METROPOLITAN
TRANSPORTATION PLANNING

SCRIPTA BOOK COMPANY
Washington, D.C.

McGRAW-HILL BOOK COMPANY
New York
St. Louis
San Francisco
Auckland
Düsseldorf
Johannesburg
Kuala Lumpur
London
Mexico
Montreal
New Delhi
Panama
Paris
São Paulo
Singapore
Sydney
Tokyo
Toronto

Metropolitan Transportation Planning

JOHN W. DICKEY, Senior Author
*Virginia Polytechnic Institute and
State University*

Robert C. Stuart
Richard D. Walker
Michael C. Cunningham
Alan G. Winslow
*All of Virginia Polytechnic
Institute and State University*

Walter J. Diewald
*Battelle Memorial Institute
Columbus, Ohio*

G. Day Ding
*University of Illinois
Urbana–Champaign*

METROPOLITAN TRANSPORTATION PLANNING

Copyright © 1975 by Scripta Book Company. All rights reserved.
Printed in the United States of America. No part of this
publication may be reproduced, stored in a retrieval system, or
transmitted, in any form or by any means, electronic, mechanical,
photocopying, recording, or otherwise, without the prior written
permission of the publisher.

2 3 4 5 6 7 8 9 0   K P K P   7 9 8 7 6

This book was set in Theme type by Scripta Graphica.
The editor was B. J. Clark; the designer was Victor Enfield;
the production supervisor was Keith Wilkinson; and the
compositor was Shirley J. McNett.
The printer and binder was The Kingsport Press.

Library of Congress Cataloging in Publication Data

Dickey, John W., date.
    Metropolitan transportation planning.

    1. Urban transportation policy. 2. Urban
transportation—Mathematical models. I. Title.
HE305.D5   388.4   73-20316
ISBN 0-07-016795-8

To my parents, Ruth C. and Franklin C. Dickey.
They showed me love, confidence, and patience.

Contents

Preface

The authors involved in the creation of this book have all had experience in teaching all or part of introductory courses in transportation planning. These courses have been mostly in the civil engineering and urban and regional planning curricula at Virginia Tech. The lack of a text covering all the items we wanted to cover was, and continues to be, a major problem. The major reasons for this seem to be twofold:

1. Most of the available texts cover subjects that are somewhat outdated.
2. Most of the available texts are directed at one discipline such as engineering or planning or economics.

Our dissatisfaction forced us to set several goals for this book. First, since no book can be kept completely up to date, especially in a fast-changing field like transportation planning, we decided to provide a modular framework within which new information can easily be incorporated. Second, we felt the book should have an orientation towards solving urban transportation problems, regardless of the disciplinary backgrounds needed to do it. Third, and finally, since urban transportation problems pervade almost all avenues of life, there should be an interdisciplinary input to the book. We feel the last goal to be particularly important since we are convinced that no real-world metropolitan transportation problem can be solved without an interdisciplinary approach (this is verified in the discussion in Chap. 8).

In keeping with our first goal, we developed the book around the concept of the "transportation planning process." This is identified in Chap. 2 as having ten stages, starting with the identification of the problem(s) and ending with the implementation, operation, and maintenance of a plan, policy, or solution to alleviate that problem. We then developed each chapter or set of chapters to correspond with each stage in the process. This setup provided two advantages:

1. Each author could see where his contribution fitted in the overall framework.
2. Each chapter or set of chapters corresponding to a stage in the process became modular. New information could be incorporated rather easily.

Concentration on a transportation planning process also allowed us to center on transportation problems, to meet our second goal. As noted, this concentration on process allowed for relative ease of input from the authors representing different disciplines.

The process-oriented approach is not without its drawbacks, however. Probably the greatest one is the emphasis on breadth over depth. This opens us to the criticism that we have not covered any single topic to the degree desired by a given discipline. Some civil engineering professionals, for example, will feel that we have slighted such important topics as drainage or structural design; some transportation planners will feel that we have not given enough attention to travel models; economists to economic analysis; sociologists and planners to social impacts; political scientists to politics and citizen participation; and so on. To all these disciplines we must confess our shortcomings and say that there are many other good books available that cover the individual topics in much more depth and with much greater skill. Our purpose was not to compete with these books, however, but to combine their thoughts into a broad, integrated spectrum of topics.

A more immediate problem is that of using this text in actual courses. We feel that it will make a good introductory book in any of the disciplines listed above (and others). Yet there must be a commitment by the particular professor to emphasize more than the discipline in which he has the most experience and therefore feels most comfortable. For example, in an introductory course in civil engineering, primary emphasis may be given to the chapters on travel and capacity, benefit-cost evaluation, geometric and pavement design, and general operation and maintenance. An introductory urban planning course, on the other hand, may emphasize the planning process, identification of problems and goals, data collection, and solution implementation. In either case, we feel that the students should be asked to read the other chapters so that they can see where the material given them fits in the larger picture. Guest lecturers from other disciplines could help in this context. Overall, we expect that there is enough material in the text to satisfy any one relevant discipline in a semester course. Thereafter, either emphasis would have to be given to other disciplines or a text going into more depth would have to be selected for the succeeding course or courses.

A final difficulty with the text is that because of its emphasis on breadth, many possibly important topics have been either left out completely or covered only briefly. Relatively little is said, for instance, about goods movement in metropolitan areas, airports, water ports, or pipelines. Nor has anything been said about such important functional topics as cost allocation among modes, taxation policies, and citizen participation strategies. Restrictions on the length of the book precluded us from discussing these and many other topics we felt were not quite as important as the ones we included. Moreover, for the same reason, we could not go into any detailed analysis of national transportation policies and decisions that have played and probably will continue to play an all-important role in helping solve metropolitan transportation problems.

Finally, we hope that the text will also prove suitable to professionals in the field who, with only a little basic background, can obtain a good picture of the present state-of-the-art in metropolitan transportation planning.

One note to all readers: the bibliography at the end of each chapter is not limited solely to those references cited in the text of the chapter. Other references have been included so that the reader will be aware of further efforts related to the topic being discussed.

It is difficult if not impossible to remember much less thank many of the people who have helped create this book over the five-year period of its conception and completion. Professor Wolfgang Homburger, from the University of California, was our primary critic and did, we feel, an important and beneficial job. Dr. Roy J. Burroughs, retired economist from HUD International, reviewed the evaluation chapter. R. Gordon Echols, head of the department of architecture at the University of Miami (Ohio), helped with comments on some of the sections related to architecture–city design. Then there were the hundreds of students who gave us their comments as we subjected them to bits and pieces of the unfinished manuscript.

The Urban Mass Transportation Administration, National Science Foundation, and Highway Research Board are due thanks for helping sponsor much of the research that ultimately helped provide material for the book.

I guess there is no way to adequately thank the many secretaries who have labored over our poor handwriting to develop a neatly typed manuscript. Our thanks go to Vickie Graham, Bonnie Gore, Gail Shepard, Dorothy Hall, Debbie Bush, Chris Duggins, Sara Reynolds, Melody Fields, Janis McDonald, and Laura Webber. There were many others who also helped in the typing, and if we forgot them, it is not from lack of appreciation.

Our final thanks go to B. J. Clark of McGraw-Hill for allowing us the unique opportunity to publish a book that does not fall strictly into any one discipline but is truly interdisciplinary.

John W. Dickey

1 The Changing Concerns of Metropolitan Transportation Planning

Those who have witnessed metropolitan transportation planning in a span of as little as 5 years know the large, and in some cases almost complete, transformation that can and has taken place. One day it seems as if the transportation system user is the only person of concern. The next day it seems as if the nonuser must be given equal if not greater concern. One day it seems as if travel time, cost, and safety are the only factors of importance. The next day the factors seem to be regional air pollution, the national economy, and the worldwide energy shortage. One day it seems as if highway engineers are perfectly capable of making complete decisions on highway planning and design. The next day, ten citizens' groups, five local planning bodies, the governor, several federal executives and legislators, and the Supreme Court all seemed to be making a variety of relevant decisions. This, then, is the rapidly changing context in which the transportation planner is involved. It will be the objective of this chapter to illustrate the history of rapid change in metropolitan transportation planning and to show the need for a more fixed but modular *process* to deal with such change. The stages in this process, to be discussed in Chap. 2, form the framework for succeeding chapters in this book.

1.1 EARLY APPROACHES TO METROPOLITAN TRANSPORTATION PLANNING

Before the early 1950s, the overwhelming concern in planning for transportation in urban areas was costs for, and benefits to, the user. In fact, it could be said that there was relatively little in the way of "planning" for "transportation" in "urban" areas. "Planning" consisted primarily of making straight-line projections of traffic counts and comparing the forecasted volumes with existing capacities. "Transportation," at least as far as government investment was concerned, consisted almost exclusively of highways; and "urban" areas were not treated too much differently than rural ones.

The first edition of one book on the topic, published in 1951 [1.1], demonstrates the state-of-the-art and the thinking at the time. About 80 percent of that book was devoted to geometric design, soils, drainage, road materials, and so forth (as opposed to about 15 percent of this text). About 15 pages of that book were devoted to urban traffic and parking surveys, with little or nothing on modeling endeavors, for example. The evaluation of alternatives was pictured almost entirely in economic terms and only with respect to the user. "Costs" were considered for roads and for vehicles; "benefits" were stated in terms of savings in distance, decreased costs of vehicle operation, decreased time to cover a given distance, and decreased accidents. (It is interesting to note that in those years many people were so happy to have a highway come to their area that they actually went out to meet highway officials to *give* part of their land for the right-of-way.)

1.2 METROPOLITAN TRANSPORTATION PLANNING IN THE 1950s

The early 1950s saw the advent of large scale urban transportation studies. While there is some argument as to which was first, the study in Detroit or in San Juan, there is not much doubt that the former one [1.3], followed by a more elaborate effort in Chicago [1.4], was the most significant. Neither could have been done had it not been for the development of the digital computer, which at that time had reached the point where a very large mass of data could be manipulated and analyzed. An emphasis thus was placed on expanding and improving the *technical* side of the metropolitan transportation planning process. Data collection efforts were initiated that cost millions of dollars for a major metropolitan area. Surveys included extensive home interviews to determine both the travel patterns and demographic characteristics of respondents. Data on land use types, intensities, and location also were collected in large quantities.

The collected data then were employed to help develop methods, such as those discussed in the first part of Chap. 6, for forecasting travel on the highway and mass transit networks for a period of as much as 25 years into the future. The greatest emphasis, however, was on the *process* of doing transportation studies, and many people made extensive charts showing how such a study should be done. Yet the problems being attacked were assumed to be about the same. Creighton lists them as being [1.2, pp. 6–13].

1. Accidents
2. Congestion
3. Inefficient investment
4. Inaccessibility

5. Ugliness   7. Air pollution
6. Strain and discomfort,
   noise, and nuisance

Prime consideration was given to the first three factors, with the others becoming recognized as time progressed. The process did, nevertheless, focus specifically on *metropolitan* areas, gave some attention to transit, and resulted in fixed *plans* for investment over the succeeding 20 or 25 years. Thus we find a major breakthrough in metropolitan transportation planning, and such studies eventually were carried out throughout the world (see, for example, Ref. [1.5]). The *Highway Act of 1962* recognized the significance of the process that had been developed and thus required all metropolitan areas with central cities having more than 50,000 persons to have a comprehensive, coordinated, and continuous transportation plan.

1.3 CHANGES IN THE 1960s

The *Highway Act of 1962* stated that its requirement for a comprehensive, coordinated, and continuous transportation plan be implemented by 1965—otherwise no federal funds, especially those for the Interstate system provided by Congress in 1956, would be forthcoming. Naturally, this requirement sent many cities and state highway departments rushing to execute and complete their metropolitan transportation planning endeavors. At the same time, several new urban transportation and related problems became apparent, and these to some extent changed the direction of thinking away from the more straightforward planning process that had developed.

One of the first problems to become apparent was that of the state of mass transit in the cities. The first year in which expenditures for transit services nationwide exceeded revenues was 1962 [1.6]. And the gap continued to widen from that point in time. The *Urban Mass Transportation Acts of 1964 and 1966* recognized the financial plight of transit as well as other problems, such as outdated equipment, poor service, and so on. About $375 million thus was allocated for a program of grants, loans, and studies for mass transit.

Two results of these acts and the studies that followed were significant. First there came about a renewed interest in transit technologies (see Chap. 9 of this book). Through a series of investigations sponsored by the Urban Mass Transportation Administration and generally known as the "New Systems Studies," a variety of innovative technologies were identified and some tested. These included various "people-mover" systems for major activity centers, rail buses, dial-a-ride systems, and so on [1.7]. Also, many service and pricing ideas were proposed and demonstrated. These ranged from the simple, such as park-and-ride systems, to the more sublime, such as telephone-retrieved minibuses featuring stewardesses serving donuts, coffee, and other liquid refreshment. Many demonstrations were not successful from a financial standpoint, but they did at least add some feasible solution ideas to those involving only massive, capital-intensive highway construction.

The second result, perhaps more important from a humanistic standpoint, was the greatly increased recognition that a significant number of people in urban areas were not being served by an auto-highway dominant form of transportation. Thus if transit were allowed to lapse, many people, primarily the poor, black, young, and old, would suffer disproportionately. These studies (most of which are abstracted in Ref. [1.8]) thereby provided a new dimension of considerations to metropolitan transportation planning—the disadvantaged.

The years that followed up to 1970 saw three acts of Congress occur that were of great significance to metropolitan transportation planning. The first was the *Urban Mass Transportation Act of 1970*. Of prime interest in that Act was the much increased funding for mass transit—$10 billion over a 12 year period. This money has and hopefully will continue to help close the financial gap for transit mentioned previously.

The other two acts were important because they helped to (1) expand the factors of concern in transportation planning, and (2) give the metropolitan areas or regions (as opposed to the localities) a review and consent power over spending on all federal-aid projects related to urban transportation. The first resulted from the *National Environmental Policy Act of 1969*, which required that environmental impact statements be developed and approved for federal-aid projects. It should be noted that the word "environmental" here has been interpreted in a very broad manner, including not only air, water, and noise pollution, but also social, economic, aesthetic, military, and other related impacts. In essence, planners and designers were asked to look at the *whole gamut* of impacts, not a small order by any means, but still an extremely important task.

The *Demonstration Cities and Metropolitan Development Act of 1966*, although coming before the *National Environmental Policy Act of 1969*, turned out to be a powerful, complementary tool in helping to foster metropolitan approaches to problems. It became difficult for one locality to "go its own way" when dealing with problems such as air pollution that had obvious metropolitanwide implications.

1.4   THE 1970s AND THE FUTURE

The beauty and the bane of the *National Environmental Policy Act of 1969* was that it forced planners and designers to consider all the significant impacts. The beauty was that persistent problems like air and noise pollution could no longer be ignored. Some plan, strategy, or design had to be developed to help alleviate the problems or else the project could easily be contested and halted in court. The bane was that Pandora's Box had been opened: many impacts are difficult to identify and define, much less reduce or enhance (whatever the case may require). Furthermore, many impacts are the antithesis of each other. Unless and until new technologies of consequence appear, there is no way to have a greater amount of comfortable and convenient travel with less air pollution or noise or energy consumption. To make matters worse, most of the decisions to be made regarding the tradeoffs between those opposing factors probably will not be done at the metropolitan level. Decisions on energy consumption, to pick the most glaring example, have been and probably will continue to be made primarily at the national and international levels. There appears to be relatively little metropolitan transportation planners can do with respect to the energy problem except respond to the above-mentioned national and international decisions.

Manheim and Suhrbier [1.10] have outlined a set of basic "principles" that are indicative of the kinds of considerations which will have to be addressed in future metropolitan transportation planning endeavors, especially if problems such as those in energy consumption are to be solved. We are not necessarily in agreement with all of these "principles," but they do provide a good basis for our discussion of future directions and likely benefits and pitfalls.

1. *Single Multimodal Transportation System*

A government transportation organization should work to provide transportation as a service, using all modes of a region and all options, including not only investment in fixed facilities but also operating and pricing policies.

As will be noted in Chap. 11 of this book, the organization created to achieve various transportation and related solutions is of great significance. Many states have set up departments of transportation in hopes that, as suggested by this principle, a greater variety of transportation (as opposed to just highway or just airport, etc.) options can be investigated and implemented. It is expected that greater integration among modes can be achieved, duplicative services removed, useful competition engendered, and, in general, a clearer role for each transportation mode evolved.

Yet, there are problems with multimodal planning that may be difficult to overcome in the future. These include greater cost, the concentration of power in organizations of increased size, and difficulties (and perhaps undesirabilities) in shifting funds from one specialized account (e.g., a highway trust fund) to another. There is, in addition, the day-to-day problems of coordinating and controlling such a massive endeavor.

2. *Alternatives and Options*

A range of transportation options are available and should be developed at all levels of technical studies to bring out the issues and to assist the community in clarifying its objectives and reaching a decision.

As will be shown in Chap. 9, there are a wide range of alternate solutions to metropolitan transportation problems in addition to the highly capital-intensive ones like freeway and rapid-rail construction.

These include:

a. New technologies such as people-movers and demand-responsive bus systems
b. Operating policies such as priority use of expressway lanes for buses, car-pooling, and scheduling adjustments
c. Pricing policies such as in transit fare and parking charge alterations

Such solutions might help to provide reduced travel time while ameliorating such adverse effects as air and noise pollution. On the other hand, many of these solutions are untested in a suitable real world situation and, because they are new, may be the source of significant problems before all the "bugs" are found and corrected.

3. Effects

Identification and prediction of social, economic, and environmental effects should be based on the group affected.

As noted in Sec. 1.1, early metropolitan transportation studies were concerned almost entirely with the *user* of the system. This limited concern perhaps was reasonable at the time, but as some of the adverse impacts of transportation became apparent, it was also recognized that the nonuser oftentimes was the recipient. Further study in the 1960s indicated that many people, particularly the poor, young, and old, would be placed at a severe disadvantage if mass transit were allowed to lapse. There thus has been an increasing emphasis on identifying the *sectors* of the population being impacted. The technology assessment approach to evaluation, described briefly in Chap. 8, represents one approach to accounting for differences in impacts among different groups of people.

Such an approach will not be without difficulties in the future. The number of groups impacted could become quite large, and this would mean that decisions would have to be made as to which ones should be given the most attention. Many more of these decisions would have to take place directly in the political arena, which might mean greater indecisiveness, more court cases, an increased bureaucracy, and longer times to implementation.

4. Analysis Tools

The technical analysis tools, particularly those for systems studies, should be responsive to the principles of supply-demand equilibrium and to community-environment impacts.

As will be seen in Chaps. 5 and 6, some models (predictive devices) are quite sophisticated. This is especially true of travel forecasting models, which show how the quantity of travel "demanded" depends on the price charged (in cost, travel time, convenience, etc.) and the "supply" (transportation system) being offered.

Future models promise to be much broader in nature and more reliable. They probably will also make greater use of man's intuition, but in a more structured manner (see Ref. [1.11] for examples). Two real dilemmas are present, however, in making forecasts in transportation planning. First, since the number of types of effects to be considered can be quite large, there may be no reliable tools available to analyze some of them correctly. Second, many transportation facilities will last for periods up to 50 years, yet it would be an extreme optimist who would put much faith in forecasts of, say, travel and air pollution levels even 20 years from now.

5. Uncertainty

The transportation decision should explicitly recognize uncertainty.

As implied above, forecasts for any extended time period are subject to far too many unexpected events: worldwide oil shortages, tax breaks to the automobile production industry, development of new and beneficial transit technologies, changes in human values, and so on. In the future, plans probably will be both more general in nature and more numerous. In other words, an attempt most likely will be made to deal less in specifics, since these would be subject to the most rapid change, and to develop several alternate plans, any one of which could be implemented depending on which major events (e.g., a gasoline shortage) took place.

6. *Evaluation*

Evaluation of a planning process should occur periodically throughout the course of studies and should guide a process by suggesting priorities for subsequent activities.

In Chap. 4 it is suggested that various goals could help to guide the planning process and that the evaluation of alternatives (Chap. 8) should depend on these goals. Goals in a community generally are not stated explicitly but must be derived from a study of past events and from continuing interaction in and among concerned agencies and citizen groups. It is anticipated that such interaction will increase, especially as planners and engineers try to determine which effects are of most concern and must thus be given the highest priority. For this endeavor to be successful in the future, however, the interaction must be continuous so that opinions are not solicited at a point after major irreversible decisions have been made.

7. *Public Involvement*

Interaction between the technical team and potentially affected communities should occur at all planning levels.

Because the *Demonstration Cities and Metropolitan Development Act of 1966* (made operational by OMB Circular Letter A-95) requires a regional review of any federally assisted projects, and because most regional agencies set up citizen committees to help in this review, public involvement in the metropolitan transportation decision making process has increased substantially. This has had many valuable ramifications. Some unwanted and undesirable freeways have not been built, citizens have identified many effects of concern that otherwise would have gone unnoticed, and some unique and valuable design features have been suggested and implemented.

The future probably will see more and better public involvement. Some questions need to be resolved, however. Among these are:

1. How are the citizens to be elected (or appointed)?
2. Who should the "citizens" represent in the community, and how?
3. Who represents people outside the community?
4. How should citizen groups relate to elected public officials?
5. What training should such groups have?
6. What vote should such citizens have in the ultimate decisions?

8.   *Decision Process*

The process through which decisions are reached should provide opportunities for negotiation among affected interest groups.

The future role of the professional probably will be quite different from that to which he or she has been accustomed in the past. Instead of making the final decision on that alternative supposedly in the overall public interest, the professional most likely will be limited to providing requested information, identifying and clarifying the issues of choice, and stimulating debate among those involved and affected. This would allow for greater negotiation among the participants and perhaps a solution more amenable to all.

The community generally is not, nor should be, the only group involved in the decision. Often there will be ramifications for underrepresented minority groups, state agencies, and even national and international organizations. Because such broader concerns are becoming more important, the decision making process of the future probably will become more interrelated and complex.

9.   *Equity*

Transportation decisions should be based on the principle of equity.

At the very least, no individual or group should lose because of a transportation "improvement." Those who are unwillingly subjected to increased air pollution or noise or relocation should be reimbursed for their disbenefits. Unfortunately, it is not always possible to determine the nature, extent, and amount of required compensation for such losses. Yet the principle remains.

Future metropolitan transportation planning endeavors most likely will give much more emphasis to the equity principle. Hopefully it would even be carried a step forward in consideration for the poor, who have much for which to be given compensation.

10.   *Institutions*

The arrangement and the organizational structure of political and technical institutions influence the degree to which social and environmental considerations are incorporated into transportation decision making.

As mentioned earlier, many states have reorganized into departments of transportation in an effort to incorporate multimodal features in planning, programming, and budgeting. Other states are giving thought to placing transportation under the broader heading of state planning and community affairs. This arrangement would cause transportation to be viewed more as an integral part of the community rather than a separate, unrelated service. There would be great difficulty, however, in properly operating and coordinating an agency of this magnitude.

Still other states have gone toward land-use control policies and corresponding agencies, in what has been termed the "quiet revolution" [1.9]. Hawaii, for example, has divided the whole state into four districts: conservation, agriculture, rural, and urban. The state land-use law authorizes land in the urban district to be utilized for whatever purpose permitted under local zoning ordinances. Lands in the agricultural and rural districts are to be employed only in compliance with regulations of the state land use commissions, and lands in the conservation district are to comply with the regulations of the State Department of Land and Natural Resources [1.9].

The important point here is that it is the *state* in this case which has made and apparently will continue to make important decisions concerning land use. The factors of primary concern are also indicated by the state. In Hawaii, these are urban and rural development (especially for tourism), agriculture (sugar cane and pineapple primarily), and environment (conservation zones). Transportation, as a result, becomes viewed not as an end in itself but as an aid in the proper development of these other factors. This attitude, we feel, is one which will become more prevalent in the future and has significant ramifications for the organization and operation of metropolitan transportation planning endeavors.

Despite all the above comments, the ultimate problem that metropolitan transportation planning has addressed and will continue to address is that of the "public good." The major problem which has existed and will continue to exist is that the sum of the parts is not equal to the whole. Millions of personal decisions of maximum benefit to each individual do not necessarily make for total maximum benefit. Webber provides good examples of this [1.12, p. 135]:

> Noxious emissions from individual vehicles are harmless; the problems arise only when the numbers of individuals gets counted in the millions . . . Externally, a few motor cars in the streets of the great cities of Europe do not really matter very much. When the numbers become large, the subtle qualities of the cities are rapidly eroded, to the loss of residents and visiting admirers as well.

Owen uses the very descriptive term, "the accidental city" [1.13]. By this is meant that:

> The basic difficulty of urban growth all over the world is that decisions about the use of urban land are being made by a host of private parties without the guidance of comprehensive plans or community goals.

What is happening is that each individual decision must be made in the context of the ones made previous to it. While these individual decisions may be optimal in their own regard, they may build on each other organically so as to spiral out of acceptable bounds. Apparently this is what has happened in many metropolitan areas—not necessarily that the area as a whole has become a comparatively disadvantageous place to live (for if it were, it certainly would be deserted by now)—but that there are many disbenefits that need not be if the atomistic approach is forsaken.

In review, then, it would appear that the future charge to metropolitan transportation planners is essentially the same as it has been in the past: plan transportation systems that provide the maximum in "public good." The context will continue to change into the future, however. The "public good" will be defined more broadly, by more people, and in such a way that considerations of equity and citizen involvement in the decisionmaking process are more common.

1.5 SUMMARY

The purpose of this chapter has been to provide an introduction to metropolitan transportation planning. The primary point is that such planning, despite the fairly constant charge to obtain the greatest "public good," has changed and probably will continue to change fairly drastically in context. In the early 1950s, when metropolitan transportation planning was being initiated in roughly the same mode as it is known now, the overwhelming concern was for the highway user: his costs, travel times, and safety. Greater emphasis also was given to the technical side of studies: data collection, modeling, and the like.

The *Highway Act of 1962* was an important evolutionary step. It required continuous, comprehensive, and coordinated transportation planning for metropolitan areas. Shortly thereafter, mass transit became a focus of concern, and many new technologies were investigated. The late 1960s and early 1970s saw the advent of increased concern for social and environmental aspects of transportation and for citizen involvement in the transportation decision making process.

The future of metropolitan transportation planning appears to be directed toward:

1. Single multimodal transportation systems
2. Increased alternatives and options
3. Increased identification of transportation effects and their ramifications for equity among groups of people
4. Better analysis tools and handling of uncertainty
5. Greater continuity in evaluation, with more public involvement and negotiation
6. Major institutional changes emphasizing transportation as one component of overall development

As mentioned, these changes most likely will alter the context but not the overriding purpose of metropolitan transportation planning. There thus appears to be a need to formulate some sort of modular framework or process for planning so that changes can be integrated without wholesale restructuring. The transportation planning process to be discussed in the next chapter is the framework we have adopted for this purpose.

BIBLIOGRAPHY

1.1   Ritter, L. J., Jr., and R. J. Paquette: *Highway Engineering*, Ronald Press, New York, 1951.
1.2   Creighton, R. L.: *Urban Transportation Planning*, University of Illinois Press, Urbana, 1970.
1.3   *Detroit Metropolitan Area Traffic Study:* Final Report (in 2 parts), Detroit, Mich., 1955.
1.4   *Chicago Area Transportation Study:* Final Report (in 3 parts), Chicago, Ill., 1959, 1960, and 1962.

1.5   The Metropolitan Transportation Committee: *Melbourne Transportation Study*, (2 vols.), Melbourne, Australia, 1969.

1.6   American Transit Association: *Transit Fact Book*, Washington, D.C., 1972.

1.7   U.S. Department of Housing and Urban Development, Office of Metropolitan Development: *Tomorrow's Transportation*, Government Printing Office, Washington, D.C., 1968.

1.8   U.S. Department of Transportation, Urban Mass Transportation Administration: *Urban Mass Transportation Abstracts*, National Technical Information Service, Springfield, Va., PB–213 212, October 1972.

1.9   Bosselman, F., and D. Callies: *The Quiet Revolution in Land Use Control*, Government Printing Office, Washington, D.C., 1971.

1.10 Manheim, M. L., and J. M. Suhrbier: *Incorporating Social and Environmental Factors in Highway Planning and Design*, Special Report 130, Highway Research Board, Washington, D.C., 1973.

1.11 Martino, J. P.: *Technological Forecasting for Decision-Making*, American Elsevier, New York, 1972.

1.12 Webber, M.: "On Strategies for Transport Planning," in *The Urban Transportation Planning Process*, Organization for Economic Cooperation and Development, Paris, 1971.

1.13 Owen, W.: *The Accessible City*, The Brookings Institution, Washington, D.C., 1972.

1.14 Department of Transportation, Urban Mass Transportation Administration: *Research, Development & Demonstration Projects*, Washington, D.C., June 30, 1972.

2 The Transportation Planning Process

One of the most interesting paradoxes in any profession is that which faces the engineer and planner who, although possessing a kitbag of mathematical and scientific tools, are called upon to perform a highly artistic task—that of problem solving. Many analysts can agree upon and accept a given method of analysis as being logically consistent and reliable, yet few will concur on the time and place that the method should be used, or on the degree of judgment needed to derive a proper solution to a problem.

A great deal of the mystery that enshrouds these types of decisions is bound up in the problem-solving process, that nebulous procedure in which the planner or engineer starts with an original statement of the problem and finishes with a rather specific and fully implemented solution. It is because the problem-solving process usually is so vague that worthwhile solutions often are obtained only through some fortunate traversal between problem statement and implementation and operation. Therefore, it would seem logical that if the design process could be mapped more precisely, better solutions might result since more persons then could follow the optimal path. It is toward this goal of better definition of the problem-solving process, especially in regard to transportation, that this chapter is directed.

2.1 MODELS

Before a discussion of the problem-solving process can proceed, it is important to delve first into the topic of models, since they are a natural adjunct to that process. A "model," according to Krick [2.3, p. 85], is: "Something which in some respect resembles or describes the structure and/or behavior of a real life counterpart. There is some correlation between the model and its corresponding reality, although obviously a less than perfect correlation." Observe that this definition "so requires that we extend our interpretation of the word 'model' considerably beyond ordinary usage, which implies a three-dimensional replica of an object or person" [2.3, p. 84]. In fact, there are actually three types of models [2.4, p. 143]:

1. Iconic: Those that look like the reality, that is, are visual geometric equivalents (e.g., a model airplane)
2. Analog: Those in which there is a correspondence between elements and actions in the model and those in reality but no physical resemblance (e.g., a football play diagram)
3. Symbolic: Those that compactly and abstractly represent the principles of the reality (e.g., $F = ma$)

It is interesting to note at this point that words in themselves are symbolic models of some reality. For example, the word "tree" is a model of a variety of items ranging from dogwoods to sequoias.

In general, a model of any situation contains the following five sets of elements:

1. Variables over which the designer has complete control: X_i.
2. Variables over which the designer has no control: Z_j
3. Variables over which the designer has indirect control: Y_k
4. General relationships between the above variables: R_m
5. Parameters (coefficients, constants, exponents, etc.) in the above relationships: P_n

Symbolically, a model M is represented by

$$M = \{X_i, Z_j, Y_k, R_m, P_n\} \qquad \text{for some or all } i, j, k, m, n \tag{2.1}$$

where the brackets indicate a *set* of items.

An example may help to clarify (Eq. 2.1). Suppose that the monthly revenue, r, from a given busline operation depends on the fare charged, f, and the monthly number of passengers, p, riding the buses. Revenue then would be the product of the fare ($/person) and the number of passengers (persons)

$$r = fp \tag{2.2}$$

It is also found that the number of passengers riding the bus in any month is a function of the number of inches of rain that month, i, and the bus fare, with the general relationship being

$$p = b/(i + 1)f^{\emptyset} \tag{2.3}$$

The "+1" after i is included so that "no rain" will not result in an infinite number of passengers (division by 0). The b and $\emptyset$ are parameters established from an analysis of past events. For example, in a hypothetical case it may have been found that the ridership is 10,000 passengers when there is no rain in a month and the fare is $1.00. This would give

$$10,000 = \frac{b}{(1+0) \ (1.00)^{\emptyset}} \qquad \text{or} \qquad b = 10,000$$

Similarly, let us assume that past data have shown that there are 40,000 passengers in a month when there is no rain and the fare is $.50. With the above value of b, these figures would lead to

$$40,000 = \frac{10,000}{(1+0) \ (0.50)^{\emptyset}} \qquad \text{or} \qquad (0.50)^{\emptyset} = \frac{10,000}{40,000} = 0.25$$

which gives $\emptyset = 2.0$.

Stopping here, we notice that the fare is a variable over which we as problem solvers hired by the bus company have control (an X_i), whereas we do not have control over the rain in a given month (a Z_j). Moreover, we have only indirect control over the number of passengers and revenue (Y_k's) since the weather influences their values. Continuing in our effort to derive a completed model, we find from Eqs. (2.2) and (2.3) and from the above discussion that

$$r = fp = f \ \frac{b}{(i+1)^{\emptyset}} \tag{2.4}$$

which leads to:

$$r = f \ \frac{10,000}{(i+1)f^2} = \frac{10,000}{(i+1)f} \tag{2.5}$$

Searching further, we may find that (2.5) holds true only for high income riders (a Z variable but stated as a category), while for lower income riders the proper relationship might be

$$r_l = \frac{12,000}{(i+1)f} \tag{2.6}$$

Equations 2.2 through 2.6 are all symbolic models and will provide the basis for the forthcoming discussions on the use of modeling in various stages of the problem-solving process. Eqs. 2.5 and 2.6 help to indicate that, in the most general situation, an indirectly controlled variable (like r) is always a function of a controllable variable (like f) and an uncontrollable variable (like i). Thus

$$Y_k = f(X_i, Z_j) \tag{2.7}$$

Equation (2.7) actually *defines* what is meant by the words "indirect control" in the sentences above Eq. (2.1).

2.2 THE PROBLEM-SOLVING PROCESS

As was remarked in the first section, the product of the problem-solving process usually is a fairly well-detailed entity, yet the actual process itself often is a rather vague and undefined procedure, so that any representation of it would not necessarily be satisfactory to all concerned. Nevertheless, there is a need for explicitness, and many authors have attempted to blueprint in some way their feelings as to a realistic interpretation of the procedure by which a solution evolves after several transformations from a problem statement. One interpretation, which is a synthesis of those formerly proposed, is presented in Fig. 2.1. This diagram will provide the framework upon which the ensuing discussion will be built.

Except for two major *feedback* loops, the 10-stage process in Fig. 2.1 is a sequential process. Each link indicates both a *direction of movement* and a *flow of information* through the process, whereas each stage, I through X, indicates an action to be taken. Some actions probably would be done concurrently in a real world situation, as would be true of *collecting data* while at the same time *defining objectives and constraints*, but simplification at this point probably will not be detrimental to the accuracy of the overall description of the process. Briefly, the actions unfold in the following manner:

I. An attempt is made to define as precisely as possible the nature of the problem and the domain within which it exists.

II. Given the problem statement, the problem solver conceives of a set of goals and objectives that indicate the direction toward which any modification should be oriented in order to become a candidate for a satisfactory solution. He also conceives of a set of constraints which cannot be exceeded in any proposed solution.

III. A model with the properties presented in Sec. 2.1 is made of the domain within which the problem has developed.

IV. Data are collected in field studies or from information given in relevant publications. These data are used both for obtaining a clear picture of the problem and problem domain and for establishing model parameters and present and past values of variables of interest.

V. The model developed in (III) is calibrated (parameters are set) and used to determine the future magnitude of the problems (*a*) if no designer changes are made, or (*b*) if the solution proposed in stage VII were to be implemented.

VI. An evaluation is made of (*a*) the future situation if no changes are made and (*b*) proposed solutions. A decision is made among the alternatives.

VII. Solutions (designer modifications) are generated and incorporated into the problem situation. These solutions are evaluated in (VI) and then (possibly) further modifications are made. This repetitive feedback

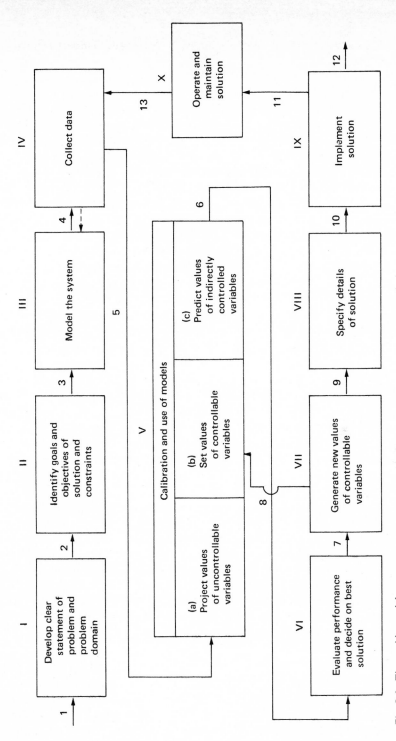

Fig. 2.1 The problem-solving process.

procedure continues until some acceptable or perhaps optimal solution is reached.

VIII. The details of the solution are evolved and specified by means of drawings, legal specifications, and so forth.

IX. The solution proposed is implemented through such procedures as physical construction, financial and budgetary measures, policy statements, and so forth.

X. The implemented solution is operated and maintained. Further data are collected to determine whether the solution has in fact led to the reduction of the problem as was predicted by the model. If this is not the case, then changes either in the model, in the modifications, or in both are needed. Continued problem solving is required as problems, goals, and so on change.

A simple example of the use of the problem-solving process can be created by referring back to the busline operation model in the previous section. Suppose that the bus company has the problem of having a revenue which is too low (stage I) and realizes that the fare charged, weather, and income status of riders all have a bearing on the problem (the problem domain). The company would like to increase its net revenue as much as possible (objective) by modifying the fare structure while at the same time taking into account relevant governmental restrictions (constraints) on the magnitude of such modifications. The models the company uses (stage III) are those in Eqs. (2.5) and (2.6). It also is found at this stage that the local regulating agency requires that the fare, f, fall within the range between 10 cents and 40 cents. The net revenue for the *next* month is calculated based on the projection that the amount of rain for that month will be 1 inch and that the fare will remain as it is today—20 cents (stage V). Under these circumstances, the total revenue is the sum of that from both the higher and lower income riders, or, from Eqs. (2.5) and (2.6):

$$r_t = \frac{10{,}000}{(1+1)\;(0.20)} + \frac{12{,}000}{(1+1)\;(0.20)} = \frac{22{,}000}{(2)\;(0.20)} = \$55{,}000/\text{month}$$

where r_t is the sum of r_h (the revenue from high income people) and r_l. This revenue is not deemed adequate (stage VI), so that a modification of the fare to 30 cents is proposed (stage VII). This modification leads to a revenue of $22{,}000/(2)\;(0.30) = \$36{,}630$ (stage V and VI again), which still is not acceptable. Finally, after several modifications, a fare of 10 cents is suggested, which leads to the greatest possible net revenue $22{,}000/(2)\;(0.10) = \$110{,}000/\text{month}$ while *at the same time* keeping within the fare limitations of the regulatory agency.

To implement this fare change, the bus company must notify prospective passengers, get new change machines for the drivers, and, in general, specify many of the details (stage VIII) needed for the satisfactory fulfillment of the innovation. Finally, the fare change is brought into effect (stage IX) and operated and maintained (stage X). After a month of experience with the modification, it turns out that the revenue received is not $110,000/month but $100,000. To locate possible causes for this discrepancy, the bus company collects more data (feedback to stage IV) and finds that Eq. (2.5) really should be:

$$r_h = \frac{8,000}{(i+1)f} \tag{2.8}$$

By entering Eqs. (2.6) and (2.8) with the values for i and f, the company then is assured that r_t = 8000/(2) (0.10) + 12000/(2) (0.10) = $100,000 per month. Similar procedures would be followed month after month to solve related problems as they arise.

2.2.1 Comments on the Problem-Solving Process

It is easy to be lulled into a sense of security when no security really exists. This is a distinct possibility in conjunction with the previous description of the problem-solving process: there are a multitude of difficulties concerning the process which appear only under further scrutiny. Several of these difficulties are listed and discussed below.

1. Various stages and links of possible importance in the problem-solving process may have been omitted from Fig. 2.1. It might happen, for example, that when an attempt is made to collect data pertinent to certain variables, it will be found that they cannot be obtained, thus requiring that an adjustment be made to the model formulated in stage III. A feedback link from stage IV to III to account for this possibility should have been incorporated in Fig. 2.1, and, in general, a case probably could be made for the inclusion of a link between any two stages.

2. Statement of the problem (stage I) often is extremely difficult, first because the problem presented to the designer usually is not the actual problem and second because problem statements generally are too narrow in scope. A good example of these two observations is the "problem" of a lack of parking spaces in city centers. In many cities spaces are available, but the real problem is that they are too far away from desired final destinations. If enough spaces were provided at the proper locations, the city center probably would have to be transformed into a large parking lot, a situation which would be undesirable insofar as overall development is concerned. Thus, the parking problem is only one part of a broad development problem.

3. Explicit objectives and constraints (stage II) are not easy to establish. If a person claims he desires "efficient" transportation, do we really have any idea of what he wants?

4. Models (stages III and V) are models. They are not reality, but contain assumptions and simplifications which allow them to represent reality in a succinct manner. Yet, it is this succinctness which detracts from a model's accuracy. Is Newton's "model" of gravity a reliable predictor when friction exists and each mass is *not* concentrated at a point?

5. Relevant data (stage IV) often cannot be obtained, due either to the great expense involved or the unwillingness of certain parties to release the information. For example, the U.S. Bureau of the Census has certain well-specified disclosure rules.[1]

6. Future values of uncontrollable variables usually must be projected or extrapolated from trends or time series information (stage V). By a similar technique [2.24], it was found that the population of the United States would never exceed 148 million people.

7. Evaluation (stage VI) oftentimes is treacherous. Is a human life worth $34,000? How is appearance to be judged relative to cost?

8. Most modifications are the result of a *creative* process which many times cannot be replicated or emulated because of the variety of the human mind and the complexity of many problem situations. Resources limitations often prevent the testing of more than a few possible modifications.

These and many other comments are pertinent to the problem-solving process. They provide the major reasons for labeling the process as "nebulous" and "artistic."

2.2.2 The Distinction between Problem Solving and Planning

Because in the next section we will be concerned with the transportation planning process, it is necessary to discuss briefly the distinction between problem solving and planning. What usually distinguishes the two is (a) the time period involved, and (b) the breadth of the situation being studied. For example, in planning we may be concerned with the location and capacity of a mass transit facility to be placed in a corridor of an urban area 15 years from now, whereas in problem solving our concern may be for the dimensions and performance of a vehicle to be placed in operation a year from now. This latter situation is narrower in scope, more detailed, and has a much shorter time dimension.

There are several natural consequences of the differences in time span and breadth found in planning and problem-solving endeavors. With respect to time span, for instance, it would be expected that forecasts of uncontrollable variables for planning purposes would have to be made further into the future, with the result being reduced reliability of the forecasted values. Obviously, a prediction of population for next year will have a much better chance of being correct than one for 20 years from now, especially because of the multitude of factors (such as wars, famines, and so forth) not considered in the predictive process but certainly likely to exert an influence on growth at some time during a 20-year span.

Another consequence of the time period difference is that the problems and objectives relevant to a planning situation may themselves change during the period so that solutions based on *present* problems and objectives may be outdated before they are implemented. The interplay between communication and transportation

---

[1] See any *Census* reports available in most libraries.

might provide a good example for this situation. Traffic congestion in urban areas often is cited as a major problem, and solutions offered are those of more highways, better mass transit, and so forth. Yet, it may be that congestion will not be a problem in 20 years *even if nothing were done about it*. Television-type telephones may be developed to such an extent that many trips needed to achieve face-to-face communication would not be necessary, thereby freeing transportation facilities from this partial burden.[2] Consequently, the objective of relieving congestion (the problem) would be antiquated. On the other hand, new problems (and corresponding objectives) of a type presently nonexistent (or unimportant) may arise within the planning period, and these should be anticipated in any planning endeavor.

A distinct advantage of the elongated time period is that presently nonexistent innovations which may lead to better solutions can be foreseen and used to complement or even replace the present solution before it is implemented. For example, if it is anticipated that pneumatic tube transportation will be significantly developed several years from now, plans for later periods could include tube transit. In fact, in some rare situations, even if tube transit were not foreseen for the near future, enough time would be available for the planner to investigate the financial and technical feasibility of developing this system so that it *would be* available several years.[3] The problem-solving process, as it is commonly understood, lacks the farsightedness to take advantage of forthcoming innovations.

A final advantage of the elongated time period is that anticipated solutions can be implemented *sequentially*, that is to say, on a *programmed basis*. Thus, instead of making improvements all at once, the planner will usually pick out a small subset to be accomplished in each subperiod of time (of, say, 5 years duration), and, if his choices are made properly, he can accrue substantial benefits over time from such a sequential procedure. Solutions arising from the problem-solving process generally cannot be programmed for sequential implementation so as to achieve benefits comparable to those derived from planning.

The second major aspect that differentiates planning from problem solving is, as previously mentioned, the breadth of the problem addressed. For example, many cities and towns are interested in providing more parking in their central areas, and parking garages and lot designs can be prescribed without too much difficulty. Nevertheless, parking is only one part of the overall transportation and urban growth situation and should be considered in this context. Future construction of mass transit facilities could reduce the need for extra parking. Planning, rather than problem solving, is the name usually given to the study of broader situations. Conversely, planning, because of its greater generality, can never be considered to have the depth of detail required for a final product, so that the problem-solving process can be considered to be an adjunct to the planning process in which

---

[2] For further elaboration of this idea, see Meier, [2.26].

[3] Because of the time and expense involved, most planning organizations do not have an opportunity to make feasibility studies for possible innovations. On a national level, however, several studies have been done. See the program for the Northeast Corridor Project [2.9] and several reports from the Department of Housing and Urban Development [2.27-2.28].

specifications of each general concept of a solution generated from the planning process are detailed.

2.3 THE TRANSPORTATION PLANNING PROCESS

The transportation planning process, as brought out above, should bear a great similarity to the problem-solving process developed in the foregoing sections of this chapter. The two major differences are that the former process is directed at the production of a rather *broad* description of a *future* transportation system, whereas the problem-solving process is much more detailed and immediate in nature. Yet, as the time for implementation nears, transportation plans also must be specified to a much greater extent.

Generally speaking, the major thrust of any transportation planning study involves the determination of the demand for travel within wide "corridors" of a region. This effort then is followed with an attempt to find those presently available or anticipated future transport systems which would meet the established travel demands in an acceptable manner. Thereafter, as time progresses, plans become more precise—proposed budget allocations are made, exact locations are determined, work programs are fixed, and so forth—until the proposed system becomes a reality. This general transportation planning process, outlined only briefly at this point, will be discussed in more detail in succeeding sections of this chapter. This presentation subsequently will form an all-important framework to which the concepts of the ensuing chapters of this text can be related in a comprehensive and logical fashion. In fact, each succeeding chapter of this text will represent one or part of one stage of the transportation planning process as it will be presented below.

2.3.1 A General Description

Any planning or design process is initiated by an attempt to define as neatly and succinctly as possible the types of problems that do or will exist and the domain in which they are set. This first stage is shown along with the remaining ones in Fig. 2.2. Almost invariably these transportation service problems are both numerous and nebulous, and they range from such mundane matters as pot holes in streets to more complex situations of development of regions. In any case, most of these problems can be reduced to that of the high cost, in time, money, and comfort (or some other measure), of getting from origins to desired destinations. The factors affecting or affected by these problems (the problem domain) usually consist of a significant portion of both the manmade and natural habitat.

Given general problem statements and a description of the problem domain similar to that above, we can go on to identify the objectives and constraints (stage II, Fig. 2.2) that will guide our search for new solutions. Example objectives might be those of minimizing travel time throughout the region, maximizing the number of people who will use public transit facilities, or influencing certain kinds of

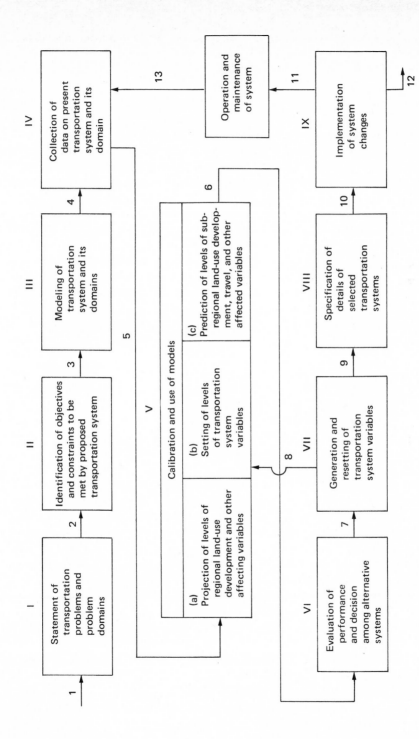

Fig. 2.2 The transportation planning process.

growth in a region through transportation improvements. Constraints relevant to these objectives may be those of the yearly budget of the local or state highway departments, federal regulations on removal of housing for construction purposes, and the quantity of certain subgrade materials available in the vicinity of the proposed improvement.

In stage III of the transportation planning process an attempt is made to model in an abstract manner the transportation system and its domain. Here the three most prominent types of models to be employed are: (1) those describing affected factors and their relation to transportation (land use development, air pollution, noise, etc.), (2) those describing travel behavior or the "demand" for transportation facilities, and (3) those describing the characteristics of various forms of transportation technologies (supply).

By having a general picture of these model types, we can proceed to a rational data collection effort (stage IV), the main purpose of which is to provide the information necessary to establish the parameters (constraints, coefficients, exponents, and so forth) for each model. The data collection stage has another important role, however—the development of more accurate statements of the problems, problem domains, objectives, and constraints. What previously may have been a general congestion problem at an intersection, after the gathering of more data, might be specified as 65.3 seconds of delay per vehicle between 4:30 and 5:30 p.m. on weekdays.

In stage V, the land use development, affected factors, travel demand, and transportation supply models are calibrated using the collected data and used in concert to predict the future state of environmental and transportation service factors *if no changes in the transportation system are made.* The consequences of such an alternative, when evaluated under stage VI of the planning process, usually are worse than those in the existing state: driving delays may be greater than at present, transit facilities may be expected to deteriorate, and the induced growth of the region may not be desirable. As a consequence of this anticipated poor performance, modifications to the present transport system must be generated (stage VII), and this generation must be done in such a manner that the objectives ascribed to in stage II are accomplished to the highest degree possible.

At this point in the process the modifications suggested should not be carried out directly, however, because of the extremely important feedback (arrow 8) which exists in most instances. The crux of this feedback is the *impact* of the modified transportation system on land use in various parts of the region, on the amount, direction, and mode of travel, and on other affected factors such as air pollution and appearance. This impact must be reevaluated in stage VI, at which point a need for further modification of the transportation system may arise. Finally, after several possible loops through these three stages (V to VII), a decision would be made among the alternative solutions that were generated. This chosen solution then would be set forth in more detailed form in stage VIII and brought into existence in stage IX, the stage of implementation.

Continued operation and maintenance would follow (stage X). This stage would conclude the main effort of the planning process, yet there would remain a continual need to collect information for the evaluation of the *actual*[4] performance of the transportation system. Moreover, planning should never be a one time endeavor, but instead should be considered a continual process, with solutions being altered as new aspects of problems arise, as goals and objectives change, and as improved technology becomes available.

2.3.2 Transportation Problems and Problem Domains

To define any type of problem and its accompanying domain often is one of the most difficult tasks to be faced by any designer or planner. Transportation problems in particular exhibit this difficulty, first because most problems occur in space as well as in time and second because the problems are hierarchical in nature. What is meant by these phrases is that the planner must be able to identify the areal region and various subparts of this region in which certain types of problems can be expected to arise at predicted times in the future. He must be capable of perceiving the whole spectrum of problems from the extremely localized ones to the regionally oriented ones. To accomplish these two tasks the planner usually would go through the following procedure:

1. He would circumscribe a *region* wherein the activities that occur are as independent from those outside the region as possible. The resulting line of demarcation usually is referred to as a *cordon line.*

2. He then would divide the cordoned region into a set of *zones* or *subregions* whose areas are small enough that most problems can be pinpointed fairly accurately and yet large enough that the study does not become inundated with data.[5] An example of a region and its zones for the Waco, Texas, area is shown in Fig. 2.3.

3. Finally, through contact with interested parties, the planner would define various transportation service problem types which fall within the broad range from regional access problems to local congestion problems and, as part of this effort, he would attempt to identify those factors in both the man-made and natural environment which would either contribute to or be a derivative of transportation system deficiencies.

The output of this three-step process would be an identification of transportation service and related problems such as:

[4] This performance constrasts with the *model-predicted* performance determined in stage VI.

[5] If the origin and destination of every trip made by each person on a given day in the New York City Metropolitan Area were recorded on computer cards, these cards would fill approximately 3,500 card boxes or 350 computer tapes: thus the need for analyzing travel and other kinds of data for groups of individuals (those in an areal zone) rather than for each and every person separately.

a. Much delay is incurred in traveling on routes through zone two
b. Many people in zone 51 have no means by which to get to worthwhile jobs
c. Pedestrian travel is too restricted in downtown zones
d. Central area stores are deteriorating
e. Growth in the region is not as rapid as that in other regions
f. Air pollution is prevalent in the region

The latter three problems generally would be considered to be contained in the transportation problem domain. The first two have special significance here,

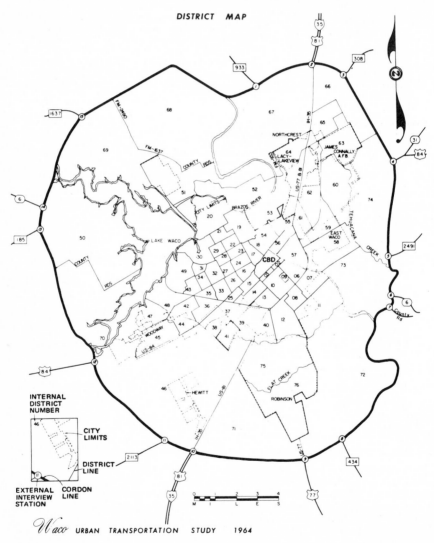

Fig. 2.3 Zonal map for cordoned area surrounding Waco, Texas. (*Waco Urban Transportation Study, 1964.*)

however, since they relate to the use to which land is put, that is *land use*. This term, interpreted in its broadest sense, refers not only to the activity classification: manufacturing, commercial, agricultural, and so forth, but also to the intensity of use, measured by employment, population, acreage, etc., by the zonal location of uses, and by the suitability of land for various activities.

Given this broad definition and recognizing that travel patterns generally are considered to be a function of the location of human activities, we can infer that travel problems are related to land use. Moreover, an extended view of the picture would show transportation affecting land use through the inducement of development in areas adjacent to transportation facilities. Taken together, these two concepts point to land use as a major element in the domain associated with transportation problems.

2.3.3. Definition of Objectives and Constraints

If the problem were the first one listed, that of too much travel delay on routes in zone two, the objective would be to minimize this delay as much as possible or to reduce it to some acceptable level. Yet this specification is not complete since we realize that there are many limitations or constraints on our endeavors to provide better solutions: time and money budgets must be adhered to, financing must be found, the political and social situation must be stable, and so forth. The output of stage II of the planning process therefore is a two part product which, if exemplified by the above problem, would be: *minimize travel delay in zone two subject to given budgetary, financial, political, and social constraints.*

2.3.4 Modeling of the Transportation System and Its Domain

The development of models to be used to represent the interrelationships between the transportation system, development, travel, and other affected factors comprises stage III of the transportation planning process. Since the calibration and use of these models (stage V) is a relevant consideration here, both of these stages will be discussed together at this time.

Figure 2.4 shows six phases basic to the modeling stage of the transportation planning process. Each of these phases corresponds to a type of model (or set of models) needed to produce inputs for the testing and evaluation stage to follow. Perhaps the most important of the six from an instructive standpoint is that of the prediction of zonal land use development levels since this phase is linked directly with the other five.

Required as inputs to this phase are three types of information: (1) projections of future regional land use variables such as population, employment, and land use acreage totals; (2) determinations of present and future levels of other affecting variables such as water, sanitary, and educational services; and (3) estimates of present and proposed transportation system performance, with the emphasis being on travel times, costs headways, and the like.

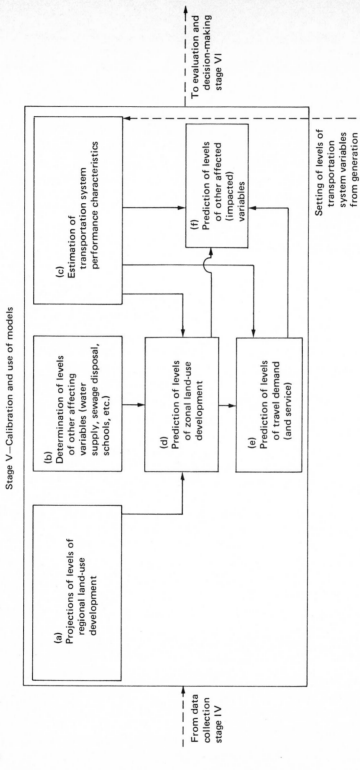

Stage V–Calibration and use of models

(a) Projections of levels of regional land-use development

(b) Determination of levels of other affecting variables (water supply, sewage disposal, schools, etc.)

(c) Estimation of transportation system performance characteristics

(d) Prediction of levels of zonal land-use development

(e) Prediction of levels of travel demand (and service)

(f) Prediction of levels of other affected (impacted) variables

From data collection stage IV

To evaluation and decision-making stage VI

Setting of levels of transportation system variables from generation stage VIII

Fig. 2.4 The six major phases in the calibration and model use stage of the transportation planning process.

A land use model now can be calibrated and employed to allocate the regional land use total among the zones in the region, thereby providing zonal estimates of land use development which in turn can be used in helping to predict travel demand (phase *e*).

Travel demand prediction usually is accomplished by means of a four step procedure which, as noted above, uses predicted future zonal land use values as well as future transportation system performance characteristics (see Fig. 2.4). The first step, *trip generation,* involves the determination of the number of trips produced by or attracted to each zone in a given time period, usually one day. Total numbers of trips are accumulated for each zone regardless of destination. A typical relationship calibrated via regression or similar techniques using existing data might be

$$T_i = \Delta P_i + bI_i + c \qquad\qquad (2.9)$$

where T_i = number of daily trips produced in zone i
P_i = resident population of zone i
I_i = average income of people in zone i
a,b,c = empirically derived parameters

Notice that two land use[6] variables are instrumental in the predictive relationship (Eq. 2.9). No transportation system characteristics are employed in Eq. 2.9, but they will become necessary in the succeeding three steps of the travel prediction procedure.

In step two the trips that are "piled up" at each zone are "dealt out" to the other zones in the region in a manner similar to the way in which individual persons are known to allocate their trips to various destinations—usually on the basis of the relative attractiveness of each zone and its distance from the zone of origin. This allocation process, referred to as *trip distribution,* in most instances uses land use variables such as ground area and floor area as measures of "attractiveness" and transportation network travel times as indicators of "distance." Thus, the trip distribution phase presents an excellent example of the joint use of land use and transportation system variables in the prediction of travel.

The third phase of travel prediction is that of *mode choice,* a phase in which, as the name denotes, estimates are made of the proportion of the interzonal trips found from the trip distribution model that travelers will choose to make by each mode.[7] Again, it is easy to see that both land use and transportation system variables are important factors in the relationships underlying mode choice since the decisions people will make probably will depend both on the characteristics of the transportation system offered (service rate, cost, travel time) and the

---

[6] Again it should be emphasized that "land use" is defined in a very broad sense and includes items such as average income and car ownership even though it is often difficult to conceive of these as ways in which land is used.

[7] Mode choice also can be the first or second step in the travel prediction process.

socioeconomic class of the traveler (e.g., higher income people are more likely to take their car instead of transit.)

The final phase of travel prediction process, *trip assignment*, involves another choice, in this case between the various routes of each mode which may be available to the traveler. For repetitive trips (and most are) this choice generally is based on either relative travel time or relative travel cost. With this last type of prediction accomplished, we then would have completed a description of the future travel on all available routes of each mode of transport in service.

Phase (*f*) of the modeling process also is significant. It is well known that a transportation system and the travel it helps to generate have both beneficial and disbeneficial impacts on factors other than land use. A complete list of factors probably would be extensive and varied, including such items as:

Air pollution   School district boundaries
Noise   Health care for the poor
Financial conditions of Crime
   private corporations   Property damage

Many of the relationships between transportation, travel, and the above items have not been established with finality. Yet more are becoming known as research progresses.

Still lacking in the overall description of the modeling process is a representation of the type and interrelationship of performance characteristics of the transportation system itself. An easy way to view the transportation system is to think of it as composed of four types of items: *vehicles, networks, terminals,* and *controls,* all mixed together in some quantity.

The product of the resultant mixture can be characterized by some of the following features:

Speeds   Dimensions
Capacities   Routes
Locations   Schedules, etc.

These features are not independent of each other, however, as is demonstrated by one relationship between the speed and volume of vehicles on an expressway [2.29, p. 334]:

$$V = 175S - 4.86S^2 \tag{2.10}$$

where V = volume of vehicles (vehicles per hour) and
     S = average speed of vehicles (mph)

Thus, to specify the performance of a particular transportation system, we must be able to identify both the relevant characteristics of the components in the system and the *relationship* between the characteristics. To accomplish this characterization we need models such as Eq. (2.10).

2.3.5 Collection of Data

While it may be true that in other fields of endeavor many models germane to the task can be employed without first investigating in detail the particular situation under study, this generally is not the case in most transportation planning efforts. The main reason for this situation is that parameters (constants, coefficients, exponents, and so forth) that remain stable from study area to study area have not been found. As a consequence, data must be collected in each transportation study to be undertaken in order to calibrate the necessary models, that is, to determine their parameters.

For example, to be able to use Eq. (2.9) for predicting future numbers of trips produced in each zone, we probably would have to compile information on present and past zonal trip productions, zonal population, and average zonal incomes and then use a regression technique (See Appendix, Sec. A.3) to find a, b, and c. Knowing these numbers, and also knowing the future values of P_i and I_i, we then would predict T_i.[8]

At this point we also should emphasize an additional purpose of data collection: to identify more precisely problems, problem domains, objectives, and constraints. In performing stages I and II of the planning process we probably would generate only vague ideas of existing problems and the directions towards which new solutions should be aimed. By gathering more information, we are able to take a problem like "lack of transit service" and specify it more explicitly as "elderly people and school children have to wait too long during daylight hours for a bus." The corresponding objective might be to "maximize the nonauto service provided these people" and a likely constraint might pertain to the yearly budget which could be allocated to the proposed service.

To summarize briefly the major needs of the data collection stage, we might classify desired information into 10 categories:

1. Statements of problems (present and anticipated future)
2. Statements of objectives and constraints (present and anticipated future)
3. Types of models (present)
4. Types, locations, and intensities of land use (past and present)
5. Transportation system features (present)
6. Travel (past and present)
7. Transportation technology (present and anticipated future)
8. Other affecting variables (present and anticipated future)
9. Evaluation procedures (present)
10. Implementation procedures (present)

It should be noted that the assembling of this vast quantity of data is a strenuous task, and, as an added burden, the engineer and planner must keep

---

[8] We also must assume that a, b, and c all will hold constant in the future, a rather daring assumption.

abreast of innovations in areas such as information detection, handling, sorting, storing, and display techniques as well as procedures for coping with sampling problems, errors, mistakes, bias, and prefabrication in data collection efforts. In fact, a summary of these and similar items would in itself constitute a supplemental set of information to be collected.

2.3.6   Evaluation of Performance and Decision Making

Suppose data have been collected for the models discussed in Section 2.3.4 and that these models have been calibrated and used in stage V of the planning process on the initial assumption that no change from the present (or committed) transportation system will be made in the future. The transformations that could come about under this "no change" situation would be those in land use development, travel, and other affected factors and these could be evaluated in stage VI (see Fig. 2.2). We would expect in this situation that the evaluated future performance of these factors generally would be worse than that which now exists; that is to say, we most likely would end up further from our stated objectives (stage II) because of probable increases in tripmaking (and consequent congestion), probable restrictions in growth in urban areas due to the lack of new transportation facilities, and probable increases in air pollution, noise, pedestrian accidents and so forth.

In any case, by making the initial supposition of no new facilities, we provide ourselves with a datum by which actual transportation modifications, to be generated in stage VII, can be judged. In other words, the performance of a modified transportation system in regard both to travel and its impact on the environment will lie somewhere between the previously noted datum and the other extreme at which there is a complete securement of the stated objectives. Given these upper and lower limits on performance, we then are able to judge each system modification when the return is made from the generation stage (stage VII) to the modeling stage (stage V) and then to the evaluation stage (stage VI).[9]

In going through the evaluation and decision making process, the planner or engineer must face some of the most vexing difficulties in the planning process. For example, the first, and perhaps most paradoxical, question concerns the role of the planner and engineer in evaluating solutions and making decisions among them. It may be that such decisions should be left entirely to the political structure of the region or to appointed citizen boards. The answer to this question is far from apparent, yet, as mentioned above, it is just one in a series of questions that may be imponderable. Several others are:

1. On what governmental level should evaluative decisions be made—local, state, or federal?
2. What variables should be considered in the evaluation—lives saved, families to be relocated, etc?

---

[9] See the corresponding feedback arrow (number 8) in Fig. 2.2.

3. How should some of these variables be measured (e.g., appearance)?

4. How should possible future risk and uncertainty be handled?

Some techniques exist for providing a rejoinder to these queries, but on the whole they are resolved through an oftentimes imperceptible interaction that occurs between all concerned parties. Whatever the nature of the evaluation process involved, decisions among alternative solutions eventually are made, but rarely through a simple and concise approach which may seem desirable.

2.3.7 Generation of the Transportation Alternatives

In the generation stage of the transportation planning process an attempt is made to bring together the four components of a transportation system (vehicles, networks, terminals, and controls) in such a way as to come as close as possible to fulfilling transportation and environmental objectives. In other words, it is the duty of the engineer or planner to pick from among all of the available components those which, when evaluated, will prove to be most beneficial or effective.

It should be noticed immediately that involved in generation is the process of creativity. Few planners or designers can deny that most of the better solutions for problems (especially those in transportation) have come to the surface through a series of intangible and untraceable steps that are an outgrowth of the creative force at work. However, it also happens that some of the worst ideas have come about through "creativity," so that in recent years many techniques have been developed as aids both in the development of better solutions and the prevention of poorer ones.

The most sophisticated of these techniques are those of mathematical programming—linear programming, nonlinear programming, dynamic programming, and so forth. The rudiments of several of these are presented in the Appendix. Mathematical programming is useful because it entails the optimization of some objective function when certain constraints are present. Clearly, if we had simple, nicely behaved, measurable objectives as well as similarly natured constraints, we could arrive at a "best" solution. Unfortunately, most objectives and constraints usually are neither explicit enough nor simple enough for such an approach.

Two other approaches to generation are those of *search* and *experimental design*. In the former approach, a set of models like those portrayed in Fig. 2.4 are employed and the values of the input variables are altered in a systematic manner according to the outputs that result from each previous alteration (or alterations). Each new solution generated usually is better than the last, so that eventually an optimum would be reached. Experimental design proceeds in approximately the same manner, but deals with experiments on the actual system, not on models of that system. Again, as in the case of the mathematical programming approaches, the vagueness and complexity of objectives and constraints usually precludes the derivation of valuable solutions from these two techniques.

The last approach, and probably the most prevalent, is that of trial and analysis, which is nothing more than an unsystematic search of a very limited set of possible modification alternatives. While the costs of the design endeavor itself are low, the trial and analysis approach does eliminate the option of obtaining better solutions through the increased probing of various transportation system possibilities.

After any one of these approaches has been used, what evolves is a broad identification of a modified transportation system composed of each of the four major components and their features. An example of such a system would be that of a hanging monorail, capable of handling 2,000 passengers per hour, running on elevated prestressed concrete beams, located in the Central Business District, with terminals costing $200,000 each, spaced at 400-yard intervals, and controlled by a railroad block-type subsystem.

Given a proposed system of this nature, we would have to return to the model use and evaluation stages of the planning process in order to determine, first, the impacts of the system on land use, travel and other affected factors and, second, the extent to which stated system objectives have been fulfilled. After going through these two stages, it may turn out that transportation system modifications again are needed. In the end, the accepted modifications would be added to (or in some cases substituted for) the committed but not already operational system.

2.3.8 Solution Specification

Up to this stage in the planning process the description of the present transportation system, the present domain, and future transportation system modifications has been a broad one, accenting only the most general features. As far as the transportation system is concerned, for example, we have been dealing only with rough estimates of costs, speeds, capacities, and so forth, these being obtained from average figures from past experiences or previous testing with similar systems. But it may be that there is little in the way of past data available on particular systems, as would be the case for downtown distribution and new aircraft systems discussed in Chap. 9.

In these situations, the only information we would have would be "guesstimates" of the costs and other characteristics involved. Thus, the task falls to the designer at the solution specification stage to specify the chosen solution much more exactly, that is, in as much detail as needed to construct and operate the actual system. For example, most highway designs require detailed geometrics, house and property line locations, highway curvature information, and fenceline and drainage pipe specifications.

It should be emphasized that the output of the solution specification stage is not always a drawing or some other kind of physical representation. Specifics may take the form of laws, policy statements, or general budget or financing procedures.

2.3.9 Implementation

The ninth stage of the transportation planning process is the actual bringing into existence of the plan or solution detailed in the solution specification stage. Naturally, construction procedures play an important role in this stage so that there must be a concern for good management practice in endeavors such as the handling of materials and the scheduling of construction projects. Yet transportation planners also must be cognizant of other aspects relevant to implementation. These may include:

Administration	Politics
Finance	Capital budgeting
Taxation	Improvement programming
Pricing	Personnel management
Cost allocation	Marketing
Among users	Advertising
Between users and nonusers	Public relations
Research and development	Accounting

On a slightly different plane there is the whole subject of *land use control*. Inherent in this item are such concepts as zoning, in which laws are made concerning the use of individual properties; subdivision regulations, which refer to the manner in which raw land under one ownership is converted into building lots, and eminent domain and condemnation, which are procedures for obtaining land and other property needed for a public use such as transportation. Taken together, the set of subjects presented in this and the previous paragraph constitute the major tools for implementing and insuring the stability of any planned solution.

2.3.10 Operation and Maintenance

The mention of the topics of zoning and subdivision regulations implies that the implementation stage is pertinent not only to the realization of the solution but also to its continued operation and maintenance (stage X). That is to say, there is a need to keep constant surveillance over the performance of the system to ensure that the intended objectives are fulfilled to the degree originally thought possible. What is required at this point then, is a control process, indicated by arrows 11 and 13 in Fig. 2.2, in which there is collection of new data, referenced to the operation and maintenance of the system, an evaluation of the newly recorded performance of the system, and specification of certain small modifications which will improve the performance to the desired level. Thus operation and maintenance really involves a continual recycling through the stages III to IX of the planning process, with the emphasis placed on refining the more detailed parts of previously obtained general solutions.

Looking at the details of the operation and maintenance stage, we usually would find a concern for some of the following items:

Operation
    Collection of fare and other charges
    Personnel management
    Keeping of accounts of revenues and expenditures
    Preparation of budgets
    Marketing and public relations
    Responding to emergencies

Training
Crime prevention, etc.
Maintenance
Grass cutting and right-of-way clearance
Inspection of components (vehicles, guideways, terminals, controls)
Overhaul and/or replacement of worn components
Snow removal
Cleaning, etc.

The list under each category could get quite long and would vary, of course, depending on the nature of the transportation system under consideration.

2.3.11   Additional Comments on the Process

The continuous nature of the planning process should be reemphasized at this point. Plans should not be so hard and fast that they cannot be subject to some revision as the types of relevant problems, the specified goals and objectives, and the technology of transportation change and evolve through time.

Another point to stress is that the transportation planning process is in most cases an expensive and time-consuming endeavor, costing in the neighborhood of $2 per capita and taking (for the initial part) 3 to 6 years in larger cities. Additionally, there usually is a considerable time span between proposal of new facilities and their construction. New freeways, for example, would be about 8 years in this stage. What is needed, then, are studies parallel to the long-term transportation planning study. These endeavors would be short-term and directed toward improvements that can be implemented within periods up to 3 years in length. Included here might be traffic engineering changes such as traffic signals, one-way streets, and additional turning lanes. Also included would be changes in bus routes, creation of special bus-only street lanes, and new ticketing arrangements (e.g., script fare systems). By working on both short- and long-term solutions, the transportation planning agency can improve both its flexibility and usefulness.

2.4 SUMMARY

The objective of this chapter has been to present a systematic version of the transportation planning process useful in organizing the approach to solving both short- and long-term transportation and related problems. This process was envisioned as having 10 stages:

1. Statement of problem and problem domain
2. Identification of goals, objectives, and constraints
3. Modeling of the system
4. Collection of data
5. Calibration and use of models
6. Evaluation of performance and decision among solutions
7. Generation of new solutions
8. Specification of chosen solution

9. Implementation of chosen solution

10. Operation and maintenance of solution

The final stage would be followed by continued checks to see if the solution were as effective as predicted. Long-term planning processes also should be accompanied by short-term, problem-solving efforts.

It is not suggested that the process discussed in this chapter is the way transportation planning should be or is being done. In different situations new stages could be added, existing stages mixed in order, and many other changes made which might lead to a process (and the solutions it generates) more effective than that portrayed here. There is a need, however, to focus on one type of process so that thinking about approaches to transportation problems can be systematized somewhat. With this idea in mind, we have organized future chapters of this book to correspond to the stages in the planning process presented here.

BIBLIOGRAPHY

2.1 Ackoff, R. L., and M. W. Sasieni: *Fundamentals of Operations Research*, Wiley, New York, 1968.

2.2 Harrisberger, L.: *Engineermanship: A Philosophy of Design*, Brooks/Cole, Belmont, Calif., 1966.

2.3 Krick, E. V.: *An Introduction to Engineering and Engineering Design*, Wiley, New York, 1965.

2.4 Woodson, T. T.: *Introduction to Engineering Design*, McGraw-Hill, New York, 1966.

2.5 Manheim, M. L.: "Principles of Transport Systems Analysis," *Highway Research Board Record*, 180, 1967.

2.6 Thomas, E. N., and J. L. Schofer: *Strategies for Evaluation of Alternate Transportation Plans*, Two Parts, The Transportation Center, Northwestern Univ., Evanston, Ill., 1967.

2.7 Chicago Area Transportation Study, vol. I, Chicago, 1959.

2.8 Moyer, R. A.: "Comprehensive Urban Transportation Study Methods," *Journal of the Highway Division, ASCE*, vol. 91, no. HW2, December 1965.

2.9 U.S. Department of Commerce, Office of High Speed Ground Transportation, Transport Systems Planning Division: *Study Design*, Northeast Corridor Transportation Project Technical Paper No. 5, Washington, D.C., July 1966.

2.10 Martin, B. V., F. W. Memmott, and A. J. Bone: *Principles and Techniques for Predicting Future Demand for Urban Area Transportation*, M.I.T., Dept. of Civil Engineering, Cambridge, Mass., January 1963.

2.11 Zettle, R. M., and R. R. Carll: *Summary Review of Major Metropolitan Area Transportation Studies in the United States*, Special Report, ITTE, Univ. of Calif., Berkeley, 1962.

2.12 U.S. Department of Commerce, Bureau of Public Roads: *Calibrating and Testing a Gravity Model for Any Size Urban Area*, Washington, D.C., October 1965.

2.13 Asimow, M.: *Introduction to Design*, Prentice-Hall, Englewood Cliffs, N.J., 1962.

2.14 Snell, J. E.: *A Framework for the Analysis of Urban Transportation Research*, Unpublished Ph.D. Dissertation, Dept. of Civil Engineering, Northwestern Univ., Evanston, Ill., 1962.

2.15 Goode, H. and R. Machol: *System Engineering*, McGraw-Hill, New York, 1957.

2.16 Hall, A. D.: *A Methodology for Systems Engineering*, D. Van Nostrand, New York, 1962.

2.17 Manheim, M. L.: *Problem Solving Processes in Planning and Design*, M.I.T., Dept. of Civil Engineering, Cambridge, Mass., January 1967.

2.18 Campbell, D. T., and J. C. Stanley: "Experimental and Quasi-Experimental Designs for Research and Teaching," in N. L. Gage (ed.), *Handbook of Research on Teaching*, Rand McNally, Chicago, 1963.

2.19 Branch, M. C.: *Planning: Aspects and Applications*, Wiley, New York, 1966.

2.20 Metropolitan Planning Commission, Kansas City Region: *Study Design for a Comprehensive Development Plan*, Kansas City, Mo., May 1967.

2.21 Quade, E.: *Analysis for Military Decisions*, Rand McNally, Chicago, 1967.

2.22 Rapoport, A.: *Operational Philosophy*, Science ed., Wiley, New York, 1967.

2.23 Altschuler, A.: *The City Planning Process—A Political Analysis*, Cornell Univ. Press, Ithaca, N.Y., 1966.

2.24 Orcutt, G. H., J. Korbel, and A. M. Rivlin: *Microanalysis of Socio-Economic Systems: A Simulation Study*, Harper and Row, New York, 1961.

2.25 Baerwald J. E.: (ed.), *Traffic Engineering Handbook* (3d ed.), Institute of Traffic Engineers, Washington, D.C., 1965.

2.26 Meier, R. L.: *A Communications Theory of Urban Growth*, M.I.T. Press, Cambridge, Mass., 1962.

2.27 U.S. Department of Housing and Urban Development: *Tomorrow's Transportation*, U.S. Government Printing Office, Washington, D.C., 1968.

2.28 Westinghouse Air Brake Company: *Study of Evolutionary Urban Transportation*, vol 1, Federal Clearinghouse, Springfield, Va., February 1968.

2.29 Wohl, M., and B. V. Martin: *Traffic System Analysis for Engineers and Planners*, McGraw-Hill, New York, 1967.

3 Transportation Problems

Almost all attempts to improve a given situation start with the recognition and statement of a problem. Where and when the problem first emerges is often difficult to tell; many are uncovered through the press, radio, television, and other mass media; still others are vocalized by citizen groups reporting to elected officials or in discussions between the elected officials themselves. Whatever the manner in which problems are identified, it is clear that certain ones come to be held as more important or of broader scope than others and thus are given consideration at higher levels of government and industry. Lacking information about many problems specific to one community or state, we have chosen to highlight in this chapter those that are deemed to have broader import. Nevertheless, local difficulties are far from unimportant, and it is hoped that procedures similar to that evolved here can be utilized to identify local problems.

This chapter is divided in three parts. In the first part, an attempt is made to define and clarify what is meant by a "problem" and its "domain." This is not an easy task by any means, with one of the primary difficulties being the complex relationship between a problem and each of its counterparts. As a consequence, in the second part of the chapter there will be a brief discussion about problem identification, problem hierarchy, and problem breadth. In the final part, a set of specific problems generally associated with transportation will be presented.

3.1 THE NATURE OF A PROBLEM

Perhaps the easiest way to avoid some of the complexity inherent in any discussion of problems is to begin with a definition. For purposes of this book, the following definition appears reasonable:

> A problem for an individual or group of individuals is the difference between the desired state for a given situation and the actual state. This difference usually cannot be eliminated immediately (if ever).

This definition brings out certain fundamental features. First, and fairly obviously, a problem relates to a given individual or group and not necessarily to the whole population. This disparity in itself often is a source of misunderstanding since those people not directly affected may find it difficult to comprehend the nature and/or magnitude of the problem.

Second, a problem arises out of an ambition to achieve the most desirable state for a given situation. However, the identification of what is "most desirable" is in itself a problem and seems to depend on the nature of goals, either conscious or unconscious, that people feel are significant. This connection of problems to goals thus implies that they both are really two sides of the same coin. They are so completely related that it is difficult to say which is the more likely definition: the problem is to meet the particular goal or the goal is to solve the particular problem. Either statement might serve well under given circumstances.

The fact that the difference between the most desirable state (goal) and actual state cannot be eliminated immediately (if ever) leads the individuals or groups involved into the characteristic psychological conditions of anger, anxiety, yearning, or even agony usually associated with a problem. In fact, if one or more of these conditions do not occur, we, as problem solvers, probably would tend to doubt the existence of a "real" problem. If it were otherwise, the situation could be readily improved to the most desirable state and the anxiety associated with the problem would not have a chance to build up.

One other feature of problems that should be recognized is that when the actual state is improved to the point where it is equivalent to the most desirable state, aspirations may subsequently rise, again creating a gap between actual and desired states. This type of occurrence is common in areas of the world where there is a "wave of rising expectations" founded upon a steadily improving economy and a relatively stable political scene. As Thomas and Schofer [3.17, p. 65] remark:

> The success or failure of a program must not be judged solely upon the basis of the satisfaction or dissatisfaction of the individuals and groups affected by it. Very successful programs may result in the elevation of levels of aspiration so that dissatisfaction still remains.
>
> ... even if urban areas were instantly rebuilt today so that every element within them were evaluated as performing perfectly, then, after the passage of time, aspiration levels would change so that performance of certain elements would again be deemed unsatisfactory.

This dilemma is a discouraging one for the problem solver, especially since it implies that most problems can never be solved "once and for all time." However, we are left with the consolation that a problem situation at least can be improved beyond its present state.

3.2 COMMENTS ON PROBLEMS

The first comment that can be made about problem statements is that they oftentimes are a reflection of cause and effect. As an illustration, consider the following quote taken from *Railway Track and Structures* [3.18, p. 26]:

> Foremost among these problems is the lack of uniformity in the grade of ties, even when cut from stands of timber in the same localities, resulting in non-uniform shrinkage and uneven depth.

In reading this, one cannot help but think that the problem of "lack of uniformity in the grade of timber ties" really is not a very important one unless this factor *has an effect on* some other, more notable conditions such as ride comfort or safety. With this example, it is easy to recognize that many problems are stated in such a way that the actual difficulty, related to the real goal or desired state, is not mentioned.

The lack of a clear declaration of the desired state to be reached creates both advantageous and disadvantageous situations. It is advantageous in that it may lead to the discovery of a factor which previously had not been recognized as being relevant to the particular situation. A good illustration would be the previous statement on nonuniformity of timber railroad ties. Until this factor had been specified as a problem, at least tentatively, no attempt would have been made to study it, and comfort and safety might have remained below par. In fact, by using this type of problem statement as a stimulant to research, the analyst is likely to locate several causative factors which then can be used to help uncover possible solutions.

On the other side of the ledger, problem statements not related to ultimate goals can be disadvantageous because they tend to mislead the investigator. It may turn out, for example, that nonuniformity of timber railroad ties had no effect whatsoever on ride comfort and safety so that any efforts expended to create uniform shrinkage and even depths would be all for naught. Perhaps, it is because past occurrences of this sort of misdirection have been numerous that the expression that "the proper identification of the problem leads one 90 percent of the way toward its solution" is so often quoted.

3.2.1 Problem Breadth

Another unfavorable aspect of problem identification made without reference to the ultimately desirable state is that the identification is apt to be concentrated on only a small set of factors and not the total set that adequately describes the actual problem situation. In other words, there is likely to be a lack of breadth in the problem statement. Krick, in his introductory book for engineers, warns that [3.19]:

> The more a total problem is subdivided into independent subproblems, the less effective the total solution is likely to be.

He then states that:

> Some of the most significant engineering contributions come about as a result of a much broader treatment of problems that were previously treated in a piecemeal fashion.

To illustrate such a situation he cites a transportation-related example in which City X, like many urban communities, is plagued by a severe parking problem in its downtown area. The proportion of its commercial district alloted to parking has reached 40 percent, which has prompted the city officials to hire a consulting engineer to design a 600-car, multistory parking facility, which is to be one of a series of similar facilities to be constructed in the congested area.

At this point the engineer notes that not only has a limited problem (parking) been given to him, but the solution (car park) as well. He realizes, however, that the "real" problem is that of transferring a large segment of the population between its place of residence and its place of business. This broad formulation opens up a whole realm of promising solutions, one of which might be a large-scale, high-speed transit system. Of course, nothing in the engineer's formulation precludes the possibility of a radically different type of urban community that reduces the need for transportation.

From this example, it becomes clear that many problem solvers have not attacked the most significant problem but instead have narrowed their analysis to a smaller portion of the situation. The result, all too often, is that the solution to the more parochial problem is in direct opposition to the solution of the large one and actually hinders further attempts at solving it.

This is not to deny the importance and difficulty of subdividing large problems into smaller, more manageable ones. This task, to be discussed later, is necessary since many real world situations are far too complex to be handled *in toto*. What is of concern here is, however, that the problem not be stated so narrowly at the beginning that its full scope and impact remains hidden.

As far as transportation problems in general are concerned, we can only feel that many of them have extremely broad implications, perhaps broader than many have imagined. This is the primary reason why we have attempted to establish a wide base for modeling and estimation in the chapter on the transportation planning process, and it is also the reason why the *domain* of a problem must be considered. The previous example of City X's parking situation provides a good illustration of this point. Even if the "correct" problem of "transferring a large segment of the population between its place of residence and its place of business" is recognized, we must also realize that a solution may bring with it certain problems that presently do not exist. In City X's case, for instance, if the city council does decide on mass transit instead of the car park, they may eventually face a financial problem since most mass transit companies have had fiscal difficulties in the past.

Yet, there is also a plus side: air pollution, noise, and automobile congestion in the CBD may be relieved to some extent. Whatever the final result, it is important for the council to acknowledge some consequences that were not of particular interest when the "problem" was initially stated. Those factors of indirect concern that either affect or are affected by the transportation system comprise the transportation *problem domain.* Also known as "concommitant outputs" or "externalities" in various academic disciplines, these factors in the problem domain generally have to be given as much or more attention as any of those of direct concern. Oftentimes it is even possible to think of *using* transportation to help achieve a desirable state for the problem environment.[1] In fact, if travel is viewed as it is by many economists as a derived demand,[2] that is, a demand that is brought about by attempts to achieve something else (e.g., a job or an education or better health through a visit to the doctor), then it follows that *all* consequences of a transportation system are concomitant and thus part of the transportation problem domain. Nonetheless, even if this concept of travel were not felt relevant, we still should be aware that factors (and associated problems) in the problem domain are of extreme importance in a transportation analysis and should, in the interests of breadth of approach, be given full consideration.

3.2.2 Identification and Classification of Problems

Even if the investigator were desirous of giving problems in the problem domain full consideration, the difficulty he then would face would be that of identifying and classifying all of the problems of concern. Without any stretch of the imagination, it is possible to make a list of at least 50 problems of importance: air pollution, noise, odor, safety, travel time, capacity, and so forth. With greater thought we may even be able to expand the list into the hundreds. The difficulties here are (1) we never know whether we have set down a complete list and (2) we never know whether we have listed a problem more than once (through an inadvertent rephrasing of the nature of the problem). In the words of the mathematician, we do not know whether or not we have achieved an exhaustive and mutually exclusive set of problems.

How to obtain a mutually exclusive and exhaustive list of problems is not at all clear at this time. The approach used in this book has been to divide all related problems into three classes: (1) those that are direct transportation service problems, that is, affect mainly the user, (2) those in the problem domain *affected* by transportation, and (3) those in the problem domain *affecting* transportation. The hope is that these three together will form an exhaustive set and separately will form mutually exclusive sets. However, we are sure that many overlaps and additions eventually will be found, thereby requiring the creation of a new and better classification system.[3] More will be said about this awkward situation while

---

[1] A good example of such a situation would be the busing of school children to achieve racial balance in schools.

[2] For a discussion of derived demand for travel, see W. Oi and P. W. Shuldiner, *An Analysis of Urban Travel Demand,* Northwestern University Press, Evanston, Illinois, 1962.

[3] A classification according to (1) man and groups (of men), (2) the man-built environment, (3) the natural environment, and (4) activities of man can be found in Sec. 4.3.

discussing goals in Chapter 4, but for now the pinpointing of identification difficulties is sufficient.

3.2.3 Problem Hierarchy

The question that should enter the reader's mind upon completing the last paragraph is that of whether the classification of problems into the above three groups is adequate from an operational standpoint. What can be done with such a classification anyway? The answer is: not much—yet. What is required is a subdivision of these three classes into more tangible and workable subcategories. We could, for example, trace down a "tree' as in Fig. 3.1 as follows:

> The sum total of all transportation problems is divided into those that are direct service problems, and those that affect, or, are affected by transportation. The service problems are further subdivided into the more specific categories of "congestion," "inadequate capacity," "lack of safety for the user," and so forth. The third of these categories is broken down into "too many accidents involving other motor vehicles," "too many accidents involving fixed objects," and so forth. And so the process continues.

Near the last stage, most people would get the feeling that they had reduced the problem to a level at which they could really cope with it. They could, for instance, try to predict the effect a new expressway would have on the number and location of accidents involving fixed objects, and this type of analysis would be sufficient for most investigations. Any studies made on higher level problems (e.g., lack of safety for user) may not be detailed enough whereas any on lower levels (e.g., accidents involving telephone poles) may be too time and effort consuming to be of any value.

The points to be made here are that, first, problems come in a hierarchy, in other words, at different levels of generality. They range all the way from "inadequate transportation" to "a recurrent pothole at such and such a street at such and such a time, etc." Second, various problems are "solved" at different levels in the hierarchy. If work is being done on an overall regional transportation problem, it may not be possible to be concerned with anything more specific than "poor accessibility."

On the other hand, if a study involves a particular route location problem, it may well be concerned with the types of accidents that occur (e.g., involving pedestrians, fixed objects, or motor vehicles) as well as ugliness and unhealthy conditions that may be fostered. The analysis of the problem, and the corresponding solution, may turn out to be very specific in this situation. Nonetheless, whatever the situation, the concept should be clear: each and every problem falls somewhere in the hierarchy and usually is solved at that level.

3.2.4 Future Problems

The final remark to be made in this section seems a bit obvious, but actually has deceptively complex connotations: the problems that we should be solving are not necessarily those that exist right now but those that will exist at the time the solution will take effect (and thereafter). When one considers the fact that the lag

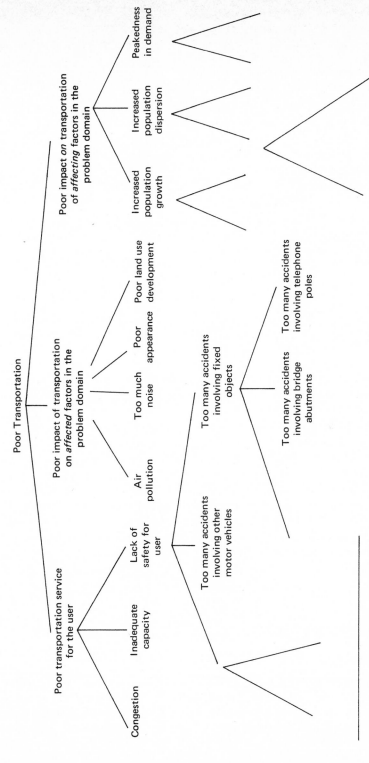

Fig. 3.1 A hierarchical "tree" of problems.

time between the formulation of a solution to many transportation problems and the implementation of that solution in the field may (and often does) exceed 10 years (especially when large-scale construction is involved), he is forced to remember that he must solve the problem that will exist *at that time*, not now.

As a practical illustration of this idea, consider the construction of a freeway. If the planner and engineer were to design the freeway for today's traffic (and the problems which it creates), they might risk the possibility of the facility being overloaded (congested) on the day of its opening. The main cause of this dilemma would be the buildup of traffic over the time period of construction, to say nothing of the additional problem created by the traffic "induced" by the new facility itself.

Working with future problems, although theoretically correct, does present at least one difficulty with which few if any researchers or practitioners have been able to come to grips: the importance attached to a given problem may change in the future. If we were to look 20 years in the past, for example, we probably would find that very little attention was directed toward such problems as air pollution, noise, lack of public transport needed for the poor to get to employment opportunities, and so forth. Even if a farsighted plan from the past did happen to take into account these problems, they probably would not have been given a very high priority. Reinterpreted, these statements indicate that in the past the difference between the desired and actual states of certain factors was very small. Now, due to probable adverse changes in the levels of these factors and also to increased public awareness of their existence and importance, the "problems" have become more severe, that is to say that difference between the desired and actual states has increased.

The question of how to predict changes over time in the perceived severity of problems actually has received little attention to date. As a consequence, this all-important consideration is left almost entirely to the subjective judgment of both the person or persons attempting to solve the problem (whatever it is at a given time) and those attempting to make decisions among alternatives proposed as solutions to the problem. The dilemma of the constantly varying importance of problems is, to our way of thinking, a frustrating one and adds even more significance to the statement that "the proper identification of the problem takes one 90 percent of the way toward its solution."

3.3 TRANSPORTATION PROBLEMS

As has been suggested several times previously in this chapter, the scope of transportation problems is extremely broad, so broad in fact that it often is difficult to identify all of the problems directly and indirectly influenced by transportation. In this section we will attempt to list and document a few of these problems and hope that the reader will be able to fill in the remainder from his own experience or particular situation.

The types of problems to be discussed are divided into three general classes:
1. Those that are direct transportation service problems
2. Those in the problem domain *affected by* (or impacted by) transportation
3. Those in the problem domain that *affect* transportation

Quotes and statistics taken from a variety of sources will help to illustrate each type of problem. The reader should be aware that many of the quotes are somewhat exaggerated for purposes of emphasis and may show only one side of an issue or problem. Some may even contain incorrect or misleading information. Still others may be stated in a highly emotional way in order to appeal to the consciences of the problem-solver and decisionmaker. What is of importance here, however, is that the planner or engineer recognize that these are the conditions in which real problems often show themselves; so that it becomes necessary to cut away the unneeded verbage and misleading information to get to the heart of the situation. A similar approach would be used in reading through the sections to follow.

3.3.1 Transportation Service Problems

Those problems that have received the most attention to date are those that affect the *user* of the transportation system. Congestion, delay, the high cost of travel, safety, and lack of privacy (for mass transit) are but a few of the many difficulties that plague the traveler. These and similar problems will be discussed in this section.

3.3.1.1 Congestion Perhaps the first problem that comes to mind in regard to transportation is congestion, which generally can be equated to long travel times and to delays in movement.

Buchanan effectively summarizes the problem of congestion in his much publicized report on *Traffic in Towns* [3.4, p. 22]. In it, he states that:

> The problems of movement are equally familiar so that there is little need to emphasize the frustrations and irritations of traffic jams, the waste of fuel, the waste of time, and the vast and essentially unproductive effort by police, wardens, and others engaged in many capacities in regulating traffic. A motor vehicle, even in its heaviest and clumsiest form, is capable of moving at a mile a minute, yet the average speed of traffic in large cities is about 11 mph.

Just how bad is the congestion problem in measurable terms? Data supplied to Wilfred Owen [3.2] by the American Transit Association and reproduced in Table 3.1 shows that speeds in the central business districts of several large U.S. cities are extremely low, especially for transit. The 4.9 mph and 5.6 mph figures for transit in downtown Dallas and Philadelphia are almost unimaginable and indicate a need for great improvements. One interesting aspect of the congestion problem is that congestion itself apparently is decreasing, yet we seem to be hearing more about it lately. Table 3.2, showing speed data in three different years in Los Angeles, illustrates the former point rather well. Speeds have increased over the years in almost all cases, but "congestion" still appears to be a problem to motorists in that city. This phenomenon of an increasing concern for a problem (in this instance, congestion) that actually is diminishing in extent, highlights rather clearly the

Table 3.1   Speed of Transit vs . Auto in the Central Business District (Miles per hour)

City	Transit	Auto
Bridgeport, Conn.	10	12.2
Dayton, Ohio	7	12–14
Detroit, Mich.	12.4	18
Louisville, Ky.	11	12–17
Philadelphia, Pa.	5.6	8.3
San Antonio, Texas	11.2	22
San Francisco, Calif.	6–9	7–13
Washington, D.C.	8	14
Dallas, Texas	4.9	8.8
Indianapolis, Ind.	13	9

Source: [3.2, p. 148]. © 1966 by the Brookings Institution, Washington, D.C.

Table 3.2   Travel Time Comparisons, Los Angeles Area, 1936, 1957, and 1960 (minutes)

From Broadway and Seventh Street to:	1936 Off-peak*	1957 Off-peak†	1957 Rush-hours	1960 Off-peak*
Pasadena	31	21†		18
South Pasadena	26	15†	21	14
San Marino	30	22†		22
Monterey Park	25	21†		18
Sierra Madre	40	34†		34
El Monte	31	26		24
Whittier	35		44	
Woodland Hills	57		64	
San Fernando	43		50	
Van Nuys	45	39		28
Universal City	32	20		16
Hollywood	23	17		16
Torrance	34		31	
Playa del Rey	37		37	
Venice	40		30	
San Pedro	48	42		35
Wilmington	39	36		29
Bell	25	22		20
Downey	33	25		24
Norwalk	37	27		26

*For this table, off-peak hours are from 9:30 A.M. to 3:30 P.M.
†Information provided by supplemental test run.
Note: Vehicle registration figures for Los Angeles County: 1936 = 967,981; 1956 = 2,741,422; 1960 = 3,360,000 (est)
Source: [3.6, p. 76].

statement by Thomas and Schofer (Sec. 3.1) that even if urban areas were instantly rebuilt to perfection, aspiration levels would rise, with the result that the performance of certain elements eventually would be deemed unsatisfactory again. People's expectations as to needed reductions in congestion apparently are increasing.

3.3.1.2 Inadequate capacity A second problem, and one that is of great significance in regard to congestion, is that of capacity: there must be sufficient facilities available to accomodate the demand for travel when and where it occurs. Examples of problems evolving when capacity becomes a scarce commodity are prevalent in most urban areas. In fact, lack of capacity generally means slow downs and delays in travel and thus really is one aspect of congestion as the traveler sees it.

The capacity problem is one that seems to be getting worse in many places as time progresses. Table 3.3 shows the ratio of peak hour volumes to design capacities on several of Chicago's main north-south arteries. Over a 2-year period the ratios associated with five of the eight arteries increased. The situation on Cicero Avenue is especially difficult since the volume grew so rapidly in the 2 years that it eventually exceeded the *predicted* capacity of the street. One can easily imagine the tieups and resulting frustrations that would result from such a situation.

The relative capacity of various modes has been a subject of much interest, and many critics of planning procedures in urban areas have jumped on the highway building program because highways just do not seem to be able to carry the great loads forced upon them. Higbee, for example, says [3.10, p. 203]:

> These are some of the rubber-tired facts of modern life: A single lane of surface street, subject to cross traffic in front and marginal friction along the sides, will allow about 1,600 persons in private automobiles to pass a given point in one hour. Trains running on a single

Table 3.3 Relationship of Peak-hour Traffic Volume to Design Capacity on North–South Arterials at Congress Street Screenline: Chicago, 1959 and 1961

Arterial	Peak-hour design capacity	Peak-hour volume (5:00 to 6:00 P.M.)		Relationship of peak-hour volume to design capacity	
		1959	1961	1959	1961
Cicero	2,130	1,730	2,290	0.81	1.08
Laramie	1,640	1,790	1,540	1.09	0.94
Central	1,640	900	1,260	0.55	0.77
Austin	1,400	1,100	1,650	0.78	1.18
Ridgeland	1,550	1,200	1,200	0.77	0.77
Oak Park	1,110	1,080	930	0.97	0.84
Harlem	1,550	1,500	1,930	0.97	1.24
Des Plaines	1,000	800	900	0.80	0.90
Total	12,020	10,100	11,700	0.84	0.97

Source: [3.6, p. 79].

track, whether above or below ground, can carry from 40,000 to 60,000 persons per hour depending on whether they run as locals or expresses.

Translated into space requirements these figures are staggering. A single railroad track, used for trains that stop briefly every half to three quarters of a mile, is worth 25 lanes of ordinary street. A single railroad track, used for trains that stop briefly every one to three miles, is worth 23 lanes of turnpike or elevated express highway.

Mumford comments on the relationship between pedestrian and vehicular capacity [3.9, p. 253]:

As for the pedestrian, one could move a hundred thousand people, by the existing streets, from, say, downtown Boston to the Common (a nearby park and historical place), in something like half an hour, and find plenty of room for them to stand. But how many weary hours would it take to move them in cars over these same streets.*

From these comments it is easy to judge the amount of importance to be attributed to the problem of inadequate capacity. In fact, capacity has been of so much concern to the traffic engineer that the Highway Research Board has produced for him an extremely detailed and complete manual [3.28] on the topic; and research continues in an effort to estimate and compare the capacities of various modes.

3.3.1.3 High user cost   Another problem, and one for which little relief is in sight, is that of the high cost of transportation to the user, in particular to those users and potential users with low incomes. A report by the Department of Housing and Urban Development to Congress points to this problem and also to some of its consequences [3.12, p. 16]:

If a man cannot afford a car, and public transit is both inadequate and too expensive, and his job has shifted to a suburb, while racial and economic segregation prevent him from following the job—that man is effectively isolated from earning a living. Further, the 40 percent in the under $4,000 income group who do own a car must bear the heavy financial burden of operating and insurance costs automobile ownership today entails.

Many measurements of operating costs for automobiles have been made. The Bureau of Public Roads (now the Federal Highway Administration) annually reports these figures, as can be seen in Table 5.7 (in Chap. 5). It is interesting to note at this point that as speed increases, the total cost per vehicle mile decreases, at least up to the 40 mph interval [3.21, p. 10]. After that, costs increase. This change at 40 mph brings to light an interesting tradeoff between travel time and operating cost. Apparently, people are willing to pay the extra cost over and above that at 40 mph to travel on the Interstate system at speeds up to 70 mph.

3.3.1.4 High facility cost and low rate of return   Along with user operation cost, there must also be a concern for the cost of the service provided to the user. We must not forget that many transportation services, whether they come from the public or private sector, are businesses and must be operated as such. If the service is a public one, there must be some assurance that it is not too great a burden on already overtaxed sources of revenue; if a private one, it should return a profit to its

---

*All quotations from Mumford are from "The Highway and the City," © 1958 by Lewis Mumford. Reprinted from his volume of the same title by permission of Harcourt Brace Jovanovich, Inc.

owners, stockholders, and other investors competitive with other investment potentials.

The transit industry is one of the most provocative examples of why there should be a concern for returns on investment. Mumford puts his finger on the problem when he discusses transit on his book on *The Highway and the City* [3.9, p. 255]:

> In order to maintain profits, or in many cases to reduce deficits, rates have been raised, services have decreased, and equipment has become obsolete, without being replaced and improved. Yet mass transportation, with far less acreage in roadbeds and rights of way, can deliver at least ten times more people per hour than the private motorcar. This means that if such means were allowed to lapse in our metropolitan centers—as the inter-urban electric trolley system, that complete and efficient network, was allowed to disappear in the nineteen-twenties—we should require probably five to ten times the existing number of arterial highways to bring the present number of commuters into the city, and at least ten times the existing parking space to accommodate them. In that tangled mass of highways, interchanges, and parking lots, the city would be nowhere: a mechanized nonentity ground under an endless procession of wheels.

As Mumford brings out, the demise of transit can have many disbeneficial ramifications for the city. Yet, until recently, transit was suffering serious declines, and present financial conditions are only slightly better than before. Table 3.4 shows several sets of nationwide data on transit for the years 1940 and 1966. One fact that stands out strongly is: total operating revenue (for all modes) increased 100.6 percent in the 26 year period, but the total payroll went up 176.4 percent in the same time span. Thus, while labor is not the only cost associated with transit, it is a large part ($994.9 million out of $1,478.5 million in 1966), and it is obvious that no business can continue to operate when its costs continue to outstrip its revenue. The future existence of transit now seems to hinge on either an increase in revenues or decrease in costs to bring about a better return on the expenditures that are made.

While the return on investment for transit seems to be endangered at this time, it is not necessarily true that all highway construction endeavors are worthwhile from an investment standpoint. The cost side of the ledger has been particularly disturbing in many instances. The cases presented in Table 3.5 are representative examples of large-scale highway construction expenditures. The Boston Central Artery stands out as the most expensive facility, and it is difficult to imagine how any highway can cost $41,667,000 a mile. Similarly, it is difficult to imagine how sufficient traffic can ever be generated, even in the middle of Boston, to develop "revenues" in the form of reduced user costs in order to justify the facility economically. Whatever the economic feasibility of this route, the important point is that this factor must be given strong consideration; otherwise, the stability of the whole system might be undermined.

3.3.1.5 Lack of safety for user   One problem which often has a great deal of personal agony involved with it is that of safety. In fact, accidents, especially those on the highway, are so common that it is a rare person who has not had a relative or friend affected by an unfortunate occurrence of this type. Also unfortunate is the fact that few of us become concerned about safety until a situation strikes close to home. The statistics show that automobile injuries accounted for more than 4

Table 3.4   Trends in Urban Public Transit Characteristics

Public transit characteristics (excluding commuter rails)	Subway and elevated rail
Revenue passengers (in millions):	
1940	2,281.9
1966	1,584.0
Change	−697.9
Percent change	−30.5
Operating revenue (in millions of dollars):	
1940	128.3
1966	306.5
Change	178.2
Percent change	138.9
Vehicle-miles operated (in millions):	
1940	470.8
1966	378.9
Change	−91.9
Percent change	−19.5
Number of employees:	
1940	*
1966	*
Change	*
Percent change	*
Payroll (in millions of dollars):	
1940	*
1966	*
Change	*
Percent change	*
Vehicles owned:	
1940	11,032.0
1966	9,273.0
Change	−1,759.0
Percent change	−15.9
Track or route mileage (miles of single track except for motor bus which is route round trip):	
1940	1,242.0
1966	1,255.0
Change	13.0
Percent change	1.0

*Not available.
Source: [3.12, p. 12].

Streetcar	Trolley bus	Motor bus	Total
4,182.5	419.2	3,620.1	10,503.7
211.0	174.0	4,702.0	6,671.0
−3,971.5	−245.2	1,081.9	−3,832.7
−95.0	−58.5	29.9	−36.5
327.8	25.0	255.9	737.0
58.7	39.2	1,074.1	1,478.5
−269.1	14.2	818.2	741.5
−82.1	56.8	319.7	100.6
844.7	86.0	1,194.5	2,596.0
42.9	40.1	1,521.7	1,983.6
−801.8	−45.9	327.2	−612.4
−94.9	−53.4	27.4	−23.6
*	*	*	203,000.0
*	*	*	144,300.0
*	*	*	−58,700.0
*	*	*	−28.9
*	*	*	360.0
*	*	*	994.9
*	*	*	634.9
*	*	*	176.4
26,630.0	2,802.0	35,000.0	75,464.0
1,407.0	1,326.0	50,130.0	62,136.0
−25,223.0	−1,476.0	15,130.0	−13,328.0
−94.8	−52.7	43.2	−17.7
18,360.0	1,925.0	78,000.0	*
898.0	676.0	122,100.0	*
−17,462.0	−1,249.0	44,100.0	*
−95.1	−64.9	56.5	*

million injuries in 1967 and, more important, for over 52,000 fatalities. To make matters worse, the number of fatalities has increased at the rate of more than 5 percent per year. Some interesting facts presented by the Department of Transportation add some depth to these figures [3.22, p. 3]:

> The grim statistics unmistakably highlight that in motor vehicle deaths the nation faces a destructive problem equal in size and complexity to other social ills such as crime, disease and poverty. Highway injuries exceed by 10 times all violent criminal acts combined, including homicides, armed robbery, rape, riot, and assault.
>
> Motor vehicle crashes rob society of nearly as many productive working years as heart disease and of more than are lost of cancer and strokes. Only about 1 of 5 expected man years of life lost to heart disease is in the age interval between 20 and 65.
>
> The dimensions of the problem extend beyond the death and injury totals, for each American family also suffered an average financial loss estimated at $291 as a result of highway crashes in 1968—a total loss of almost $15 billion.

Table 3.6 gives a breakdown of yearly accident figures by various categories. A particularly discouraging aspect of these figures is that the number of accidents in several of the classes had been decreasing for a period of time, but now seems to be holding steady. This change may be attributed to a growing population and a related increase in automobile usage, but the problem is that, despite a general reduction in the number of deaths per 100 million vehicle miles of travel (see [3.23]), the number of deaths per 100,000 population is increasing. The implication of this differentiation is that each person is becoming more exposed to death and injury on the highway and thus views the problem as a worsening condition.

An intermodal comparison of accident data also brings out some interesting features. As can be seen in Fig. 3.2, the accident rate per 100 million passenger miles for motor vehicle travel exceeds by far that for any of the other modes. Notice in particular that the rate for motor vehicle travel is roughly nine times that for bus travel, yet both types of vehicles use the same facilities! This considerable difference under similar circumstances opens the way for some interesting

Table 3.5   Cost of Urban Highways

Expressway	Total cost (in thousands)	Miles	Cost per mile (in thousands)
Hollywood Freeway	$ 55,000	10	$ 5,500
Arroyo Seco Freeway	11,000	8	1,375
John Lodge and Edsel Ford Expressway ..	207,000	24	8,625
Major Deegan Expressway	63,600	7.5	8,480
Cross-Bronx Expressway	112,000	5	22,450
Penn Lincoln Parkways	150,000	20	7,500
Boston Central Artery	125,000	3	41,667
Congress Street Expressway	50,000	8	6,250
Schuykill Expressway	80,000	17	4,705

Source: [3.2, p. 49]. © 1966 by the Brookings Institution, Washington, D.C.

Numbers of fatalities per 100,000,000 passenger miles

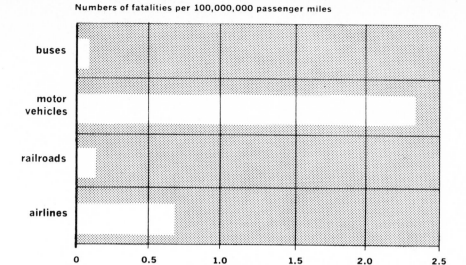

Fig. 3.2 Average passenger accident fatality rates, 1960–65. [3.12, p. 14].

speculation as to the causes of highway accidents. Another significant point is that the airline accident rate is approximately one-third that of the motor vehicle rate. Yet, we seem to be much more aware of airline crashes, perhaps because of their spectacularity and the resultant news coverage which follows any accident of this sort. Nevertheless, for whatever the reason, airline fatalities *seem* to be a bigger problem to people than motor vehicle fatalities and, interestingly enough, many more people are afraid of flying than driving despite the fact that they have three times the chance of getting killed in the process of getting to the airport.

3.3.1.6 Requirement of user operation The problems of congestion, cost, and safety are explicit, confronting us almost every time we travel. Many other problems are not as obvious, but still may have an equivalent or greater amount of importance. Primary among these latter types is that of requirements for operation which several present day transportation systems (in particular, the auto-highway system) put on the user. If a transportation system is created in which the user has to play an active, physical role in his own travel, then it stands to reason that many people physically disabled for one reason or the other will not be capable of using such a system. Moreover, the unfortunate ones generally are those already disadvantaged in some way—the young, handicapped, and so forth. As the previously mentioned Department of Housing and Urban Development (HUD) report brings out [3.12, p. 17]:

> The poor are not the only nondrivers. The handicapped, the elderly, and the young also suffer from a transportation system that makes the individually owned automobile almost a necessity unless they are able to pay for someone to drive them. Today, 19 million Americans are over age 65: of these, over 6 million live in poverty . . . by 1980, over 100 million persons will be under 18 or over 65 years old. The problem of the unserved is not

limited to central cities. In suburban areas there is frequently no public transit. For all but two- and three-car families, intrasuburban transportation to shopping and to recreation is almost impossible. Even where there are two cars, someone must always assume the burden of driving for the rest of the family.

As the HUD report neatly summarizes the problem [3.12, p. 17]:

If transit service continues to be reduced, many of these nondrivers will be destined to be isolated more and more in their narrow neighborhood worlds while all around them the advantages of automobile mobility benefit the relatively affluent majority more each year.

Table 3.6 Motor Vehicle Deaths by Type of Accident and Number of Nonfatal Injuries, 1938 to 1963

| | | | Deaths from | |
| | | | | |
Year	Total deaths*	Pedestrians	Other motor vehicles	Railroad trains
1938–42 ave	33,550	12,440	9,500	1,620
1943	23,823	9,900	5,300	1,448
1944	24,282	9,900	5,700	1,663
1945	28,076	11,000	7,150	1,703
1946	33,411	11,600	9,400	1,703
1947	32,697	10,450	9,900	1,736
1948	32,259	9,950	10,200	1,474
1949	31,701	8,800	10,500	1,452
1950	34,763	9,100	11,650	1,541
1951	36,996	9,200	13,100	1,573
1952	37,794	8,600	13,500	1,429
1953	37,955	8,700	13,400	1,506
1954	35,586	8,000	12,800	1,269
1955	38,426	8,200	14,500	1,490
1956	39,628	7,900	15,200	1,377
1957	38,702	7,850	15,400	1,376
1958	36,981	7,650	14,200	1,316
1959	37,910	7,850	14,900	1,202
1960	38,137	7,850	14,800	1,368
1961	38,091	7,650	14,700	1,267
1962	40,804	7,900	16,400	1,245
1963	43,600	8,200	17,600	1,340
				Percentage
1953 to 1963	+15%	−6%	+31%	−11%
1962 to 1963	+7%	+4%	+7%	+8%

*Yearly totals do not quite equal sums of the various types because totals for most types are estimated, and these have been made only to the nearest 10 deaths for some types and to the nearest 50 deaths for others.

3.3.1.7 Lack of privacy Another less obvious problem with many transportation systems (in particular, mass transit systems) is that they do not allow for personal privacy. One could hardly feel happy about being squeezed together with the rest of mankind in a crowded subway, elevated train, or bus. Certainly such an occurrence is degrading to the mass transit traveler and has the perhaps undesired effect of making automobile travel all the more appealing.

collision with					
Street-cars	Bicycles	Animal-drawn vehicle or animal	Fixed objects	Deaths from noncollision accidents	Approximate totals of nonfatal injuries†
140	750	210	1,050	7,840	1,180,000
171	450	160	700	5,690	800,000
175	400	140	700	5,600	850,000
163	500	130	800	6,600	1,000,000
174	540	130	950	8,900	1,200,000
102	550	150	1,000	8,800	1,150,000
83	500	100	1,000	8,950	1,100,000
56	550	140	1,100	9,100	1,100,000
89	440	120	1,300	10,600	1,200,000
46	390	100	1,400	11,200	1,300,000
32	430	130	1,450	11,900	1,350,000
26	420	120	1,500	12,200	1,350,000
28	380	90	1,500	11,500	1,250,000
15	410	90	1,600	12,100	1,350,000
11	440	100	1,600	13,000	1,400,000
13	460	80	1,700	11,800	1,400,000
9	450	80	1,650	11,600	1,400,000
6	480	70	1,600	11,800	1,400,000
5	460	80	1,700	11,900	1,400,000
5	490	80	1,700	12,200	1,400,000
0	500	90	1,750	12,900	1,500,000
10	570	80	1,900	13,900	1,600,000
changes					
−62%	+36%	−33%	+27%	+14%	+11%
—	+14%	−11%	+9%	+8%	+7%

†Estimates of injuries that were disabling beyond the day of accident.
   Note: Deaths are based on data from the National Vital Statistics Division, state traffic authorities, and Interstate Commerce Commission.
   Source: [3.23, pp. 48, 50].

Even in a place like New York City where travel by auto is relatively expensive and time consuming, a person who drives at least has a chance to collect his thoughts in peace, and, perhaps more importantly, to chose the people with whom he wishes to come in close contact. The statement to follow is all but priceless in describing some of the benefits associated with privacy in the automobile [3.24, p. 11]:

> I ask myself why, as an idealogical urbanite, I am in favor of mass transit and yet I rarely use it. That is, when I can avoid it, I do. There are little things that the auto gives you. It delivers a lot of service and chronologically it's important. For one thing, it's a portable closet. You pick up stuff and you throw it in the car and then you can sort of go on to your next errand. It's a marvelous thing that no real mass transit has attempted. The only consolation is the rental locker which is developed in the most densely used parts of the mass transit. One of the nice things about the auto is that it's not transparent—it gives you a lot of shield to pick your nose or scratch your crotch (even more easily than you can pick your nose, unless you have a little window shade in your car). The point is, you quickly move away, you don't stay with the same traffic—it gives you independence or just shielding in a general way. Let's say, you have to pick up something downtown. If you're going on mass transit, maybe you'll have to change your clothes whereas you can just hop in your car and really not be in any kind of social situation while you're there but run in, run out.

The problem of lack of privacy in transportation vehicles, especially in those designated by that impersonal word "mass" transit, does not seem to be improving. Instead, as Table 3.7 seems to indicate for three recent rail rapid transit installations, the load per seat runs as high as 275 percent. One can hardly have much feeling of privacy when crushed in this bulk of humanity.

3.3.1.8 Discomfort A set of factors somewhat complimentary to privacy in creating a general feeling of comfort and physical satisfaction while traveling is that composed of all those elements affecting the physical senses of the user: noise, appearance, temperature, humidity, precipitation, air flow, smell, dirt, sway, jerk, vibration, and so forth. The list of these features could be quite extensive, but the main idea is that these are the ones that relate to the user's basic "creature comfort." The automobile ranks high on creature comfort just as it did on privacy.

Table 3.7 Peak-hour Passenger Volumes: Three Recent Rail–Rapid Transit Installations

City	Section length (mi)	Stops (no.)	Seats (no.)	Load seats (%)	Trains (no.)	Passengers		Speeds	
						Peak hour (no.)	15'–20' rate (no.)	Trains (mph)	Autos (mph)
Toronto	4.6	10	496	275	28	35,166	39,840	17.6	12.3
Chicago	1.0	2	294	204	25	10,376	14,542	24.5	—
Cleveland	7.0	6	238	189	20	6,211	8,349	28.0	—

Source: [3.21, p. 29].

With good heating, air conditioning, and ventilation systems; with stereo tape cartridges and FM radios; and with bucket seats, arm rests, and leather interiors, it is easy to see why the automobile is such an attractive means of transportation. In contrast, many mass transit vehicles can only be called "shabby." One of the main reasons for this situation is the age of the vehicles. As the previously quoted HUD report notes [3.12, p. 10]:

> According to American Transit Association figures, 2,891 of the 9,273 subway and elevated cars in operation in 1966 were cars that also were in operation in 1940—and as many rapid transit passengers can testify, the other new 6,382 cars are, at most, only slightly less bumpy, better lit, or more comfortable.

Also, in many cities it is not difficult to see that a large proportion of the buses, the most common means of mass transit, are older than their generally accepted service life of 12 to 15 years [3.6]. Thus, there is a definite problem with urban mass transit systems from the standpoint of comfort, and much needs to be changed in this area of concern.

3.3.2 Problems in the Problem Domain Affected by Transportation

The foregoing discussion of transportation service problems has been far from complete. A more exhaustive presentation might identify many additional problems of immediate and obvious importance both to the user of a system and, subsequently, to the planners and engineers who must design for the user. Yet, as has been emphasized before, the discussion in this chapter must not be limited to the service problems themselves, but also to the less direct problems that may influence or be influenced by a transportation system. The latter of these two types of problems will be explored in this section.

3.3.2.1 Air pollution The problem of air pollution is one that affects many of us. Although the extent of the consequences of air pollution has not been fully gauged at this time, several significant facts about such adverse elements as fumes and smell have been pointed out by Buchanan in his report to the British Ministry of Transport [3.4, p. 26]:

> These fumes and smell constitute a further unpleasant by-product of the motor vehicle. Fumes are emitted mainly from engine exhausts, but also from ventilation holes in carburetors and tanks, and from "breathers" in crankcases. They contain amongst other substances, carbon monoxide (especially from petrol as opposed to diesel fuel), unburnt elements of fuel, and carbon dust. Carbon monoxide is toxic, and carbon dust can act as a carrier for cancer-producing compounds. In sunny weather, fumes can develop as eye and throat irritants.

As can be seen in Table 3.8, various air pollutants such as sulfur oxides and carbon monoxide can cause acute and chronic leaf injury, irritate the eyes and upper respiratory tract, may be cancer producing, and can in some cases impair mental processes. These, in addition to corrosion of metals, obviously are problems of some seriousness.

Table 3.8   Effects Attributed to Specific Pollutants

Air pollutant	Effects
Particulates	Speed chemical reactions; obscure vision; corrode metals; cause grime on belongings and buildings; aggravate lung illness
Sulfur oxides	Cause acute and chronic leaf injury; attack wide variety of trees; irritate upper respiratory tract; destroy paint pigments; erode statuary; corrode metals; ruin hosiery; harm textiles; disintegrate book pages and leather
Hydrocarbons (in solid and gaseous states)	May be cancer-producing (carcinogenic); retard plant growth; cause abnormal leaf and bud development
Carbon monoxide	Causes headaches, dizziness, nausea; absorbed into blood, reduces oxygen content; impairs mental processes
Nitrogen oxides	Cause visible leaf damage; irritate eyes and nose; stunt plant growth even when not causing visible damage; create brown haze; corrode metals
Oxidants: ozone	Discolors upper surface of leaves of many crops, trees, shrubs; damages and fades textiles; reduces athletic performance; hastens cracking of rubber; disturbs lung function; irritates eyes, nose, throat; induces coughing
PAN (peroxyacetyl nitrate)	Discolors lower leaf surface; irritates eyes; disturbs lung function

Sources: [1]HEW, National Air Pollution Control Administration, *The Effects of Air Pollution*, No. 1556, revised 1967. [2]NAPCA, *Air Pollution Injury to Vegetation*, No. AP-71, 1970. [3]American Association for the Advancement of Science, *Air Conservation*, Pub. No. 80, 1965. [4]National Tuberculosis and Respiratory Disease Association, *Air Pollution Primer*, 1969.

Transportation, unfortunately, is a major **contributor** to air pollution. With respect to nationwide emissions of various pollutants in 1968, transportation sources as a whole contributed 42.3 percent of the 213.8 million tons of emissions that year. Particularly high contributions were made by transportation sources to the amounts of carbon monoxide (63.8 tons), hydrocarbons (16.6 tons), and nitrogen oxides (8.1 tons) in the air [3.24]. With the consequences from these as indicated above, air pollution from transportation would appear to be a major and costly concern both for governmental agencies and private firms.

3.3.2.2 Noise   A problem that bears similar characteristics to that of air pollution is noise. It has that same ability to pervade the environment close to the transportation system, it is irritating, and it may, in the long run, be harmful to a person's health. Research is still progressing on the noise problem and its impact, but Buchanan has placed a great deal of emphasis on it in his study [3.4, p. 25]:

In addition to danger and anxiety, the motor vehicle is responsible for a great deal of noise. This has recently been under consideration, along with other aspects of noise, by an official committee set up by the Minister for Science. In their report, the committee concluded that "in London (and no doubt this applies to other large towns as well) traffic is, at the present time, the predominant source of annoyance, and no other single noise is of comparable importance." The committee distinguished five main kinds of noise from vehicles: propulsion noises (from engines, gears, transmissions, and exhausts), horns, brake squeal, door slamming, and loose loads or bodies.

Our own conclusion, based on observation and many discussions, is that traffic noise is steadily developing into a major nuisance, seriously prejudicial to the general enjoyment to towns, destructive of the amenities of dwellings on a wide scale, and interfering in no small degree with efficiency in offices and other business premises. But again, this is something we have mostly grown up with, and we tend to take it very much for granted.

More detailed studies and measurements seem to bear out some of these conclusions. Judged in comparison to some common noise levels, as displayed in Table 3.9, transportation noises can be significant. Airplanes, of course, contribute heavily. As can be noted in Table 3.10, a four engine jet plane at takeoff produces about 115 decibels even at a distance of 500 feet. This sound pressure level is almost equivalent to that from rock music with amplifiers in a closed room (Table 3.9). Motor buses, subway and railroad trains, and heavy trucks all contribute average noise levels of 85 decibels or above at a distance of 20 feet. This means that passersby and those living in closely abutting buildings are continually subject to noises equivalent to that of a vacuum cleaner. Obviously, when such noise continues, rest and sleep is difficult, radios and televisions are not heard, and in some instances physical damage to the ear may occur. In any case, annoyance and frustration is built to produce an undesirable situation.

3.3.2.3 Visual intrusion and poor appearance One aspect of the impact of transportation on its environment is the visual aspect. Naturally, nothing creates more arguments than a discussion over what is "good looking" and what is not; it is often said that nothing is more difficult to measure than "beauty." Nevertheless, it is important to try to design transportation facilities that have a nice appearance,

Table 3.9 Noise (Sound Pressure) Levels of Common Sources

Source	Decibel level
Conversation	55–60
Industrial processes known to cause hearing loss	84
Vacuum cleaner	85
Motorcycle revving up	110
Rock music with amplifiers	120
Pneumatic rivetor	130
Threshold of pain	140
Jet plane at takeoff	150

Source: The Tidewater (Norfolk, Virginia Area) *News,* Thursday, April 15, 1971. p. 2.

Table 3.10   Average Noise (Sound Pressure) Levels*
of Some Transportation Sources

Source	Decibel level	Source	Decibel level
Heavy trucks	86	Subway trains	90
Motor buses (starting)	85	Old street cars	88
Trolley buses	75	Railroad trains	
		(diesel, steam)	85
Light trucks	74	New PCC cars	75
Automobiles	71	Electric railroad trains	75
20,000-lb thrust 4-		10,000 MP 4-engine	
engine jet airliner		propeller aircraft	
at takeoff (500 ft		at takeoff (500 ft	
away)	115	away)	99

*At 300 cps re 0.0002 microbar. Measurements made 20 ft from source except in the case of steam and diesel trains. Adapted from C. M. Harris (ed.), *Handbook of Noise Control*, McGraw-Hill, New York, 1957, pp. 35-2, 35-3.

both as they stand by themselves and in the context of the environment in which they are placed. As Mumford says about highways [3.9, p. 247]:

> In many ways, our highways are not merely masterpieces of engineering, but consummate works of art: a few of them, like the Taconic State Parkway in New York, stand on a par with our highest creations in other fields. Not every highway, it is true, runs through country that offers such superb opportunities to an imaginative highway builder as this does: but then not every engineer rises to his opportunities as the planners of this highway did, routing the well-separated roads along the ridgeways, following the contours, and thus, by this single stratagem, both avoiding towns and villages and opening up great views across country, enhanced by a lavish planting of flowering bushes along the borders. If this standard of comeliness and beauty were kept generally in view, highway engineers would not so often lapse into the brutal assaults against the landscape and against urban order that they actually give way to when they aim solely at speed and volume of traffic, and bulldoze and blast their way across country to shorten their route by a few miles without making the total journey any less depressing.

The problem of visual intrusion can take many forms other than just the simple "brutal assaults against the landscape" and the buildings that comprise a community. There is the visual intrusion by the multitude of signs and signals—directional, one way, no parking, and so forth—that often crop up on city streets and give that "scattered debris" look. Then there is the all too familiar intrusion of parked vehicles in the spaces between city buildings. It is unfortunate but true that the recent great increase in the number of automobiles in the United States and elsewhere has brought a corresponding need to store them, and usually the only place where this can be done is in the already crowded confines of city streets and open spaces.

Finally, at the end of its useful lifetime, the automobile can have a detrimental visual effect on it surroundings. Almost every large city is familiar with the problems of abandoned cars on the streets, but the problem to the average citizen is that unsightly, half wrecked cars or trucks often are left to mar the appearance of the neighborhood and detract from its daily stimulus value.

Buchanan summarizes rather well the thinking on both sides of the issue of visual intrusion and appearance. As he states [3.4, p. 27]:

> Visual intrusion, out of all the matters mentioned, is the most debatable. Some people will say that the motor vehicle "is part of modern life and must be frankly accepted as such." The counter-argument is that indifference to visual intrusion leads eventually to a slovenly disregard for the quality of surroundings. Permanent parking at the kerbside, for example, gets accepted, then maintenance and running repairs are accepted, derelict cars are allowed to stay, the street garbage and litter are accepted for they cannot be swept away, the oil stains and grease accepted. The open parking lot is accepted and with it the damaged kerbs, broken railings, and battered signs that hard usage invariably leads to. And so it goes on. With it all, it can be argued, comes increasing disrespect for the whole architectural and historic heritage.

3.3.2.4 Excessive right-of-way and relocation requirements In addition to the

problems of poor appearance and visual intrusion brought about by urban transportation facilities, there are also the difficulties associated with the excessive right-of-way and relocation requirements of most facilities. These two problems arise because of the need for a commodity especially valuable in urban areas: land. First, rights-of-way are required for the facility itself, and acquisition is expensive, both in initial cost and from the standpoint of productive land taken from the tax rolls. The second part of the problem is that people usually are living on the desired land, and relocation often is a bitter and trying experience, both to those who must move and leave what may have been fairly desirable and inexpensive quarters and also to those who must face the thankless task of reestablishing those displaced. These difficulties are demonstrated all to clearly by the often heard complaint, particularly by ghetto residents, that "highway building is Negro removal." Mumford is especially critical of the work of the highway engineer in urban areas [3.9, p. 246, 246]:

> Unfortunately, highway engineers, if one is to judge by their usual performance, lack both historic insight and social memory: accordingly, they have been repeating, with the audacity of confident ignorance, all the mistakes in urban planning committed by their predecessors who designed our railroads. The wide swaths of land devoted to cloverleaves, and even more complicated multi-level interchanges, to expressways, parking lots, and parking garages, in the very heart of the city, butcher up precious urban space in exactly the same way that freight yards and marshalling yards did when the railroads dumped their passengers and freight inside the city.

He continues by giving some pertinent examples:

> Like the railroad, again, the motorway has repeatedly taken possession of the most valuable recreation space the city possesses, not merely by thieving land once dedicated to park uses, but by cutting off easy access to the waterfront parks, and lowering their value for refreshment and repose by introducing the roar of traffic and the bad odor of exhausts, though both noise and carbon monoxide are inimical to health. Witness the shocking spoilage of the Charles River basin parks in Boston, the arterial blocking off of the Lake Front in Chicago (after the removal of the original usurpers, the railroads), the barbarous

sacrifice of large areas of Fairmount Park in Philadelphia, the partial defacement of the San Francisco waterfront, even in Paris the ruin of the Left Bank of the Seine.

Quite obviously, it is difficult to take almost any land in urban areas since someone is bound to be adversely affected, either directly because he must move, or indirectly because his favorite or closest social, recreational, or commercial spot has been eliminated. The hardship and disturbance associated with relocation may never be completely eradicated. Added to all this is the fact that streets, railroads, and parking facilities generally consume more urban land than any other category of land use and, leaving aside single family residences, consume more land than all other uses *combined* [3.2]. One cannot help but wonder how transportation manages to take up more urban space than almost all other "living" needs added together.

3.3.2.5 Inordinate changes in land values Still another aspect of the relationship between transportation facilities and their effect on land use is that of changes in land value. While not necessarily a harmful influence, a new transportation facility can cause problems in the land market by increasing land values, thereby bringing large profits to those fortunate (or with great foresight) enough to have land in the path of the new facility. This profit is extracted, of course, from those individuals who wish to locate close to the facility after it is completed. Ritter and Paquette bring out some excellent examples of the impact highways (in particular) can have on land values over a short period of time [3.25, p. 54, 55]:

1. Land and improvements on it located on the Dallas Central Expressway rose about 780 percent in value during a 10-year period that spanned the construction and opening of the highway. Land in a two-block-wide strip adjacent to property abutting the Expressway had an increase in value, including improvements on it, of only 104 percent; land beyond this strip showed a gain of about 47 percent.
2. Before U.S. 50 was relocated and improved near Lawrenceville, Illinois, land that now faces the expressway's frontage roads abutted a local road. This land was developed to single-family residences and increased in value more than nine times during an 18-year period; similar land located along a secondary road increased in value only 1½ times.
3. The impact of the New York State Thruway on land values has been dramatic (the over-all impact of the Thruway has been compared with the impact of the long-ago construction of the Erie Canal, in the same state). Land values at Rochester Interchange have risen 700 percent and more. Some land acquired by the state for rights-of-way at $500 per acre later was worth ten times that amount. Near Syracuse, a 21-acre site near the Thruway sold for $15,000 in 1951; in 1955, slightly over half that acreage sold for ten times the former value.

Of course, the effects on land value may not always be positive. Especially in rural areas, old routes may be cut off by bypasses and new sections of the Interstate highway system, with the result being that motels, service stations, and the like on the old route essentially are disenfranchised. Also, farm property values may be lowered due to the severance of previously convenient access roads. Thus, it appears that the engineer and planner cannot count on any totally positive or negative problems insofar as land values are concerned. He only knows that the effect will be substantial.

3.3.2.6 Inappropriate or undesirable land development Another aspect of the relationship between land value and transportation is that between land development and transportation (or, more specifically, the potential access to land which transportation provides). The preceeding examples from Ritter and Paquette show clearly that increase in land value, and hence development, go hand-in-hand with access. Again, the question of whether these changes are beneficial or not is difficult to answer. If the situation falls under the latter category, then of course we are faced with a problem.

The increase in land use intensity around route 128, the circumferential skirting Boston, is an interesting case. Bone and Wohl indicate fairly clearly [3.26] that there has been a substantial outmigration of industry from the central Boston area to the belt of land straddling the circumferential. In fact, a Wilbur Smith report summarizing the earlier Bone and Wohl study states that [3.8]:

> As of September, 1957, there were 99 new industrial and commercial plants located along the highway, costing over $100 million and employing 17,000 persons; more than 70 plants were previously located within a four-mile radius of Boston.

The effects of these moves are both advantageous and disadvantageous. On the positive side, industries probably were able to acquire relatively inexpensive land and ship their goods at a lowered cost. Surrounding counties most likely also benefited since they obtained new sources of public income from their taxes. On the negative side, however, travel of employees to their jobs became much more difficult and the City of Boston lost many of its highly valued revenue sources. These two latter aspects definitely must be regarded as problems that arise from changes in transportation.

The longer travel requirement for employees suggests that equality of access to employment and other opportunities may be a desirable attribute of a transportation system. Thus, planners and engineers must take cognizance of the problems which their plans create for the disadvantaged, especially insofar as they are affected by land management. Higbee states the charge very precisely when he says [3.10, p. 190]:

> This authority to lay out the arteries and veins of circulation is the authority to establish the guide lines of future real-estate development and the whole course of evolution of the landscape.

Mumford sees similar development problems and lays the blame partially on the American people as well as on the engineer [3.9, p. 245]:

> As long as motorcars were few in number, he who had one was a king; he could go where he pleased and halt where he pleased; and this machine itself appeared as a compensatory device for enlarging an ego which had been shrunken by our very success in mechanization. That sense of freedom and power remains a fact today only in low-density areas, in the open country; the popularity of this method of escape has ruined the promise it once held forth. In using the car to flee from the metropolis the motorist finds that he has merely transferred congestion to the highway and thereby doubled it. When he reaches his destination, in a distant suburb, he finds that the countryside he sought has disappeared: beyond him, thanks to the motorcycle, lies only another suburb . . . In short,

the American has sacrificed his life as a whole to the motorcar, like someone who, demented with passion, wrecks his home in order to lavish his income on a capricious mistress who promises delights he can only occasionally enjoy.

From these statements and examples we would have a difficult time not concluding that there are development problems which are a direct function of transportation and thus should be given considerable attention in the transportation planning process.

3.3.2.7 Moral, religious, biological, and other related problems
With transportation (or the lack of it) already being held responsible for several of the major physical, social, and economic problems in our cities and rural areas, it would seem that all of its negative aspects had been uncovered. Nonetheless, some additional evidence, albeit not too prevalent or easy to trace, indicates that still more problems may be attributed to transportation. For example, Abigail Van Buren has said that the automobile has been one of the most influential forces in shaping the morals of American youth. She says:[4]

... today almost every boy, upon reaching the legal age to drive, has a car of his own, or can borrow one at a moment's notice. And if he can't get a car, the girl can. The automobile has become the modern tribal symbol of manhood. With five gallons of gas, in 20 minutes our young people can be transported into a private world of their own to enjoy hours of uninterrupted privacy. If that doesn't spell trouble for healthy normal adolescents, I don't know what does.

Another interesting effect comes from the religious side of life. A minister[5] has said that after a highway bisected his parish area, people from the sector on the far side of the facility from the church attended services less often than they did before the highway was built. So it seems (again on very superficial evidence) that transportation facilities may even affect our choices and strengths of religious activity.

A final example comes from a third, completely unrelated area of concern—the natural environment. Rachael Carson, whose book, *Silent Spring*, attracted the attention of both conservationists and nonconservationists alike, has written that [3.27, p. 69]:

There is a steadily growing chorus of outraged protest about the disfigurement of once beautiful roadsides by chemical sprays, which substitute a sore expanse of brown, withered vegetation for the beauty of fern and wildflower, of native shrubs adorned with blossom or berry.

She continues by giving an example from her own personal experience:

I know well a stretch of road where nature's own landscaping has provided a border of alder, viburnum, sweet fern, and juniper with seasonally changing accents of bright flowers, or of fruits hanging in jewelled clusters in the fall. The road had no heavy load of traffic to support; there were few sharp curves or intersections where brush could obstruct the driver's vision. But the sprayers took over and the miles along the road became something

---

[4] *Family Circle*, vol. 76, no. 1, January 1970, p. 37.
[5] Personal communication.

to be traversed quickly, a sight to be endured with one's mind closed to thoughts of the sterile and hideous world we are letting our technicians make.

It is obvious that Miss Carson feels strongly that someone is causing environmental problems which, with some intelligent effort, could be alleviated. As is usually the case, the responsibility for making this effort falls mostly on the transportation engineer or planner. Thus we see once again that transportation (or some small aspect of it) can affect parts of our environment in many ways we do not immediately realize.

3.3.2.8 Unequal impact upon certain population groups To talk about the *overall* significance of various problems related to transportation in an urban area is not necessarily the same as talking about their significance to any one individual or group of individuals. Unfortunate as it is, the impact (both good and bad) of transportation does not appear to fall evenly across the whole urban area:

1. The nonuser may be subject to the noise and air pollution caused by the automobile user.
2. The trucker and public may gain competitively at the expense of the railroad when new highway facilities are built.
3. The poor person may get much worse transit service than the rich.

This list could be extended considerably, but the important point is that not all people stand to gain from transportation, and this differential can be a problematic situation.

Tomorrow's Transportation summary focuses rather sharply on some of the contrasts that may occur, especially in regard to the poor and disadvantaged [3.12, p. 15]:

> *The Unserved:* Ironically, metropolitan transportation systems too often leave unserved those who most need service: the poor, the handicapped, the secondary worker, the elderly, and the young.
>
> Typically, the poorer people are, the more dependent they are on public transportation. Car ownership statistics document this strikingly. According to a recent survey, 76 percent of households with annual incomes of less than $1,000 owned no car; in the $1,000 to $1,999 class, the percentage was 69; it was 24 percent in the $3,000 to $4,999 class, 11 percent in the $6,000 to $7,499 class; and 4 percent in the over $10,000 class. Less than half of all families with incomes under $4,000, half of all Negro households, and half of all households with heads over 65 years old own no automobiles.

The report continues:

> The beeline distance between South Central Los Angeles and Santa Monica, a center of employment, is 16 miles; to make the trip by public transportation takes an hour and 50 minutes, requires 3 transfers and costs 83 cents one way. The Department of Housing and Urban Development (HUD) demonstration project in Watts has shown that when direct transportation service was provided for residents of that district to jobs and other opportunities in other parts of the city, ridership increased from 800 to 2,800 daily in 3 months. Many of the new riders were bound for work.
>
> As more central business district jobs become white-collar, and an ever larger proportion of unskilled and semiskilled jobs move to outlying sections, poor people are more disadvantaged than ever by public transportation systems which focus on central

business districts and also stop at city limits. A New York study reports, "The employment of suburban areas of both poverty and nonpoverty workers residing in the areas studied in New York City (poverty areas) appears to be almost insignificant." One reason is an often cited figure: It would cost a resident of central Harlem in New York some $40 a month to commute by public transportation to an aircraft factory in Farmingdale, Long Island.

The poor are not only isolated from jobs, but also from social and health services, recreation areas, and social contacts outside the immediate neighborhood. A HUD demonstration project in Nashville, Tenn., has provided bus service for outpatients and employees linking nine major medical centers with downtown Nashville and a hospital connecting service. In the first 2 months of actual operation, the medical center express service line showed a 61-percent increase in passengers, while the hospital connecting service line showed a 73-percent increase in ridership.

Quite obviously any study having as its purpose the betterment of transportation must identify special groups of interest and not treat the population of the urban area homogenously. Otherwise problems like those quoted above may unsuspectingly arise for one or more sets of people and cause them much psychological distress and perhaps even physical harm.

3.3.3   Problems in the Problem Domain Affecting Transportation

Up to this point we have concentrated on the impacts of transportation on various aspects of the physical environment, human characteristics, and human activities. Yet it is not difficult to reverse the roles of these entities, with transportation being the affected entity rather than the affecting one. What, then, are some of the factors which create changes (or a need for change) in transportation? Those identified most frequently are overall population growth, the contrasting forces of urbanization and suburbanization, increases in automobile ownership (and corresponding decreases in transit ridership), and, finally, changes in lengths, numbers, and times of trips. Each of these will be briefly discussed in turn in the paragraphs to follow.

3.3.3.1   Increased population growth and dispersion Perhaps one of the foremost problems transportation must deal with is the ever increasing number of persons it must serve. The two charts in Fig. 3.3 are taken from a Wilbur Smith and Associates report and show both the growth and rural-urban distribution of population in the United States since 1790. The trends look somewhat ominous, especially because of the increased growth rate indicated in the top diagram. If we are experiencing difficulty now providing services for the present population, think of the problems when, by the year 2000, there will be 100 million additional people in the country, almost all of whom will be in urban areas. Since this figure is almost the same as the total urban population in 1960, future prospects can only be viewed with some alarm.

The distribution as well as the amount of population is also quite important in relation to transportation needs. Obviously, if people are massed in several small areas of the country, the use of transit becomes feasible. But transportation also becomes more expensive, as was well demonstrated by the case of the

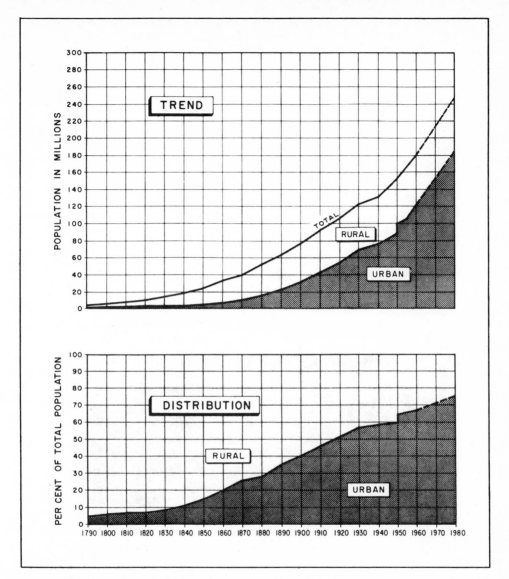

Fig. 3.3 Population trends: United States, 1790–1980 [3.8, p. 9].

$42,000,000-a-mile Boston Central Artery. Thus, a switch from a predominately rural to predominately urban population has varied but significant impacts on transportation.

Similarly, the trend toward suburban as opposed to central city living has significant import for urban transportation. The greater spread of activities implied by the suburbanization process automatically means longer distances to be traveled to get to any one activity and, correspondingly, fewer people taking the same paths of travel. Mass transit, in its present form, does not appear to be an useful form of transportation in this type of situation, and highways, while relatively inexpensive on a per-mile basis, are needed in greater lengths, creating an additional cost which tends to cancel out the comparatively low suburban land costs. Thus, suburbanization, increasing as is in the United States [3.8], can create real problems for the transportation planner as he attempts to keep within ever present budgets.

3.3.3.2 Increased automobile ownership There cannot be much doubt that the automobile is both a popular and useful means of transport. Its innate popularity is of importance here, especially because there seems to be no end to the desire of Americans to purchase more and more cars. Figure 3.4 illustrates the rapid growth of the motor vehicle in the United States. When one compares this growth to that of population, he immediately recognizes that cars are increasing more rapidly than people: in fact, at approximately twice the rate! Consequently, if one has trouble comprehending an increase in population of 100,000,000 by the year 2000, he might have even more difficulty comprehending an additional 200,000,000 motor vehicles. Of course, present trends are not expected (or hoped) to continue, but the numbers of vehicles still will increase markedly, creating a deluge in the city that will be difficult to divert or decrease in scale.

The other half of the vehicle growth picture is the decline of transit ridership. These two factors go hand in hand as can be demonstrated by comparing numbers in Fig. 3.4 with those in the top part of Table 3.4. In the period since 1940, motor vehicle registrations have risen sharply, whereas the number of passengers per year

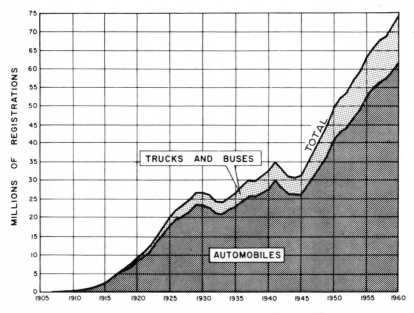

Fig. 3.4 Motor vehicle registration trends, United States [3.8, p. 29].

on all modes of transit has dropped off correspondingly. Therefore, it appears that for the transportation planner to be successful in developing a suitable transportation system, he will have to overcome or circumvent the "natural" and problematic tendencies described above and make transit a viable mode of travel in the face of enlarged car ownership. To accomplish such a task will not be easy.

3.3.3.3 Peakedness in the amount and timing of travel Two other "natural" problems that have a direct effect on the need for transportation are the quantity and temporal pattern of travel. Perhaps due to the rise in per capita income or to the transportation system itself, the amount of travel in the United States has risen sharply. With 1940 considered as a base of 100, the vehicle miles of travel in 1960 stood at the 238 level [3.8, p. 33]. By way of comparison, the gross national product of the country stood at 212 while total population was at 136. Thus, we see a greatly increased desire to travel that must be met by the transportation system, and, with travel outstripping all other relevant quantities, it appears that a greater amount of resources must be expended to keep up with the rapidly expanding demands for transportation.

To make matters worse, we must also allow for the significant hourly peaking in travel that takes place in urban areas. As can be seen in Fig. 3.5, there usually are two general peaks—the rush hours—in which travel is much heavier than at other times. The evening peak in Chicago, for example, may amount to approximately 11 percent of the total trips in a day. Yet, if there were no peaks, we would only have to provide for $\frac{1}{24}$ or about 4 percent of all daily trips in 1 hour. Temporal variations in tripmaking thus require that we provide for roughly three times as many trips as would occur otherwise.

The situation for transit is even more difficult. Referring again to Fig. 3.5, we see that almost all transit trips occur during the peak periods, with the result being that most of the transit stock will lay idle during the rest of the day. Moreover, the cost of labor for transit is affected greatly since it usually takes more than one shift of drivers and other personnel to cover the two peaks.

3.4 SUMMARY AND CONCLUDING COMMENTS

Table 3.11 summarizes much of the material concerning the effect of many factors in the problem domain on the need for transportation. Most apparent are the extremely rapid growths of travel, vehicle registrations, and gross national product (GNP). It appears that there is a strong correlation between the first two entities and the latter one so that we can expect that if economic conditions continue on the rise, there will be an ever increasing number of cars in use for an ever increasing amount of travel. In addition, with population gaining as it is, especially in urban areas, we might anticipate great pressures on urban transport systems as they attempt to handle the increased burdens placed upon them. These pressures represent the essence of all the factors in the problem domain affecting transportation.

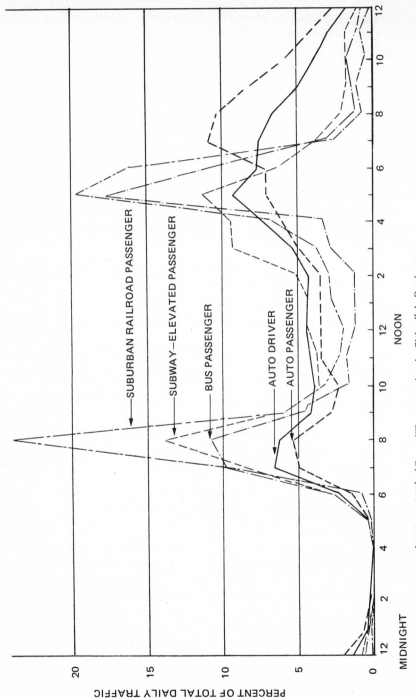

Fig. 3.5 The "peak" problem [3.29, p. 165]. (*From "Transporation in Cities," J. Dyckman. Copyright © 1965 by Scientific American, Inc. All rights reserved.*)

The chart axes:

PERCENT OF TOTAL DAILY TRAFFIC

MIDNIGHT ... NOON

Legend labels:
SUBURBAN RAILROAD PASSENGER
SUBWAY–ELEVATED PASSENGER
BUS PASSENGER
AUTO DRIVER
AUTO PASSENGER

**Table 3.11 Summary Transportation Indices in Relation to
Economic Growth 1940–1959 (1940 = 100)**

				Item				
Year	Total popu- lation*	Urban popu- lation	Gross national product†	Manu- facturing employ- ment	Total vehicle regis- trations	Vehicle miles of travel	Transit riders	Commuter railroad passengers
1940	100	100	100	100	100	100	100	100
1941	101	101	116	113	108	110	108	101
1942	102	101	130	124	102	89	137	125
1943	103	102	145	131	95	69	168	136
1944	105	100	156	129	94	70	176	139
1945	106	100	153	125	96	83	178	141
1946	107	111	136	129	106	113	178	149
1947	109	113	135	136	117	123	172	150
1948	111	114	142	139	127	132	163	145
1949	113	116	141	135	138	140	145	135
1950	115	119	154	140	151	152	132	99
1951	117	120	165	148	160	163	123	117
1952	119	122	171	151	164	170	115	114
1953	121	122	178	155	173	180	106	112
1954	123	124	176	151	181	186	95	109
1955	125	125	188	156	193	200	88	108
1956	127	139	193	161	201	208	84	108
1957	130	146	198	163	207	214	79	109
1958	132	153	193	157	211	220	74	104
1959	135	159	206	162	217	230	73	97
1960‡	136	161	212	165	228	238	NA§	NA

*Includes Armed Forces.
†In constant 1947 dollars.
‡Preliminary.
§NA—not available.
Source: [3.8, p. 33].

Factors in the problem domain were only one of three types discussed in this chapter, however. The other two were: (1) those relating directly to transportation service, and (2) those in the problem domain affected or impacted by transportation.

The distinction between the three types probably is not entirely clear, but this is to be exptected when one considers the subject matter involved. What is important at this stage, however, is that we as transportation engineers or planners try to make ourselves cognizant of the great range of consequences that result from the many decisions made concerning transportation systems of various types. Perhaps for a given situation the kinds of problems discussed in this chapter are not significant, or perhaps the real problems have not been covered here, or perhaps certain problems have not been given enough attention. Whatever the case, we must recognize (1) that the problem identification stage of the planning process is critical, (2) that too few transportation studies have expended enough effort in trying to pinpoint actual problems (going on the assumption that problems are more or less universal), and (3) that problems will change, acquiring different degrees of importance, as time progresses. The upshot of these conditions is that the planner or engineer must be prepared to devote resources to problem identification; otherwise he opens himself to the mistrust of citizens who have made comments such as those that follow [3.24, p. 8] :

> I don't think there has been any planning, meaningful planning, anywhere in the United States.
> A number of people think they're engaged in meaningful planning. I think that's what annoys us. When I draw up a ——·—— plan and produce it on a slick brochure then that's profundity—you better believe it because it has my name at the bottom of it. How many of *those* have we seen?
> I think most of the planning is very, very opportunistic for the guys who are doing the planning, trying to get some money and really no thought given to how it's going to fit into a total scheme of things—no thought given to how these people are going to live there, and it goes on and on.

BIBLIOGRAPHY

3.1   Alexander, C., and M. L. Manheim: "The Design of a Highway Interchange," *Highway Research Board Record* 83, Washington, D.C., 1965.

3.2   Owen, W.: *The Metropolitan Transportation Problem*, rev. ed., The Brookings Institution, Washington, D.C., 1966.

3.3   Owen, W.: *Cities in the Motor Age*, The Viking Press, New York, 1959.

3.4   *Traffic in Towns*. The specially shortened edition of the Buchanan Report, Penguin Books Ltd., Hamondsworth, England, 1963.

3.5   Alexander, C.: *Notes on the Synthesis of Form*, Harvard Press, Cambridge, 1964.

3.6   Meyer, J. R., J. F. Kain, and M. Wohl: *The Urban Transportation Problem*, Harvard Press, Cambridge, 1965.

3.7   Fabre, M.: *A History of Land Transportation*, Hawthorne Books, New York, 1963.

3.8   Wilbur Smith and Associates: *Future Highways and Urban Growth*, New Haven, Conn., 1961.

3.9   Mumford, L.: *The Highway and the City*, Mentor, New York, 1953.

3.10 Higbee, E.: *The Squeeze—Cities Without Space*, Apollo Editions A-43, William Morrow & Co., New York, 1960.

3.11 McMillan, R. K., and H. Assael: *National Survey of Transportation Attitudes and Behavior: Phase I Summary Report*, NCHRP Report 49, Highway Research Board, Washington, D.C., 1968.

3.12 U.S. Department of Housing and Urban Development, Office of Metropolitan Development: *Tomorrow's Transportation*, U.S. Government Printing Office, Washington, D.C., 1968.

3.13 Pell, C. De B.: *Megalopolis Unbound*, F. A. Praeger, New York, 1966.

3.14 Duhl, L. J. (ed.): *The Urban Condition*, Basic Books, New York, 1963.

3.15 Gordon, M.: *Sick Cities*, MacMillan, New York, 1965.

3.16 Bello, F.: "The City and the Car," in *The Exploding Metropolis*, The Editors of Fortune, Doubleday, Garden City, New York, 1958.

3.17 Thomas, E. N., and J. L. Schofer: *Strategies for Evaluation of Transportation Plans,* NCHRP Report 96, Highway Research Board, Washington, D.C., 1970.

3.18 Devalle, J. W.: "Concrete Ties for Timber Trestles," *Railway Track and Structures,* vol. 64, no. 9, Sept. 1968.

3.19 Krick, E. V.: *An Introduction to Engineering and Engineering Design,* Wiley, New York, 1965.

3.20 Fleisher, A.: "On Prediction and Urban Traffic," *Papers and Proceedings of the Regional Science Association,* vol. 7, 1961.

3.21 Berry, D. S. et al.: *The Technology of Urban Transportation,* Northwestern Univ. Press, Evanston, Ill., 1963.

3.22 U.S. Department of Transportation: *Second Annual Report to the Congress on the Administration of the Highway Safety Act of 1966,* U.S. Government Printing Office, Washington, D.C., 1969.

3.23 National Safety Council: *Accident Facts,* Chicago, 1964.

3.24 Barton-Aschman Associates, Inc.: *Guidelines for New Systems of Urban Transportation, Vol. II: A Collection of Papers,* Federal Clearinghouse, Springfield, Va., April 1968.

3.25 Ritter, L. J., and R. J. Paquette: *Highway Engineering,* 2d ed., Ronald Press, New York, 1960.

3.26 Bone, A. J., and M. Wohl: "Massachusetts Route 128 Impact Study," *Highway Research Board Bulletin* 227, 1959.

3.27 Carson, R.: *Silent Spring,* Faucett Publications, Greenwich, Conn., 1962.

3.28 Highway Research Board: *Highway Capacity Manual, 1965,* Special Report 87, Washington, D.C., 1965.

3.29 Dychman, J.: "Transportation in Cities," *Scientific American,* vol. 213, no. 3., Sept. 1965.

3.30 Hall, F. D.: "Transportation," *Vital Speeches of the Day,* vol. 33, no. 1, August 15, 1967.

3.31 Bartholomew, H.: "Metropolitan Transportation Problem," *Proceedings of the American Society of Civil Engineers,* vol. 91, July 1965.

3.32 Hulbert, S. F.: "Human Factors and Traffic Engineering," *Traffic Engineering,* vol. 28, no. 12, Sept. 1968.

3.33 *Civil Engineering,* vol. 38, no. 9, Sept. 1968.

3.34 League of Women Voters of the United States: "A Congregation of Vapors," *Facts and Issues,* Washington, D.C., Sept. 1970.

4 Transportation Goals and Objectives

The starting point of all planning and programming is some definition of the result toward the achievement of which efforts are to be directed. "Goals" are desired ends expressed in the broadest sense, derived from a consideration of "values" and conducive to a further delineation of program objectives, alternative approaches, and definitive plans and schedules of action.

Transportation programs have generally been characterized by a lack of clear statements of broad overall goals, probably because the complexity of the transportation condition makes such statements difficult to compose, and because programs have generally been devised to meet a given "problem," such as low revenues, or congestion, or antiquated equipment.

Nonetheless, there is an existing structure of transportation goals at both national and local levels. However loosely they may be defined and however lacking in cohesive, assembled form, overall goals have been expressed in the development of legislation, in party platforms (see Fig. 4.1) and the statements of elected leaders, in comprehensive plans, in judicial decisions, in the stated aims of interest groups and in other reflections of consensus. Although much needs to be done to expand and refine (or perhaps reconsider) existing transportation goals, an immediate problem is how to understand those that do exist and apply them in the guidance of efforts to improve urban and rural conditions.

The sensible approach to problems facing us in the seventies.

High-quality education is a necessity. Virginia needs more and better schools, highly qualified teachers, additional emphasis on early childhood education, a complete special education program, a full system of community colleges, vocational education, and increased opportunities for our children in higher education.

Efficient and responsive government at lowest cost must be insured by a series of studies aimed at effective tax collection procedures and a reorganization of mushrooming State agencies. Areas like Southwest and Northwest Virginia need to be brought into closer contact with State government.

Safe streets and colleges require firm action if disturbances should erupt in Virginia, well-trained law enforcement officials, concern for the rights of society as well as those of the accused, immediate steps to combat drug abuse, and a concerted attack on the growing death rate on our highways.

A comprehensive transportation policy which treats all Virginians fairly and gives proper emphasis to secondary roads has become essential.

Economic development can lighten local tax burdens. A first-rate effort to attract industry to provide new jobs and to promote Virginia's ports, railroads, and airfields is imperative.

The welfare system must be reformed to provide training and rehabilitation for recipients so they can be removed from the rolls and lead useful and productive lives.

The quality of rural life must be enhanced. Affiliation of hospital complexes in Roanoke and Winchester with the U. Va. medical school to provide more doctors and health care, a workable system of tax deferral on farm and open space land, and increased agricultural research and education can help stem the urban crisis.

Battle for Governor The sensible choice

Fig. 4.1 An example of goal statements in political situations.

Understanding and pursuing broad goals is especially critical in the planning of transportation, for it is all too easy (as the record bears out) to view transportation simply as a supporting "service" to be projected in response to demands emanating from other actions or decisions. To the contrary, as was shown in the previous chapter, transportation is an element of the urban structure so pervasive in its influence that it must be considered an area for key decision making in the shaping of both urban form and environment. Transportation decisions are, furthermore, only infrequently related to the immediate future and, hence, seldom can be readily reversed if they turn out to be "wrong," in the sense that they fail to contribute to or even hamper the achievement of high-level goals in urban improvement.

In this chapter a loosely structured hierarchy of urban values and corresponding transportation goals and objectives is described. The intent is to summarize the principal goals which appear to be operative in recent thinking about transportation and development activities and then indicate briefly (and as a prelude to Chap. 8) how these goals might vary from person to person.

The chapter is divided into seven sections. First, a brief résumé of basic urban values and goals is presented. Second, two basic transportation goals, one for those factors of direct concern to transportation service and the other for those factors impacted by transportation, are discussed in general terms. These are then used in the third section as a guide for the identification of a select set of more detailed goals. In the fourth section, these detailed goals are transformed into specific objectives containing relevant criteria. Thereafter follows a discussion of the weightings of importance of different objectives and variations in these weightings for different groups of people. The final section contains summary comments on the difficulties associated with identifying transportation problems and goals.[1]

4.1 BASIC URBAN VALUES AND GOALS

All goals and objectives stem from basic *values* that are important to people. There are many ways of describing these values. A "good" city is popularly referred to in everyday terms such as "vital," "warm and friendly," "dynamic," "safe," "exciting," "full of opportunity," and "beautiful." A "bad" city is described as "dirty," "ugly," "dangerous," "hostile," "impersonal," "confusing," "overwhelming," "time-consuming," "congested," or "wasteful." A more formal listing of abstract values would include terms such as "freedom," "liberty," "dignity," "health and safety," "amenity," "diversity," "economy," "ownership," "mobility," and "affluence."

In most general terms, then, a value can be defined as:

Value: An element of a shared symbolic system (referred to as a value system), acquired through social learning, which serves as a guide for the selection from among perceived alternatives of orientation.

Indications of the types of values held by individuals in a given society should be of great concern to planners, engineers, and designers, particularly since these values form the basis for the development of goals for the activities and characteristics of the population and the use of resources in a region. For instance, at the highest and most general level, there should be little disagreement that governmental interest in urban development relates to two major goals:

First, that the quality of life be improved in the whole variety of ways that reflect the common values so often expressed in personal reactions to "the city."

Second, that the metropolitan area itself be strengthened in terms of its productive capacity, its democratic institutions, and its ability to allocate and use its natural and human resources to best advantage in each community.

As can be seen, these goals rest heavily on inherent values, and this fact serves to emphasize the definition of a goal which is as follows:

---

[1] Much of the wording in the beginning sections of this chapter is taken from the report in [4.27], which we felt described even better than we could ourselves the concept of the nature and structure of goals.

Goal: An articulation of values, formulated in light of identified issues and problems, toward the attainment of which policies and decisions are directed.

Two points regarding this definition need further elaboration. For one, goals are an outgrowth of identified *issues and problems* and usually do not stand on their own. We would not, for example, be concerned about "strengthening democratic institutions" in metropolitan areas, as stated in the second value above, if we happened to be working for a totalitarian government. But, as a second point, we should not *limit* our set of goals to correspond only to problems that presently exist because in many cases solutions which are proposed bring about unanticipated new types of problems. To repeat an example given in the previous chapter (Sec. 3.2.1), we cannot afford to narrow our consideration of parking in the central business district only to that problem. If we did, we might overlook additional problems such as that of the transfer of large segments of the population between their places of residence and places of business, or that of noise, or air pollution, or congestion near parking facilities, and so forth. The set of goals associated with transportation must therefore relate to more than existing problems; otherwise, proposed solutions will bring about new and unexpected difficulties.

Creating an amalgam of values and goals is a complicated process that has by no means been fully developed in the field of transportation planning and design. Among the complications is the fact that values or goals are not necessarily mutually supporting. Indeed, they are often in polar-like opposition, so that the problem in goal formulation is one of emphasis and balance among values. The process is also complex because points of balance are constantly shifting in time and from place to place. Technological, economic, social, and institutional changes are continually altering the extent to which individual values may be capable of being achieved. This means that the establishment of goals and the determination of relative emphasis to be placed upon various goals is a continuing process that must be applied at many levels and in many places.

Another apparent difficulty in developing goals is that they, like problems, seem to be hierarchical.[2] Statements of goals usually begin with broad generalizations and then are developed at more detailed levels to guide the various types and stages of planning and design activities. However, we should realize that goals are intended to be broad, extensive statements that form the basis for comprehensive concepts for our undertakings. Thus, we should not be quick to give into the tendency to try to avoid generalizations inherent in goal statements and thus avoid the accusation of a lack of specificity and "practicality."

4.2 BROAD GOALS FOR TRANSPORTATION

The two broad goals for urban development presented in the previous section probably would be at the top of any goal hierarchy. Proceeding down from these

---

[2] For a hierarchical structure of problems for which a corresponding pattern of goals could be constructed, see Chap. 3, Fig. 3.1; and also Fig. 4.2 in this chapter.

would be a wide variety of goals pertaining to various aspects of human characteristics, human behavior, and the physical environment. We, of course, are particularly interested in transportation in this context and in the previous chapter subdivided transportation problems into three classes: (1) those that are "direct" or transportation service problems; (2) those in the problem environment *affected by* transportation; and (3) those in the problem environment *affecting* transportation.

A similar classification can be employed for transportation goals and will be developed in this section. However, it should be realized at this point that the setting of goals for the last class of transportation problems probably is not a worthwhile exercise. The reason is that goals can logically be created only for factors over which some control can be exerted. Since we as local transportation planners or engineers can do relatively little to influence factors such as overall population growth, income levels, and so forth, the discussion to follow on goals for transportation will not relate to these type of factors.

4.2.1 Goals for Direct or Transportation Service Factors

The primary, although certainly not exclusive purpose of transportation is to serve the user or potential user of the system, that is, to provide accessibility to land and mobility between desired trip ends.

Beneficial transportation for the user would be most obvious in the form of increased access to opportunities for achievement, most notably in employment, purchase of goods, health care, and education. In the short run transportation development should aim to compensate for disparities inherent in such current phenomena as shifts in employment and living patterns which tend to reduce ready access to a variety of opportunities. To do this requires the provision of transportation to both centrally located employment, commercial, health, and educational centers and to new centers in outlying areas. It also means designing transportation improvements to enable a range of choice and diversity of urban experience.

Efficiency and economy in the use of public and private corporation funds also is of direct importance in transportation service, especially since these are virtually standard requirements in all forms of investment. It is apparent, for example, that many public and private transportation operations have had to maintain a continuing vigil on expenses in order that they could achieve a respectable rate of return on their investments. Similarly, it is clear that funds from local, state, and federal sources are limited and must be allocated to their best use.

4.2.2 Goals for Factors in the Problem Domain Affected by Transportation

An environment which responds to human needs and sensibilities and to the requirements of enterprise should be sought, thus helping to enlarge urban opportunity. This goal is concerned with rational arrangement, amenity, and fostering of the forms of development that are characterized by the variety-diversity and ease of contact that they offer.

Rational arrangement makes it possible for people to understand the city's layout and be able to move about more readily. Thus, it is easier to plan and locate enterprises and institutions in desirable relationship to the rest of the city's activities.

Amenity has to do with positive qualities of convenience, safety, healthfulness, and beauty as opposed to the negative qualities of inconvenience, hazard, pollution, and ugliness.

Variety and ease of contact are two of the most dominant motivations in the growth of urban areas. They are concerned not only with transportation efficiency, but also with the design of large-scale development. It is the latter with which this goal is chiefly involved. For example, there is a strong trend (apparently reinforced by both internal and external economies) toward the development of new multipurpose centers or subcenters (business, educational, research, housing) throughout metropolitan areas. Despite the improvement in variety and ease of contact that such centers offer, their development is frequently inhibited by lack of transportation facilities.

Conservation of natural resources is an associated goal reflecting society's growing awareness of the limitations of air, water, land, and other natural resources needed in urban development and maintenance of all forms of life. Transportation planning can contribute to this goal in its support of concepts fostering the multiple use of land (including both multiple-use projects and conservation of land used for transportation facilities). The provision of adequate transportation services supporting high intensity of land-use in and around special resource areas (water frontages, areas of unusual aesthetic or historical value) will permit greater use of these resources. Different types of transportation facilities and different designs (for example, elevation or depression according to microclimatological requirements) may be devised or selected in the interest of better natural resource management.

Transportation, as a facet of spatial organization, can play a major, although not an exclusive, role in the accomplishment of all of these goals. It may do this in terms of pricing (making available services within the ability of people to pay), in terms of speed (placing distant locations in improved time relationships), and in terms of other operating characteristics. It may also do this in terms of availability of service, a function of system design. It may contribute to equitable access through its influence on the arrangement of land use. Quite obviously, all of these goals are important, and methods needed to achieve them are of general concern to the public.

4.3 IDENTIFICATION OF MORE DETAILED GOALS

The two sets of goals brought out above, one for transportation service and the other for transportation impact on the environment, provide very general directions towards which transportation system modifications and control should evolve. More detailed and tangible goals and objectives are needed, however, so that solutions to certain specific problems can be evaluated. To develop such a detailed set is not easy since many important considerations do not present themselves until solutions with characteristics different from the present situation are suggested. Moreover, if adequate thought is given to goal identification procedures, the resulting list of goals can become quite long, and additional efforts must be devoted to ensure that the items on the list are fairly exclusive and exhaustive and that they are representative of the group of people they are intended to serve.

Dickey and Broderick [4.31] have developed one technique useful for being more exhaustive in identifying transportation service, impact, and affecting factors. Their technique involves a classification with four major components: (1) man (and groups), (2) the natural environment, (3) the manmade environment, and (4) activities.

Each of these components are further subdivided, as can be seen in Tables 4.1 to 4.4. These tables also serve as a checklist. By way of illustration, an often forgotten group in many urban planning and design situations consists of those people who

Table 4.1 Man (and Groups)

Component I

Individuals and/or households

I-1	By age (including unborn, those that will die, etc.)
I-2	By race, religion, color, ethnic background
I-3	By locality (and future locality)
I-4	By sex
I-5	By employment category
I-6	By political leaning
I-7	By income
I-8	By educational background
I-9	By personality types (including deviants)
I-10	By occupation
I-11	By social status
I-12	By leisure pursuits
I-13	By power/control

Firms and institutions

I-14	Firms
I-15	Institutional groups
I-16	Governmental agencies, legislatures, and judiciaries
I-17	Social groups and clubs
I-18	Political groups
I-19	By locality (and future locality)
I-20	Military organizations
I-21	Unions
I-22	Peer groups

Table 4.2   Elements of the Natural Environment

Component II

II-1	Earth materials
II-2	Physiographic system (including land surface, etc.)
II-3	Hydrologic system (land-related surface and subsurface waters, etc.)
II-4	Climate (micro and macro)
II-5	Vegetation (forests, flowers, grass, etc.)
II-6	Wildlife (aquatic animals, land animals, insects, etc.)
II-7	Marine and estuarine systems
II-8	Time
II-9	Atmosphere

Table 4.3   Elements of the Manmade Environment

Component III

III-1	Food, drink, tobacco, drugs
III-2	Clothing
III-3	Raw materials; intermediate and final goods (including crops, domestic animals, etc.)
III-4	Housing (including institutional)
III-5	Communication facilities (including mail, television, telephone, radio, etc.)
III-6	Transportation facilities (including vehicles, guideways, terminals, and controls)
III-7	Educational and cultural facilities (including schools, museums, libraries)
III-8	Water supply, sewage disposal, solid waste disposal, and drainage facilities
III-9	Health facilities (including hospitals, mental institutions, nursing homes)
III-10	Energy creation and supply facilities (including electric, coal, oil, natural gas, etc.)
III-11	Production facilities (including office buildings, machinery, storage areas, warehouses)
III-12	Sales, administrative, and service facilities (including wholesale and retail)
III-13	Military facilities (including bases, training camps, storage areas, etc.)
III-14	Governmental, police, fire, judicial, and welfare facilities
III-15	Leisure and recreational facilities (including parks, clubs, fraternal organizations, etc.)
III-16	Information
III-17	Monetary capital (stocks, bonds, cash, etc.)
III-18	Laws (including police power, eminent domain, zoning, etc.)
III-19	Energy

Table 4.4 Activity Elements and Agents

Component IV

Agent		Activity
IV-1	Individuals and Households	Income producing
IV-2		Child raising and family
IV-3		Educational and intellectual
IV-4		Spiritual development
IV-5		Social
IV-6		Recreation and relaxation
IV-7		Clubs
IV-8		Community service and political
IV-9		Associated with food, shopping, health, etc.
IV-10		Travel
IV-11	Firms	Goods producing
IV-12		Service
IV-13	Institutions	Human development
IV-14		Basic community service
IV-15		For welfare and special groups
IV-16	All (long-term)	Migration
IV-17		Investment
IV-18		Crime, war

do not at present live in the urban area being planned or designed. This group would have to be considered, for example, in planning for new towns or new developments involving vacant land within the boundaries of an existing urban area. This group is element I-3 in Table 4.1. Two other groups of possible interest consist of those individuals not born yet or those living now who may not be when actual developments take place in the distant future. These groups are included in the category of Individuals By Age (including unborn, those that will die, etc.), item I-1 in Table 4.1.[3]

As mentioned, the elements presented in Tables 4.1 to 4.4 serve as a good checklist. Yet, it is also important to determine the *characteristics* of interest for each element in these tables. Dickey and Broderick searched the *Thesaurus* [4.34] and produced a list of 49 characteristics that could possibly describe each element (see Table 4.5). These characteristics then were cross-referenced with each element to produce a matrix of items (possible goals or problems) like that suggested in Table 4.6. As an example of the use of this kind of table, consider element III-6 of Table 4.3, the "transportation system," and characteristic C-3 of Table 4.5, "technical." If we combine these two entities we might be led to think of those people under 16 years of age, those handicapped, and those too old to be capable (technically) of driving an automobile. One detailed goal, then, for a transportation

---

[3] With the recent emphasis on advocacy planning, it is surprising that the planner often forgets he is one of the few advocates for the future generation.

Table 4.5 Characteristics to be Used in Conjunction with Elements in Tables 4.1 to 4.4

C-1	Religious-moral-ethical		C-26	Beautiful
C-2	Free		C-27	Quiet
C-3	Technical		C-28	Healthy
C-4	Stable		C-29	Safe
C-5	Private		C-30	Informed
C-6	Cheap		C-31	Liberal
C-7	Accessible		C-32	Upper class
C-8	Active		C-33	Polluted
C-9	Defended (militarily)		C-34	Nicely shaped
C-10	Large		C-35	Dark
C-11	Comfortable		C-36	New
C-12	Wealthy		C-37	Fragrant
C-13	Just		C-38	Hot
C-14	Happy		C-39	Windy
C-15	Parochial		C-40	Wet
C-16	Natural		C-41	Flexible
C-17	Numerous		C-42	Open
C-18	Organized		C-43	Biased
C-19	Time consuming		C-44	Hungry
C-20	Law abiding		C-45	Thirsty
C-21	Tasty		C-46	Angry
C-22	Exciting		C-47	Powerful
C-23	Affiliative		C-48	Fearful
C-24	Symbolic		C-49	Productive
C-25	Inducive to communication			

system may be to reduce the technical requirement for operation (that is, user operation). In a similar way, a variety of other goals can be identified.

This identification technique has several drawbacks:

1. Not all characteristics in Table 4.5 are descriptive of the elements in Tables 4.1 to 4.4 (e.g., "nicely shaped" (C-34) and "unions" (I-21) do not go together).
2. The elements (and characteristics) are not mutually exclusive (e.g., individuals of certain age classes (I-1) are also of certain races and religions (I-2)).
3. The number of items in Table 4.6 can become quite large.

These drawbacks can be reduced somewhat through various means, but what is important is that the technique can be employed to identify *ahead of time* a large percentage of possible goals of relevance to transportation planning and design.

4.3.1 Example Sets of Goals

Many different sets of goals have been proposed in transportation and related studies. As expected, the goals are specified at different levels of the hierarchy and in many cases are somewhat vague in nature. Further, there is no general agreement on major categories of goals (as, for example, the transportation service and impact categories employed in this book). These problems, while somewhat significant, can be tolerated if one does not become overly concerned with precision in an endeavor which is not relatively understood or agreed upon. Greater precision is needed, however, when objectives and criteria (measures) are developed for each goal (Sec. 4.4).

An example on a broad level of goal specification (actually potential benefit specification) can be found in the (San Francisco) Bay Area Rapid Transit District's *Composite Report,* which was presented to the voters in the region just before a bond issue referendum:

1. It (the BART system) would aid future growth by (*a*) maintaining and encouraging concentration of business and industry and lessening sprawl, (*b*) improving living and working conditions, (*c*) preserving and increasing property values, and (*d*) permitting more economic use of land.
2. It would benefit state and local governments by (*a*) reducing the need for highway funds in the central cities and releasing them for suburban areas, (*b*) containing urban sprawl, thereby lessening costs of public services, (*c*) protecting and increasing public revenues by inducing greater economic growth, and (*d*) reducing usurpation of tax and job-producing lands by highway facilities.
3. It would benefit families and individuals in the three counties by (*a*) increasing mobility and job potentials of users, (*b*) providing transportation

Table 4.6 Urban Element–Performance Characteristic Items

	Performance characteristics				
Urban elements	C-1 Religious-Moral-Ethical	C-2 Free	C-3 Technical	...	C-49 Productive
Man (and groups)					
I-1 Individuals and/or households by age					
$\vdots$					
I-22 Peer groups					
Natural environment					
II-1 Earth materials					
$\vdots$					
II-9 Atmosphere					
Manmade environment		Items			
III-1 Food, drink tobacco, drugs					
$\vdots$					
III-19 Energy					
Activities					
IV-1 Income producing					
$\vdots$					
IV-18 Crime, war					

for those without automobiles, and (c) expanding social, educational, and recreational opportunities.

As noted, these goals are somewhat broad but do seem to cover most important aspects.

In Dallas, 87 people from diverse backgrounds were chosen to participate in a 3-day conference which produced a set of goals to be considered by citizens in town meetings. The resulting goals for transportation are reproduced in Table 4.7. A general goal statement is made first, followed by a set of specific recommendations. Many of the latter are perhaps overly specific and presuppose a solution. The fifth goal, for example, stresses more adequate taxi service as a need. Yet it may be

Table 4.7   Transportation Goals for Dallas, Texas

General goal

Dallas must recognize and improve its position as a major transportation and communication center. In order that we may continue to grow and compete successfully with other metropolitan regions, we should work constantly to improve transportation and communications facilities. Within the city and the region, people must be able to move rapidly, pleasantly, safely, and economically from their homes to work, to schools, to shopping areas, and to recreational and cultural facilities. Transportation of goods within the city and region should be efficient without interfering with the citizen's enjoyment of his city.

Specific goals

1. Continue to expand and improve transportation service to the metropolitan areas and nations at reasonable rates.
2. Secure with the support of other governmental units in the region, enabling legislation for a Transit Authority or Authorities which would:
   a. Serve as large an area initially as is practical and be designed ultimately for the entire metropolitan region. Membership would include representatives of the areas served.
   b. Study the technology of rapid transit to select the system or systems which can best satisfy our needs.
   c. Assume ownership and operation of the Dallas Transit System and extend its services to satisfy as many needs as the Authority can justify economically.
   d. See to it that Dallas and other municipalities protect and, if possible, preserve at today's price, right-of-way for future rapid transit.
   e. Consider subsidy of public transit by the metropolitan region.
3. Bring the Dallas-Fort Worth airport to its fullest potential as a regional and world air center. Develop more private aircraft and short-hop commercial facilities.
4. Maintain a perpetual list of the community's needs in communications and take effective action to assure postal, telephone, and telegraph services which meet the needs.
5. Make available adequate taxi service in all parts of the city and at all hours.
6. Design transportation facilities and services to satisfy the needs of users without dissatisfying other people. For example, when transportation changes are needed, sufficient right-of-way should be acquired to protect adjacent land.

Source: [4.36, pp. 12–13].

that the kind of service desired could be fulfilled by other means (e.g., mini-bus). The main point is nevertheless that some general directions for improvement in Dallas' transportation system have been determined.

Perhaps the most exhaustive set of goals is that proposed by Winfrey and Zellner [4.32]. These are reproduced in Table 4.8. The authors divided all goals (consequences) into 15 general categories and then subdivided these even further. They also attempted to determine whether the impacts associated with each goal or consequence would be urban or rural in nature, economic or social, on a particular geographic level (from the transportation system right-of-way to the regional level), and would occur at particular times relative to the completion of construction. In terms of our classification by transportation service or impact, all goals in Table 4.8 fall into the latter class except those in major category 13 (Road User). Table 4.8 represents one of the most detailed sets of goals found in the literature. Such a set would be most useful for, say, final design and solution specification, while a broader based set (as for BART) might be more appropriate for general policy statement.

4.4 GOAL-RELATED OBJECTIVES AND CRITERIA (MEASURES)

Up to this point little has been said about measurable entities that can be used to give explicit assessment of suggested solutions for metropolitan transportation. These more tangible entities are known as *objectives* and contain measurable attributes or quantities known as *criteria:*

Objective: A specific statement denoting a measurable end to be reached or achieved for a particular group of people, usually in a particular span of time.

Criterion (measure): An explicit attribute or characteristic used for the purpose of comparative evaluation.

Associated with each goal should be at least one strongly defined objective and a corresponding criterion (or criteria). In a study done for the Baltimore region [4.32], Ockert and Pixton identified a set of goals and associated measures. One goal, illustrated in Table 4.9, was that of provision of access to activities. Several possible *criteria* were listed and one was picked as a single measure of success in meeting the goal. As can be seen, the chosen *criterion* is very specific in terms of (a) income levels associated with the jobs and (b) travel times and headways associated with the transportation system. The *objective* would be to minimize the number of employment opportunities without "adequate" (as defined explicitly in the table) transportation. No time period to reach a certain level of the objective was given.

Some additional examples of criteria are presented in Table 4.10. These are Phase I specifications part of the Federal Clean Car Incentive Program sponsored by the Environmental Protection Agency. The criteria are divided into six categories— emissions, safety, performance, serviceability, fuel availability, and noise level. Within each of these categories are sets of desired measures to be employed in testing the success of automobile designs.

Table 4.8 Social and Economic Consequences (Goals) of Highway Improvement (by Area, Type, Location, and Timing)

Social and Economic Consequence Variables / Goal	Area		Type		Location				Timing			
	Urban	Rural	Economic	Social	Right-of-way	Corridor	Community or system	Region or nation	Before construction	During construction	After construction - short term	After construction - long term
1. Aesthetics												
A. The view from the road	X	X		X	X	X					X	X
B. The view of the road	X	X	X	X	X	X					X	X
C. Highway-mode-induced aesthetic effects	X	X	X	X	X	X	X				X	X
2. Agriculture												
A. Access to improved road		X	X	X		X	X				X	X
B. Economic units (size of farm unit)		X	X		X	X				X	X	X
C. Productivity		X	X			X	X	X		X	X	X
D. Dislocation		X	X	X	X	X			X	X	X	X
3. Commercial												
Commercial sales receipts and incomes:												
A. Change due to dislocation and relocation	X		X		X	X			X	X	X	
B. Change due to barrier	X		X		X	X				X	X	
C. Change due to population change	X		X			X					X	X
D. Change due to income group change	X		X			X				X	X	X
E. Change due to traffic volume change (bypass effect)	X		X				X				X	X
F. Change due to accessibility change (trade area)	X		X			X					X	X

Item											
G. Change due to community price change (resulting from transportation)	X						X			X	X
H. Rental property receipts	X						X			X	X
I. Employment	X					X	X	X		X	X
J. Land use	X					X	X	X		X	X
K. Land value	X				X	X	X			X	X
L. Effect on public transportation	X			X		X	X		X	X	X
M. Parking	X					X	X		X	X	X
4. Community government											
A. Community services and facilities	X					X	X			X	X
B. Park, recreation and open space	X		X			X				X	X
C. Non-highway government revenue and expenditures changes	X	X					X	X	X	X	X
D. Public policy and laws	X	X				X	X	X	X	X	X
E. Community goals	X	X				X	X	X	X	X	X
5. Construction											
A. Community social and economic effects during construction				X		X	X	X	X		
B. Immediate effects on highway construction industry	X			X				X	X		
C. Long term effects on non-highway construction industry	X			X			X	X		X	X
6. Employment											
A. Employment change due to new land use development	X	X		X		X	X		X	X	
B. Employment change due to dislocation and relocation	X	X		X		X	X	X	X	X	
7. Environment											
A. Noise	X	X		X		X	X	X		X	X
B. Air pollution	X	X		X		X	X			X	X
C. Vibrations	X		X				X	X	X	X	X
D. Drainage patterns	X	X		X		X	X			X	X

Table 4.8 Social and Economic Consequences (Goals) of Highway Improvement (by Area, Type, Location, and Timing) *(Continued)*

Social and Economic Consequence Variables

Goal	Area Urban	Area Rural	Type Economic	Type Social	Location Right-of-way	Location Corridor	Location Community or system	Location Region or nation	Timing Before construction	Timing During construction	Timing After construction - short term -	Timing After construction - long term -
8. Industrial												
A. Industrial development	X		X			X	X	X			X	
B. Industrial dislocation	X		X	X	X			X	X			
C. Industrial relocation	X		X			X	X			X	X	X
D. Industrial land use	X		X	X		X	X			X	X	X
E. Industrial land value	X		X			X	X				X	X
9. Institutions												
A. Institutional dislocation and relocation	X		X	X	X					X	X	X
B. Institutional accessibility and patronage change	X		X	X		X				X	X	X
10. Population												
A. Population growth	X	X		X		X	X					
B. Population density	X	X		X		X	X					
C. Population geographic shifts	X	X		X			X	X				
D. Population distribution	X			X			X					
11. Public utilities												
A. Utility joint-use of right-of-way	X	X	X		X				X	X	X	X
B. Utility dislocations and relocations	X	X	X		X	X			X	X	X	
C. Utility patterns and costs	X		X			X	X				X	X

92

	1	2	3	4	5	6	7	8	9	10	11	12
12. Residential neighborhoods												
A. Rents, costs and prices of replacement housing	X		X			X	X		X	X	X	
B. Residential relocation costs	X		X		X				X			
C. Social and economic relationships of dislocatees	X		X	X	X	X			X	X		
D. Quality of neighborhood life	X				X	X	X		X			
E. Property values in right-of-way before taking	X		X			X			X			
F. Neighborhood and community stability	X		X	X	X	X			X			
G. Neighborhood and community linkage patterns	X		X	X		X					X	
H. Residential land development	X		X			X	X				X	X
I. Residential property values	X			X		X	X				X	X
J. Neighborhood and community patterns	X			X		X	X				X	X
K. Social life and social patterns	X			X		X	X				X	X
13. Road user												
A. Accident and safety	X	X	X	X	X	X	X	X			X	X
B. Running costs—distance related	X		X		X	X	X				X	X
C. Running costs—land use intensity and population density related	X		X		X	X	X				X	X
14. Spatial and geographical changes												
A. Local	X	X	X	X	X		X		X	X	X	X
B. Metropolitan	X	X	X	X			X				X	X
C. Regional	X	X	X	X				X			X	X
15. Urban form and development												
A. Land-use inventory	X		X			X			X	X	X	
B. Land values general	X		X		X	X				X	X	
C. Central business district	X		X	X	X	X	X	X		X	X	X
D. Urban form and development patterns	X		X	X		X	X	X		X	X	
E. Real property and land taken for right-of-way; use and value	X		X			X			X	X		

Source: [4.32, pp. 226-7].

An important point to be made here is that it is not necessary to have *quantifiable* criteria, just measurable ones. Guilford [4.25] defines these terms as:

Measurement: The *assignment of numbers* to objects according to logically accepted rules, and

Quantification: The *ordering* of something according to quantity or amount.

Since it is possible to assign a number to something without ordering it (e.g., male = 1, female = 2), we can employ such criteria as "presence (or lack) of food services in a terminal," or "operation of vehicle by user required or not required." These criteria are nominal (name or categorical) in scale, not ordinal (e.g., army ranks), interval (e.g., °F), or ratio (e.g., yards) in scale. While nominal measures are not as precise in nature as the latter three, they are useful in situations where well-defined and accepted measures are not available. Moreover, because quantification is not a strict necessity in developing criteria, we can feel free to use completely subjective measures derived, for example, from responses of citizens concerned with the appearance of a proposed elevated highway. These responses could be measured on a semantic differential scale [4.26], which has a range from -3 for "very ugly" to $+3$ for "very beautiful." A 0 rating would indicate indifference—"neither ugly nor beautiful."

Table 4.9 Example of a Goal and Related Criteria

Goal: Increase activity access

Possible criteria (measures):	Units
Number of employment opportunities without adequate transportation	Jobs
Accumulated shortage of parking space	Parking spaces
Number of employment opportunities directly served by expressways	Jobs
Number of employment opportunities directly served by rapid transit	Jobs
Number of shopping trips without direct arterial highway access	Shopping trips

Suggested single criterion:

Number of employment opportunities without adequate transportation

Formulation:

$$J = J_{wc} + J_{bc}$$

where J = number of employment opportunities without adequate transportation (jobs)

         J = number of high income ($> \$7,500/\text{yr}$) jobs > 5 min. driving time from an arterial street and > 5 min. walking time from transit stop having < 30 min. headways (jobs)

        J_{bc} = number of low income ($< \$3,500/\text{yr}$) jobs > 5 min. walking time from transit stop having $\leqslant 30$ min. headways (jobs)

Adopted from [4.37, p. A-4].

Table 4.10 Example Criteria and Standards

Criteria	Standard
I. *Emissions* (for 4,000 miles)	
1. Hydrocarbons: grams per vehicle mile measured by the 1975 Federal Test Procedure	0.41
2. Carbon monoxide: grams per mile	3.4
3. Oxides of nitrogen: grams per mile	1.0
4. Evaporative hydrocarbons: grams per test	2.0
5. Smoke: percent capacity during (*a*) acceleration and (*b*) lugging	(*a*) 30 (*b*) 15
II. *Safety*	
1. Compliance with Federal Motor Vehicle Safety Standards and inherent safety of the vehicle and power plant	—
III. *Performance*	
1. Startup time: seconds at 60°F	30
2. Acceleration: seconds on level surface from 0–60 mph	16
3. Top speed: mph for 1 mile on level surface	75
4. Range: miles at (*a*) 50 mph and (*b*) 65 mph	(*a*) 200 (*b*) 150
IV. *Serviceability*	
1. Equivalent to 1972 model year vehicles	—
V. *Fuel availability*	
1. Million vehicle-miles per year fuel quantity available (also must be capable of being stored and dispensed by existing methods)	2.5
VI. *Noise level*	
1. Maximum dBA at 50 ft	80

Adopted from *Commerce Business Daily*, Issue No. PSA–5529, March 16, 1972.

The creation of measurable objectives and corresponding criteria completes the makeup of a second type of hierarchy which starts with values and goals. Figure 4.2 gives a general schematic representation of this other kind of hierarchy and emphasizes the idea that there is not necessarily a one-to-one relationship between criteria, objectives, goals, and values. Several criteria may relate to one objective, one objective to several goals, and so forth.

4.5 CONSTRAINTS AND STANDARDS

A complete discussion of values, goals, objectives, and criteria for transportation must also take into account constraints and standards (desired levels). These

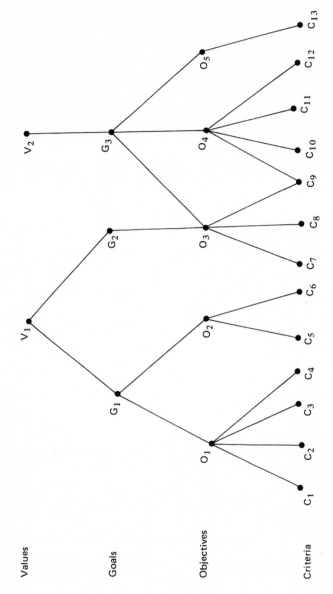

Fig. 4.2 Hierarchical interrelationships among values, goals, objectives, and criteria. [4.20, p. 2–15].

two elements are relevant since there often are certain criteria which people would like to minimize or maximize, such as accidents, while there are others whose values only have to be kept above or below a certain level. A government transportation budget provides a good example. Often a set amount of funds is allocated for, say, highway improvements. The aim then is to go as far as possible toward relevant goals while keeping within the limit of the budget. The budget in this example would be a *constraint*, not a goal or objective.

A *standard* is a *particular desired level* of the criterion which should not be exceeded or undercut (or both), depending on the particular situation. An example of a standard relates to temperature control. Usually, it is desirable to have the temperature in a vehicle kept at about 70°F, neither above nor below. Hence, an attempt would be made to design the heating and/or air conditioning systems to achieve this level. Examples of other standards are those associated with the previously discussed criteria for the Federal Clean Car Incentive Program. These can be seen in Table 4.10. Whether in a certain situation one would be dealing with objectives and criteria or constraints and standards is difficult to tell but seems to depend on how much importance people attach to levels of a criterion beyond its commonly accepted value. If, for example, it were not important as to how much a budget is underspent, then no one is expected to *minimize* expenses and the budget should be taken as a constraint to spending, not an objective for it.

4.6 WEIGHING THE IMPORTANCE OF OBJECTIVES

Not only must transportation planners and engineers be concerned with identifying and listing the various goals, objectives, constraints, and standards relating to a given problematic situation, but in some cases they must also determine the relative weights of importance carried by the stated goals and objectives. For instance, the goal of creating a transportation system that "offers novelty" has evoked little attention to date, whereas, offering low door-to-door travel time has been of such interest that it probably can be considered the prime mover in stirring people to act in solving their transporation problems.[4] No attempt will be made in this section to make specific judgments about the relative weights of importance of various objectives, but several illustrations will be given to demonstrate the contributions which can come from efforts to define weightings of importance.

Actually, except for some preliminary studies, relatively little is known from a research standpoint about the weights of importance of different transportation goals. Perhaps the most interesting procedure developed so far for determining weights is that by R. L. Wilson (in [4.16, Chap. 11]) in his study of the desires of people in Greensboro and Durham, North Carolina.

---

[4] See, for example, the introductory discussion in the "Red Book" [4.11] of the American Association of State Highway Officials.

In his study, Wilson presented to a sample of people in each city a chart or "game" board like that shown in Fig. 4.3. He also gave each respondent a number of "markers" with which to "pay" for lower density development and for "the closeness of neighborhood things to the house." For example, a 60 ft by 100 ft lot cost 18 markers while a 3-min *walk* to a grocery store cost 5 markers and a 10-min *drive* cost only 2 markers. The number of markers associated with each item on the game board was supposed to be in rough proportion to the expenditures needed to provide that item, and the total number of markers given to the respondents was supposed to be in rough proportion to the average income of residents in the particular city—40 markers in Greensboro and 36 in Durham.

The results of one survey are shown in Table 4.11. It seems that most people in these two cities were desirous of obtaining low density living (categories 4 and 5), even to the point where they would be willing to "spend" over half their markers for this privilege. This result in itself is of extreme importance to transportation planners since it implies that people generally will spend the travel time gains they achieve from transportation improvements by purchasing homes in lower density (usually suburban) developments. For the most part, this move to lower density has been what has happened in American cities—a direct outgrowth of the importance attached to the goal of lower living density.[5]

The rank ordering or choices as to what neighborhood facilities people would like to have nearby also is interesting. In both Greensboro and Durham the religious building is placed at or near the top in importance. This outcome is almost completely unanticipated and should prove to have some interesting ramifications for neighborhood layout and circulation design. Following the religious building in importance are those kinds of facilities visited most frequently—elementary schools, grocery stores, and so forth. Those places not visited often, such as the movie theatre, the shoe store, and the library, generally are found at the bottom of the list. These rank orders give the planner and engineer a rough idea of how much importance should be attached to the objectives of connecting places of various types together by means of transportation.

Another interesting conclusion from the Wilson study comes from an inspection of the third column in Table 4.11. The group of respondents in Durham were given a second turn at allocating their markers but with no constraint on how many they could spend. The results indicate that, *with unlimited resources,* people in Durham seemed to have an increased desire for access to shopping centers, neighborhood parks, playgrounds, and community centers. When resources are binding, however, these activities are somewhat subjugated to the more mundane matters of getting to the grocery and drug stores. We can conclude, therefore, that (1) desires (the importance of goals or objectives) will change as incomes and total resources increase, and that (2) what people may desire ultimately is somewhat different from what they may desire when forced to stay within the constraints (especially budgetary) of the real world. Both these considerations should play an important

---

[5] See Chap. 3, Sec. 3.3.3.1 for further verification of this point.

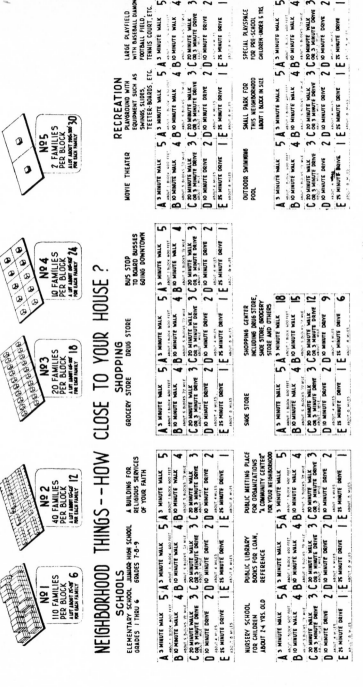

Fig. 4.3 "Game board used to evaluate aspects of neighborhood density and distance relationships. Original, 28 × 45 in., included five photographs of building types typical of the five densities at the top of board to assist in conveying concept of relative densities. [4.17, p. 389]".

Table 4.11 Rank Order, Percentage of Respondents Who Chose Neighborhood Facilities in Figure 4.3

Proportion of responses in each density category (percent)

	1	2	3	4	5	Total %	Total no.
Greensboro	1.1	2.7	23.2	55.7	17.3	100.0	185
Durham	0	1.9	24.7	35.8	37.7	100.0	162

Greensboro 40 markers	Durham "A" 36 markers	Durham "B" no limit
1. Religious building	1. Bus stop	1. Religious building
2. Elementary school	2. Grocery store	2. Shopping center
3. Grocery store	3. Religious building	3. Bus stop
4. Junior High school	4. Drug store	4. Neighborhood park
5. Bus stop	5. Elementary school	5. Elementary school
6. Shopping center	6. Shopping center	6. Junior high school
7. Drug store	7. Junior high school	7. Playground
8. Library	8. Movie theater	8. Movie theater
9. Community center	9. Neighborhood park	9. Community center
10. Swimming pool	10. Library	10. Swimming pool
11. Neighborhood park	11. Playground	11. Library
12. Playground	12. Community center	12. Playfield
13. Movie theater	13. Swimming pool	13. Grocery store
14. Playfield	14. Playfield	14. Drug store
15. Nursery	15. Nursery	15. Preschool play space
16. Preschool play space	16. Preschool play space	16. Nursery
17. Shoe store	17. Shoe store	17. Shoe store

Source: [4.17, p. 391].

role in the planner's or engineer's thinking when designing and locating future transportation systems.

Despite the fact that many of Wilson's findings are of interest, they may not apply elsewhere and we must conclude that it is the technique which is important at this point. More mathematically sophisticated techniques are available, but this one has the advantages that it is simple to understand and apply and takes into account constraints as well as objectives.

4.7 VARIATIONS IN WEIGHTINGS BETWEEN GROUPS OF PEOPLE

Another study dealing with weightings of importance was that by Golob et al. [4.33]. This study is of double interest here in that it was concerned with potential user preferences for a public transportation system and with variations in these preferences among different user groups. Using semantic differential scales (see

Sec. 4.4 and [4.26]) and paired comparison techniques [4.38], the investigators determined relative weights of importance for a large number of system characteristics. This determination was accomplished through a sample survey of families in a residential suburb of Detroit. The results of the survey of 786 persons are summarized in Fig. 4.4.

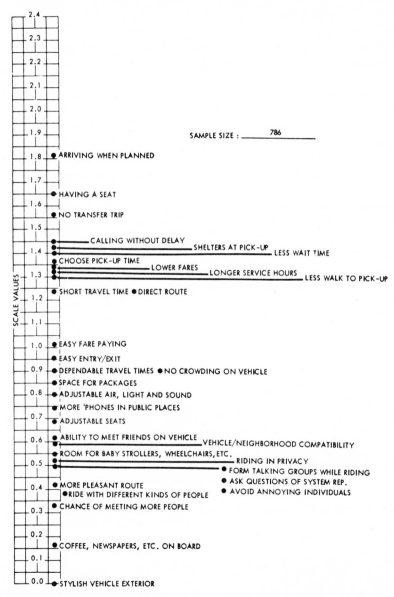

Fig. 4.4 Weightings of importance given system characteristics by the total population. [4.33].

It is interesting to note that "lower fares" is not given the highest preference among all characteristics. In fact, it ranks eighth on the list behind such factors as "less wait time" and "arriving when planned." Also, "short travel time" ranks lower in importance than comfort factors such as "having a seat" and "shelters at pick-up." It would seem, then, that on an overall basis, transit users would like a type of system in which dependability ("arriving when planned." "calling without delay," etc.), basic creature comforts ("having a seat," "shelters at pick-up," etc.), and reduced excess time ("no transfer time," "less walk to pick-up," etc.) are stressed, even over travel cost and time—the two items of greatest concern in most traditional transportation studies. Of course, the survey by Golob et al. posed questions about many characteristics outside the experience of the average transit patron (e.g., "calling without delay"), so that it may be that *actual* responses may differ from those on the survey. Yet the relative weightings of factors do suggest the need for a broader outlook in most transportation studies.

In looking at variations in weightings between potential user groups, Golob et al. determined that while there were some minor differences between certain groups—nondrivers, housewives, and so on—only three groups were really distinct. These were elderly, low-income, and young people. The weighting scales for the first two groups are displayed in Figs. 4.5 and 4.6.

In the first figure it can be seen that the elderly focus more of their attention on the special physical problem they face: getting on and off the vehicle. They appear to want to be able to sit down and not to transfer. Also, since time generally is less important to them and cost more, they put a lesser value on "short travel time" and a greater on "lower fares." It should be noticed, too, that the preference scale is more dispersed for the elderly than for the total population. This, the authors indicate, shows that a greater proportion of respondants have similar preferences.

Low-income people probably are users of present transit systems and seem to conceive only of waiting on a corner for pick-up. They thus focus on waiting times, shelters at pick-up, and longer service hours (see Fig. 4.6). Interestingly, "lower fares" does not rank any higher in order for low income people than for the population as a whole (although it does have a higher scale value). The conception that poorer people are concerned almost entirely with cutting travel expenses thus could be misleading to those concerned with making policy regarding transit regulations for a city.

The above results show that in transportation planning and design efforts, some attention ought to be given to the variety of groups of people that may be affected. Otherwise, the system will not serve its intended purpose and may be a source of dissatisfaction.

4.8 COMMENTS ON TRANSPORTATION PROBLEMS AND GOALS

The preceding material in this chapter has been presented in an effort to uncover and establish thinking about directions and desires for transportation and

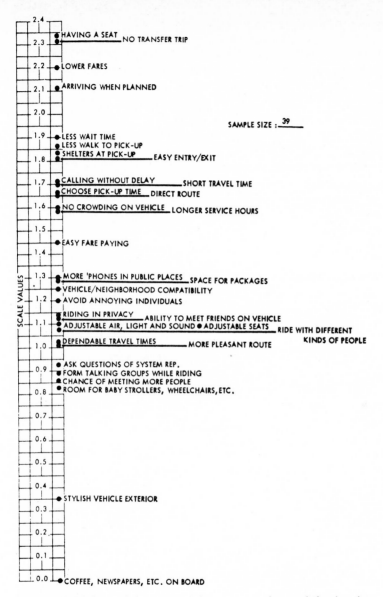

Fig. 4.5 Weightings of importance given system characteristics by the elderly. [4.33].

for the factors it affects. The discussion ranged from the most general aspirations for urban development—basic urban values and goals—through descriptions of broad goals for transportation, then to more detailed goals, objectives, and criteria, and finally to the weighing of importance of objectives. This procession from the most general levels to the more specific and applicable criteria follows to some extent the

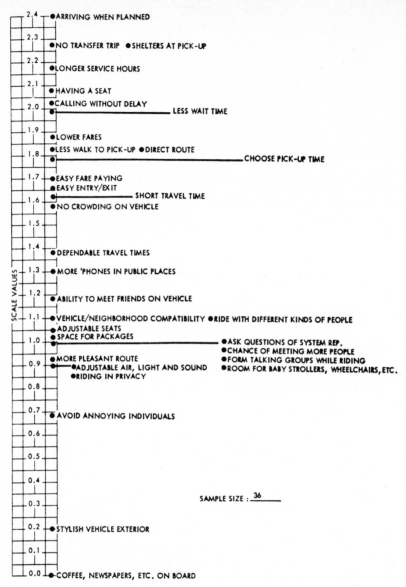

Fig. 4.6 Weightings of importance given system characteristics by those with low incomes. [4.33].

thought process that should, and usually does, take place in the minds of the engineer, planner, and finally the decision-maker as they attempt to come to grips with the perplexing, multifaceted problems so common to transportation and related endeavors.

Perhaps the most important points that emanate from the discussion in this chapter are (1) the need for goals and objectives is an ever present one, and (2) existing efforts aimed at formulating and utilizing goals and objectives are not very systematic endeavors and, in fact, are not even very commonplace. These two points, taken together, are disturbing. It is not difficult to get most people to agree that it is an eminently reasonable procedure to set goals and objectives if only for the purpose of preventing us from "not being able to see the forest because of the trees." Some significant considerations somehow always escape the scrutiny of even the most well-intentioned and intelligent planners and engineers. A goal checklist often prevents such occurrences. A more important reason for goals and objectives is, however, that the real needs of the citizenry be served. If we simply *assume* what these needs and desires are, we run the risk of planning, designing, and constructing a transportation system for the wrong purpose. To have to rebuild the system or operate it in an unintended fashion is a luxury that can be ill-afforded.

There are many reasons, nonetheless, why explicit goals and objectives do not exist or, when they do exist, why they are not readily applicable for planning and design work. Many of these reasons are a direct outgrowth of the difficulties alluded to in this and the previous chapter on transportation problems.

First, there is the general confusion over problem or goal identification. A primary difficulty here is the inadvertent statement of problems or goals related to means, not ends. A good example of such a situation was that in the previous chapter where the problems of safety and comfort on the railroad were partially transformed into the "problem" of lack of uniformity in timber railroad ties. An illustration more relevant to broader goal statements might evolve about a decision to build more parking garages in a downtown area. It would then be all too easy to say that "our goal is to provide 3,000 more garage parking spaces downtown by the year ———." This type of goal is a *means* to an end, not an end itself (which may be "more employment downtown," or "revitalization of center city shopping," or something else). One way to help avoid substituting means for ends as goals is to continually ask the question, "Why do we want to achieve goal X"? If an answer such as "... because we want to do Y" is readily forthcoming, this would imply that Y is the actual desired end, not X. If the answer is "... just because," then it is likely that X is an actual end in itself.

Difficulties involved in exposing *all* problems or goals also hinder efforts to be more systematic. Table 4.8 is a result of an endeavor to be as comprehensive as possible about goal identification. Yet without a doubt, anyone could add more goals or restate those already in the table in a more definitive manner. One goal not given explicit treatment in that table, for instance, is that of "desirable impact on religious activities." Noting that people in Durham and Greensboro, North Carolina, placed a high value on nearness to a religious building and that church attendance is affected by highways, we might conclude that such a goal would be a desirable addition. The fact that some important factors often go unnoticed indicates rather well why a broad attack on problems (Sec. 3.2.1) is difficult to achieve.

Still another difficulty in being systematic about problems and/or goals and objectives is that the weightings of importance given to various factors are subject to change. Everyday experience tells us that different people attach different amounts of importance to various objectives and that, even for one person, the extent of importance varies over time (a condition which at the extreme results in fads). Naturally, these variations are perplexing to those who must plan and design for the benefit and welfare of the public, but they do lead to two considerations that should be taken into account;

1. Because there are variations in weightings between people, any solution for transportation problems should incorporate a flexibility and diversity somewhat commensurate with these variations.[6] A single plan or design, intended for universal application, probably is not realistic.

2. Because there are variations in weightings over time for each individual, future problems generally will not be exactly the same as present ones (Sec. 3.2.4). Thus, the planner or engineer probably should design for an average (over time) level of importance for each objective if the solution is to be successful.[7]

The final and perhaps greatest hindrance to the systematizing of problems, goals, and objectives is that there is rarely any explicit indication given as to the relative priorities to be attached to the desires of one individual or group of individuals as opposed to another. In fact, up to this point in this chapter we have temporarily ignored a question central to study in the fields of welfare economics and political science: that of which individuals or groups *should* benefit (or be disbenefited) from various public "improvements" such as transportation facilities. In welfare economics, for example, a commonly held objective known as the *Pareto optimum* [4.24] is "the condition in which it is impossible to make some individual 'better off' without making any other 'worse off'."

Similarly, political science often has been referred to as "the study of who gets what," so that, again, gains and losses to individuals are significant matters. What is important at this point, however, is that in contrast to welfare economics and political studies, overall transportation studies rarely delineate the degree of emphasis given to one segment of the population as opposed to another. The result for the study is that the relative priorities are implied and thus not open to scrutiny and easy change. The result for the practice of problem and goal formulation is vagueness and confusion. In any case, the question of who should gain (or who does gain inadvertently)—the rich or the poor or the handicapped or the trucker or the downtown merchant, and so forth—is one that should nag at the conscience of the planner or engineer as he attempts to create solutions for present and anticipated transportation problems. More will be said about this question in the discussion of evaluation and decision making in Chap. 8.

---

[6] Anderson [4.23] has some interesting thoughts on planning for flexibility and diversity.

[7] Actually, little is known about predicting variations in weightings of importance, so that this last statement can only be viewed as tentative.

BIBLIOGRAPHY

4.1   Automotive Safety Foundation:*Urban Highways in Perspective*, Washington, D.C., 1968.

4.2   U.S. Department of Transportation: *The Freeway in the City*, Publ. No. TD2.102: F 87, U.S. Government Printing Office, Washington, D.C., 1968.

4.3   Schimpeler, C. C., and W. L. Grecco: "System Evaluation: An Approach Based on Community Structure and Values," *Highway Research Board Record* 238, 1968.

4.4   Falk, E. L.: "Measurement of Community Values: The Spokane Experiment," *Highway Research Board Record* 229, 1968.

4.5   Von Neumann, J., and O. Morganstern: *Theory of Games and Economic Behavior*, (3rd ed.), Princeton Univ. Press, Princeton, N. J., 1953.

4.6   Fishburn, P. C.: *Decision and Value Theory*, Wiley, New York, 1964.

4.7   Churchman, C. W., and R. L. Ackoff: "An Approximate Measure of Value," *Operations Research*, vol. 2, 1954.

4.8   Manheim, M. L.: *Highway Route Location as a Hierarchically-Structured Sequential Decision Process*, Dept. of Civil Engineering, M.I.T., Cambridge, 1964.

4.9   L. C. Fitch and Associates: *Urban Transportation and Public Policy*, Chandler Press, San Francisco, 1964.

4.10 Wohl, M., and B. V. Martin: *Traffic System Analysis for Engineers and Planners*, McGraw Hill, New York, 1967.

4.11 American Association of State Highway Officials: *Road User Benefits Analyses for Highway Improvements*, Washington, D.C., 1960.

4.12 Mohring, H., and M. Harwitz: *Highway Benefits: An Analytical Framework*, Northwestern Univ. Press, Evanston, Ill., 1962.

4.13 Wachs, M.: "Relationships Between Drivers' Attitudes Toward Alternate Route and Driver and Route Characteristics," *Highway Research Board Record* 197, 1967.

4.14 Gerlough, D. L., and F. A. Wagner: *Improved Criteria for Traffic Signals at Individual Intersections*, NCHRP Report 32, Highway Research Board, Washington, D.C., 1967.

4.15 Hitch, C. J., and R. N. McKean: *The Economics of Defense in the Nuclear Age*, Atheneum, New York, 1966.

4.16 Chapin, F. S., Jr., and S. F. Weiss (eds.): *Urban Growth Dynamics in a Regional Cluster of Cities*, Wiley, New York, 1962.

4.17 Chapin, F. S., Jr.: *Urban Land Use Planning*, Univ. of Illinois Press, (2d ed.), Champaign-Urbana, Ill., 1965.

4.18 Kent, R. J., Jr.: *The Urban General Plan*, Chandler, San Francisco, 1964.

4.19 Haworth, L.: *The Good City*, Univ. of Indiana Press, Bloomington, 1963.

4.20 Berry, B. J. L., et al.: *A Goal Achievement Framework for Comprehensive Social-Physical Planning in the City of Chicago*, Center for Urban Studies, The University of Chicago, Chicago, June, 1968.

4.21 Fishburn, P. C.: "A Note on Recent Developments in Additive Utility Theories for Multiple Factor Situations," *Operations Research*, vol. 14, no. 6, Nov.–Dec., 1966.

4.22 Hille, S. J., and T. K. Martin: "Consumer Preference in Transportation," *Highway Research Board Record* 197, 1967.

4.23 Anderson, S. (ed.): *Planning for Diversity and Choice; Possible Futures and Their Relations to the Man-Controlled Environment*, M.I.T. Press, Cambridge, Mass., 1968.

4.24 Little, I. M. D.: *A Critique of Welfare Economics*, Oxford University Press, London, 1950.

4.25 Guilford, J. P.: *Fundamental Statistics in Psychology and Education*, McGraw-Hill, New York, 1956.

4.26 Osgood, C. E., G. J. Suci, and P. H. Tannenbaum: *The Measurement of Meaning*, Univ. of Illinois Press, Urbana, 1957.

4.27 Barton-Aschman Associates, Inc.: *Guidelines for New Systems of Urban Transportation*, vol. 2, Chicago, April, 1968.

4.28 American Association of State Highway Officials: *A Policy on Geometric Design of Rural Highways,* Washington, D. C., 1965.

4.29 American Association of State Highway Officials: *A Policy on Arterial Highways in Urban Areas,* Washington, D.C., 1969.

4.30 Pardee, F. S., et al.: *Measurement and Evaluation of Transportation System Effectiveness,* Memorandum RM–3869–DOT, The Rand Corporation, Santa Monica, Calif., September, 1969.

4.31 Dickey, J. W., and J. P. Broderick: "Toward a Technique for a More Exhaustive Evaluation of Urban Area Performance," *Environment and Planning,* vol. 6, no. 1, March 1972.

4.32 Winfrey, R., and C. Zellner: *Summary and Evaluation of Economic Consequences of Highway Improvements,* NCHRP Report 122, Highway Research Board, Washington, D.C., 1971.

4.33 Golob, T. F., E. T. Canty, R. L. Gustafson, and J. E. Vitt: "An Analysis of Consumer Preferences for a Public Transportation System," *Transportation Research,* vol. 6, no. 1, March, 1972.

4.34 Zettle, R. M.: "On Studying the Impact of Rapid Transit in the San Francisco Bay Area" *Highway Research Board Special Report 111,* Washington, D.C., 1970.

4.35 Roget, P. M.: *Thesaurus of English Words and Phrases,* Longmans, Green and Co., Ltd., London, 1936.

4.36 Goals for Dallas: *Goals for Dallas: Submitted for Consideration by Dallas Citizens,* Graduate Research Center of the Southwest, Dallas, 1966.

4.37 Ockert, C. W., and C. E. Pixton: *A Strategy for Evaluating a Regional Highway-Transit Network,* Regional Planning Council, Baltimore, 1968.

4.38 Thurstone, L. L.: *The Measurement of Values,* 4th Impression, University of Chicago Press, Chicago, 1967.

4.39 De Chiara, J., and L. Koppelman: *Planning Design Criteria,* Van Nostrand Reinhold, New York, 1969.

4.40 Highway Research Board: "Measures of the Quality of Traffic Service," *Special Report 130,* Washington, D.C., 1972.

5 Transportation System Performance and Land Use Models

In Chap. 2 reference was made to models and their use in the transportation planning process. In that chapter a model was defined as "something which in some respects resembles or describes the structure and/or behavior of a real life counterpart." A model was also said to consist of five basic elements:

1. Variables over which the designer has complete control (X_i's)
2. Variables over which the designer has no control (Z_j's)
3. Variables over which the designer has indirect control (Y_k's)
4. Relationships between variables (R_m's)
5. Parameters (specific coefficients, constants, exponents, etc.) (P_n's)

In this and the following chapter an attempt will be made to explore several of the various types of models relevant to transportation planning and design.

In addition to identifying model types, these two chapters also will deal with the calibration and use of models, since these two aspects are so closely related. In other words, the discussion will cover both the third and fifth stages of the transportation planning process as described in Chap. 2.

This particular chapter will focus on three major types of models: (*a*) transportation system interrelationships, (*b*) zonal land use development, and (*c*) regional population and employment growth.

In Chap. 6, we will discuss models of travel behavior and other transportation system impacts. Topics to be included under the latter category will be housing relocation, appearance, noise, and land values. It should be noted that some models are not as well developed as others. For example, it is difficult to measure the appearance of a future transportation system much less predict the reaction of people to it. This kind of problem should be expected, however, and those factors that cannot be predicted with much certainty still should be accorded the significance they deserve in the evaluation process.

5.1 MODELS IN THE TRANSPORTATION PLANNING PROCESS

The modeling stage of the transportation planning process has been divided into six phases in Chap. 2. These phases and their interconnections are diagrammed in Fig. 5.1. It is perhaps easiest to understand this diagram by first looking at the inputs and outputs of the calibration and model use stage (stage V) itself and then looking at its internal workings.

The major inputs to all phases of stage V come from the data collection stage (stage IV) of the transportation planning process. In addition, phase c of stage V—Estimation of Transportation System Performance Characteristics—can only be accomplished through knowledge of the type of transportation system being considered as a solution. This input would come from stage VIII (generation of alternative solutions stage) where new solutions are formulated. This connection is represented by the dashed vertical arrow on the right hand side of Fig. 5.1. The *outputs* of the calibration and model use stage serve as inputs to the evaluation and decision making stage (VI).

Looking now at the internal workings of stage V, we see that the prediction of zonal land use development levels (phase d) requires informational inputs from three of the other five phases and, as such, provides a good basis for explaining the interaction between the phases. To elaborate further, *a land use model* is one which is used to estimate the future zonal locations and intensities of population, employment, and land areas.[1] The factors which seem to affect the level of land use development in any section of a metropolitan region are: (1) the projected overall growth of the region, (2) the past and present intensity of land use developments in each zone, and (3) the past, present, and future levels of certain other variables, primarily transportation, water supply, and sewage disposal facilities, zoning and the quality of schools and other municipal services. Inputs from phases a, b, and c of Fig. 5.1 thus can be identified directly, with the projected levels of regional growth of population and employment coming from phase a, information on present and future municipal services other than transportation coming from b, and, of course, the transportation system performance characteristics coming from c. Information on *present* zonal land use is drawn from the output of the data collection stage of the planning process.

---

[1] In Chap. 2 "land use" was interpreted in its broadest sense, referring not only to an activity classification—manufacturing, commercial, residential, and so on—but also to the intensity of use as measured by employment, population, acreage, and so forth.

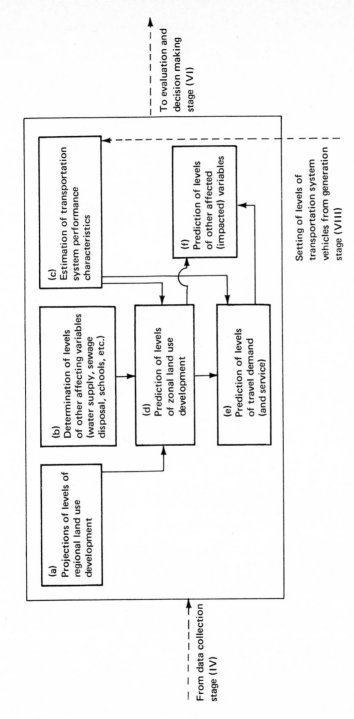

Fig. 5.1 The six major phases in the calibration and model use stage of the transportation planning process.

Looking again at Fig. 5.1, we see that both the level of future zonal land use and the performance characteristics of the proposed transportation system are the principle factors which influence future travel patterns. This relationship, to be discussed in more detail in the next chapter, is a natural one since population and employment centers are the focus of most travel and since this travel cannot be done without transportation facilities.

The final relationship in Fig. 5.1 involves other affected factors such as noise levels, appearance, smell, community disruption, and so forth. Most of these impacts stem directly from the transportation system, travel on it, and land use. Noise, for example, might be created by traffic on a street (transportation system) and is heard by residents of abutting buildings (land use).

After estimating these additional impacts, we would proceed to the evaluation stage where all future impacts—land use, travel, noise, relocation, and so on—would be examined and compared to established goals and objectives. If deemed unsatisfactory, these impacts could be altered through modifications of the transportation system. These changes, which would be made in the generation stage (stage VII) of the planning process (see dashed arrow in Fig. 5.1), would be fed back to the transportation system in phase c, which in turn would be fed into and influence subsequent changes in zonal land use, travel, and the other affected factors. After several iterations through this feedback process, (hopefully) desirable patterns of impacts would evolve, at which time the corresponding transportation system modifications would be specified in more detail (stage VIII), implemented (stage IX), and then operated and maintained (stage X).

From the preceding description of the phases of the calibration and model use stage it should be apparent that all five elements of a model are involved. First, it is generally assumed that the transportation planner or engineer has complete control of the transportation system and can mold its component parts—vehicles, networks, terminals, and controls—to any type of transportation solution that may seem desirable.[2] The transportation system thus is considered to be an X variable.

Other factors cannot be controlled by the transportation planner or engineer, however. The growth of regional population and employment usually is assumed to be independent of his actions as is the quality, location, and timing of construction of water supply and sewage disposal facilities, schools, and other public services. These generally are under the control of other agencies and firms and thus must be considered as uncontrollable or Z variables. Even some transportation system performance characteristics are affected by factors (not shown in Fig. 5.1), such as climate and geologic conditions, that have to be accepted as uncontrollables by the designer. The only action he can take with respect to these factors is to estimate their future levels and use these estimates to help predict zonal land use, travel demand (and service), and other relevant impacts.

---

[2] In reality the planner or engineer obviously does not have complete control over the entire transportation system. However, he assumes this because in his role he generally can make *recommendations* concerning most of the system.

We see from the above discussion that zonal land use, travel demands, and other impacts are indirectly controllable variables (Y's). Transportation system changes (X's) can be created which can affect, say, subregional land use growth. The construction of radial freeways, for example, might encourage the flight of higher income families to the suburbs. Yet this migration probably would also be aided by changes in school systems, existing land use patterns, regional growth and many other factors (Z's) outside the control of the transportation planner or engineer. Hence, transportation plays only a partial role in land development, which thus must be considered a Y variable.

The relationships and parameters in models connecting the X, Y, and Z variables will not be discussed in detail at this point. One example may prove helpful, however. In the *Chicago Area Transportation Study* [5.19], the percent of urban trips by transit was found to correlate with the population per 1,000 sq ft of residential land (considered here to be a Z variable) and the number of autos per 1,000 people in a zone (considered here to be an X variable). The associated equation was (from Ref. [5.20])

$$Y = 15.5 + 21.745 \log Z - 16.72 \log X \tag{5.1}$$

The relationship between variables is a linear one except that a logarithm is taken of each independent variable before the additions are made. The parameters are the constant 15.5 and the coefficients 21.745 and 18.72. In other cities, these parameters may vary, but they are treated as constants in Chicago.

Additional relationships will be displayed throughout this and the succeeding chapter. In many cases it will be difficult to specify controllable, uncontrollable, and indirectly controllable variables. This will be left to the reader. Nonetheless, the distinction should be kept in mind since it is desirable to foresee which variables have to be forecasted before using a particular model, which are forecast within the model, and which can be varied by the planner or engineer.

5.2 TRANSPORTATION SYSTEM PERFORMANCE MODELS

Transportation system modifications proposed by planners or engineers do not usually have a direct influence on land use, travel, and other relevant impacts. Travel time can not be controlled entirely by the designer, for example, because it is often a function of traffic volumes, weather conditions, accidents, and so forth. As another example, vehicular appearance cannot always be controlled. Dirt and corrosion can mar appearance as can vandalism and lack of maintenance. All these generally are beyond the designer's perogative. The purpose of this section is to show some examples of models relating designer-proposed modifications and certain other affecting factors to transportation system performance characteristics. These examples will be concentrated on vehicular acceleration and deceleration characteristics; speed, volume, and density relationships in a traffic stream; highway capacities; and transportation system costs. The latter item will be discussed at some length since it plays an important role in the evaluation process.

5.2.1 Transportation Performance Characteristics

In Chap. 9 transportation systems are described as being composed of four major components—vehicles, networks, terminals, and controls. Each of these components has certain performance characteristics, some of which are listed in Table 5.1. In this table, the characteristics are divided into two categories: (a) mechanics and (b) construction and operation. The former category contains those characteristics commonly associated with the motion of a transportation system while those in the latter category are more akin to the physical development of a system and its use. As an example, costs, while related to the characteristics of strength and power, fall more reasonably under the heading of a "construction and operation" characteristic.

Each of the four transportation system components generally has each of the characteristics listed in Table 5.1, although there are many exceptions. A good illustration is that of capacity. Vehicles have capacities—50 seated persons per bus; networks have capacities—2,000 vehicles per hour per lane on a freeway; and terminals and control systems have capacities—a Greyhound Bus terminal recently built in Los Angeles can handle 500 buses and 14,000 passengers per hour [5.21], while a fixed-time traffic signal, under ideal conditions, can pass from 1,200 to 1,500 vehicles per hour of green time. Table 5.1 thus contains a list useful for identifying and modeling many of the important performance characteristics of most transportation system components.

Table 5.1 Some Performance Characteristics of Transportation Systems

I Mechanics (statics, kinematics, and dynamics)

1. Strength	5. Speed-velocity	9. Lift
2. Weight	6. Acceleration	10. Drag
3. Stress	7. Power	11. Friction
4. Strain	8. Stability	12. Heat-temperature

II Construction and operation

1. Volume	9. Cleanliness	17. Service life
2. Density	10. Sanitariness	18. Costs
3. Headway	11. Appearance	(a) Construction or purchase
4. Spacing	12. Privacy	(b) Land
5. Capacity	13. Smell	(c) Labor
6. Safety	14. Comfort	(d) Fuel
7. Flexibility	15. Light	(e) Operation and maintenance
8. Reliability	16. Noise	(f) Finance
		(g) Engineering and management

5.2.2 Models of Acceleration, Deceleration, and Top Speed

Primary constraints on top speed for any passenger carrying vehicle are its acceleration and deceleration characteristics. At a given acceleration, it takes a finite time and distance for a vehicle to reach its top speed. The same is true for decelerating to a stop. The distance remaining between two terminals after acceleration and deceleration would be traveled at the top speed.

For constant acceleration and starting at zero initial velocity

$$s_a = \tfrac{1}{2} at^2 \qquad (5.2)$$

and since

$$t = v/a \qquad (5.3)$$

then

$$s_a = \tfrac{1}{2} v^2/a \qquad (5.4)$$

where v = top speed
a = rate of acceleration
s_a = distance covered
t = time

If there were a situation requiring a low initial velocity, such as maintaining a low constant speed until the vehicle was a certain distance from the terminal, then

$$s_a = \tfrac{1}{2} at^2 + v_0 t_0 \qquad (5.5)$$

where v_0 is the initial speed and t_0 is the time at the initial speed. Or

$$s_a = \tfrac{1}{2} v^2/a + v_0 t_0 \qquad (5.6)$$

So it can be seen that the distance required for a vehicle to accelerate to its top speed is primarily dependent upon acceleration. The maximum acceleration possible depends upon the design capability of the vehicle, the track or roadway, and the passenger. For a nonair cushion vehicle, the amount of friction available between the wheels and the roadway becomes a determining factor, as illustrated in Fig. 5.2.

In this figure

$$\Sigma F_x = 0 \qquad (5.7)$$

or

$$W_x + f - M_a = 0 \qquad (5.8)$$

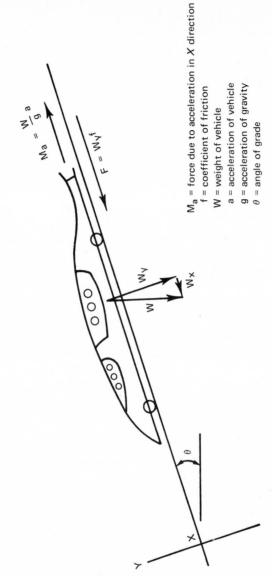

M_a = force due to acceleration in X direction
f = coefficient of friction
W = weight of vehicle
a = acceleration of vehicle
g = acceleration of gravity
θ = angle of grade

Fig. 5.2 Forces in a transportation vehicle going up a grade.

or

$$W \sin \theta \ + \ Wf \cos \theta \ - \ \frac{W}{g} \, a \ = \ 0 \tag{5.9}$$

Considering that θ is small, it can be assumed that (approximately) $\sin \theta = \tan \theta$ and $\cos \theta = 1$. Further, $\tan \theta = G$ or percent gradient/100. Equation (5.9) then becomes

$$G \ + \ f \ = \ a/g \tag{5.10}$$

or

$$a \ = \ g(G + f) \tag{5.11}$$

where G must be negative for the uphill conditions and positive for downhill. As an example of the significance of Eq. (5.11), assume a flat grade $(G = 0)$ and a maximum coefficient of friction of 0.4 (a not uncommon value for rubber wheels on a wet pavement). By Eq. (5.11)

$$a_{max} \ = \ 32.2 \ (0.4) \ = \ 12.9 \ \text{ft/sec}^2 \quad \text{or 8.8 mph/sec}$$

An acceleration of this magnitude would not be too severe providing the passengers were either facing forward or were adequately strapped in their seats. It would be much too high if it were desired to be doing other activities (such as serving meals). If 8.8 mph/sec could be tolerated, and if a high speed vehicle were desired at about 200 mph top speed, then by Eq. (5.4) and converting mph to ft/sec

$$s_a \ = \ \tfrac{1}{2} \, v^2/a \ = \ \tfrac{1}{2} \ (200 \times 1.47)^2/12.9 \ = \ 3{,}333 \ \text{ft}$$

or about two-thirds of a mile. If a more comfortable acceleration were used, say on the order of 2 mph/sec, the distance to reach top speed would be

$$\frac{8.8}{2} \ \times \ 3{,}333 \ = \ 14{,}665 \ \text{ft}$$

or about $2\frac{3}{4}$ miles. An uphill gradient would, of course, increase this value.

On the deceleration phase, everything is reversed but the same arithmetic applies except that gradient G is subtractive from the coefficient of friction, f, for the downhill situation and additive for the uphill. At high deceleration rates, passengers sitting face forwards must be strapped in their seats. Again, for $G = 0$ and a maximum f value of 0.4, maximum deceleration would be 8.8 mph/sec. About 2 mph/sec would again represent a slow, comfortable deceleration, similar to that of an automobile slowing down in gear with only slight brake application.

From this discussion it can be seen that where comfort is to be maximized (low acceleration and deceleration rates) and a high top speed is to be used, long distances between stops are required to take advantage of the high speed capabilities of the equipment. Where short distances between stops are required, the high speed capability would be wasted.

5.2.3 Models of Radial Acceleration

A vehicle of any type rarely is always able to go in a straight line, but must at some time change direction by use of a curve. Whether the vehicle is an automobile, railroad car, airplane, or some other type of conveyance, the forces placed on the passenger are an important consideration to the design of the curves or paths to be followed.

For illustrative purposes some principles concerning the design of highway curves will be presented here, but to be followed by discussion concerning the applicability to other systems.

If one were to tie a stone or weight to a cord and whirl it around, a force is felt to pull outward, and conversely the hand must exert an inward pull on the stone. This force produces a radial acceleration, a_n, and the direction of the force must be in the same direction as the acceleration and is called centripetal force.

Assume that a vehicle is going around a curve of radius, R, at a velocity v (Fig. 5.3). Since, after going around the curve a distance ds, the velocity component, v, is going in two different directions, with the result of producing a normal velocity component, v, toward the center of the circle. Since very small angles and distances are involved, the solution for radial acceleration is as follows

$$\sin d\theta = d\theta = \frac{dv_n}{v} \tag{5.12}$$

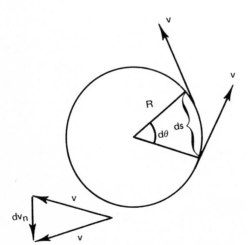

Fig. 5.3 Velocity vectors for a vehicle going around a horizontal curve.

or

$$dv_n = vd\theta \qquad (5.13)$$

or, since

$$ds = Rd\theta \qquad (5.14)$$

or

$$d\theta = \frac{ds}{R} \qquad (5.15)$$

then

$$a_n = \frac{dv_a}{dt} = \frac{vd\theta}{dt} = \frac{vds}{Rdt} \qquad (5.16)$$

since

$$v = \frac{ds}{dt} \qquad (5.17)$$

then

$$a_n = \frac{v^2}{R} \qquad (5.18)$$

where v is the velocity of the vehicle and R is the radius of the curve.

Because of the radial acceleration developed while a vehicle goes around a curve, the amount of roadway slope and side friction available determines whether or not the vehicle will stay on the road and if it does not, whether it will tip over or slide (Fig. 5.4). The relationship between slope, friction, and velocity can be developed as follows for the case when sliding of the vehicle is imminent

$$\Sigma F_x = 0 \qquad (5.19)$$

$$2F + W_x - C_x = 0 \quad \text{or} \quad 2F = C - We \qquad (5.20)$$

$$\Sigma F_y = 0 \qquad (5.21)$$

$$2N - W_y - C_y = C \quad \text{or} \quad 2N = Ce + W \qquad (5.22)$$

By definition the coefficient of friction f equals F/W

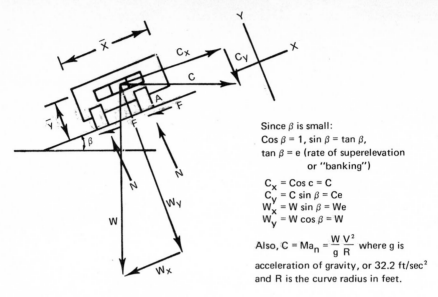

Since β is small:

Cos β = 1, sin β = tan β,

tan β = e (rate of superelevation or "banking")

C_x = Cos c = C
C_y = C sin β = Ce
W_x = W sin β = We
W_y = W cos β = W

Also, $C = Ma_n = \dfrac{W}{g}\dfrac{V^2}{R}$ where g is acceleration of gravity, or 32.2 ft/sec^2 and R is the curve radius in feet.

Fig. 5.4 Forces on a vehicle going around a vertical curve.

$$\frac{2F}{2N} = \frac{F}{N} = \frac{C - We}{Ce + W} = f \tag{5.23}$$

Substituting for C

$$\frac{\dfrac{W\,v^2}{g\,R} - We}{\dfrac{W\,v^2}{g\,R}e + W} = f \tag{5.24}$$

which results in

$$v^2 = gR\ \frac{e + f}{1 - ef} \tag{5.25}$$

Since e and f are small numbers, their product can be neglected, resulting in

$$e + f = v^2/gr \tag{5.26}$$

where e and f are unitless, v is in ft/sec, g in ft/sec,^{2} and R is in feet. If it is desired to have v in mph, Eq. (5.26) becomes

$$e + f = v^2/15R \tag{5.27}$$

For the case when tipping is imminent instead of sliding (which occurs with high centers-of-gravity), the following relationship can be developed:

Assume that the vehicle will tip about point A,

$$\Sigma M_A = 0 \tag{5.28}$$

$$C_x \bar{y} - W_x \bar{y} - C_y \bar{x} - W_y \bar{x} = 0 \tag{5.29}$$

$$C\bar{y} - We\bar{y} - Ce\bar{x} - W\bar{x} = 0 \tag{5.30}$$

$$\frac{W}{g} \frac{v^2}{R} \bar{y} - We\bar{y} - \frac{W}{g} \frac{v^2}{R} e\bar{x} - W\bar{x} = 0 \tag{5.31}$$

which results in

$$v^2 = gR \frac{(\bar{y}e + \bar{x})}{(\bar{y} - 2.75e)} \tag{5.32}$$

5.2.4 Definitions and Models of Volumes, Speeds, and Densities in a Traffic Stream

Perhaps the most discussed characteristics of highway traffic are those of volume, speed, and capacity. Volume, as defined in the *Highway Capacity Manual* [5.15] *is a flow*, not a static quantity or amount. Properly expressed, volume is "the number of vehicles that pass over a given section of a lane or a roadway during a time period of one hour or more." Oftentimes it is necessary to refer to various averages and peaks of volumes occurring during different periods of time. The most common definitions are:

Average annual daily traffic (AADT)—The total yearly volume divided by the number of days in the year.

Average daily traffic (ADT)—The total volume during a given time period in whole days greater than one day and less than one year divided by the number of days in that time period.

Tenth, twentieth, thirtieth, etc. highest annual hourly volume (10HV, 20HV, 30HV, etc.)—The hourly volume on a given roadway that is exceeded by 9, 19, 29, etc. hourly volumes, respectively, during a designated year.

Peak Hour Traffic—The highest number of vehicles found to be passing over a section of a lane or a roadway during 60 consecutive minutes.

Rate of Flow—The hourly representation of the number of vehicles that pass over a given section of a lane or a roadway for some period less than 1 hour.

This list of definitions starts with the longest time period usually considered, the year, and ends with the shortest, some period less than an hour. Each attempts to indicate expected variations in traffic volumes. The last one corresponds to the shortest time period. A flow of, say, 600 vehicles in 15 min would be presented as an hourly volume of 2,400 vph *if the flow were to continue at its present rate*.

The concept of speed,[3] like volume, also can be expressed in a variety of ways. The most important distinction arises from the manner in which speed is measured—either in terms of time taken to pass a given (small) length of traveled way or in terms of distance covered in a very small interval of time. The former of these two concepts leads to the idea of "spot speed" where

Spot Speed—The time a vehicle takes to cover a specified (small) length on a roadway divided into that length. The averaging of spot speeds creates an "average spot speed" or, as it is better known:

Space mean speed $(\bar{U}_s)$—The total of the small, given distances on a roadway traveled by a set of vehicles divided by the sum of the times all vehicles take to traverse that distance. Stated symbolically this definition becomes

$$\bar{U}_s = \frac{n\Delta x}{\displaystyle\sum_{i=1}^{n} \Delta t_i} \tag{5.33}$$

where $\bar{U}_s$ = space mean speed for a set of n vehicles

Δx = a fixed, small distance on a roadway

Δt_i = time vehicle i takes to traverse distance Δx

The second means of measurement of average speed, involving a fixed time interval instead of a fixed distance, is

Time mean speed $(\bar{U}_t)$—The sum of the distances on a roadway traversed by a set of vehicles divided by the total (over all vehicles) of the small, given intervals of time needed by each vehicle to traverse the corresponding distance. Put in a form comparable to that of Eq. (5.33), the time mean speed is

$$\bar{U}_t = \sum_{i=1}^{n} \Delta x_i / n\Delta t \tag{5.34}$$

where Δx_i = the distance traveled by vehicle i in fixed time interval Δt.

The actual difference between these two definitions of speed may not be obvious until one considers two hypothetical situations involving the use of a series of time-coded movie films of traffic flow along a freeway lane on which stripes are painted at 1-ft intervals. In both situations, two drivers are given instructions to drive at a speed (car speedometer) of 20 and 40 ft/sec (13.5 and 27 mph), respectively, but in the first situation we determine how much time it takes for each car to cover an 80 foot section of the freeway lane, whereas, in the second, we determine the distance which each car travels in 1 second. Thus, $\Delta x = 80$ ft, $\Delta t_1 =$

---

[3] The word "speed" usually is used in Traffic Engineering instead of "velocity" since the direction of the motion of the vehicle is apparent.

80 ft/20 fps = 4 seconds, Δt_2 = 80 ft/40 fps = 2 seconds, and Δt = 1 second, Δx_1 = 20 fps (1 second) = 20 ft, and Δx_2 = 40 fps (1 second) = 40 ft. Then $\bar{U}_s$ can be calculated as

$$\bar{U}_s = \frac{2 (80 \text{ ft})}{4 \text{ sec} + 2 \text{ sec}} = \frac{160}{6} = 26.67 \text{ ft/sec}$$

while

$$\bar{U}_t = \frac{20 \text{ ft} + 40 \text{ ft}}{2 (1 \text{ sec})} = \frac{60}{2} = 30.00 \text{ ft/sec}$$

An obvious difference exists, indicating that any further description of the average speed of a transportation mode ought to be referenced to the type of measurement performed. Otherwise some discrepancies might arise. Unfortunately, the means of measurement usually is not specified in many studies so that the reader must judge from the general context of the presented information whether he is dealing with a time mean speed or a space mean speed.

For example, if the average speed of vehicles on a transit facility were given, one might suspect that it was calculated by using various time measurements over the prescribed transit route, thereby leading to a space mean speed. On the other hand, if the average speed of automobiles on a highway were computed using readings from the speedometer of each car, the average speed in this case probably would be a time mean speed since speedometers generally measure the number of revolutions of the wheel, and therefore the distance traveled, per unit of time,[4] (note that in the previous example the average of the speedometer speeds was (40 + 20)/2 = 30 fps = $\bar{U}_t$).

A final illustration concerning the definition and measurement of speed regards the situation in which neither the distance nor time intervals are fixed for measurement. In this case an average equal to neither $\bar{U}_t$ or $\bar{U}_s$ might be found. If, for instance, the 20 and 40 ft/sec speedometer measurement were made for time a duration of 3 and 5 seconds, respectively, (implying that different distances were covered), the average speed would be

$$\frac{20 \text{ ft/sec} (3 \text{ sec}) + 40 \text{ ft/sec} (5 \text{ sec})}{3 \text{ sec} + 5 \text{ sec}} = \frac{60 + 200}{8} = \frac{260}{8} = 32.50 \text{ fps}$$

The result is a mean speed differing from both of the previous two. No specific name has been given to this, perhaps because it is hoped that no one will be tempted to calculate an average speed in this manner. However, measurements of this sort can be made inadvertently as, for example, by summing bus travel times over routes of varying lengths and then making the division. To eliminate such

---

[4] The unit of time is implicit in the mechanical operation of the speedometer.

occurrences, the analyst must keep constant watch on the manner in which various travel time and distance data are combined.

Other speed definitions of relevance to the specification of transportation systems are:

Design speed—A speed selected for purposes of design and correlation of those features of a traveled way, such as curvature, superelevation, and sight distance, upon which the safe operation of vehicles is dependent.

Average highway speed (*AHS*)—The weighted (by length of subsection) average of the design speeds within a section of a traveled way, when each subsection within the section is considered to have an individual design speed.

Operating speed—The highest overall speed at which a vehicle can travel on a given traveled way under favorable weather conditions and under prevailing traffic conditions without at any time exceeding the safe speed as determined by the design speed on a section-by-section basis.

The definitions are almost self-explanatory, but will be discussed in more detail in Chap. 10.

Density was the third characteristic mentioned earlier in conjunction with volume and speed. Also referred to as *concentration,* it can be defined as:

Density (D)—The number of vehicles occupying a unit length of the through lanes of a traveled way in any period (very small) of time.

The easiest way to visualize what is meant by density is to consider an aerial photograph of a highway at some "instant" (actually the small time interval needed to take the picture). A count could be made of the number of vehicles along, say, a measured mile of the highway, giving the density in vehicles per mile. Again, as was true of speed, we could fix either the time period or distance in defining an average density. However, the usual definition is that where the latter entity is held constant. Volume, too, usually is "averaged" over time so that it would be consistent to use figures for volume measured over a fixed small distance in conjunction with space mean speeds and densities.

Several other characteristics of a traffic stream should be defined explicitly. Their meaning is fairly straightforward:

Delay—The time consumed while traffic or a specified component of traffic is impeded in its movement by some element over which it has no control.

Vehicular gap—The interval in time or distance between individual vehicles measured from the rear of one vehicle to the head of the following vehicle.

Spacing—The interval in *distance* from head to head of successive vehicles.

Headway—The interval in *time* from head to head of successive vehicles as they pass a given point.

These characteristics will be alluded to throughout the remainder of the text.

Some of the relationships between volume, speed, density, spacing, headway, and unit (per distance) travel time can be stated quite simply. For instance

$$V = \bar{U}_s D \tag{5.35}$$

$$\bar{U}_s = Vs \qquad (5.36)$$

$$D = Vm \qquad (5.37)$$

$$s = \bar{U}_s h \qquad (5.38)$$

$$h = ms \qquad (5.39)$$

$$m = Dh \qquad (5.40)$$

where V = volume

      $\bar{U}_s$ = space mean speed[5]
      D = density
      m = spacing
      h = unit travel time
      h = headway

The first equation, while not having an obvious interpretation, perhaps can be understood by imagining a paper with a given density of dots on it being slid past a point (represented by the arrow). The greater the density of points on the paper

$$\boxed{\cdot\;\cdot\;\cdot\cdot\cdot\cdot\cdot\cdot\;\cdot\;\cdot\cdot\quad\cdot\quad\cdot\;\cdot\cdot\cdot\cdot\cdot\cdot\cdot} \quad \bar{U}_s \;\rightarrow$$
$$\uparrow$$

and the greater the speed at which it is pulled, the greater the number of dots that will pass the point per unit of time—a greater volume. An analogous relationship would exist in freeway flow, with the density and speed variables being multiplied together in order to obtain consistent units

$$\left(\frac{veh}{mi}\right) \times \left(\frac{mi}{hr}\right) = \left(\frac{veh}{hr}\right)$$

Similar analogies can be developed to explain the remaining relationships, yet the "consistent units" idea is one of the easiest ways to remember and understand each equation. For example, if we know the average headway (sec/veh) and wanted to determine the average spacing ft/veh, we would have to multiply the headway by ft/sec or the speed $\bar{U}_s$ to get the correct units. This would mean that

$$s \quad = \quad h \qquad \bar{U}_s$$
$$\left(\frac{ft}{veh}\right) = \left(\frac{sec}{veh}\right) \times \left(\frac{ft}{sec}\right)$$

which is equivalent to Eq. (5.38).

---

[5] For the most part we will be dealing with averages over time (with distance fixed) so that the space mean speed is the proper measure to be employed.

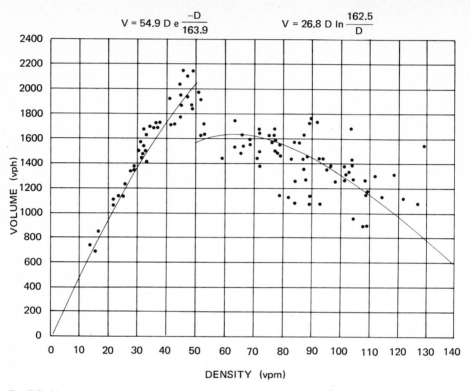

Fig. 5.5 Volume-density relationship—Edie hypothesis. *Source:* [5.23].

The relationship between certain characteristics many times cannot be established as easily as was done in the previous paragraph. Often observations must be obtained from the field and curves must be "fitted" to these observations either by hand or through some technique such as regression. Figures 5.5 through 5.7 exhibit three pairs of empirically established relationships between volume, density, and speed for uninterrupted flow [5.23]. It has been found that the data points can be approximated best with two-part logarithmic functions suggested by Edie, with the break point coming, interestingly enough, at the point where the volume of traffic is approximately equal to the lane capacity.[6] Actually, this occurrence would come as no surprise to anyone who has observed flow on a heavily traveled freeway for any period of time. In order to get capacity flow, traffic must proceed in an extremely orderly fashion. Otherwise, any small disturbance, such as a quick acceleration or deceleration, would create large headways between vehicles and subsequent smaller volumes. With capacity flow being so sensitive to small interruptions, a rather unstable condition at capacity can be expected, a situation which is reflected in the breakpoints in the volume-density-speed relationships.

[6] See Sec. 5.2.5 for definitions and models of capacity.

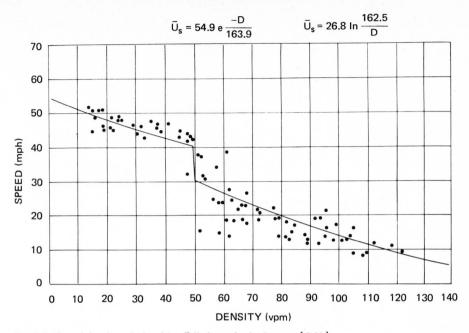

Fig. 5.6 Speed-density relationship—Edie hypothesis. *Source:* [5.23].

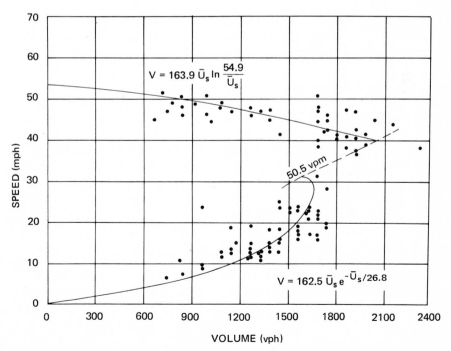

Fig. 5.7 Speed-volume relationship—Edie hypothesis. *Source:* [5.23].

While it is difficult to remember the values of each parameter in the mathematical equations indicated in Figs. 5.5 through 5.7, the reader should be able to recall the *general form* of each by thinking of them as being essentially continuous in nature and by bearing in mind the boundary conditions for each characteristic. If, for instance, vehicles averaging 20 ft in length were lined up solidly along a 1-mile stretch of roadway lane, the density would be 5,280 (ft mile)/20 ft/veh = 264 veh/mile, and we could anticipate that the speed as well as the volume would be zero[7] since no vehicles would be moving in this situation.

At the other extreme of density—only a single vehicle on the 1-mile stretch—the speed probably would be very high because of the lack of interference, whereas the volume, as in the preceding case, woud be very low (almost 0). These conditions, along with the constraint that the volume cannot exceed the capacity (which occurs at some intermediate density and speed), would lead to the type of diagrams in Fig. 5.8. The average speed of vehicles on a section of road is called the *mean free speed* and is denoted by $\bar{U}_f$.

Returning to the Edie models of density, volume, and speed, we find that the model relating the latter two characteristics is fairly reliable, with a correlation coefficient of 0.83 and a standard error of regression of 3.55 mph. The analyst can therefore place some amount of faith in the relationship although, as is demonstrated by the scatter of observation points in Fig. 5.7 as well as by the correlation coefficient, *complete* trust is not warranted.

5.2.5 Definitions and Models of Capacity

Capacity is another characteristic of all traveled ways of great importance in the planning endeavor. Capacity is a volume, specifically a maximum volume that passes by a point (a small distance) during a given time period. It should be recognized that the maximum volume theoretically can be very high, especially if we were to consider a series of racing cars driven extremely close to each other and "slipstreaming" or "drafting" at very high speeds. This would be an unusual and perhaps contrived case, however, but still enough of a possibility that we should incorporate in our definition the idea of a maximum volume which has a *reasonable expectation* of occurrence. The complete definition then becomes:

Capacity—The maximum number of vehicles which has a reasonable expectation of passing over a given section of a lane or a roadway in one direction
during a given time period under prevailing roadway and traffic conditions.

It should be noticed that for any given section of an actual lane or roadway the capacity as defined may vary from moment to moment due to weather conditions, upstream and downstream bottlenecks, accidents, and so forth. Nevertheless, the capacity of a section generally can be considered to be constant for most analyses. The limited access freeway or expressway, because it has no interruptions from sources external to the traffic stream, provides a relatively simple example situation

---

[7] The volume would be 0 since no vehicles could move in order to pass a point on the roadway.

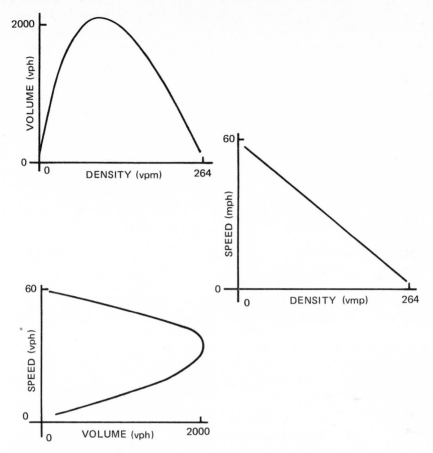

Fig. 5.8 General relationships between speed, volume, and density.

from which capacity estimates can be made. We thus concentrate on these facilities rather than more complex ones such as at-grade intersections and nonaccess controlled highways.

The capacity of a freeway in a section removed from any major interferences such as on- or off-ramps is dependent upon seven major factors:

1. Number of lanes
2. Width of lanes
3. Lateral clearance to obstructions on either side of the roadway from the outside of the traffic lanes (ft)
4. Percentage of trucks and city buses in the traffic stream
5. Percentage of intercity buses in the traffic stream
6. Length of grade (miles)
7. Percent grade

The model to be presented here is not a mathematical one, although it was evolved from a series of statistical analyses [5.24] using the factors listed above. Instead the model is implicit in a set of tables given in the *Highway Capacity Manual* [5.15]. The model also rests on the assumption, based on a multitude of observations of freeways in various cities, that the capacity of a freeway under the most *ideal conditions* will be 2,000 vph/lane. Thus, before we can use the tables that represent the model, we must know the ideal condition for each of the seven independent variables. Deviations from these ideals then are employed to make reductions in the 2,000 vph/lane figure because of the nonideal conditions.

The ideal value of each of the seven factors is set in the *Highway Capacity Manual* [5.15] as follows:

1. Number of lanes—(depends on lateral clearance and lane widths)
2. Width of lanes—12 ft or more
3. Lateral clearance—6 ft or more
4. Percentage of trucks—0 percent
5. Percentage of intercity buses—0 percent
6. Length of grade—0 miles
7. Percent grade—0 percent

These values are employed in conjunction with Tables 5.2 through 5.5, reproduced from the *Highway Capacity Manual*. In Table 5.2, the first three factors

Table 5.2 Combined Effect of Lane Width and Restricted Lateral Clearance on Capacity and Service Volumes of Divided Freeways and Expressways with Uninterrupted Flow

Distance from traffic lane edge to obstruction (ft)	Adjustment factors, *W*, for lane width and lateral clearance							
	Obstruction on one side of one-direction roadway				Obstructions on both sides of one-direction roadway			
	12-ft lanes	11-ft lanes	10-ft lanes	9-ft lanes	12-ft lanes	11-ft lanes	10-ft lanes	9-ft lanes
(a) 4-lane divided freeway, one direction of travel								
6	1.00	0.97	0.91	0.81	1.00	0.97	0.91	0.81
4	0.99	0.96	0.90	0.80	0.98	0.95	0.89	0.79
2	0.97	0.94	0.88	0.79	0.94	0.91	0.86	0.76
0	0.90	0.87	0.82	0.73	0.81	0.79	0.74	0.66
(b) 6- and 8-lane divided freeway, one direction of travel								
6	1.00	0.96	0.89	0.78	1.00	0.96	0.89	0.78
4	0.99	0.95	0.88	0.77	0.98	0.94	0.87	0.77
2	0.97	0.93	0.87	0.76	0.96	0.92	0.85	0.75
0	0.94	0.91	0.85	0.74	0.91	0.87	0.81	0.70

Source: [5.15, p. 256].

Table 5.3   Passenger Car Equivalents of Trucks on Freeways and Expressways, on Specific Individual Subsections or Grades

Grade (%)	Length of grade (mi)	Passenger car equivalent, E_T				
		3% Trucks	5% Trucks	10% Trucks	15% Trucks	20% Trucks
0–1	All	2	2	2	2	2
2	$\frac{1}{4}$ to $\frac{1}{2}$	5	4	4	3	3
	$\frac{3}{4}$ to 1	7	5	5	4	4
	$1\frac{1}{2}$ to 2	7	6	6	6	6
	3 to 4	7	7	8	8	8
3	$\frac{1}{4}$	10	8	5	4	3
	$\frac{1}{2}$	10	8	5	4	4
	$\frac{3}{4}$	10	8	5	4	5
	1	10	8	6	5	6
	$1\frac{1}{2}$	10	9	7	7	7
	2	10	9	8	8	8
	3	10	10	10	10	10
	4	10	10	11	11	11
4	$\frac{1}{4}$	13	9	5	4	3
	$\frac{1}{2}$	13	9	5	5	5
	$\frac{3}{4}$	13	9	7	7	7
	1	13	10	8	8	8
	$1\frac{1}{2}$	13	11	10	10	10
	2	13	12	11	11	11
	3	13	13	14	14	14
	4	13	14	16	16	15
5	$\frac{1}{4}$	14	10	6	4	3
	$\frac{1}{2}$	14	11	7	7	7
	$\frac{3}{4}$	14	11	9	8	8
	1	14	13	10	10	10
	$1\frac{1}{2}$	14	14	13	13	13
	2	14	15	15	15	15
	3	14	17	17	17	17
	4	16	19	22	21	19
6	$\frac{1}{4}$	15	10	6	4	3
	$\frac{1}{2}$	15	11	8	8	8
	$\frac{3}{4}$	15	12	10	10	10
	1	15	14	13	13	11
	$1\frac{1}{2}$	15	16	15	15	14
	2	15	18	18	18	16
	3	15	20	20	20	19
	4	20	23	23	23	23

Source: [5.15, p. 258].

Table 5.4 Passenger Car Equivalents of Intercity Buses on Freeways and Expressways, on Specific Individual Subsections or Grades

Grade* (%)	Passenger car equivalent,† E_B
0–4	1.6
5‡	2
6‡	4
7‡	10

*All lengths.
†For all percentages of buses.
‡Use generally restricted to grades over .5 mile long.
Source: [5.15, p. 260].

are considered, and a separate adjustment factor, *W*, is specified for each combination. If, for example, each lane of a six lane freeway were 9 ft wide and an obstruction, perhaps a sign support or a bridge abutment, were located at a distance of 4 ft from one edge of a traffic lane, the adjustment factor from Table 5.2 would be 0.77. This would imply a 23 percent reduction in the ideal capacity of 2,000 vph/lane.

The remaining four characteristics also form an interrelated set similar to that of the first three. In this case, however, a transformation first is made of trucks and intercity buses driving on a given length and percent of grade to an equivalent number of passenger cars (E_T and E_B, respectively). Then the adjustment factors, designated by *T* for trucks and *B* for intercity buses, are determined based on the previously found equivalency values. The reason for this intermediate transformation lies in the theory that a truck or bus, because of its slowness in climbing various lengths and steepnesses of grades, takes up a space or creates a headway in the traffic stream that could be filled by some much greater, equivalent number of passenger cars. In any real situation the equivalency will vary according to the speed of the truck or bus at the bottom of the hill, the number of similar vehicles directly following each other, the horsepower and torque of the vehicles, and so forth, so that the equivalency number actually pertains to the "average" influence of a truck or bus.

The charts for determining the passenger car equivalents and corresponding adjustment factors are displayed in Tables 5.3 and 5.4. The second of these is for bus equivalents and, as can be seen, gives numbers which generally are lower than for trucks. The bus or truck equivalents then are entered into the left hand column of Table 5.5, and the adjustment factor is found under the respective percentage column. By way of illustration, suppose that there were ten percent trucks (and city buses) and five percent intercity buses on a three percent grade 1 mile long. What would be the values for *T* and *B*? We find from Table 5.3 that $E_T = 6$ while

Table 5.5 Adjustment Factors* for Trucks and Buses on Individual Roadway Subsections or Grades on Freeways and Expressways (Incorporating Passenger Car Equivalent and Percentage of Trucks or Buses)†

Passenger car equivalent, E_T or E_B	Truck adjustment factor T, (B for buses)‡ Percentage of trucks, P_T (or of buses, P_B) of:														
	1	2	3	4	5	6	7	8	9	10	12	14	16	18	20
2	0.99	0.98	0.97	0.96	0.95	0.94	0.93	0.93	0.92	0.91	0.89	0.88	0.86	0.85	0.83
3	0.98	0.96	0.94	0.93	0.91	0.89	0.88	0.86	0.85	0.83	0.81	0.78	0.76	0.74	0.71
4	0.97	0.94	0.92	0.89	0.87	0.85	0.83	0.81	0.79	0.77	0.74	0.70	0.68	0.65	0.63
5	0.96	0.93	0.89	0.86	0.83	0.81	0.78	0.76	0.74	0.71	0.68	0.64	0.61	0.58	0.56
6	0.95	0.91	0.87	0.83	0.80	0.77	0.74	0.71	0.69	0.67	0.63	0.59	0.56	0.53	0.50
7	0.94	0.89	0.85	0.81	0.77	0.74	0.70	0.68	0.65	0.63	0.58	0.54	0.51	0.48	0.45
8	0.93	0.88	0.83	0.78	0.74	0.70	0.67	0.64	0.61	0.59	0.54	0.51	0.47	0.44	0.42
9	0.93	0.86	0.81	0.76	0.71	0.68	0.64	0.61	0.58	0.56	0.51	0.47	0.44	0.41	0.38
10	0.92	0.85	0.79	0.74	0.69	0.65	0.61	0.58	0.55	0.53	0.48	0.44	0.41	0.38	0.36
11	0.91	0.83	0.77	0.71	0.67	0.63	0.59	0.56	0.53	0.50	0.45	0.42	0.38	0.36	0.33
12	0.90	0.82	0.75	0.69	0.65	0.60	0.57	0.53	0.50	0.48	0.43	0.39	0.36	0.34	0.31
13	0.89	0.81	0.74	0.68	0.63	0.58	0.54	0.51	0.48	0.45	0.41	0.37	0.34	0.32	0.29
14	0.88	0.79	0.72	0.66	0.61	0.56	0.52	0.49	0.46	0.43	0.39	0.35	0.32	0.30	0.28
15	0.88	0.78	0.70	0.64	0.59	0.54	0.51	0.47	0.44	0.42	0.37	0.34	0.31	0.28	0.26
16	0.87	0.77	0.69	0.63	0.57	0.53	0.49	0.45	0.43	0.40	0.36	0.32	0.29	0.27	0.25
17	0.86	0.76	0.68	0.61	0.56	0.51	0.47	0.44	0.41	0.38	0.34	0.31	0.28	0.26	0.24
18	0.85	0.75	0.66	0.60	0.54	0.49	0.46	0.42	0.40	0.37	0.33	0.30	0.27	0.25	0.23
19	0.85	0.74	0.65	0.58	0.53	0.48	0.44	0.41	0.38	0.36	0.32	0.28	0.26	0.24	0.22
20	0.84	0.72	0.64	0.57	0.51	0.47	0.42	0.40	0.37	0.34	0.30	0.27	0.25	0.23	0.21
21	0.83	0.71	0.63	0.56	0.50	0.45	0.41	0.38	0.36	0.33	0.29	0.26	0.24	0.22	0.20
22	0.83	0.70	0.61	0.54	0.49	0.44	0.40	0.37	0.35	0.32	0.28	0.25	0.23	0.21	0.19
23	0.82	0.69	0.60	0.53	0.48	0.43	0.39	0.36	0.34	0.31	0.27	0.25	0.22	0.20	0.19
24	0.81	0.68	0.59	0.52	0.47	0.42	0.38	0.35	0.33	0.30	0.27	0.24	0.21	0.19	0.18
25	0.80	0.67	0.58	0.51	0.46	0.41	0.37	0.34	0.32	0.29	0.26	0.23	0.20	0.18	0.17

*Computed by $100/(100 - P_T + E_T P_T)$, or $100/(100 - P_B + E_B P_B)$. Use this formula for larger percentages.

†Used to convert equivalent passenger car volumes to actual mixed traffic; use reciprocal of these values to convert mixed traffic to equivalent passenger cars.

‡Trucks and buses should not be combined in entering this table where separate consideration of buses has been established as required, because passenger car equivalents differ.

Source: [5.15, p. 261].

from Table 5.4 that $E_B = 1.6$. Entering Table 5.5, we then determine that the adjustment factor for trucks (T) is 0.67 and for buses (B), through interpolation, is 0.94.

The calculation of the actual capacity of a section of a freeway now can be found by multiplying the 2,000 vph/lane figure by the number of lanes and the three adjustment factors, W, T, and B. Thus

$$c = 2,000\,NWTB \tag{5.41}$$

where c is the capacity of a given section of freeway and N is the number of lanes. Using the preceding example situation and adjustment factors, we would arrive at a (one-directional) capacity of

$$c = 2,000\ (3)\ (0.77)\ (0.67)\ (0.94) = 2,910 \text{ vph}$$

The preceding discussion has been directed toward the estimation of freeway capacities. What should be emphasized at this point is that, as proposed earlier, we are attempting to relate one characteristic of a transportation system to several others. In this case capacity is taken as the dependent variable, whereas the dimensions of the roadway (number and widths of lanes, lateral clearance) and the mechanics of vehicle operation (acceleration and power of different types of vehicles) are the independent variables, the latter type being implicit in the passenger car equivalency factors. The estimation of freeway capacity thus demonstrates the interrelationship of characteristics involved.

Still lacking in the freeway capacity model, however, is some statistic, such as a correlation coefficient, that would indicate the reliability and possible estimation accuracy of the model. Unfortunately, such a measure or index is not given in the *Highway Capacity Manual*, with the result being that the analyst is likely to place undue faith in his predictions, having no reason to think otherwise. To provide some perspective on this question, one study of *intersection* capacities [5.14] showed that about 67 percent of the estimates were within ±406 vph of the actual capacity. Obviously this is not a good record, and despite the fact that freeway traffic is subject to fewer interferences than that at intersections, we still should maintain some skepticism of freeway capacity estimates.

5.2.6 Models of Transportation Costs

One of the most important characteristics of any proposed solution to a transportation problem is the cost of the solution. Not only must there be a concern for the amount of funds required to purchase and construct or install the proposed system but also to operate and maintain it at an appropriate level. Also to be taken into account are the funds needed to plan and design the changes from the present situation. These are just a few of the many costs associated with any proposed solution.

In this section several sets of cost data from previously built or anticipated transportation systems will be presented. Most of the figures will not be in a form detailed enough for final cost estimates. Nor are the figures recent enough for such an endeavor. Instead the emphasis will be on presenting costs that show in rough terms the dollar magnitudes that may be involved. Some figures have been derived from rather crude estimates, others from slightly more detailed studies.[8] As a consequence, it should be stressed that most of the costs should not be taken as fixed and final.

The discussion of costs is broken in several categories. First there is a division according to whether the costs are for vehicles, networks, terminals, or control systems. Then there is a secondary division into purchase and construction or installation costs, operating costs, and maintenance costs. Thereafter follows a brief statement about the effects of inflation and rising prices on yearly costs levels. Finally, an entirely new transportation system, the Transit Expressway, is costed in order to exemplify and summarize much of the proceding presentation.

5.2.6.1 Transportation vehicle costs Most of us are familiar with the costs of various types and makes of automobiles so that it will not be necessary to go into this cost item here. Table 5.6 shows costs for different kinds of urban transit vehicles. As can be seen, the average cost for a typical bus is $26,000, a figure which comes out to about $10/sq ft of vehicle floor space. In another case, buses bought in 1961 for use in Memphis cost $30,300 a piece. Part of the additional cost can be attributed to air conditioning units, which at the time sold for $4,180 per unit. Rail rapid transit vehicles are more expensive than buses on a per square foot basis, ranging from $10/sq ft up to $17/sq ft. Some units, like the double deck ones, are not self-propelled and thus require an external motive power source such as the diesel-electric locomotive indicated at the bottom of Table 5.6 Cost comparisons between vehicles are not easy since they generally have different expected service lives, different numbers of seats, and oftentimes serve different purposes.

Vehicle operation and maintenance costs, on an average yearly basis, often equal or exceed purchase costs. Table 5.7 shows the average cost over a 10-year period to an owner of a medium priced 4-door sedan purchased for $3,185. The total cost per mile is 11.89¢, of which only 3.19¢ is for depreciation (payment) for the car. Repairs and maintenance average 1.56¢/mile and gasoline and oil (not inluding tax) 1.89¢ mile. Interestingly enough, the tax money collected and eventually used for highway construction and maintenance amounts to only 1.35¢/mile, less than the cost of either insurance for the car or repairs and maintenance.

Operation and maintenance costs for mass transit vehicles are much more than one would at first imagine, partially because of the cost of labor for driving the

---

[8] The reader is referred to Chap. 10 where some slightly more refined cost prediction relationships are used to demonstrate one aspect of the transportation solution specification process.

Table 5.6 Mass Transit Vehicle Costs

	Cost per unit	Interest and amortization	Approximate annual cost per		
			Unit	Sq ft	Seat
Motor bus	$ 26,000	12%	$ 3,000	$10	—
Rail rapid transit cars					
Light-weight	90,000	7%	6,300	14	—
Heavy-weight	125,000	7%	8,800	15	—
Commuter railway cars					
Single-deck trailers	140,000	7%	9,800	12	80
Multiple unit cars	200,000	7%	14,000	17	110
Double-deck (trailer)	150,000	7%	10,500	10	65
Diesel-electric locomotive (2,000 hp)	200,000	7%	14,000	—	—

Source: Berry, D. A., Blomme, G. W., Jones, J. H., and Shuldiner, P. W. *Technology of Urban Transportation*, Northwestern University Press, Evanston, Illinois, 1963.

vehicle. In Memphis, for example, the costs per vehicle mile for the city bus operation in 1964 were as follows [5.40]

  44.9¢ Operations
  1.3¢ Taxes (excluding federal income)
  1.7¢ City gross receipts payments
  1.2¢ Interest
  5.4¢ Depreciation

  54.5¢ Total

This cost actually is fairly low. Other figures for other localities and situations are: Chesapeake, Va. 64.8¢/bus mile (1967, [5.26]) and New York City, 65¢/bus mile [5.27]. Berry [5.25] has indicated that the per vehicle mile costs for rail rapid transit cars would be about 55¢ and for MU (multiple unit) commuter railway cars about $1.00.

Other interesting costs: ˙
Boeing 747 Jumbojet: $23,000,000 (1969, [5.28])
Automatic bus washing and cleaning facility: $60,000 (1961, [5.29])

5.2.6.2 Transportation network costs Costs for transportation networks include those for guideways, intersections or interchanges, and bridges. Construction costs are, of course, a major consideration for networks on the ground. The cost of land or right-of-way for transportation also becomes a significant component in this instance.

For highways, cost estimates for planning purposes generally are obtained by using unit prices such as those shown in Table 5.8. These then are multiplied by the

Table 5.7 Estimated Cost of Operating an Automobile (Total costs in dollars, costs per mile in cents)

Item	First year (14,900 miles)		Second year (13,000 miles)		Tenth year (5,700 miles)		Totals and averages for ten years (100,000 miles)	
	Total cost	Cost per mile	Total cost	Cost per mile	Total cost	Cost per mile	Total cost	Cost per mile
Costs including taxes:								
Depreciation	955.00	6.59	538.00	4.29	50.00	.88	3,485.00	3.19
Repairs and maintenance	72.51	.50	94.58	.73	30.38	.53	1,520.78	1.52
Replacement tires	17.23	.12	15.43	.12	46.49	.82	385.00	.39
Accessories	1.19	.01	1.06	.01	3.23	.06	28.13	.03
Gasoline	251.43	1.73	225.38	1.73	98.71	1.73	1,733.23	1.73
Oil	15.40	.11	15.40	.12	12.60	.22	157.50	.16
Insurance	208.95	1.44	198.58	1.53	149.08	2.61	1,722.23	1.72
Garaging, parking, tolls, etc.	207.73	1.43	198.65	1.53	134.48	2.71	1,805.00	1.80
Total	1,729.44	11.93	1,307.10	10.06	544.97	9.56	10,936.87	10.54
Taxes and fees:								
State:								
Gasoline	73.64	.51	66.01	.51	28.91	.51	507.64	.51
Registration	20.00	.14	20.00	.15	20.00	.35	200.00	.20
Titling	136.97	.94	—	—	—	—	136.97	.13
Subtotal	230.61	1.59	86.01	.66	48.91	.86	844.61	.84
Federal:								
Gasoline	42.08	.29	37.72	.29	6.52	.29	290.08	.29
Oil*	.33	—	.33	—	.27	—	3.38	—
Automobile and tires†	57.97	.40	36.22	.26	6.10	.11	215.32	.32
Subtotal	100.58	.69	72.27	.35	2.89	.40	508.78	.51
Total taxes	330.99	2.28	158.28	1.21	78.10	1.26	1,393.39	1.35
Total of all costs	2,060.43	14.21	1,465.38	11.27	616.10	10.82	11,890.26	11.89

*This estimate covers the total costs of medium priced 4-door sedans purchased for $3,185 ($3,374 if the federal excise tax is included), operated 100,000 miles over a 10 year period, then scrapped. Baltimore prices, considered to be in a middle range, were used.

†Where costs per mile were computed to be less than $\frac{1}{20}$ cent, a dash appears in the column.

Source: Bureau of Public Roads, Office of Planning, Highway Statistics Div.

quantities of materials needed as determined in the solution specification stage. An example of such calculations for an actual bidded highway job in North Carolina can be seen in Table 5.9. This table, taken from *Engineering News Record,* is much too detailed to be discussed fully here. It has been presented to give the reader some feeling for the level at which actual cost estimates are made.

On a more general basis, Table 5.10 indicates average costs per centerline mile for federally aided highways built in the U.S.A. in 1964. The costs are divided into engineering, right-of-way, earthwork and drainage, structures, and flexible pavement components. A further division is by Interstate rural and urban, primary rural and urban, and secondary rural and urban highways. As can be seen, the costs vary widely between different parts of the country and between the different types of

Table 5.8   Unit Prices of Various Highway Construction Items

Item	Unit	Unit prices
Clearing and grubbing	Acre	$1,000.00
Building demolition	Ea.	400.00
Regular excavation	C.Y.	1.25
Borrow excavation	C.Y.	1.50
Pavement		
Complete	S.Y.	8.00
Surfacing only	L.F.	1.00
Concrete curb and gutter	L.F.	3.25
Concrete sidewalks	S.Y.	5.00
Raised concrete median (4-ft)	L.F.	9.00
Raised grass median (16-ft)	L.F.	6.50
Topsoil and seeding	Acre	900.00
Fencing	L.F.	3.00
Paved shoulders	S.Y.	2.50
Guard rail	L.F.	5.00
Drainage		
12″ pipe	L.F.	$ 4.00
15″ pipe	L.F.	5.00
18″ pipe	L.F.	7.00
24″ pipe	L.F.	9.00
30″ pipe	L.F.	12.00
36″ pipe	L.F.	16.00
42″ pipe	L.F.	22.00
48″ pipe	L.F.	27.00
54″ pipe	L.F.	32.00
60″ pipe	L.F.	40.00
Reinforced concrete	C.Y.	115.00
Drop inlet	Ea.	500.00
Manhole	Ea.	300.00
Curb	L.F.	2.50

Source: [5.30, p. 80].

Table 5.9   Example of Unit Price for a Highway Job in North America

1C	Nello L. Teer Co., Durham, N.C.; James T. Tripplett, Inc., Chester S.C.; L. R. Ryan, Inc., Chester, S.C., joint venture	$10,652,395
2	Asheville Paving Co., Asheville, N.C.; Ballenger Paving Co., Greenville, S.C.; Structures, Inc., Greenville, S.C., joint venture	11,141,181
5	Blythe Brothers Co., Charlotte, N.C.	12,965,774
EE:	N.C. State Highway Commission, Raleigh, N.C.	10,758,411

Bids: 11/25/69

Items:	Unit	Number	IC Bid	2 Bid
Mobilization	ls	job	120,000	384,000
Clear and grub	ls	job	225,000	90,000
Exc, uncl	cy	4,641,000	0.53	0.70
drain ditch	cy	26,000	1.00	1.50
CABC stab subgr	ton	12,000	3.00	2.85
Sand, base				
drainage	cy	9,800	5.50	5.00
CABC	ton	141,500	2.66	2.75
Plant mix,				
prime coat	gal	56,200	0.22	0.22
asph cmt	ton	1,110	31.00	31.00
Bit conc, base				
crse	ton	13,300	7.32	7.32
surf crse	ton	4,975	7.63	7.63
RC br appr				
slabs, rigid	sy	825	16.00	15.00
crc pvmt	sy	3,325	17.50	16.00
PCC pvmt, 8″	sy	128,300	6.25	4.68
9″	sy	54,300	5.96	5.96
Conc, endwalls,				
cl A	cy	54	110.00	130.00
cl C	cy	45	100.00	130.00
CMP, 16 ga. 18″	lf	256	6.00	5.50
BCCMP, ty B,				
16 ga 15″	lf	6,336	7.00	3.60
18″	lf	6,948	7.50	4.25
24″	lf	6,146	10.00	5.75
14 ga 30″	lf	5,374	12.00	8.00
36″	lf	1,724	15.00	10.00
12 ga 42″	lf	1,744	18.00	13.20
Str plate pipe,				
72″, 12 ga	lf	320	71.00	35.00

Source: Reprinted from *Engineering News Record*, (March 12, 1970), copyright McGraw-Hill, Inc. All rights reserved.

Table 5.10 Dollars per Centerline Mile Cost of Complete Highway Construction or Reconstruction by Highway System and Census Division (Based on Federal-Aid Projects for 1964)

Highway system and census division	Engineering	Right of way	Earthwork and drainage	Structures	Flexible pavement	Total
A. Interstate rural						
1. New England	86,389	116,987	256,698	272,134	176,893	909,101
2. Middle Atlantic	113,944	154,302	288,492	363,916	249,575	1,170,299
3. South Atlantic North	147,827	200,186	224,568	290,639	254,570	1,117,790
4. South Atlantic South	52,315	70,845	121,153	134,860	128,434	507,607
5. East North Central	76,671	101,827	188,089	225,736	194,143	788,466
6. West North Central	51,411	69,621	125,504	115,857	153,142	515,535
7. East South Central	59,407	80,448	141,234	154,266	204,122	639,477
8. West South Central	64,119	86,830	153,951	175,403	179,025	659,328
9. Mountain	49,294	66,754	193,443	86,603	91,994	488,088
10. Pacific	68,079	92,192	211,516	186,928	159,756	718,471
B. Interstate urban						
1. New England	320,070	997,356	664,264	1,895,066	180,129	4,056,885
2. Middle Atlantic	590,662	1,840,532	746,539	2,247,594	254,678	5,680,005
3. South Atlantic North	433,368	1,350,396	581,122	2,007,453	251,906	4,624,245
4. South Atlantic South	179,028	557,860	313,511	501,801	130,234	1,682,434
5. East North Central	340,043	1,059,592	486,722	1,481,890	194,220	3,562,467
6. West North Central	187,135	583,123	324,770	1,001,001	156,144	2,252,173
7. East North Central	218,661	681,360	365,475	1,174,574	225,411	2,665,481
8. West South Central	199,334	621,134	398,885	650,445	174,394	2,044,192
9. Mountain	163,159	508,412	500,579	423,322	99,956	1,695,428
10. Pacific	355,210	1,106,853	547,346	1,559,994	160,893	3,730,296

C. Primary rural

1. New England	47,000	137,918	61,472	57,948	160,239	464,577
2. Middle Atlantic	52,852	155,001	68,854	46,234	216,478	539,210
3. South Atlantic North	43,852	120,656	57,356	30,777	215,898	468,539
4. South Atlantic South	35,005	65,093	45,784	23,332	118,537	287,751
5. East North Central	39,556	101,056	51,737	26,414	163,054	381,817
6. West North Central	19,407	35,504	25,384	16,485	75,314	172,094
7. East South Central	22,797	39,954	29,817	32,169	99,975	224,712
8. West South Central	19,386	43,551	25,356	21,432	84,615	194,340
9. Mountain	17,256	54,723	22,570	13,488	45,801	153,838
10. Pacific	33,982	59,836	44,446	43,658	131,530	313,452

D. Primary urban

1. New England	86,006	287,096	193,324	190,250	162,160	918,836
2. Middle Atlantic	93,936	322,656	211,150	179,210	217,910	1,024,862
3. South Atlantic North	76,025	251,162	170,889	130,440	223,839	852,355
4. South Atlantic South	57,078	135,500	128,301	111,801	118,064	550,744
5. East North Central	70,624	210,362	158,750	141,507	165,764	747,007
6. West North Central	26,782	60,550	60,201	36,549	79,173	263,255
7. East South Central	29,902	68,139	67,215	44,259	108,341	317,856
8. West South Central	28,789	74,274	64,712	55,410	86,462	309,647
9. Mountain	27,409	93,327	61,611	37,214	50,388	269,949
10. Pacific	72,442	102,047	162,836	271,490	148,722	757,537

E. Secondary rural

1. New England	17,475	46,160	11,979	20,338	73,756	169,708
2. Middle Atlantic	19,122	51,887	13,108	15,845	92,593	192,555
3. South Atlantic North	15,556	40,382	10,664	6,745	88,250	161,597
4. South Atlantic South	13,009	21,786	8,980	5,326	52,747	101,938
5. East North Central	14,690	33,822	10,070	6,115	71,316	136,013
6. West North Central	13,870	22,568	9,508	4,626	64,399	114,971

Table 5.10 Dollars per Centerline Mile Cost of Complete Highway Construction or Reconstruction by Highway System and Census Division (Based on Federal-Aid Projects for 1964) (*Continued*)

Highway system and census division	Engineering	Right of way	Earthwork and drainage	Structures	Flexible pavement	Total
7. East South Central	15,503	10,627	25,397	12,463	80,071	144,061
8. West South Central	12,978	8,896	27,684	6,606	67,102	123,266
9. Mountain	12,347	8,464	34,785	6,568	41,937	104,101
10. Pacific	14,159	9,706	38,035	7,809	55,996	125,705
F. Secondary urban						
1. New England	4,201	9,820	66,144	78,129	76,241	234,535
2. Middle Atlantic	4,510	10,542	74,337	71,782	98,107	259,278
3. South Atlantic North	3,486	8,148	57,865	36,961	101,529	207,989
4. South Atlantic South	2,870	6,708	31,218	33,817	56,066	130,679
5. East North Central	3,240	7,574	48,465	40,589	73,213	173,081
6. West North Central	2,475	5,785	32,339	13,639	62,228	116,466
7. East South Central	5,569	13,017	36,392	25,662	84,550	165,190
8. West South Central	2,496	5,834	39,669	18,090	68,918	135,007
9. Mountain	2,603	6,084	49,845	20,879	42,410	121,821
10. Pacific	3,803	8,890	54,502	68,593	66,073	201,861

Source: [5.31, p. 252].

roads built. Interstate highways in urban areas naturally are most expensive to build, averaging as much as $5,680,005 per mile in the heavily populated Middle Atlantic region of the United States. As could be expected, structures and right-of-way are the most costly items for this type of facility.

Individual large scale bridges and tunnels are perhaps the most expensive items of all. A good example is the Straights of Bosphorous Bridge in Turkey which is a suspension structure almost one mile long and is expected to cost $185 million. Costs for similar kinds of projects can be noted in Table 5.11.

As mentioned before, right-of-way costs are the other big expense item for urban highways (and terminals). Generally these costs are obtained by looking at

Table 5.11   Approximate Costs and Dates of Construction of Various Bridges and Tunnels Around the World

Cost (in millions of dollars)	Date	Description	Reference
70	1970	Eight lane sunken tube tunnel under Thames River in London; 1/2-mile long	ENR* March 12, 1970
67	1970	Four lane tube tunnel under Mersey River in Liverpool, England; 1.5 miles long	ENR March 12, 1970
185	1969	5,118-ft Turkish bridge over the Straights of Bosphorous	ENR Dec. 4, 1969
69.5	1969	3,500-ft four track tunnel under the East River and Welfare Island in New York City	Civil Engineering Dec., 1969
45	1969	Kniebrucke (bridge) across the Rhine River at Dusseldorf, Germany; 1,800-ft span, tunnel approach, and 4,300-ft underwater section—all 92 ft wide	ENR Nov. 26, 1969
57.6	1970	9,000-ft Mersey River Bridge in Liverpool, England	ENR Oct. 16, 1969
10.1	1969	Silver Bridge, Pt. Pleasant, West Virginia; 1,800-ft long with four lanes	ENR Nov. 6, 1969
23.7	1970	1.072-mile long tunnel in Virginia (2 tunnels each 26 ft wide and 16.5-ft high	ENR Sept. 18, 1969
180	1970	San Francisco Bay Area Rapid Transit (BART) tube across bay—3.6 miles long, 48 ft wide and 24 ft high	A BART Publication

Engineering News Record.

local tax assessors' records to determine the assessed value of land in a given city. Where property taxes are not incurred, such as in many rural areas, land costs of past projects may be the only guide by which to make estimates. Figure 5.9 portrays the manner in which land values vary within a city—in this case, Topeka, Kansas. Construction which involves the taking of land (and buildings) in center city areas obviously is going to be extremely expensive. In downtown Hartford,

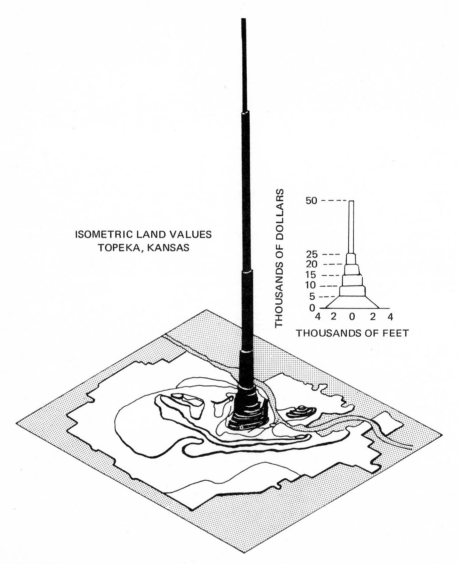

Fig. 5.9 Representation of the structure of urban land values. *Source:* Deane S. Knox, *Distribution of Land Values in Topeka, Kansas, Lawrence.* Center for Research in Business, The University of Kansas, May 1962.

**Table 5.12   Costs of Construction for Various
Types of Two-Track Rail–Rapid Transit Facilities
(1959–1960 Prices)**

	Costs in thousand of dollars	
Type of facility	Average cost per route mile*	Cost range for a station†
Cut and cover subway	14,000 (9,900–17,800‡)	420–2,400
Tunnel	15,300	—
Elevated	3,200	480–720
Open cut	2,600	400–600
At level (median strip)	2,100	320–480
Escalators (each)	—	32–40

*Includes costs of track and structures, relocation and maintenance of utilities, power supply and distribution systems, transmission systems, and signal systems. Right-of-way costs and costs of engineering and contingencies are not included.

†These costs are for stations to accommodate trains up to 600 feet in length. They are "station finish" costs which do not include the cost of track and structures contained within the station limits. The wide range in costs reflects variations attributed largely to whether single-level or multi-level arrangements are used.

‡The wide range in costs is due in part to variations in soil conditions, cost of underpinning, etc.

Source: Soberman, R. *A Study of the Characteristics of Rail Transit Systems,* Master's Thesis, Massachusetts Institute of Technology, January, 1961.

Connecticut, for instance, land values exceeded $50 per sq ft in 1963 [5.12, p. 100]. In other areas of the city, values will be relatively lower except, perhaps, at major outlying commercial areas.

Construction of transportation guideways other than for the automobile also can be expensive propositions. Table 5.12 gives some rough estimates of costs for building two track rail rapid transit facilities. As could be expected, tunneling usually is an extremely costly alternative, being as much as five times as expensive as building an elevated, open cut, or at grade (level) route. Also included in this table are the costs for stations. A very large station, built in connection with a cut and cover subway, could run as much as $2,400,000 by itself (as can be seen, the station is about $\frac{1}{10}$ of a mile long).

The continued operation and maintenance of networks and guideways is a far from inexpensive item. On a per centerline mile basis, the costs do not appear to be high. The state of Illinois, for instance, spent an average of only $5,296 to maintain each mile of Interstate highway in 1965 (Table 5.13). In contrast to the construction cost, this figure seems very low; however, it should be remembered

Table 5.13 Maintenance and Operating Expenses for 1965–Illinois Division of Highways (Expenses are in dollars per centerline mile)

Class of work	Urban expressways	Interstate highways	Regular state highways
Maintenance			
Wearing surface	$ 7,818	$ 494	$ 768
Shoulders, ditches, cuts, and fills	553	664	397
Large bridges (100 ft length and over)	786*	92*	719*
Culverts and other drainage facilities	478	54	27
Small bridges (less than 100 ft length)	—	10	19
Miscellaneous structures and facilities	453	15	13
Service drives	—	105	1.36
Total maintenance	$12,242	$1,462	$ 1,303
Operation			
Cutting and clearing vegetation	$ 3,050	$1,071	$ 419
Snow removal and ice control	14,350	957	581
Clearing dirt and debris	10,514	655	257
Roadside planting maintenance	1,426	425	34
Upkeep of guardrail	1,672	147	31
Subway and drainage pumping	1,701	19	11
Electric lighting	—	—	0.40
Traffic operation	21,326	504	476
Rest area operation	—	56	—
Total operation	$54,041	$4,834	$ 1,809
Total maintenance and operation	$66,283	$5,296	$ 3,112
Weighted average miles maintained	105.13	626.68	14,330.71

*Cost per bridge.
Source: [5.31].

that there are many more miles to operate and maintain than are constructed in any one year. The net result is that many highway departments end up spending as much as 30 percent of their annual budget on operation and maintenance.

5.2.6.3 Transportation terminal costs Terminals for transportation services may be a very large part of the budget of many governmental bodies. Airport terminals in particular have been rather expensive items, yet ones in which most governmental bodies (especially municipalities) have been willing to invest. Two good examples are the new airport facilities being constructed in the Dallas–Ft. Worth area and in Philadelphia. The former is intended to cover an area of 30 sq miles, have a 105 gate, two row, three level, terminal building 3.25 miles long, and cost $600,000,000.[9] The Philadelphia airport plans include a 90-gate passenger terminal, a 217-acre "cargo city" complex, a 10,500-ft runway, and 25,000 parking

[9] *Engineering News Record,* Nov. 6, 1969.

Table 5.14 Physical and Financial Facts Regarding San Francisco Garages, 1959

Item	Fifth and Mission garage	Butler–Stockton garage	Civic center garage
Parking area	399,000 sq ft	390,600 sq ft	355,674 sq ft
Store area	—	31,300 sq ft	—
Total area	399,000 sq ft	421,900 sq ft	355,674 sq ft
Number of parking stalls			
Self-parking	1,023	932	954
Attendant-parking	—	—	1,461
Construction contract price	$1,500,000	$2,530,000	$3,392,460
Demolition cost	105,000	212,000	—
Engineer and architects' fees (computed at 6% of contract)	90,000	151,103	203,540
Surface restoration expense	—	—	154,000
Total construction cost (including all other fees, commissions, and interest reserves)	$2,135,000	$3,680,000	$4,500,000
Land acquisition cost	1,600,000	2,550,000	—
Total acquisition cost	$3,735,000	$6,230,000	$4,500,000
Construction contract price			
Per square foot	$ 3.76	$ 6.00	$ 9.53
Per stall	1,835.00	3,714.00	3,556.00*
			2,322.00†
Total construction cost			
Per square foot	$ 5.37	$ 8.72	$ 13.40
Per stall	1,971.00	3,948.00	4,717.00*
			3,080.00†
Land acquisition cost per stall	$1,477.00	$2,736.00	$4,717.00*
Total project cost per stall	$3,448.00	$6,684.00	$3,088.00†

*Self-parking.
†Attendant-parking.
Source: [5.33].

spaces for cars in garages. The total cost of all this is estimated to be $400,000,000.[10]

Another type of terminal important to urban areas is that for downtown (or major activity center) parking. Information presented in *Parking Garage Operation* [5.33] and Table 5.14 indicates that for 18 municipally developed garages the

[10] *Engineering News Record*, Dec. 18, 1969.

Table 5.15 Annual Cost-Income Data for 18 Selected Municipal Garages

A. Itemized breakdown of annual operating costs

Fiscal item	Cost per space		Cost per parker	
	Self-parking	Attendant-parking	Self-parking	Attendant-parking
Salaries	$ 76.68	$115.64	$0.134	$0.248
Insurance	8.36	8.36	0.018	0.018
Utilities	11.90	11.90	0.021	0.021
Maintenance and other	23.69	23.69	0.044	0.044
Management fee	15.97	15.97	0.031	0.031
Total	$136.60	$175.56	$0.248	$0.362
Total excluding management fee	$120.63	$159.59	$0.217	$0.331

Source: [5.33].

average capital cost per parking space was $3,687, of which $1,597 was for land, $1,817 for construction, and $273 for other expenses.

The operation and maintenance of these parking facilities also is a costly item. The data in Table 5.15 show, for example, that depending on whether a facility has attendant or self-parking, the annual average operating and maintenance cost per space could be as much as $175 (with attendants) or $136 (self-parking). The average cost per parker would be either $.36 or $.25, respectively, for the two conditions above.

Airport terminal and runway maintenance also is expensive. It cost $7,720,000 to rip up and replace a 10,000-ft runway and apron at the Atlanta, Georgia airport;[11] $2,560,000 to overlay and provide centerline lighting for a 7,750-ft by 150-ft runway in Dallas;[12] and, most interestingly, $0.40 per lineal foot just to clean and reseal joints in a pavement at another airport.[13] Obviously any transportation terminal with its related facilities requires a continuing expenditure of funds to keep it in good operating order.

5.2.6.4 Transportation control system costs The final major cost component for a transportation system is that for controls. For automotive traffic, controls would consist of markings, signs, signals, and other street furniture. Table 5.16 shows unit costs for many of these items. The data were obtained from the purchasing records of the city of Dallas, Texas. To the uninitiated what is most surprising is that a simple item such as a stop or yield sign costs as much as $15 to purchase and install. Moreover, the maintenance costs of these signs run around $2.25/yr. These costs are not high, however, in contrast to traffic signals. A

---

[11] *Engineering News Record*, Dec. 4, 1969.
[12] *Engineering News Record*, Oct. 16, 1969.
[13] *Civil Engineering*, Dec. 1969.

Table 5.16 Cost Data for Traffic Signs and Signals Dallas, Texas

Component	Unit	Number of components used	Individual cost of component	Total annual component cost	Site work cost	Installation cost	Estimated life	Total cost installed component	Annual operation and maintenance costs	Total annual cost of installed components
Signs										
Stop	24" × 24"	2,900	$ 7.30	$ 21,200.00	$ 3.00	$ 5.00	5 years	$ 15.30	$ 2.45	$ 44,370.00
Yield	30" × 30"	70	6.25	438.00	3.50	5.50	5 years	15.25	2.25	1,068.00
Misc.	18" × 24"	330	6.25	2,063.00	3.50	5.50	5 years	15.25	2.35	5,033.00
One way	18" × 24"	1,500	6.25	8,775.00	3.50	5.50	5 years	15.25	2.35	22,875.00
No parking	12" × 18"	900	3.35	3,015.00	3.50	5.50	5 years	12.35	1.77	11,115.00
School warning	30" × 30"	350	7.70	2,695.00	3.50	5.50	2 years	16.70	6.60	5,845.00
School cross	24" × 30"	350	6.95	2,433.00	3.50	5.50	2 years	15.95	6.23	5,583.00
Misc.	24" × 24"	300	7.50	2,250.00	3.50	5.50	5 years	16.50	2.60	4,950.00
Street name	2 blades, 4 faces	1,500	14.22	21,330.00	2.00	10.00	5 years	26.22	4.00	39,330.00
Bus stop	oval w/pole	300	11.00	3,300.00	3.00	9.00	5 years	23.00	1.00	6,900.00
Portable information	18" × 24"	100	6.25	625.00	3.50	3.00	1 year	12.75	9.25	1,275.00
Pole	10' 6" pole and cap	3,400	4.20	14,280.00	3.00	5.50	20 years	12.70	.10	43,180.00
Signals										
Head-traffic	3 lights	40	80.00	3,200.00	5.00	227.00	20 years	312.00	14.00	12,480.00
Head-pedestrian	2 lights	300	105.00	31,500.00	5.00	66.00	20 years	176.00	11.00	52,800.00
Controller	3D-NA(S)	8	600.00	4,800.00	10.00	100.00	20 years	710.00	102.00	5,680.00
Controller	3D-NA(I)	12	800.00	9,600.00	10.00	100.00	20 years	910.00	102.00	10,920.00
Controller	8P-solid state	25	8,500.00	212,500.00	10.00	328.00	20 years	8,838.00	110.00	212,500.00
Detector	Loop		180.00						20.00	
Detector	Pressure	400	420.00	119,200.00	10.00	465.00	20 years	895.00		119,200.00
Pole	30' mast arm		425.00							
Pole	10' 4" pipe		12.00							

Source: Urban America, Inc., *Center City Transportation Project Workshop Reports*, Washington, D.C., 1969.

Table 5.17   Price Index Changes Over Time for Various Highway Construction Items

	Price index 1957–59=100			Percentage changes this quarter from	
	Fourth quarter 1969	Third quarter 1969	Fourth quarter 1968	Third quarter 1969	Fourth quarter 1968
Excavation	135.7	137.4	157.6	–1.2	–13.9
Surfacing:					
Portland cement concrete	128.1	125.8	117.9	+1.8	+8.6
Bituminous concrete	111.5	100.4	101.4	+11.1	+10.0
Composite surfacing	119.4	112.6	109.3	+6.1	+9.3
Structures:					
Reinforcing steel	121.8	113.8	102.7	+7.1	+18.6
Structural steel	166.1	191.4	128.2	–13.2	+29.6
Structural concrete	167.5	149.9	137.9	+11.8	+21.5
Composite structures	158.8	156.6	128.4	+1.4	+23.7
Composite price index	138.7	136.3	132.3	+1.7	+4.8

The U.S. average contract unit prices for the index items during the third and fourth quarters of 1969, and during calendar years 1968 and 1969 are:

	Unit	Third quarter 1969	Fourth quarter 1969	1968	1969
Excavation	Cu yd	$ .58	$ .57	$ .55	$ .58
PCC surface	Sq yd	5.51	5.61	4.86	4.96
Bituminous concrete surface	Ton	6.69	7.43	6.68	6.96
Structural reinforcing	Lb	.147	.157	.131	.142
Structural steel	Lb	.373	.323	.249	.316
Structural concrete	Cu yd	81.20	90.75	72.70	81.88

Source: Reprinted from *Engineering News Record,* (March, 1970), copyright McGraw-Hill, Inc. All rights reserved.

sophisticated eight-phase solid state traffic controller for one intersection costs $8,500, and a 30-ft mast arm pole to which the traffic signal heads would be attached would cost $425.

The costs for operation of a control system can be demonstrated through another example—that of freeway control. In a bus-freeway surveillance system proposed by researchers at Texas A&M [5.35] for the John Lodge Freeway in Detroit, the annual operating costs would be $287,800. It was suggested that television cameras be positioned at 13 locations along the freeway. These would allow for the priority entry of buses onto the freeway from selected bus ramps. Required also for this operation would be 345 detectors costing a total of $207,000, 47 signal installations for $94,000, and a control center for $35,000. The 13 TV installations would cost $156,000.

5.2.6.5 Increases in prices over time Obviously all the costs and prices quoted above should be considered relevant to other costs at the particular point in time at which they are incurred; otherwise some large discrepancies may result. Inflation, of course, will have a major influence on the rise in prices over time, and this rise can be significant. Table 5.17 illustrates this point. At the bottom can be seen unit prices for several major highway construction items in 1968 and 1969. At the top are the changes in the prices of these items with the 1957–59 period taken as a base (of 100). In the 10 year span between 1958 and 1968, excavation prices rose by 57.6 percent, Portland cement concrete surfacing by 17.9 percent, and so on. Over all items considered, the composite price increase was 32.3 percent or roughly $\frac{1}{3}$. This shows the importance of taking into account price changes over time.

5.2.6.6 Summary: A new system To help summarize some of the preceding thinking on transportation costs, we will utilize some figures developed for a relatively new system—the Transit Expressway. As pictured in Chap. 9, the Transit Expressway consists of automatically controlled bus-like vehicles running on a specially designated guideway. In a hypothetical case, the guideway would be 10 doubletrack miles long, would utilize 110 vehicles, and, in 1969 (the year for which all costs have been calculated) would employ as many as 115 people in associated labor force positions. Under these and other conditions too numerous to specify, vehicle capital costs would total $10,330,110 or $93,900 per vehicle. The overall costs to construct a route mile of double track would be $5,769,369 (the guideway is assumed to go through rather rugged terrain). These capital costs, along with those for underground, at-grade, and aerial stations are summarized in Table 5.18*a*, *b*, and *c*.

Operating and maintenance costs for the system are expected to total $1,252,336 for the year. Of this, roughly $440,000 could be considered as maintenance costs. The various categories of these expenses can be seen in Table 5.19. By viewing these and the capital cost items, the reader hopefully can obtain some insight into the magnitude of costs involved for each transportation system component.

5.3 LAND USE MODELS

As emphasized in the beginning of this chapter, land use models are the focal point for inputs from the majority of the other types of models in the calibration and model use stage. Prediction of zonal land use development is difficult, however, especially since it is not easy to see that a relationship with transportation and other factors does exist. Certainly this reaction is to be expected since the causal influence is a gradual one, appearing only after 5, 10, or an even greater number of years after changes in the transportation system and other facilities. Nevertheless, as can be seen in Fig. 5.10, the actual changes can be dramatic. In this figure, the growth in various parts of the Chicao Metropolitan Area is shown, and while the development which appears cannot all be attributed to the transportation system itself, the fact that most of it is within a short distance of these facilities provides a strong indication of the importance of the transportation system, and possibly other public and private facilities in development.

Table 5.18a Construction Costs of Hypothetical Transit Expressway System (1969)

Item	Unit cost
Tunnel, mixed earth and rock	$10,654,622
Tunnel, rock	9,811,623
Stations, underground	4,824,418
Stations, at-grade	3,178,884
Stations, aerial	2,960,336
Track, in tunnels	723,646
Track, at-grade	3,393,452
Track, aerial	9,356,849
Transfer switches	350,402
Transfer tables	95,074
Bridges	3,790,112
Track heaters	419,270
Tunnel lighting	36,148
Automatic train operating system	1,539,770
Power system	4,754,797
Maintenance and repair facilities	631,336
Audio and visual communications systems	439,064
Auxiliary mobile equipment	233,890
Spare parts	500,000
Vehicles	10,330,100
Total	$68,023,793

Source: [5.36, p. 245].

Table 5.18b Unit Costs of Some Transit Expressway Items (1969)

Item	Unit Cost
Overall cost per route mile including	
rolling stock	$6,802,379
Per lineal foot double track	1,288
Overall cost per route mile excluding	
rolling stock	5,769,369
Per lineal foot double track	1,093
Underground station*	2,412,209
Per square foot	111
At-grade station*	794,721
Per square foot	67
Aerial station*	740,084
Per square foot	63

*Exclusive of tracks, etc.
Source: [5.36, p. 245].

Table 5.18c Construction Costs of Transit Expressway Guideway Per Double Track Mile Under Different Conditions (1969)

Item	Roadway in earth tunnel	Roadway in rock tunnel	At-grade roadway	Aerial roadway
Tunnel	$11,228,659	$ 9,811,613	—	—
Track	350,170	350,170	$ 822,677	$2,079,317
Lighting	23,126	11,563	37,805	37,805
Auto train operation	138,653	138,653	138,653	138,653
Power	428,313	428,313	428,313	428,313
Communications	39,600	39,600	39,600	39,600
Total	$12,208,521	$10,779,912	$1,467,048	$2,723,688

Source: [5.36, p. 246].

Table 5.19 Yearly Operating and Maintenance Costs of Hypothetical Transit Expressway System (1969)

Electric power		Yard operations	
Energy charge	245,950	Supervision	21,964
Demand charge	21,704	Hostlers	54,300
Total	267,654	Cleaners	24,638
		Supplies	2,468
Automatic train operation		Total	103,366
Supervision	7,731		
Console operators	57,414	Vehicle maintenance	
Maintenance	27,328	Superintendent	7,732
Total	92,473	Supervision	27,110
		Mechanic and electricians	81,342
Station operations		Inspectors	20,710
Supervision	10,296	Labors	21,212
Guard attendants	99,942	Clerical	12,000
Custodians	29,458	Tire replacements	31,750
Escalator M&R	22,205	Other materials and parts	69,573
Other equipment M&R	4,176	Subsystem overhaul	18,450
Station M&R	18,030	Total	289,879
Station and shop heat	1,570		
Total	185,857	General and administrative	
		Insurance	87,145
Roadway maintenance		General administrative	174,836
Supervision	10,296	Total	261,981
Track and power crew	19,937		
Ways crew	12,727	Total operating costs	1,252,336
M&R materials	8,166		
Structure painting	—		
Resurfacing	—		
Total	51,126		

Source: [5.36, p. 262].

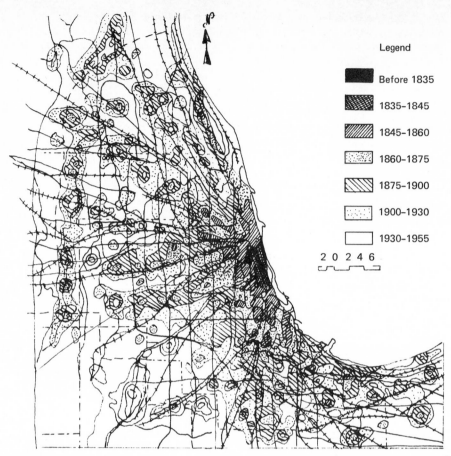

Fig. 5.10 Chicago growth patterns. The urbanized area has spread out in waves from the site of the original settlement. The finger development has followed the suburban railroad line. *Source:* [5.19, vol. 1, p. 15].

5.3.1 Some Simple Theories

There are a number of very simple models and theories which address the topic of land use change. Some of these were developed by urban geographers and sociologists as much as 45 years ago. While they are not really very helpful in terms of increasing our ability to forecast land use, they are discussed briefly here to help guide us conceptually when we talk about more detailed models.[14]

According to Park [5.41], most urban processes derive their energy from the expansion of the city's population and the city's area in a concentric ringlike fashion over time. Observation (at first on an informal basis) of Chicago revealed

[14] Much of the discussion here comes from Berry and Horton [5.45].

that the process of upward social mobility involved geographic migration: the population group which had resided in the city for the longest time would move from their original homes to newer homes in the city's periphery as their economic status improved; they would be replaced at the center of the city by new arrivals, to whom the older housing stock would "filter down." Thus, a distinctive spatial pattern of activity and residence zones, Burgess's concentric zones (Fig. 5.11 and [5.44]) emerged, the definitions of which are based on principal land uses (zone I, commercial; zone II, industrial; zones IIb to V, residential), and within the residential category by the type of resident (zone III, zone of workingmen's homes; zone V, commuter's zone), both use and tenants changing in time as a result of the filtering down of property. The broadly defined zones are divided into smaller natural areas (Fig. 5.11) on the basis of race (the Black Belt), or ethnicity (Little Sicily), or the type of residence (residential hotels).

An alternative model of the changing spatial structure of the city was put forward by Homer Hoyt [5.41]. On the basis of an intensive study of some 142 cities for which eight variables [5.42] were mapped by blocks, Hoyt was able to say that the high and low rent neighborhoods occupied distinct subareas of the city and that these were not aligned concentrically about the city center but, rather, distributed in a sectoral fashion. The spatial pattern of the city's rental areas was determined, in Hoyt's view, by the choice of those who could afford the highest rents. They preempt the land along "the best existing transportation lines, high ground—free from the risk of floods, and land along lake, bay, river and ocean fronts where such water fronts are not used for industry" [5.42]. Hoyt showed that highgrade residential areas of Chicago follow such a pattern and that there is a concomitant tendency for the innermost parts of the high-rent sectors to become low-grade residential areas, except in the case of the Gold Coast. But Hoyt's view of the city is at best partial, constrained by his narrow focus of interest on housing characteristics in general and on rent in particular. He gave little consideration to the characteristics of the inhabitants who occupied the structures.

Since the time of these simple explanations of urban growth, many more sophisticated models have been developed. Several such models are discussed by Berry and Horton [5.45] and Blunden [5.47]. Several models applied on a large scale are those by Hamburg and Sharkey [5.3] for the Chicago Area Transportation Study and by Rosenthal et al. [5.46] in relation to the BART system in San Francisco. We have elected here to discuss in detail the EMPIRIC land use model, which has been utilized extensively in Boston, Washington, D.C., and elsewhere.

5.3.2 The EMPIRIC Land Use Model

Any land use model should incorporate the transportation—land use relationship as well as the others represented by the linkages to phased (land use) in Fig. 5.1. Specifically, future zonal (subarea) land use development in any given region should be a function of:

1. Past and present zonal land use
2. Past, present, and proposed transportation systems

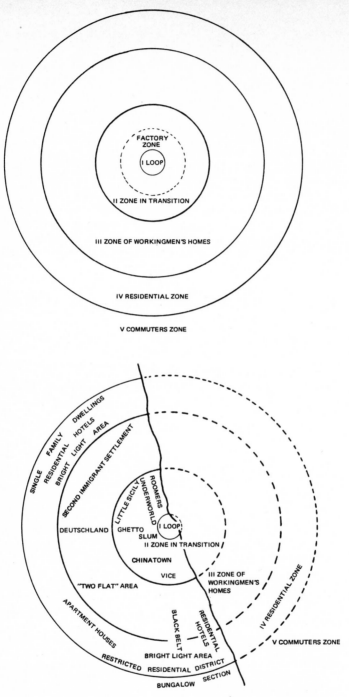

Fig. 5.11 Burgess' spatial model. *Source:* Robert E. Park and Ernest W. Burgess, *The City*, Chicago, University of Chicago Press, 1925, pp. 51, 53.

Table 5.20 Basic Inputs to the EMPIRIC Model

Present zonal land use variables (zone h), V_{ih} (t)

V_{1h} (t) = Number of families with an annual income less than \$5,000
V_{2h} (t) = Number of families with an annual income between \$5,000 and \$9,999
V_{3h} (t) = Number of families with an annual income between \$10,000 and \$14,999
V_{4h} (t) = Number of families with an annual income equal to or greater than \$15,000
V_{5h} (t) = Number of persons in manufacturing and construction employment (S.I.C.*
$\quad\quad\quad$ Codes 15-39)
V_{6h} (t) = Number of persons in wholesale, transportation, communication, utilities and
$\quad\quad\quad$ government employment (S.I.C. Codes 1-14, 40-50, 91-99)
V_{7h} (t) = Number of persons in retail employment (S.I.C. Codes 52-59)
V_{8h} (t) = Number of persons in service employment (S.I.C. Codes 70-89)
V_{9h} (t) = Number of persons in finance, insurance, and real estate employment (S.I.C.
$\quad\quad\quad$ Codes 60-67)

Present zonal land area variables (zone h)

NAP_h (t) = Net residential area, in acres
NAM_h (t) = Net manufacturing area, in acres
NAR_h (t) = Net retail area, in acres
ODA_h (t) = Other development area, in acres
DA_h (t) = Developable area, in acres
UA_h (t) = Total used area = $NAP_h(t) + NAM_h$ $(t) + NAR_h$ $(t) + ODA_h$ (t)
GA_h (t) = Gross area = UA_h $(t) + DA_h$ (t)

*The letters S.I.C. stand for the Standard Industrial Classification of land use activity taken from: Bureau of the Budget, *Standard Industrial Classification Manual*, U.S. Government Printing Office, Washington, D.C., 1957.

   3. Past, present, and proposed municipal services such as sewage disposal, water supply, and educational facilities; and, from exogenous models

   4. Projected future *regional* land use totals

To incorporate all of these variables, a model necessarily must be complex, yet from a practical standpoint it must be both easy to understand and capable of being put into operation immediately.

A good example of a model that fits these criteria is the EMPIRIC land use model [5.5], which has been employed successfully in the Eastern Massachusetts region. This particular model utilizes as its inputs most of the present (time t) and projected or proposed future (time $t + 1$) variables listed above. Referring to Tables 5.20 through 5.22, we see that land use variables for each zone h, $V_{ih}(t)$, are expressed in terms of number of families within different yearly income classes, number of employees in various types of employment categories, and area of land[15] devoted to different functions. The transportation system, both present and future, is represented by interzonal *travel times* by automobile and by transit, while the other municipal services, both present and future, are represented by the type of

[15] These variables, as seen in Table 5.20, are not treated as land use variables but instead are designated as "present land area variables." This definition conflicts with the usual one in that land area commonly is utilized as an indication of intensity of land use.

Table 5.21   Basic Inputs to the EMPIRIC Model

Present municipal service variables (zone h)

w_h (t) = Water supply index, ranging from 1 through 7, indicating
type of water supply service

s_h (t) = Sewage disposal index, ranging from 1 through 5, indicating
type of sewage disposal service

Present transportation system variables

TA_{gh} (t) = Travel time by automobile from zone g to h, in minutes
TT_{gh} (t) = Travel time by transit from zone g to h, in minutes

Water supply index

Code number	Type of system
1	Individual wells
2	Combination of individual wells and municipal supply
3	Municipal surface supply
4	Combination of municipal surface and ground supply
5	Municipal ground supply
6	Municipal and metropolitan district corporation supply
7	Metropolitan district corporation supply

Sewage disposal index

Code number	Type of system
1	Septic tank
2	Combination septic tanks and municipal system
3	Municipal system
4	Combination of septic tanks and/or municipal system and metropolitan district corporation system
5	Metropolitan district corporation system

water supply and sewage disposal systems in each zone. Each type is depicted by means of an index, shown in Table 5.21, which ranges from 1 to 7 for the water system and 1 to 5 for the sewage disposal system. The lower numbers correspond to the least sophisticated type of system. The final group of inputs, as displayed in Table 5.22, is a set of projected future regional land use totals, $T_j(t)$, for each of the land use variables indicated in Table 5.20.

Given the above mentioned inputs, the EMPIRIC model distributes the projected quantities of each regional land use variable into each and every zone. The result is a prediction of the number of families of different income levels and number of employees of different types in each zone, $V_{ih}(t + 1)$. Table 5.23 gives the complete list of outputs while Fig. 5.12 portrays diagrammatically these outputs along with the previously mentioned inputs.

With the large number of variables to be accounted for within the EMPIRIC model, it can be anticipated that the relationships between them would be fairly complex; and, as it turns out, they are. Furthermore, the model is complicated by several additional but necessary features:

1. The influence of travel on intraurban migration is decreased as travel time itself increases. This idea is incorporated through the creation of the terms $\exp(-B \cdot TA_{gh})$ and $\exp(-B \cdot TT_{gh})$ where B is an empirically derived coefficient depending on the type of transportation system and land use.

2. The persuasiveness of transportation is specified further by considering along with the travel time factor the amount of area in a zone devoted to certain types of development (residential, manufacturing, retail, and other) and the number of families and employees in *all other zones* who desire to profit by these developments. Taken in total, these two considerations and those in (1) imply that the effect of transportation becomes more significant when large developments in a subregion are located at short travel distances from a preponderance of families and potential employees.

Table 5.22   Basic Inputs to the EMPIRIC Model

Future municipal service variables (zone h)

$w_h(t+1)$ = Water supply index, ranging from 1 through 7, indicating type of water supply service

$s_h(t+1)$ = Sewage disposal index, ranging from 1 through 5, indicating type of sewage disposal service

Future transportation system variables

$TA_{gh}(t+1)$ = Travel time by automobile from zone g to h, in minutes

$TT_{gh}(t+1)$ = Travel time by transit from zone g to h, in minutes

Future regional land use variables, $T_i(t+1)$

$T_1(t+1)$ = Total number of families with an annual income less than \$5,000

$T_2(t+1)$ = Total number of families with an annual income between \$5,000 and \$9,999

$T_3(t+1)$ = Total number of families with an annual income between \$10,000 and \$14,999

$T_4(t+1)$ = Total number of families with an annual income equal to or greater than \$15,000

$T_5(t+1)$ = Total number of persons employed in manufacturing and construction employment

$T_6(t+1)$ = Total number of persons in wholesale, transportation, communication, utilities, and government employment

$T_7(t+1)$ = Total number of persons employed in retail employment

$T_8(t+1)$ = Total number of persons employed in service employment

$T_9(t+1)$ = Total number of persons employed in finance, insurance, and real estate employment

Table 5.23   Outputs from the EMPIRIC Model

Future zonal land use variables (zone h), V_{ih} $(t + 1)$

V_{1h} $(t + 1)$ = Number of families with an annual income less than $5,000

V_{2h} $(t + 1)$ = Number of families with an annual income between $5,000 and $9,999

V_{3h} $(t + 1)$ = Number of families with an annual income between $10,000 and $14,999

V_{4h} $(t + 1)$ = Number of families with an annual income equal to or greater than $15,000

V_{5h} $(t + 1)$ = Number of persons in manufacturing and construction employment (S.I.C. codes 15–39).

V_{6h} $(t + 1)$ = Number of persons in wholesale, transportation, communication, utilities, and government employment (S.I.C. codes 1–14, 40–50, 91–99)

V_{7h} $(t + 1)$ = Number of persons in retail employment (S.I.C. codes 52–59)

V_{8h} $(t + 1)$ = Number of persons in service employment (S.I.C. codes 70–89)

V_{9h} $(t + 1)$ = Number of persons in finance, insurance, and real estate employment (S.I.C. codes 60–67)

---

3. The water supply and sewage disposal indices also are transformed according to the total used (developed) area of the zones to which they correspond.

4. Certain "land developability" variables are defined which symbolize the extent of use of land in a zone for either residential, manufacturing, or retail use (Table 5.24).

5. The model predicts *changes* (Δ) in the zone to region *share* of the land use variables, not their actual future values. However, these changes can be converted immediately to actual values since the levels of present and future regional land use development as well as present *zonal* land use developments already are known.

The set of equations for $W_{3h}(t)$ to $W_{8h}(t)$ at the bottom of Table 5.24 is representative of the discussion in (1) and (2) above. Travel time, by both automobile and transit, is taken as an exponent of e, the base of the natural logarithms. The effect is to reduce the importance of travel time as a factor in the growth of a zone when it is located at distances which make it relatively inaccessible to most family and work trips. On the other hand, these equations have been developed in recognition of the idea that travel time is not the only determinant of accessibility.

Also relevant is (a) the extent to which a zone has been developed, thus making it attractive to tripmaking and further growth, and (b) the extent to which families and potential employees are in close proximity to the zone. Figure 5.13 depicts this situation for a given zone h surrounded by the remaining $G - 1$ zones in a

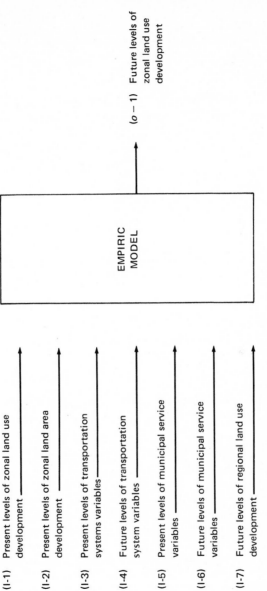

Period t inputs

Period (t + 1) outputs

(I-1) Present levels of zonal land use development

(I-2) Present levels of zonal land area development

(I-3) Present levels of transportation systems variables

(I-4) Future levels of transportation system variables

(I-5) Present levels of municipal service variables

(I-6) Future levels of municipal service variables

(I-7) Future levels of regional land use development

EMPIRIC MODEL

(o − 1) Future levels of zonal land use development

Fig. 5.12 Major inputs and outputs for the EMPIRIC land use model.

Table 5.24   Transformed Inputs to the EMPIRIC Model

Present family and employment variables, $U_{zh}(t)$

$U_{1h}(t) = V_{1h}(t) + V_{2h}(t) + V_{3h}(t) + V_{4h}(t)$ = total families
$U_{2h}(t) = V_{1h}(t) + V_{2h}(t)$ = number of families with an annual income less than \$10,000
$U_{3h}(t) = V_{3h}(t) + V_{4h}(t)$ = number of families with an annual income greater than \$10,000
$U_{4h}(t) = V_{5h}(t) + V_{6h}(t) + V_{7h}(t) + V_{8h}(t) + V_{9h}(t)$ = total employment

Present transformed variables (water and sewer)

$W_{1h}(t) = UA_h(t)\, s_h(t)$
$W_{2h}(t) = UA_h(t)\, w_h(t)$

Present transformed transportation system variables

$$W_{3h}(t) = \sum_{g=1}^{G} UA_h(t)\, U_{1g}(t)\, \exp\left[-B \cdot TA_{gh}(t)\right]$$

$$W_{4h}(t) = \sum_{g=1}^{G} UA_h(t)\, U_{4g}(t)\, \exp\left[-B \cdot TA_{gh}(t)\right]$$

$$W_{5h}(t) = \sum_{g=1}^{G} UA_h(t)\, U_{3g}(t)\, \exp\left[-B \cdot TA_{gh}(t)\right]$$

$$W_{6h}(t) = \sum_{g=1}^{G} UA_h(t)\, U_{1g}(t)\, \exp\left[-B \cdot TT_{gh}(t)\right]$$

$$W_{7h}(t) = \sum_{g=1}^{G} UA_h(t)\, U_{4g}(t)\, \exp\left(-B \cdot TT_{gh}(t)\right]$$

$$W_{8h}(t) = \sum_{g=1}^{G} UA_h(t)\, U_{2g}(t)\, \exp\left[-B \cdot TT_{gh}(t)\right]$$

---

designated region. In the equation for $W_{3h}(t)$, for example, the extent of development of zone h is represented by $UA_h(t)$, the present amount of the total used (developed) area in a zone h, whereas the availability of total families in any surrounding zone g is represented by the number of families in the zone, U_{1g}, weighted by the function of auto travel time from zone g to h, $\exp\left[-B \cdot TA_{gh}(t)\right]$.

If all of these factors are combined, terms of the form $UA_h U_{1g} \exp [-B \cdot TA_{gh}(t)]$ are obtained. These then are summed over all zones to portray the presence of availabile families in the whole region.

The resulting equation, along with others of similar form but different kinds of access (e.g., transit access of employees in zone g to opportunities in zone h), are presented in Table 5.24. Similar equations also can be seen in the top section of Table 5.25. These are referenced to the future (time $t + 1$) instead of the present (time t). The significance of the remaining equations in Tables 5.24 and 5.25 hopefully can be deduced directly from the discussion under (3) and (4) above.

As pointed out in item (5) of the preceding list, the EMPIRIC model does not predict directly the future zonal levels of each land use variable, $V_{ih}(t + 1)$, but instead predicts *changes in the zone to region share* of the variable. Each $V_{ih}(t + 1)$ then can be extracted from this share. For example, the share presently held by zone 1 of the families in the region whose income is less than \$5,000 is

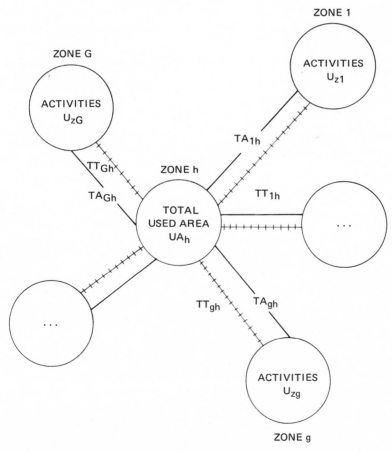

Fig. 5.13 Accessibility of zone h as related to the other zones in the region.

$$R_{11} = \frac{V_{11}(t)}{\sum\limits_{h=1}^{H} V_{1h}(t)} \tag{5.42}$$

where $R_{11}(t)$ = the share of the regional level of land use variable 1 (families with income less than \$5,000) presently held by zone 1

Table 5.25 Transformed Inputs to the EMPIRIC Model

Future transformed variables (water and sewer)

$W_{1h}(t+1) = UA_h(t) s_h(t+1)$
$W_{2h}(t+1) = UA_h(t) w_h(t+1)$

Future transformed transportation system variables

$$W_{3h}(t+1) = \sum_{g=1}^{G} UA_h(t) U_{1g}(t) \exp\left[-B \cdot TA_{gh}(t+1)\right]$$

$$W_{4h}(t+1) = \sum_{g=1}^{G} UA_h(t) U_{4g}(t) \exp\left[-B \cdot TA_{gh}(t+1)\right]$$

$$W_{5h}(t+1) = \sum_{g=1}^{G} UA_h(t) U_{3g}(t) \exp\left[-B \cdot TA_{gh}(t+1)\right]$$

$$W_{6h}(t+1) = \sum_{g=1}^{G} UA_h(t) U_{1g}(t) \exp\left[-B \cdot TT_{gh}(t+1)\right]$$

$$W_{7h}(t+1) = \sum_{g=1}^{G} UA_h(t) U_{4g}(t) \exp\left[-B \cdot TT_{gh}(t+1)\right]$$

$$W_{8h}(t+1) = \sum_{g=1}^{G} UA_h(t) U_{2g}(t) \exp\left[-B \cdot TT_{gh}(t+1)\right]$$

Land developability variables, $L_{jh}(t)$

$L_{1h}(t) = NAP_h(t) [GA_h(t) - UA_h(t)] / GA_h(t)$
$L_{2h}(t) = NAM_h(t) [GA_h(t) - UA_h(t)] / GA_h(t)$
$L_{3h}(t) = NAR_h(t) [GA_h(t) - UA_h(t)] / GA_h(t)$

$V_{11}(t)$ = the present level of land use variable 1 in zone 1, and
$\qquad$ H = the total number of zones in the region ($=G$).

The denominator represents the present total of the particular land use variable in the region. A general form of Eq. (5.42) then can be presented as

$$R_{ih}(t) \ = \ \frac{V_{ih}(t)}{\displaystyle\sum_{h=1}^{H} V_{ih}(t)} \tag{5.43}$$

For the future year, the share $R_{ih}(t+1)$ is denoted by

$$R_{ih}(t+1) \ = \ \frac{V_{ih}(t+1)}{T_i(t+1)} \tag{5.44}$$

where $V_{ih}(t+1)$ is the future level of land use variable i in zone h and $T_i(t)$ is the projected regional level of land use variable i. Thus, the *change in the share* from the present to the future, ΔR_{ih}, is

$$\Delta R_{ih} \ = \ \frac{V_{ih}(t+1)}{T_i(t+1)} \ - \ \frac{V_{ih}(t)}{\displaystyle\sum_{h=1}^{H} V_{ih}(t)} \tag{5.45}$$

As mentioned, the EMPIRIC model predicts the ΔR_{ih}'s not the $V_{ih}(t+1)$'s so that, given the former values, the latter ones can be calculated through a rearranged version of Eq. (5.45)

$$V_{ih}(t+1) \ = \ \left[\Delta R_{ih} \ + \ \frac{V_{ih}(t)}{\displaystyle\sum_{h=1}^{H} V_{ih}(t)} \right] T_i(t+1) \tag{5.46}$$

The other transformed input variables also are represented as shares or changes in shares in the EMPIRIC model, leading to the defining equations

$$Z_{kh}(t) \ = \ \frac{W_{kh}(t)}{\displaystyle\sum_{h=1}^{H} W_{kh}(t)} \tag{5.47}$$

$$Z_{kh}(t+1) = \frac{W_{kh}(t+1)}{\displaystyle\sum_{h=1}^{h} W_{kh}(t+1)} \tag{5.48}$$

$$\Delta Z_{kh} = Z_{kh}(t+1) - Z_{kh}(t) \tag{5.49}$$

and

$$M_{jh}(t) = \frac{L_{jh}(t)}{\displaystyle\sum_{h=1}^{H} L_{jh}(t)} \tag{5.50}$$

where $Z_{kh}(t)$ = present share of transformed variable k held by zone h
       $Z_{kh}(t+1)$ = future share of transformed variable k held by zone h
           ΔZ_{kh} = change in share of transformed variable k in zone h
         $M_{jh}(t)$ = present share of land developability variable j held by zone h
$W_{kh}(t)$, $W_{kh}(t+1)$, and $L_{jh}(t)$ are as indicated in Tables 5.24 and 5.25.

The equations comprising the EMPIRIC land use model now can be stated in the general form

$$\Delta R_{ph} = f[R_{ih}(t), \Delta R_{ih}, Z_{kh}(t), Z_{kh}(t+1), \Delta Z_{kh}, M_{jh}(t)] \tag{5.51}$$

where ΔR_{ph} is the change in share of land use variable p in zone h. As can be seen, this change is a function of the *present share* of certain land use variables in zone h; the *change in share* of certain land use variables in h; the present, future, and change in share of transportation system and other variables in zone h; and, finally, the present share of land developability variables held by h. There is an equation in the overall EMPIRIC model for each land use variable p ($p = 1, \ldots 9$) and for each zone h ($h = 1, \ldots H$), so that values for all ΔR_{ph}'s are obtained by simultaneous solution of each of the H sets of 9 equations.

The specific equations developed by the Traffic Research Corporation are shown in Table 5.26. These were derived using multiple linear regression and can be solved by hand but more easily with readily available computer programs. The reliability of the equations is fairly high. After extensive testing and development, the Traffic Research Corporation found that for a 104 zone division of the Eastern Massachusetts region the correlation coefficients were as indicated next to the respective equations in Table 5.26. All of these coefficients are fairly high, which is a good sign; however, in a second test [5.37] with 453 zones, several of the correlations dropped to as low as 0.70, thus implying that when used in

Table 5.26 EMPIRIC Land Use Model Equations *

Equation 1: $\Delta R_{1h} = .637\,\Delta R_{2h} - .295\,\Delta R_{3h} + .018\,\Delta R_{8h} + .133\,R_{1h}\,(t)$
$- .109\,R_{3h}\,(t) + .044\,Z_{2h}\,(t) - .298\,\Delta Z_{4h}\,/0.05/$
$- 0.68\,Z_{4h}\,(t)\,/0.15/ \quad [r = 0.995]$

Equation 2: $\Delta R_{2h} = .530\,\Delta R_{1h} + .337\,\Delta R_{3h} + .022\,\Delta R_{7h} + .060\,\Delta R_{8h}$
$- .101\,R_{2h}\,(t) + .036\,R_{8h}\,(t) + .044\,Z_{1h}\,(t+1)$
$+ .025\,M_{1h}\,(t) + .302\,\Delta Z_{4h}\,/0.05/ + .114\,\Delta Z_{6h}\,/0.005/$
$[r = 0.976]$

Equation 3: $\Delta R_{3h} = -.125\,\Delta R_{1h} + .627\,\Delta R_{2h} + .294\,\Delta R_{4h} - .224\,R_{3h}\,(t)$
$+ .196\,Z_{1h}\,(t) + .145\,\Delta Z_{1h} \quad [r = 0.957]$

Equation 4: $\Delta R_{4h} = -.282\,\Delta R_{2h} + .603\,\Delta R_{3h} - .278\,R_{4h}\,(t) + .145\,Z_{2h}\,(t)$
$+ .118\,Z_{1h}\,(t) + .046\,M_{1h}\,(t) - .384\,\Delta Z_{5h}\,/0.15/$
$+ .093\,\Delta Z_{7h}\,/0.15/ \quad [r = 0.963]$

Equation 5: $\Delta R_{5h} = .220\,\Delta R_{6h} - .302\,R_{5h}\,(t) - .015\,R_{9h}\,(t) + .138\,M_{2h}\,(t)$
$+ .278\,\Delta Z_{8h}\,/0.05/ + .121\,Z_{3h}\,(t)\,/0.05/ \quad [r = 0.930]$

Equation 6: $\Delta R_{6h} = .456\,\Delta R_{5h} + .081\,\Delta R_{7h} - .132\,\Delta R_{9h} + .106\,R_{5h}\,(t)$
$- .194\,R_{6h}\,(t) - .144\,\Delta Z_{4h}\,/0.15/ + .095\,Z_{6h}\,(t)\,/0.05/$
$[r = 0.987]$

Equation 7: $\Delta R_{7h} = .440\,\Delta R_{6h} - .117\,R_{4h}\,(t) + .126\,R_{6h}\,(t) - .363\,R_{7h}\,(t)$
$+ .165\,M_{3h}\,(t) + .213\,\Delta Z_{3h}\,/0.15/ + .064\,Z_{6h}\,(t)\,/0.05/$
$[r = 0.975]$

Equation 8: $\Delta R_{8h} = - .252\,\Delta R_{6h} - .510\,R_{8h}\,(t) + .022\,R_{9h}\,(t) + .620\,\Delta Z_{2h}$
$+ .240\,\Delta Z_{1h} + .564\,\Delta Z_{6h}\,/0.15/ + .390\,Z_{3h}\,(t)\,/0.05/$
$[r = 0.939]$

Equation 9: $\Delta R_{9h} = - .614\,\Delta R_{6h} + .020\,R_{8h}\,(t) - .159\,R_{9h}\,(t) + .110\,Z_{6h}\,(t)\,/0.05/$
$[r = 0.999]$

---

*The numbers between the slash (/ /) marks are the values of B in the particular expression.
Source: [5.37].

conjunction with a study area containing over 200 zones, the EMPIRIC model should be applied with caution and results checked for reasonableness against other available estimates.

5.3.3 Example Application of the EMPIRIC Model

Finding a simple example to demonstrate the use of the EMPIRIC model is difficult due to the complexity of the model. Certainly, it would not be feasible to show the simultaneous solutions of the 9 linear equations for each zone. Consequently, we will present the inputs for a small, semihypothetical example problem and then give the outputs without showing any of the multitude of intermediate calculations.

The example involves six zones from the eastern Massachusetts region pictured in Fig. 5.14. Data for each of these zones are presented in Table 5.27. These have been taken for the most part from *1960 Census* reports. Other data not available from the *Census* have been obtained from highway and United States Geological Survey maps and, when no information was readily available, from educated guesswork. The future levels of *regional* land use development, shown in Table 5.28, were calculated simply by extrapolating from past trends[16] in the Eastern Massachusetts area. Interzonal auto and transit travel times were assumed to be as shown in Table 5.29, and for simplicity, all *B* values (Tables 5.24 and 5.25) were set at 0.10. No changes were made from present to future transit times and auto travel times were altered only in four cases (pairs 1 to 1, 1 to 2, 1 to 4, and 1 to 6). These few changes had the effect of making zone 1 (Boston) more accessible.

For comparison's sake, the EMPIRIC model actually was employed twice, once in conjunction with the four highway improvements listed above and again when there were no changes from the present highway system. The outcomes of these two applications, shown in Table 5.30, provide interesting, and perhaps somewhat counterintuitive results. First, it might be expected that in the case where auto travel times related to Boston (zone 1) were decreased, there would be greater growth, comparatively speaking, in Boston than in the other zones. As it turns out, there is only a negligible increase: 442,754 families and employees with the improvements versus 436,310 in the case without the improvements. Similarly, we might expect large gains in zone 6 (Stoneham) since the link from there to Boston is improved considerably. But again the difference is negligible: 17,817 versus 17,461. Thus, it appears that in the example situation outlined here, the influence of certain transportation changes is minimal.

One important feature of the model which should be noted is that it does not necessarily give predictions of individual zonal land use variables which, when totaled for all zones, equal the corresponding exogenously projected future values. A comparison of the last two columns in Table 5.28 shows this clearly. The discrepancies usually are not great, but in one case in the example situation, $T_7(t+1)$,

---

[16] Actual methods for making predictions of this sort are presented in the next section of this chapter.

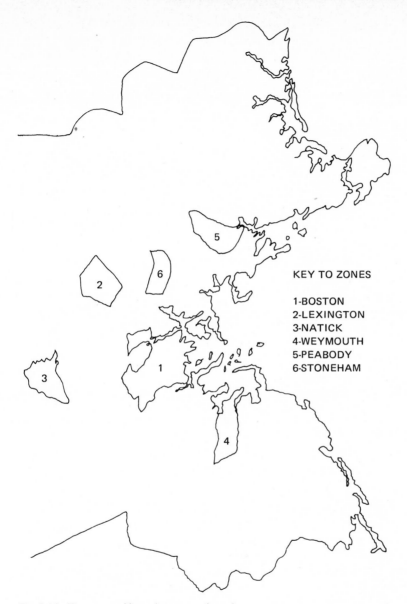

Fig. 5.14   The eastern Massachusetts study region.

the difference was too large to ignore. The presence of such large differences might be thought of as detrimental to the validity of the model, and this is true to some extent. On the other hand, these differences also might point to unsuitable input data. This is a strong possibility in this example since some of the data were obtained through "educated" guesswork, so that we should not expect overly accurate outputs as a result.

Table 5.27 1960 Land Use Data, Land Area Data, and Water Supply and Sewage Disposal Indices

	Zone					
Var.	1	2	3	4	5	6
V_{1h}	63,946	817	1,259	2,505	2,148	956
V_{2h}	77,955	2,976	3,936	7,106	5,026	2,614
V_{3h}	16,869	1,662	1,392	1,821	950	715
V_{4h}	5,445	1,094	531	422	344	197
V_{sh}	82,716	3,092	3,523	6,405	6,200	2,609
V_{6h}	77,294	1,736	2,086	3,523	2,016	1,428
V_{7h}	41,793	1,145	2,087	2,670	2,080	964
V_{8h}	59,191	2,550	2,595	2,814	1,888	1,389
V_{9h}	18,224	587	612	1,046	401	443
GA_h	32,563	11,673	10,956	11,878	11,776	4,403
UA_h	29,306	4,669	4,382	3,563	5,888	2,201
DA_h	1,628	4,669	4,382	4,751	3,532	1,320
ODA_h	1,628	2,335	2,191	3,563	2,366	882
NAP_h	11,608	1,301	1,226	997	1,648	616
NAM_h	1,887	263	274	200	332	124
NAR_h	973	123	110	94	156	58
W_h	7	5	5	4	5	5
S_h	5	3	4	3	4	4

5.3.4 Comments on the EMPIRIC Model

As can be seen from the preceding example, the EMPIRIC model can be quite complicated. This is not unexpected, however, seeing that the urban area or region being modeled also is extremely complicated in nature. But the major problem still remains—most people and many professionals do not have the mathematical capabilities to understand, much less apply, a model like EMPIRIC.

Table 5.28 Projections of Future (1970) Levels of Regional Land Use Development

Land use variable	Present level	Projected level	
$T_1 (t + 1)$	71,631	77,832	families
$T_2 (t + 1)$	99,613	129,721	families
$T_3 (t + 1)$	23,409	36,322	families
$T_4 (t + 1)$	8,033	15,566	families
$T_5 (t + 1)$	104,545	108,262	employees
$T_6 (t + 1)$	88,083	90,686	employees
$T_7 (t + 1)$	50,739	47,775	employees
$T_8 (t + 1)$	70,427	94,647	employees
$T_9 (t + 1)$	21,313	25,726	employees

Despite its complexity, EMPIRIC still has many theoretical difficulties which, in comparison to the ideal, leaves much to be desired. First is the question of the time period involved. EMPIRIC usually would be calibrated over a 5 to 10 year period and then employed recursively for forecasting up to 20 years into the future. Such forecasts should be suspect since the forecast period is greater than the calibration

**Table 5.29   Interzonal Travel Times
By Automobile and Transit (min)**

Zonal pair	Present auto travel times	Present transit travel times	Future auto travel times	Future transit travel times
1-1	15	15	10	15
1-2	25	25	20	25
1-3	25	25	25	25
1-4	20	20	14	20
1-5	45	45	45	45
1-6	20	20	10	20
2-1	25	25	25	25
2-2	6	6	6	6
2-3	25	25	25	25
2-4	60	60	60	60
2-5	30	30	30	30
2-6	12	12	12	12
3-1	25	25	25	25
3-2	25	25	25	25
3-3	5	5	5	5
3-4	40	40	40	40
3-5	45	45	45	45
3-6	30	30	30	30
4-1	20	20	20	20
4-2	60	60	60	60
4-3	40	40	40	40
4-4	6	6	6	6
4-5	52	52	52	52
4-6	40	40	40	40
5-1	45	45	45	45
5-2	30	30	30	30
5-3	45	45	45	45
5-4	52	52	52	52
5-5	6	6	6	6
5-6	15	15	15	15
6-1	20	20	20	20
6-2	12	12	12	12
6-3	30	30	30	30
6-4	40	40	40	40
6-5	15	15	15	15
6-6	6	6	6	6

Table 5.30 1970 Land Use Levels Resulting from Highway Improvements, and 1970 Land Use Levels with No Highway Improvements

Var.	Zone 1	2	3	4	5	6	Total	Projected
With highway improvements								
V_{1h}	68,751	938	1,424	2,501	2,841	1,045	77,460	77,832
V_{2h}	94,340	4,413	6,417	8,505	9,601	3,554	126,830	129,721
V_{3h}	21,467	2,809	3,030	3,039	3,178	1,445	34,968	36,322
V_{4h}	8,527	2,236	1,572	1,288	1,496	677	15,796	15,566
V_{5h}	65,351	6,968	7,260	9,152	8,210	3,941	100,882	108,262
V_{6h}	62,699	4,950	5,095	6,886	3,871	2,999	86,500	90,686
V_{7h}	23,199	1,902	2,784	2,836	2,843	1,153	34,717	47,775
V_{8h}	65,653	4,526	4,257	6,202	3,119	2,713	86,470	94,647
V_{9h}	23,767	270	315	816	207	330	25,705	25,726
Without highway improvements								
V_{1h}	69,949	683	1,183	2,094	2,722	828	77,460	77,832
V_{2h}	91,203	5,075	7,047	9,576	9,912	4,017	126,830	129,721
V_{3h}	21,333	2,813	3,053	3,111	3,188	1,470	34,968	36,322
V_{4h}	9,248	2,048	1,421	1,081	1,420	576	15,796	15,566
V_{5h}	66,562	6,703	7,015	8,748	8,089	3,763	100,882	108,262
V_{6h}	67,312	3,941	4,162	5,341	3,413	2,324	86,500	90,686
V_{7h}	23,229	1,896	2,774	2,825	2,846	1,146	34,717	47,775
V_{8h}	64,440	4,791	4,502	6,606	3,239	2,890	86,470	94,647
V_{9h}	22,964	446	478	1,083	287	447	25,705	25,726

period. Then too, one must always be suspicious of the input data to the calibration phase since they are quite numerous, somewhat expensive to collect, and subject to some error of measurement and/or interpretation.

Another theoretical question concerns the linearity of the relationships in EMPIRIC. While certain basic variables have been transformed in a nonlinear fashion (Table 5.25), the overall model has linear relationships between the transformed variables. There really is no theoretical justification for this type of relationship, but easy-to-use methods for nonlinear simultaneous regression are not presently available. This situation leads us to be suspicious of the parameters in EMPIRIC, especially if (1) they are assumed to hold constant for 20 years into the future, and (2) they are employed in a situation where the model might inadvertently be utilized outside of the range of the variables with which it was calibrated.

A final difficulty with EMPIRIC is the uncertainty associated with the input variables, including those not actually employed in the model. As far as the *actual* inputs are concerned, many have to be forecast themselves: future highways and transit travel times, water and sewer facilities, and regional population and employment. There thus is some question about possible forecast errors in the input variables which may be reflected in errors in the EMPIRIC model outputs.

The second part of the difficulty—uncertainty with variables *not* employed in EMPIRIC—is, we feel, most serious. There are so many factors that can affect land use development that it is almost impossible to include all of them in *any* model. These factors range from "too small closets in a house" (thereby inducing people to move) to "excessive national capital gains taxes" for industry. Between are a variety of factors including changes in attitudes toward environmental preservation, development, and subsidy of complete new towns in a region, and changes in sewage treatment technology (e.g., complete in-house recycling of wastes). EMPIRIC, like any land use model, thus must be utilized with a significant amount of judgment on the part of many persons, including those familiar both with land use modeling and with the geographic area being modeled.

5.4 MODELS OF REGIONAL POPULATION AND EMPLOYMENT GROWTH

In this section we will be concerned with models by which future *regional* land use can be forecasted so as to be employed in a land use model similar to that just described. The discussion here will be brief, however, since these types of models usually fall within the domain of demographers and economists.

5.4.1 Regional Population Models

Population projections have been the center of attention of researchers for many years. This emphasis has been due to the integral part such projections play in any planning endeavor, be it urban, corporate, or even defense. Prime among the techniques available are the three to be discussed here. They are:

1. Extrapolation
2. Gompertz or logistics curves
3. Growth composition analyses[17]

5.4.1.1 Extrapolation of population The extrapolation technique, simply stated, is one in which a line is extended from past data points into the future and the population for the future period is found by "reading" the value for the particular year in question. Figure 5.15 indicates such a procedure. Data have been taken from past *Census* studies, a hand drawn smooth line has been created and extrapolated into the future, and the population for 1990 calculated. This line need not be linear nor must it always be hand drawn. Regression often has been used to establish the relationship between population and time.

Difficulties with the extrapolation technique are many. Most important, underlying causal factors, essentially covered over by this crude model, may change considerably, thereby creating entirely different growth rates. An example of this

[17] See [5.1] and [5.4] for detailed discussions of these and other techniques.

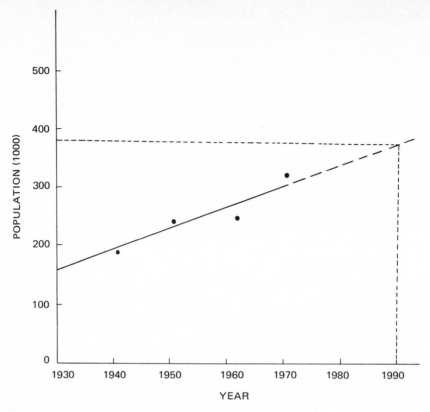

Fig. 5.15 Extrapolation of population from 1970 to 1990.

kind of situation would be the construction of a large manufacturing plant in an area previously lacking substantial employment opportunities. People would tend to accumulate in nearby residential areas and thus increase the population of these areas.

5.4.1.2 Gompertz or logistics curves Another difficulty with extrapolation is that the potential maximum growth limit of a region is not taken into account. The Gompertz Curve technique eliminates this problem by considering population growth to start out slowly, building cautiously on a small base, then increasing fairly rapidly, and finally slowing down again as the maximum population that a region can "hold" is approached. The result is an S-shaped curve of population growth over time whose general form is

$$P_{t + \theta} = ka^{b\theta} \tag{5.52}$$

where $P_{t + \theta}$ is the population at a time θ years from the present time (t) and k, a, and b all are parameters whose values are established through some kind of curve fitting procedure (like regression) utilizing past data.

A similar model of population growth is that of the logistic curve whose formula is

$$P_{t+\theta} = \frac{k}{1 + e^{a+b\theta}} \tag{5.53}$$

where $P_{t+\theta}$ k, a, and b are the same as in Eq. (5.52) and e is the base of the natural logarithms. Both of these models have been used quite extensively, but they suffer from the same drawback as the extrapolation technique—no underlying causal factors are identified, and these, if significant, may lead to large, unexpected changes.

5.4.1.3 Growth composition analysis To help reduce the above-mentioned deficiencies in population growth models, several analysts have employed models that include four important variables: births, deaths, in-migration, and out-migration. The equation for this model is

$$P_{t+\theta} = P_t + B_\theta - D_\theta + I_\theta - O_\theta \tag{5.54}$$

where P_t = the present (time t) population
B_θ = the births during period θ
D_θ = the deaths during period θ
I_θ = the in-migration during period θ
O_θ = the out-migration during period θ

A basic need for a model such as Eq. (5.54) is to have estimates of B_θ, D_θ, I_θ, and O_θ for the upcoming period θ. To obtain such information requires that projections of these values be available and also reliable, a situation which brings us back to the extrapolation technique as a necessary tool for all predictions. In other words, somewhere in the prediction process we eventually must rely on some sort of extrapolation into the future.

5.4.2 Regional Employment Models

Also required as input to most land use models is the future number of persons falling in certain employment categories. Usually, although not always, these inputs are obtained through models which relate future employment to future population, present employment, and interindustry production and consumption relations, which are assumed to hold constant into the future. The input-output model [5.4] is representative of this kind of concept.

5.4.2.1 The regional input-output model This type of model relies heavily on data concerning the amount of money spent by an industry in a region for goods and services from other industries in the region. As an example, consider the purchases and sales in Table 5.31 by two industries which, for simplicity, are assumed to be the only ones in a region, that is, with the exception of the households in the region, which also purchase industry goods, like food and furniture, for final consumption. The values in each row of Table 5.31 actually correspond to an equation of the form

$$X_i - x_{i1} - x_{i2} = Y_i \quad \text{(all } i)\tag{5.55}$$

where X_i = the gross output of industry i
$\quad x_{i1}$ = sales of industry i to industry 1 (agriculture)
$\quad x_{i2}$ = sales of industry i to industry 2 (manufacturing)
$\quad Y_i$ = final (household) demand for outputs of industry i

Thus, for row one we have equalities $10 - 5 - 3 = 2$ and for row two: $9 - 4 - 1 = 4$. Now, excluding the final demands, let us divide each x_{ij} by X_j to determine the *percentage* of goods purchased by industry i from industry j, a_{ij}. Thus

$$x_{ij} = a_{ij} X_j \tag{5.56}$$

which leads to the set of production coefficients displayed in Table 5.32.

Now assume that the final demand by households for goods and services is known, estimated perhaps on the basis of future population and average household income projections. All other variables in Eq. (5.55) are to be predicted. Thus, there are six unknowns: x_{11}, x_{12}, x_1, x_{21}, x_{22}, and x_2, and there also are six equations

$$X_1 - x_{11} - x_{12} = Y_1 \tag{5.57}$$

$$X_2 - x_{21} - x_{22} = Y_2 \tag{5.58}$$

$$x_{11} = a_{11} X_1 \tag{5.59}$$

$$x_{12} = a_{12} X_1 \tag{5.60}$$

$$x_{21} = a_{21} X_1 \tag{5.61}$$

and

$$x_{22} = a_{22} X_2 \tag{5.62}$$

Table 5.31   Input–Output Matrix (Dollar's Worth of Products)

From	To			
	Agri-culture	Manu-facturing	Final demand	Total
Agriculture	5	3	2	10
Manufacturing	4	1	4	9
Total	9	4	6	19

**Table 5.32 Input–Output Production
Coefficient Matrix**

	To	
From	Agri- culture	Manu- facturing
Agriculture	0.50	0.33
Manufacturing	0.40	0.11

If Y_1 = \$4 × 10^6, Y_2 = \$6 × 10^6, and the a_{ij}'s are as in Table 5.32, we can solve Eq. (5.17) to (5.22) simultaneously by inserting the equalities (5.59) through (5.62) where needed in the first two equations and get

$$X_1 - 0.50\,X_1 - 0.33\,X_2 = 4 \tag{5.63}$$

and

$$X_2 - 0.40\,X_1 - 0.11\,X_2 = 6 \tag{5.64}$$

which lead to X_1 = \$17.82 × 10^6, X_2 = \$14.74 × 10^6, x_{11} = \$8.91 × 10^6, x_{12} = \$4.91 × 10^6, x_{21} = \$7.12 × 10^6, and x_{22} = \$1.62 × 10^6.

We thus have found the gross output of each industry at some given future point in time. What remains to be done is to use either some present or extrapolated ratio of employees/dollars of gross output, r_i, to obtain the number of employees. For instance, if at present r_1 = 2 × 10^{-4} employees/dollar of gross output and r_2 = 1 × 10^{-4} employees/dollar of gross output, the future number of employees in agriculture will be $r_1 X_1$ = (2 × 10^{-4}) (4.49 × 10^6) = 2,212 and in manufacturing (1 × 10^{-4}) (4.49 × 10^6) = 449.

5.4.2.2 Comments on input-output models Several comments should be made about the advantages and disadvantages of an Input-Output model:

1. It can be expanded to take care of any number or different categories of industry so that it could be easily adapted to producing employment inputs for a land use model like EMPIRIC.
2. Data on sales and purchases of many industries often are difficult to find.
3. Production coefficients and ratios of employment to gross output may not be constant over time due to technological, union, management, and governmental changes.
4. No account is made of trade with industries outside the region (although such input-output models have been developed).
5. The complexity of the model is such that most studies probably would be willing to sacrifice reliability to get predictions in a quicker and less expensive manner.

5.5 SUMMARY

In this chapter an attempt has been made to demonstrate three basic categories of models: (a) those showing the interrelationship between transportation system performance characteristics; (b) those showing how land use develops in various parts of an urban area; and (c) those showing how regional population and employment grows (or shrinks). Several types of models were discussed relevant to the first category. These included models for acceleration and deceleration of a vehicle, traffic stream relationships, capacity, and transportation system costs.

These models provided inputs to the land use modeling process, category (b) above. Land use was viewed as being affected in a very complicated way, not only by the transportation system characteristics but also by present land use, water and sewer facilities, available land of different types, and by regional growth in population and employment.

Models for the latter two factors above were presented as the final part of the chapter. For regional population growth, three common models were discussed:

1. Extrapolation
2. Gompertz or logistics curves
3. Growth composition analyses

The input-output model was presented as an example of one method for predicting employment growth in a region.

The interrelationships between the phases in the modeling stage of the transportation planning process were discussed in conceptual terms in the beginning of the chapter. It can be seen, however, that many of the models are fairly complex and that it would be difficult to interrelate them in a real world situation.

BIBLIOGRAPHY

5.1 U.S. Department of Commerce, Bureau of Public Roads, Urban Planning Division: *The Role of Economic Studies in Urban Transportation Planning*, U.S. Government Printing Office, Washington, D.C., August, 1965.

5.2 U.S. Department of Commerce, Bureau of Public Roads: *Population Forecasting Methods*, U.S. Government Printing Office, Washington, D.C., June, 1964.

5.3 Hamburg, J. R., and R. H. Sharkey: *Land Use Forecast*, Chicago Area Transportation Study, Chicago, 1961.

5.4 Isard, W.: *Methods of Regional Analysis: An Introduction to Regional Science*, M.I.T. Press, Cambridge, Mass., 1961.

5.5 Hill, D. M., D. Brand, and W. B. Hansen: "Prototype Development of a Statistical Land Use Prediction Model for the Greater Boston Region," *Highway Research Board Record* 114, 1966.

5.6 Irwin, N. A.: "Review of Existing Land Use Forecasting Techniques," *Highway Research Board Record* 88, 1965.

5.7 Horwood, E. M., C. A. Zellner, and R. L. Ludwig: *Community Consequences of Highway Improvement*, NCHRP Report 18, Highway Research Board, Washington, D.C., 1965.

5.8 Highway Research Board: *Urban Development Models*, Special Report 97, Washington, D.C., 1968.

5.9 CONSAD Research Corp.: *Impact Studies: Northeast Corridor Transportation Project*, vol. II, Federal Clearinghouse, PB 177 611, Springfield, Va., January, 1968.

5.10 Bureau of Public Roads, Dept. of Commerce: *The Role of Economic Studies in Urban Transportation Planning*, U.S. Government Printing Office, Washington, D.C., August, 1965.

5.11 Goodman, W. I., and E. C. Freund (eds.): *Principles and Practice of Urban Planning*, International City Managers Association, Washington, D.C., 1968.

5.12 Chapin, F. S., Jr.: *Urban Land Use Planning*, University of Illinois Press, (2d ed.), Champaign–Urbana, Ill., 1965.

5.13 Institute of Traffic Engineers: *Capacities and Limitations of Urban Transportation Modes*, Washington, D.C., May, 1965.

5.14 Wohl, M., and B. V. Martin: *Traffic System Analysis for Engineers and Planners*, McGraw-Hill, New York, 1967.

5.15 Highway Research Board: *Highway Capacity Manual–1965*, Special Report 87, Washington, D.C., 1965.

5.16 Wohl, M.: "Costs of Urban Transport Systems of Varying Capacity and Service," *Highway Research Record* 64, 1965.

5.17 Drew, D. R.: *Traffic Flow Theory and Control*, McGraw-Hill, New York, 1968.

5.18 Lang, A. S., and R. M. Soberman: *Urban Rail Transit; Its Economics and Technology*, M.I.T. Press, Cambridge, Mass., 1964.

5.19 *Chicago Area Transportation Study* (3 vols.), Chicago, 1959, 1960, 1962.

5.20 Baerwald, J. E.: *Traffic Engineering Handbook*, Institute of Traffic Engineers, Washington, D.C., 1965.

5.21 American Society of Civil Engineers, Committee on Terminals: "Terminal Planning for Future Highways," *Journal of the Highway Division*, ASCE, vol. 92, no. HW2, October, 1966.

5.22 Highway Research Board: *Measures of the Quality of Traffic Service*, Special Report 130, Washington, D.C., 1972.

5.23 Drake, J. S., J. S. Schofer, and A. D. May, Jr.: "A Statistical Analysis of Speed Density Hypotheses," *Highway Research Record* 154, Washington, D.C., 1967.

5.24 C.E.I.R., Inc.: *Final Report on Intersection Traffic Flow*, Arlington, Va., 1960.

5.25 Berry, D. S. et al.: *The Technology of Urban Transportation*, Northwestern Univ. Press, Evanston, Ill., 1963.

5.26 Wilbur Smith and Associates: *Chesapeake Mass Transportation Demonstration Project*, New Haven, Conn., January, 1969.

5.27 Meyer, J. R., J. F. Kain, and M. Wohl: *The Urban Transportation Problem*, Harvard Univ. Press, Cambridge, Mass., 1965.

5.28 Kolk, F. W., and D. R. Blundell: "Evolution and Revolution With the Jumbo Trijet," *Astronautics and Aeronautics*, vol. 6, no. 10, October, 1968.

5.29 Day and Zimmerman, Inc.: *Potential Near Term Improvements in Urban Transportation*, Federal Clearinghouse, Springfield, Va., PB 178 278, March, 1968.

5.30 Hayes, Seay, Mattern, and Mattern: *Danville Area Transportation Study*, vol. III, Roanoke, Va., 1968.

5.31 Winfrey, R.: *Economic Analysis for Highways*, International Textbook Co., Scranton, Pa., 1969.

5.32 Hall, Peter (ed.): *Land Values*, Sweet and Maxwell, London, 1965.

5.33 Whiteside, R. E.: *Parking Garage Operation*, The Eno Foundation, Saugatuck, Conn., 1961.

5.34 Urban America, Inc.: *Center City Transportation Project Workshop Reports*, Washington, D.C., 1969.

5.35 Texas Transportation Institute: *A System to Facilitate Bus Rapid Transit on Urban Freeways*, Federal Clearinghouse, Springfield, Va., PB–183390, December, 1968.

5.36 MPC Corporation: *Transit Expressway Report*, Pittsburgh, Pa., February 20, 1967.

5.37 Traffic Research Corporation: *EMPIRIC Land Use Forecasting Model, Calibration Report: 626 Traffic Zones,* Boston, December, 1966.

5.38 Traffic Research Corporation: *EMPIRIC Land Use Forecasting Model Reliability Report: 626 Traffic Zones,* Boston, January, 1967.

5.39 Barton-Aschmann Associates: *The Impact of Transportation Staging on Metropolitan Growth,* Chicago, February, 1970.

5.40 Memphis Transit Authority: *Mass Transportation Studies in Memphis,* Memphis, March, 1965.

5.41 Park, R.: "Human Ecology," *American Journal of Sociology,* vol. XLII, no. 2, July, 1936.

5.42 Hoyt, H.: *One Hundred Years of Land Values in Chicago,* Univ. of Chicago Press, Chicago, 1933.

5.43 Hoyt, H.: *The Structure and Growth of Residential Neighborhoods in American Cities,* U.S. Government Printing Office, Washington, D.C., 1939.

5.44 Burgess, E. W.: "The Growth of the City: An Introduction to a Research Project," in *The City,* R. E. Park, E. W. Burgess, and R. D. McKenzie (eds.), Univ. of Chicago Press, Chicago, 1925.

5.45 Berry, B. J. L., and F. E. Horton: *Geographic Perspectives on Urban Systems,* Prentice-Hall, Englewood Cliffs, N.J., 1970.

5.46 Rosenthal, S. R. et al.: *Projective Land Use Model—PLUM (3 vols),* Institute of Transportation and Traffic Engineering, Univ. of California, Berkeley, 1972.

5.47 Blunden, W. R.: *The Land Use/Transport System,* Pergamon Press, Oxford, England, 1971.

6 Transportation System Travel and Impact Models

The preceding chapter dealt with transportation system performance models and with methods for predicting zonal land use development after regional population and employment forecasts had been made. A review of Fig. 5.1 indicates that there are two remaining types of models to be discussed—transportation system travel and impact models. These two provide an interesting contrast for this chapter. Travel models, to be discussed in the first section, have received much attention and are highly sophisticated from a mathematical standpoint. Impact models, to be discussed in the second section, often are comparatively crude and in many cases are only descriptive in nature. It should not be inferred from this situation, however, that impacts are less important than travel. While this may have been the case in the past, recent changes in attitudes are placing an ever greater emphasis on the impacts that transportation systems have on the urban dweller and his environs.

6.1 TRAVEL ESTIMATION MODELS

The estimation of travel given information about both future levels of land use development and anticipated transportation system modifications is a task which has received a considerable amount of attention in transportation planning endeavors. Engineers and planners have gotten away from the previously common technique of estimating the future usage of a transportation system simply by projecting past trends in constant increments into the future. Now most efforts are directed toward collecting data for use in identifying the complex land use-transportation system-travel relationships alluded to above. Once these have been established, they then can be utilized for making the needed travel estimation.

Perhaps the major reason for this change in approach has been that projections could not be made for completely new facilities or for facilities passing through areas yet to be developed. In other words, for anticipated new facilities there were no past data from which trends for projections could be established. Moreover, as Kanwit, Steel, and Todd [6.27] pointed out at the time, trending often was treacherous.

To make up for deficiencies in projection techniques, transportation planners came up with two important assumptions (or hypotheses) which have formed the basis for almost all recent travel modeling efforts. These assumptions are brought out explicitly in the report of the Chicago Area Transportation Study (CATS), in which it is stated at the outset that [6.20, pp. 5, 6] : ". . . the study worked on the hypothesis that there is a measurable relationship between land use and the amount and distribution of traffic," and that: "Since land use can be predicted with some assurance, future traffic demands can also be predicted."

Figure 6.1 shows diagrams of daily trip ends and square feet of floor area by zone for the Chicago region, aptly demonstrating the existence of a correlation between the two variables. From the evidence presented, it therefore can be concluded that travel can be estimated more reliably by working through relationships with predicted future land use (and transportation system) character-istics, many of which also have to be estimated, rather than by projecting present and past travel trends directly. This conclusion provides the setting for the forthcoming discussion of travel models.

6.1.1 The Travel Estimation Process

The four general steps by which future travel patterns are determined have been presented earlier in this chapter and in Chap. 2. They are *trip generation, trip distribution, mode choice,* and *route choice* or *trip assignment.* To repeat what was said there, *trip generation* is concerned with the prediction of the number of trips per time period made to or from a given areal unit or zone (regardless of the trips' origins or destinations), *trip distribution* is concerned with finding the zones to or from which the generated trips are directed, *mode choice* is concerned with the determination of the particular mode of transportation used for the zone-to-zone trips, and *trip assignment* is concerned with the prediction of the particular route that will be selected by travelers going between each pair of zones on each mode of transport.

Figure 6.2 gives a schematic portrayal of the division of generated (produced or attracted) trips into subcategories according to zone origin and destination, mode, and route. This figure also shows the type of results desired from travel estimation models and, in a sense, provides a *definition* of *travel* or *travel patterns.* By knowing the values of all T_{ijm}'s and the time period to which they correspond, we can obtain a fairly complete description of a trip as:

> A one-way journey made within a given time period between two places (usually two areal zones, i and j) on a certain route (r) of a certain mode of transport (m).

Travel would be simply the overlay of all component types defined above. Of special interest in Fig. 6.2 is the fact that the number of trips from a given zone (i) to any other zone (j), T_{ij}, is not necessarily equal to T_{ji}. Nor for that matter is the trip production of any zone i, P_i, necessarily equal to the trip attraction, A_i, of that zone. Only over a 24-hr period is $T_{ij} = T_{ji}$ and $P_i = A_i$, and even for this interval of time, the use of equalities may not be exactly correct because of long weekend and holiday exoduses from certain localities.

In general, then, the absence of these equalities is an indication of variations and peaks in tripmaking, the most familiar of these being in the morning and evening rush hours. Since these two peaks are so distinct and sizable, they have been the source of most of the attention of transportation planners. The usual approach to predicting the amount and pattern of travel within these periods has been first to calculate average 24-hour trip volumes through the 4-step procedure shown in Fig. 6.2 on the assumption that $T_{ij} = T_{ji}$ and $P_i = A_i$ and then to multiply the resulting values by suitable peak to average ratios to obtain the peak volumes. In other words, to complete the picture of the overall travel estimation modeling process, we would need to add a further step to the form shown in Fig. 6.2. In this step, the 24-hour T_{ijmr}'s would be divided into various time period categories.

6.1.2 Trip Generation from Residences

Any trip has both an origin and a destination, or, saying this another way, a zone where it is produced and a zone where it is attracted. A common simplifying assumption is that most trips are produced at residences (home) and are attracted at nonresidences. Trip production thus is equated to residential trip generation and trip attraction to nonresidential trip generation.

The most common technique employed in establishing residential trip generation relationships is that of linear regression[1] utilizing *present* zonal tripmaking and demographic data. Used as the independent variables are such factors as total population, number of household units, average family size, average automobile ownership per household, and so forth. Figures 6.3 and 6.4 show some of the simpler relationships which have been found, while Table 6.1 gives an additional set of relationships, some of which are more complex owing to their multivariate and nonlinear nature. The correlation coefficients associated with these equations are unusually high as compared to most found in practice although the estimation of *zonal* trip generation using *averages* of dwelling unit values often is more reliable than attempting to estimate the number of trips generated by each *individual* household and then adding them.

[1] See Appendix.

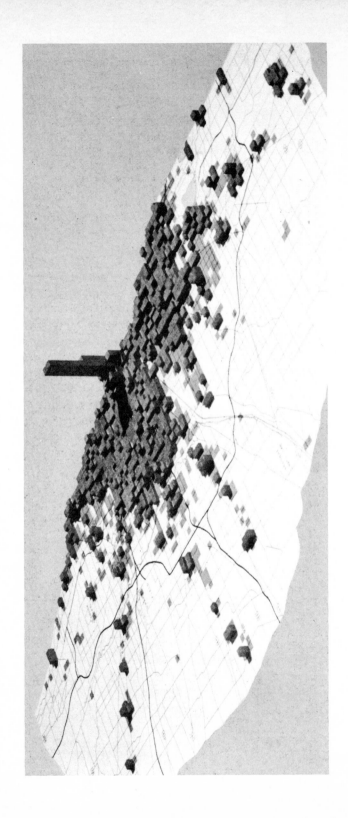

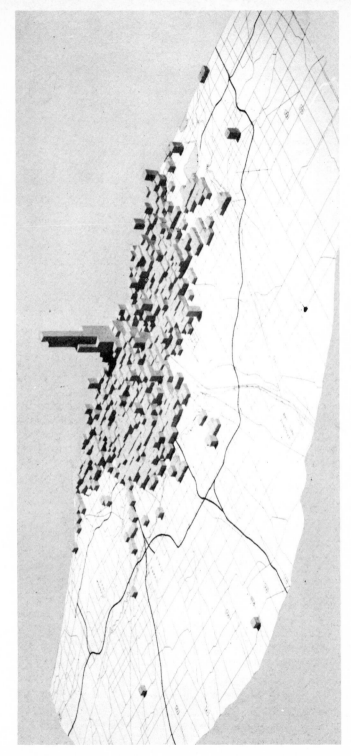

Fig. 6.1 Total person trip destinations and floor area models, Chicago, 1956. The highest block in the top model represents 144,000 trip destinations per quarter square mile. The highest in the lower model represents 32,000,000 sq ft per quarter sq mile. [6.20, pp. 23, 25].

185

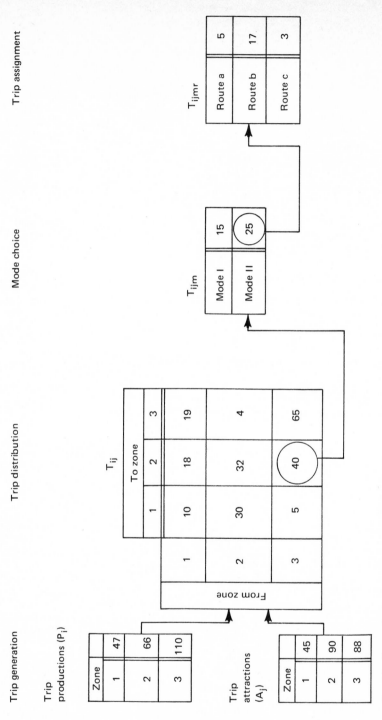

Fig. 6.2 Example of steps in the travel estimation process.

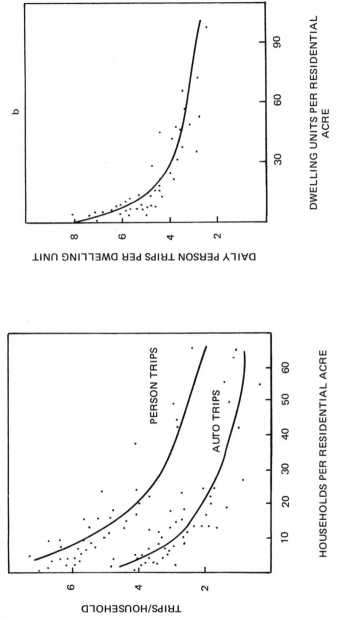

Fig. 6.3 Effect of residential density on trip production by districts: (a) Pittsburgh and (b) Washington, D.C., [6.5, p. 8].

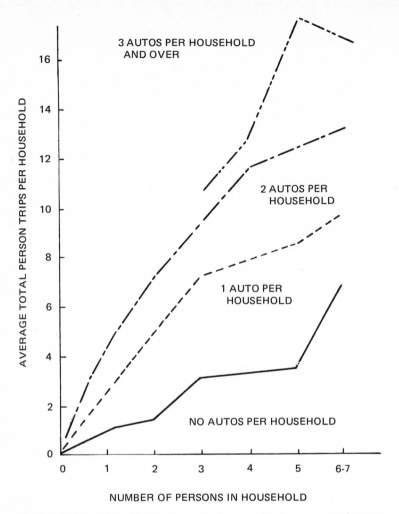

Fig. 6.4 Relationship of family size and auto ownership to average total person trips per dwelling unit. [6.5, p. 20].

As stated, the regression equations are derived using present travel and zonal characteristics. Unfortunately it often turns out that a set of equations must be found for each new study area, mainly because of the significant differences between geographic areas in travel behavior and in the manner in which zones are delineated. Yet regression techniques are easy to use (and abuse), especially with the aid of the digital computer, so that the necessity for establishing new relationships is not necessarily bothersome. What is disturbing, however, is the lack of a general forecasting model, since one is not as yet available.

After the regression equations are found, the assumption then is made that the coefficients and other parameters thus established will hold constant into the

Table 6.1 Effects of Density on Total Trip Generation: Illustrative Examples

Study	Year	Equation number	Equation*	Coefficient of correlation (r)
Between several cities:				
Future Highways and Urban Growth 1961	A		$Y_1 = 2.7 - 1.17\, x_1$	Hand fit
"Some Aspects of Future Transportation in Urban Areas" 1962	B		$Y_1 = 2.6 - 0.092\, x_6$	Hand fit
	C		$Y_1 = 2.6 - (0.092)\, x_1/x_3\,(10^{-3})$	Hand fit
Within cities:				
Detroit Area Transportation Study 1953	D		$Y_2' = 15.07 - 4.23 \log x_2$	-0.75
	E		$Y_2' = 1.87 + 4.26 \log x_4$ $-1.60 \log x_2$	0.83
"A Study of Factors Related to Urban Travel"† 1957	F		$Y_2 = 7.22 - 0.013\, x_2$	0.72
	G		$Y_2 = 4.33 + 3.89\, x_3 - 0.005\, x_2$ $-0.128\, x_4 - 0.012\, x_5$	0.84
	H		$Y_2 = 3.80 + 3.79\, x_3 - 0.0033\, x_2$	0.84
St. Louis Metropolitan Area Transportation Study 1959	I		$Y_6 = 0.261 - 0.017\, x_7$	Not cited
Chicago Area Transportation Study 1956	J		$Y_4 = 6.64 - 2.43 \log x_2$	-0.95
	K		$Y_5' = 4.32 - 1.90 \log x_2$	-0.96
	L		$Y_2 = 11.80 - 4.246 \log x_2$	-0.97
	M		$Y_3 = 7.34 - 3.29 \log x_2$	-0.96
Pittsburgh Area Transportation Study 1962	N		$Y_2 = 9.62 - 4.19 \log x_2$	-0.88
	O		$Y_3 = 5.55 - 2.64 \log x_2$	-0.91
	P		$Y_4 = 5.02 - 2.17 \log x_2$	-0.87
	Q		$Y_5 = 3.35 - 1.35 \log x_2$	-0.90

*Dependent variables:

Y_1—Total internal person-trips per capita
Y_2—Person-trips per family
Y_2'—Person-trips per dwelling place
Y_3—Auto-trips per family
Y_4—Person-destinations per dwelling place
Y_5—Auto-destinations per dwelling place
Y_5'—Vehicle-destinations per dwelling place
Y_6—School trips per person

†Independent variables:

x_1—Gross urbanized-area density
x_2—Dwelling places per residential acre
x_3—Autos per dwelling unit
x_4—Distance from CBD
x_5—Family income
x_6—(Households per car) × urbanized area population density × 10^{-3}
x_7—Thousands of people per square mile

‡*Public Roads*, vol. 29, no. 7 (April, 1957), based on Washington, D.C.

Source: Herbert S. Levinson and F. Houston Wynn, "Effects of Density on Urban Transportation Requirements," *Community Values as Affected by Transportation*, Highway Research Board, Washington, D.C., Highway Research Record, No. 2 (1963), p. 49.

future. Then by knowing the *future* values of zonal characteristics (from the land use development models), all that must be done is to insert these into the correct equation and calculate the future number of trips. For example, if Eq. H in Table 6.1 were utilized and the future (average) number of autos per dwelling unit (x_3) were 1.00, the future (average) number of dwelling places per residential acre (x_2) were 10.0, and the future total number of families in the zone were 2,000, then:

$$Y_2 = 3.80 + 3.79 \ (1.00) - 0.0033 \ (10.0) = 7.56 \text{ person trips/family}$$

and the future total number of (daily) person trips generated in the zone would be (7.56) (2,000) = 15,320.

6.1.3 Trip Generation of Nonresidences

In contrast to residential trip generation is that from nonresidences, and it is with these kinds of trips that the importance of the interrelationship between tripmaking and land use becomes most apparent. In fact, the models used for estimation of nonresidential trip generation often speciy the classification and intensity of land use activities as causal factors. Consequently, the most prevalent models are simply cross-classification summaries of *rates* of tripmaking (per acre or per square foot) for the various land use activity classes. These rates are assumed to hold constant into the future.

An example of a cross-classification scheme is given in Table 6.2 where the number of daily person trips made in the Chicago study in 1956 is divided into different categories depending on the type of land use—manufacturing, transportation, commercial, public buildings, and public open space—and distance from the

Table 6.2 1956 Person Trip Generation Rates

| Ring | Average distance from loop (mi) | Person trip destinations per acre | | | | |
		Manu- facturing	Trans- portation	Commercial	Public buildings	Public open space
0	0.0	3,544.7	273.1	2,132.2	2,013.8	98.5
1	1.5	243.2	36.9	188.7	255.5	28.8
2	3.5	80.0	15.9	122.1	123.5	26.5
3	5.5	86.9	10.8	143.3	100.7	27.8
4	8.5	50.9	12.8	212.4	77.7	13.5
5	12.5	26.8	5.8	178.7	58.1	6.1
6	16.0	15.7	2.6	132.5	46.6	2.5
7	24.0	18.2	6.4	131.9	14.4	1.5
Average for study area		49.4	8.6	181.4	52.8	4.2

Source: [6.5, p. 16] .

loop, the central business district (CBD) of Chicago. Each trip total within the table subsequently is divided by the number of acres of ground area of the respective land use in the ring of territory whose average distance from the CBD is as indicated. The result of this procedure is a rate which in this case is specified in terms of daily person trip destinations per acre of ground area. When assumed to hold constant into the future, each of these rates can be employed in conjunction with exogeneously predicted land acreage figures (at the given distance from the CBD) to give the future quantity of trip destinations.

As an example of the use of these models[2] for prediction of nonresidential trip generation, consider the rate in Table 6.2 of 132.5 person trips per acre for commercial land uses lying at a distance of between 14 and 20 miles from the CBD. It may be that for a time 20 years hence, land use model predictions may have indicated a growth from 150 to 350 acres in this category, thereby giving an expected increase in trip generation from 132.5 (150) = 19,875 daily person trips to 132.5 (300) = 39,750 daily person trips.

The greatest advantage of the cross-classification estimation technique is its simplicity. Yet this simplicity can be misleading and often is achieved at the price of accuracy. It can be misleading in that, in most cases, no measure of *variability* in trip generation rates for different parcels within each cross-classification is presented along with the rate. The result is that this variability, which often is substantial [6.5], is reflected in the variability (lack of reliability) in the resultant predictions. To obtain more exact estimates, then, requires more complex models.

The most common way for obtaining greater reliability is by combining regression and cross-classification, that is, by establishing a regression equation within each and every class. Illustrations of this technique can be seen in Table 6.3 where regression equation models have been established within each of several manufacturing subclasses (regardless of distance from CBD). The numbers in the second, third, and fourth columns represent the parameters from the general model

$$Y_{ij} = b_{1j}X_{1ij} + b_{2j}X_{2ij} + a_j \tag{6.1}$$

where Y_{ij} = total daily person trips to land use j in zone i
$\quad\quad X_{1ij}$ = floor area of land use j in zone i
$\quad\quad X_{2ij}$ = number of employees associated with land use j in zone i

The correlation coefficients corresponding to each subclass model are presented along with the parameters and appear to be fairly high, thus providing the analyst with the satisfaction of knowing that his models are reliable, at least if used to estimate present trip generation. Nonetheless, for prediction of trips to be made at some distant time in the future, possibly 20 years hence, he will have to accept the assumption, made also in residential trip generation models, that the parameters will be the same at that future date. At that time the number of daily person trips

---

[2] Simple as these rates may be, they still are "models" in the sense of the definition in Chap. 2.

Table 6.3   Total Person Trips vs Floor Area and Employment*

Land use (j)	a_j	Floor area (b_{1j})	Employment (b_{2j})	r^2
Food and kindred products	17	−0.003	1.24	0.959
Tobacco manufacturers	−5	−0.001	1.14	0.998
Textile mill products	53	0.005	1.05	0.959
Apparel	−8	0.003	1.12	0.994
Lumber	5	0.009	1.21	0.997
Furniture and fixtures	303	0.034	0.77	0.889
Paper	63	0.220	1.08	0.996
Printing	53	−0.001	1.08	0.961
Chemicals	−101	0.209	0.50	0.822
Petroleum refining	51	0.019	1.04	0.993
Rubber and plastics	47	−0.021	1.24	0.986
Leather products	18	0.053	0.57	0.914
Stone, clay, and brass	−3	0.000	1.25	0.972
Primary metals	48	0.044	0.96	0.999
Fabricated metals	−35	0.017	1.09	0.998
Mechanical machinery	−23	0.012	1.17	0.997
Electrical machinery	−47	0.038	1.00	0.989
Transportation equipment	13	0.002	1.37	0.947
Scientific instruments	−1	0.031	1.10	0.990
Miscellaneous manufacturing	67	0.023	1.01	0.913

*Data derived from *Chicago Area Transportation Study*.
Source: Table partially restructured from [6.21, p. 121] .

to, say, apparel manufacturing plants in a zone with 50 apparel employees and 40,000 sq ft of apparel floor area would be predicted as

$$Y = 0.003 \,(40{,}000) + 1.12 \,(50) - 8 = 168 \text{ person trips/day}$$

Table 6.4 shows variables used in modeling efforts in several other planning studies where the classification was based on the *purpose* of the nonresidential trips rather than on the land use activity category and distance from the CBD. The variety of entries in this table emphasizes the differences in tripmaking between cities: differences which, as was mentioned under residential generation, point to the need for distinct models for each individual study area.

In making parallel determinations of residential and nonresidential trip generation, it may turn out that the region-wide totals of each may not be equivalent, or at least nearly equivalent. This type of occurrence obviously is indicative of unreliable models and can be corrected only by developing better predictive relationships. What is to be stressed at this point, however, is that these two totals can and should provide controls by which the accuracies of the two different sets of models can be judged. It might also be noted here that many trip

Table 6.4 Factors Used to Estimate Trip Attractions

Study Year-pop.	Home-based Work	Shop	Soc.-rec.	Other	Special	Non-home based	Trucks
Washington, D.C. 1963-2,900,000	E	S_R	S_R,DU	E,S_R,DU	[1]A_{SC}, DU	E,S_R DU	
New Orleans 1960-645,000	NRD,DU,S_R E,A_C,I,DRD	NRD,DU,C S_R,DRD	DU,P,C P_S,S_R	[2]C,E DRD	[3]NRD,P/C,S_R E,I,H,DRD	NRD,DU,C S_R,E,A_C,SC	DU,D,E A_C,SC
Kansas City, Kan.-Mo. 1959-643,000	[4]E,D	[4]S_R,D	[5]P,DU		[5],[6]P	[5]D	
Ft. Worth, Tex. 1964-540,000	E	[7],[8]E_C		P,E_C E_M,E_O		P,E_C E_M,E_O	P,E_C E_M,E_O
Charleston, W. Va. 1965-250,000	[9]E,E_V	E_R,SC,S_P		[9]S_V,E_V,DU A_R,SC_V,I	[10]SC_V	[9]E,E_V,SC_V SC,DU,A_R,I	[9]E_V,T S_V,I
Nashville, Tenn. 1961-250,000	[11]E,E_W,E_B	[11]A_C,D	[11],[12]P,I	[13]A_C	[14]SC,I	A_C,D	
Chattanooga, Tenn. 1962-240,000	E	[15]A_C	[15],[16]P,I	[16],[17]A_C	[15],[18]SC,I	A_C	
Waterbury, Conn. 1963-190,000	E	E_R		P,E_C E_M,E_O		P,E_C E_M,E_O	P,E_C E_M,E_O
Erie, Pa. 1963-140,000	E	[19]E_R	P,E_R,E_O			P,E_R E_M,E_O	[20]P,E_R E_M,E_O
Greensboro, N.C. 1964-130,000	E	E_R		P,E_C E_M,E_O		P,E_C E_M,E_O	P,E_C E_M,E_O
Fargo, N.D. 1965-70,000	E,E_R	[21]P,E_R,E_O		P,DU C,E	[22]DU,E_R,E_O	DU,E,E_R	C,E,E_R
Appleton, Wis. 1965-55,000	[23]E,D A_{PU},A_I			[23]DU,A_{PU},A_I A_C,E		D,E,A_C A_I,A_{PU},DU	DU,E A_C,A_I

Comments

[1] School trips
[2] Personal business
[3] School trips
[4] Different procedures used for stable and unstable zones
[5] Different procedures used depending on type of zone
[6] School trips
[7] Includes related business, eat, and convenience and shopping goods
[8] Gross sales and floor area suggested as possible alternatives
[9] Different factors used to estimate AM and PM peaks
[10] School trips
[11] Different procedures used for stable and unstable zones
[12] Recreation trips computed by uniform factor expansion
[13] Business trips
[14] School trips
[15] Different procedures used for stable and unstable zones
[16] Recreation trips distributed in proportion to surveyed recreation trips
[17] Business trips
[18] School trips
[19] Special adjustments made for shopping centers
[20] Special adjustments made for areas adjacent to major railroads
[21] Retail employment alone used for CBD and outlying areas
[22] Personal business trips
[23] Different factors used to estimate origins and destinations

Key to entries

Employment: E = Total employment; E_R = Retail employment; E_M = Manufacturing employment; E_C = Commercial employment; E_O = Employment other than retail and manufacturing; E_W = White collar employment; E_B = Blue collar employment; E_V = Various specialized employment.

Sales: S_R = Retail sales; S_C = Convenience goods retail sales; S_P = Personal service sales; S_V = Retail sales by various specialized categories.

Area: A_{PU} = Acres of public and semipublic land; A_I = Acres of industrial land; A_C = Acres of commercial land; A_R = Acres of residential land; A_{SC} = Acres of school land.

School Enrollment: SC = Total school enrollment; SC_V = School enrollment by various grade levels.

Household Characteristics: P = Population; P_s = Persons five years of age or older; H = Persons per dwelling unit; DU = Number of dwelling units; NRD = Persons per net residential acre; DRD = Dwelling units per net residential acre; I = Income; C = Number of automobiles.

Miscellaneous: D = Distance from CBD; T = Truck ownership.

Source: [6.22, p. 77].

distribution models employ as inputs not the *number* of trips attracted to a zone but the relative trip "attractiveness" of a zone. This concept will be demonstrated in the upcoming discussion of the gravity model. Floor area or employment often are utilized as measures of relative attractiveness.

6.1.4 Major Generators

While models similar to those presented in the previous two sections provide the engineer or planner with much information on future trip generation, there are several types of urban facilities which because of their large size and innate attractiveness to tripmakers should be handled on a separate basis. The three to be examined here are airports, shopping centers, and large industrial plants. It should be noted that we probably will be concerned with travel to and from these kinds of facilities in the more immediate future (1–5 years), especially for the purposes of gauging parking and traffic control equipment needs. Consequently, we can use independent variables that are much more precise in nature than those employed in, say, 20-year forecast models. The designers of these soon-to-be constructed major generators usually will have detailed data on the characteristics of the development.

6.1.4.1 Airports Figure 6.5 shows data on the number of annual air-passengers originating at 180 Standard Metropolitan Statistical Area (SMSA)[3] airports as related to SMSA population. The relationship appears to be reliable except, perhaps, at the points most distant from the origin. Air-passenger trips are not the only source of travel to airports, however, as is indicated in Table 6.5 and 6.6 where social-recreation (serve passenger and sight-seeing) trips and especially work trips are seen to be numerous, often outnumbering the actual passenger trips.

Further study of trip generation of airports by Keefer [6.6] has led to the three regression equations in Table 6.7. The dependent variables are expressed in terms of passenger originations while the independent variables cover a wide range of characteristics of the SMSA such as population per square mile (X_2), percent of population that is high school graduates (X_6), and so forth. Correlation coefficients are high in the cases of Y_1 and Y_2 but do not appear to be very substantial for Y_3. Thus, any predictions made with the latter equation should be utilized with caution.

6.1.4.2 Shopping centers The number of shopping centers in the United States has risen remarkably: from about 2,000 in 1957 to nearly 10,000 in 1965 [6.6]. Moreover, these types of commercial areas attract unusually high numbers of trips as compared to other uses, so that it is important to gauge the impact of such centers on travel in surrounding territories. Of course, many factors can be easily recognized as influencing tripmaking to shopping centers—the amount and quality of merchandise available there, the distance or travel time to the center, the number of parking spaces, and perhaps even the weather (Table 6.8). While it is not possible to take all of these factors into account, Keefer [6.6] employs many of them in

---

[3] For simplicity, an SMSA can be thought of as any metropolitan area (city plus suburbs) associated with a city with a population greater than 50,000 people.

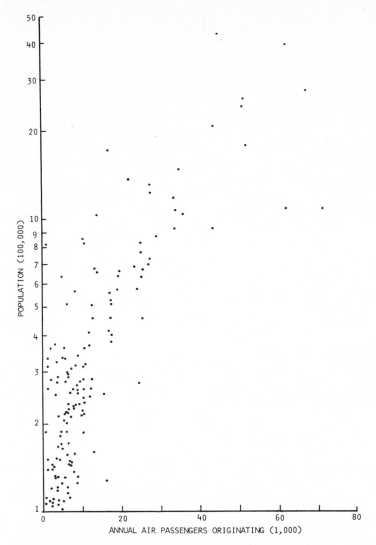

Fig. 6.5 Annual air passengers originating per 100,000 population, 180 standard metropolitan statistical areas, 1960. [6.6, p. 22].

determining relationships relevant to trip generation. A set of three multiple regression models developed in the report are displayed in Table 6.9. The correlation coefficients fall into the "fairly high" bracket, suggesting that most predictions made with the equations will be fairly accurate, particularly if the predictions are not made for the too distant future. It should be noted that the independent variables utilized in the regression models are restricted almost entirely to characteristics of the center, not of the population in the surrounding market

Table 6.5 Purpose Distribution of Person Trips to and from Selected Airports, All Travel Modes*

Airport	Trips to airport (%)			Trips from airport (%)		
	To work	To soc.-recr.	To air travel	To home	To pers. business	To other
Atlanta	67.8	5.8	26.4	—	—	—
Buffalo	23.3	33.7	43.0	55.7	14.1	30.2
Chicago (Midway)	34.7	25.7	39.5	82.6	6.0	11.4
Minneapolis–St. Paul	46.8	19.7	33.6	80.3	7.1	12.6
Philadelphia	24.2	32.8	43.1	70.0	9.7	20.3
Pittsburgh	43.0	20.6	36.5	85.9	4.7	9.3
Providence	39.8	37.7	22.5	—	—	—
San Diego	45.9	21.6	32.4	—	—	—
Seattle–Tacoma	35.0	24.2	40.8	81.3	12.4	6.3
Washington (National)	69.8	15.8	14.4	80.1	9.9	10.0

*From transportation study data (home interviews) for the various cities.
Source: [6.6, p. 8].

Table 6.6 Definition of Variables Used in Multiple Regression, Airports

Variable type	Symbol	Definition
Dependent	Y_1	Total aircraft departures performed in scheduled service, calendar year 1960
	Y_2	On-line revenue passenger originations in scheduled service, calendar year 1960
	Y_3	Y_2/100,000 SMSA population
Independent	X_1	Population, thousands
	X_2	Population, per square mile
	X_3	Nonwhite population, 0.1%
	X_4	Median age, 0.1 year
	X_5	Families with incomes over $10,000, 0.1%
	X_6	High school graduates, 0.1%
	X_7	Manufacturing employment, hundreds
	X_8	Transportation employment, hundreds
	X_9	Trade employment, hundreds
	X_{10}	Institutional employment, hundreds
	X_{11}	Manufacturing establishments with at least 100 employees
	X_{12}	Services receipts, million
	X_{13}	Unemployment rate

Source: [6.6, p. 106].

Table 6.7 Selected Multiple Regression Results, Airports (N = 176)

Equation	r^2	Standard Error*
$Y_1 = -63 + 0.17X_3 + 0.78X_5 - 0.06X_7 + 0.76X_8$ $+ 0.19X_9 - 0.43X_{12} - 0.62X_{13}$	0.86	60
$Y_2 = -2{,}977 - 3.36X_1 + 2.50X_3 + 16.43X_5 - 2.27X_7$ $+ 12.32X_8 + 13.06X_9 - 2.09X_{10} - 3.09X_{12}$	0.92	73
$Y_3 = -944 - 0.06X_2 + 0.69X_3 + 1.49X_4 + 3.01X_5$ $+ 0.58X_6 - 0.48X_7 + 0.95X_9 - 0.41X_{10} + 0.33X_{11}$ $+ 0.30X_{12} + 1.51X_{13}$	0.35	83

*As percentage of $\bar{Y}$.
Source: [6.6, p. 107].

area. This restriction could be harmful in that an urban center and a rural center with similar characteristics would be predicted to have the same number of attracted auto driver trips. Quite obviously this would not be realistic, so that a warning must be issued concerning the injudicious insertion of values into the model equations in a strictly "mechanical" manner.

6.1.4.3 Manufacturing plants Major industrial plants many times are the producers of significant traffic congestion, the problem being doubly acute when an entire shift of plant employees is released at the same time that other smaller establishments are closing for the day. In small towns, this concurrent influx of traffic onto the transportation system can be particularly bothersome and not

Table 6.8 Definition of Variables Used in Multiple Regression, Shopping Centers

Variable type	Symbol	Definition
Dependent	Y_1	All auto driver trips
	Y_2	Auto driver trips to shop
	Y_3	Other auto driver trips
Independent	X_1	Number of parking spaces
	X_2	Total person work trips
	X_3	Distance from major competition, 0.1 mile
	X_4	Age of study data, years
	X_5	Age of center at time of study, years
	X_6	Reported travel speed of tripmakers, mph
	X_7	Floor space for convenience goods, 1,000 sq ft
	X_8	Floor space for shopping goods, 1,000 sq ft
	X_9	Floor space for other uses, 1,000 sq ft

Source: [6.6, p. 108].

Table 6.9   Selected Multiple Regression Results, Shopping Centers

Equation	r^2	Standard error*
$Y_1 = 3,875 + 5.35X_2 + 291.9X_3 - 578.5X_4 - 0.65X_6$ $- 22.31X_9$	0.920	21
$Y_2 = 2,841 + 3.23X_2 + 241.4X_3 - 410.8X_4 - 0.34X_6$ $- 10.45X_7 + 4.32X_8 - 25.70X_9$	0.892	25
$Y_3 = 801 + 0.06X_1 + 0.90X_2 + 31.2X_3 - 108.0X_4$ $+ 35.7X_5 - 0.18X_6 - 1.47X_7 - 2.36X_8$ $+ 1.67X_9$	0.985	14

*As percentage of $\bar{Y}$.
Source: [6.6, p. 109].

susceptible to much relief since it usually would be impractical and costly to provide sufficient capacity for these large but not very lengthy peaks (Table 6.10).

Keefer also has produced multiple regression equation models for determining the quantity and percentage of various types of trips made to manufacturing plants. These equations, shown in Table 6.11, deal with daily automobile driver and transit passenger trips based on characteristics of the plant site, the employees, and the region within a three mile radius of the plant. In using these and other regression

Table 6.10   Definition of Variables Used in Multiple Regression, Manufacturing Plants

Type	Symbol	Definition
Dependent	Y_1	Auto driver trips
	Y_2	Transit passenger trips
Independent	X_1	Population within 5-mile radius, thousands
	X_2	Automobiles within 5-mile radius, thousands
	X_3	Residential land within 5-mile radius, 0.1 acre
	X_4	Net residential density in plant zone, persons/acre
	X_5	Net manufacturing density in plant zone, persons/acre
	X_6	Plant site area, acres
	X_7	Prime shift percentage, three highest morning hours
	X_8	Employees from car-owning households
	X_9	Employees not licensed to drive
	X_{10}	White-collar employees
	X_{11}	Male employees
	X_{12}	CBD-plant distance/CBD cordon line distance
	X_{13}	Average distance, home to work, 0.01 miles
	X_{14}	Total work trips to plant
	X_{15}	Total manufacturing work trips, plant zone

Source: [6.6, p. 109].

Table 6.11   Selected Multiple Regression Results, Manufacturing Plants

Equation	r^2	Standard error*
$Y_1 = 1{,}449 - 3.02X_4 + 1.34X_5 + 1.18X_6 - 9.46X_7$ $- 0.97X_8 - 1.58X_9 - 0.79X_{10} - 0.62X_{11}$ $- 0.64X_{12} - 1.22X_{13} + 2.32X_{14} - 0.01X_{15}$	0.98	13
$Y_2 = -287 + 0.78X_9 + 0.43X_{10}$	0.82	64

*As percentage of $\bar{Y}$.
Source: [6.6, p. 110].

models, the analyst should attempt to gather as much relevant additional information as possible in order to make independent checks of model-calculated trip generation figures.

6.1.5   Trip Distribution Models

After having predicted the number of trips produced by a zone or attracted to it, the next step in the overall travel estimation process is that of "linking" the productions with the attractions, that is, determining how the trips produced in a zone are distributed among all of the other zones. Stated in a behavioral context, we are trying to predict how people who are about to make trips decide on their possible destinations. Obviously there are a multitude of reasons why one destination would be chosen over another: lack of jobs in certain zones, better highways between certain points, dangerous neighborhoods which must be traversed, and so forth. Generally speaking, then, traffic distribution can be considered a function of [6.8, p. I-1]:

1. The type and extent of transportation facilities available in an area.
2. The pattern of land use in an area, including the location and intensity of land use.
3. The various social and economic characteristics of the population of an urban area.

Many mathematical models have been developed to explain and predict the distribution of traffic. As a matter of fact, researchers probably have centered more interest on trip distribution than on any other phase in the travel estimation process. The results of these efforts are models such as the Fratar Grow Factor Model [6.11], the Gravity Model [6.8], the Intervening Opportunity [6.9], and Competing Opportunity [6.23] Models, the Linear Graph Theory Model [6.24], and others. Of course it would not be possible to discuss all of these in this text, so that we have chosen to present the Gravity Model since it more than likely is the most widely used and easiest to understand of the group. However this decision should not be taken as an indication that the other models are not comparable in sophistication of concept and in accuracy. This certainly is not the case.

The gravity model, as its name implies, is adopted from the "law" of gravity as advanced by Newton in 1686 to explain the force between (and consequent motion of) the planets and stars in the universe. As originally proposed, the model equation for the force between two bodies was

$$F_{12} = G \frac{M_1 M_2}{d_{12}^2} \tag{6.2}$$

where F_{12} = the gravitational force between bodies 1 and 2
   M_1 = mass of body 1
   M_2 = mass of body 2
   d_{12} = distance between bodies 1 and 2
   G = a constant

In viewing this model, travel researchers noted an interesting analog, especially in regard to shopping travel: M_1 might represent the "mass" of trips available at, say, a residential area; M_2 the "mass" or attractiveness of a shopping area; d_{12} the distance between the two areas; and F_{12} the number of trips between the two areas. These interpretations would imply through the gravity model that the greater the size or attractiveness of the two areas (masses) and the less the distance between them, the more would be the number of interarea trips. This was found to resemble many real world situations.

When the effect of several competing attraction areas (i.e., multiple masses) was taken into account, the gravity trip distribution model became

$$T_{ij} = P_i \frac{A_j/d_{ij}^b}{(A_1/d_{i1}^b) + (A_2/d_{i2}^b) + \ldots + (A_j/d_{ij}^b) + \ldots + (A_n/d_{in}^b)} \tag{6.3}$$

where T_{ij} = number of trips produced in zone i and attracted to zone j
   P_i = number of trips produced by zone i
   A_j = number of trips attracted to zone j
   d_{ij} = distance between zone i and zone j, generally expressed as the total
     travel time (t_{ij}) between i and j
   b = an empirically determined exponent which expresses the average
     area-wide effect of spatial separation between zones on trip interchange

What this formula states in essence is that the percentage of the P_i trips produced by zone i allocated to destination zone j is dependent upon both the attractiveness (A_j) of and travel time to that zone *relative to* the same features of all other attracting zones. Thus a zone in which a new shopping center is built (increased A_j) or to which a new transportation facility is constructed (decreased d_{ij}), increases its relative "pull" on the P_i trip productions and subsequently draws a greater proportion of these productions to itself.

The gravity model has undergone an additional change in form in order to make it more general in concept. As used in most applications, it now appears as

$$T_{ij} = P_i \frac{A_i F_{ij} K_{ij}}{\displaystyle\sum_{j=l}^{n} A_l F_{il} K_{il}} \tag{6.4}$$

where F_{ij} is called the "travel time factor" (specified as $1/(t_{ij}^b)$ above) and where K_{ij} is a specific zone-to-zone adjustment factor for taking into account the effect on travel patterns of defined social or economic linkages not otherwise incorporated in the gravity model formulation (somewhat equivalent to the "G's" in the Newton's gravity model). One major change to be noted here is that we no longer are required to have a travel time function of the form $1/(t_{ij}^b)$ but could have others such as

$$F = a \, t_{ij}^{-b} \tag{6.5}$$

$$F = ate^{-bt^2 + ct + d} \tag{6.6}$$

$$F = \frac{1}{a + bt} \tag{6.7}$$

All of these express the general idea of a drop in F as t increases, but one may lead to more reliable trip distribution estimates than the others under certain circumstances. The second major change is, of course, in the inclusion of the K_{ij} factors, these being added because of some unusual differences in travel distributions noted in some cities and attributed to the social and economic makeup of the travelers. For example, higher income persons have a greater tendency to make longer work trips than their lower income counterparts [6.8].

6.1.5.1 Calibration of the gravity model After establishing a minimum path tree from each zone centroid to all others,[4] the engineer or planner would have available to him all the necessary input data for the gravity model and therefore *should* be able to make predictions of future trip distributions. Unfortunately, this is not the case, as the example to follow will show. In this example, presented in Fig. 6.6, we have taken a hypothetical 4 zone city, 2 zones of which are strictly residential and the other 2 of which are strictly commercial (shopping). The present productions, attractions, and interzonal trips,[5] all obtained from a travel survey, are given along with the travel times, which are placed next to their respective links. At this juncture, it should be noted that the gravity model should be able to reproduce the present interzonal trip figures circled on each link. So

$$T_{13} = 500 \left[\frac{300(1/5^2)(1)}{300(1/5^2)(1) + 800(1/10^2)(1)} \right] = 500 \left(\frac{12.00}{12.00 + 8.00} \right) = 300 \text{ trips}$$

---

[4] See Appendix.
[5] Shown circled on corresponding link. It is assumed in the example that no trips are produced at the shopping centers nor attracted at the residential areas.

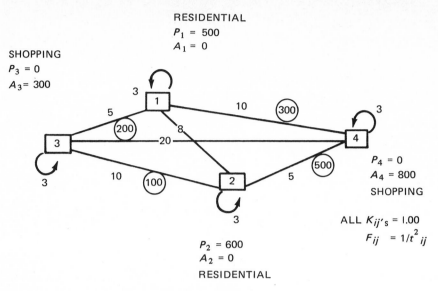

Fig. 6.6   Example situation for gravity model utilization.

$$T_{14} = 500 \left[\frac{800(1/5^2)(1)}{300(1/5^2)\,(1) + 800(1/10^2)\,(1)} \right] = 500 \left(\frac{8.00}{12.00 + 8.00} \right) = 200 \text{ trips}$$

$$T_{23} = 600 \left[\frac{300(1/10^2)(1)}{300(1/10^2)\,(1) + 800(1/5^2)\,(1)} \right] = 600 \left(\frac{3.00}{3.00 + 32.00} \right) = 51 \text{ trips}$$

$$T_{24} = 600 \left[\frac{800(1/5^2)(1)}{300(1/10^2)\,(1) + 800(1/5^2)\,(1)} \right] = 600 \left(\frac{32.00}{3.00 + 32.00} \right) = 549 \text{ trips}$$

and $T_{11} = T_{12} = T_{21} = T_{22} = T_{31} = T_{32} = T_{34} = T_{44} = T_{41} = T_{42} = T_{43} = T_{44} = 0$ trips since either the corresponding P_i or $A_j = 0$. In comparing these calculated values to the ones found circled in Fig. 6.6, it becomes obvious that the gravity model is not very reliable in *reproducing present trip distribution* in this example. Moreover, the sum of the trips into each attracting area does not equal the number of trip attractions: for instance, $T_{13} + T_{23} = 300 + 51 = 351 \neq A_3 = 300$.

The present feeling as to the cause of the two types of discrepancies brought out above is that: (1) the A_j's are not absolute measures of the attraction of trips to a zone, but instead are relative measures which could have different absolute magnitudes, and (2) travel time alone is not sufficient to give an indication of the "friction" on travel caused by distance, so the F_{ij}'s, which supposedly represent the influence of "friction," are only *approximated* by a term such as $1/t_{ij}^2$.

These two explanations now have become the *reason d'etre* for making changes in the A_j's and F_{ij}'s, which are modified as demonstrated below, again using the example in Fig. 6.6. The A_j's are changed first, then the F_{ij}'s, and this sequence is followed several times. Each separate use of the gravity model with a new set of A_j's or F_{ij}'s is called an *iteration*. To start, let us modify the A_j's by setting

$$b_j^{(1)} = \frac{A_j}{\displaystyle\sum_{i=1}^{n} T_{ij}^{(0)}} \tag{6.8}$$

where $b_j^{(1)}$ signifies the first modification coefficient and the $T_{ij}^{(0)}$'s are the previously calculated interzonal trip estimates. Then, in general, let

$$T_{ij}^{(c)} = P_i \frac{A_j b_j^{(c)} F_{ij} K_{ij}}{\displaystyle\sum_{j=1}^{n} A_j b_j^{(c)} F_{ij} K_{ij}} \tag{6.9}$$

where $b_j^{(c)}$ is the cth modification (iteration coefficient). For the zones in the example

$$b_3^{(1)} = 300/(300 + 51) = 0.857$$

$$b_4^{(1)} = 800/(200 + 549) = 1.068$$

Therefore

$$T_{13}^{(1)} = 500 \frac{300(0.857)\,(1/5^2)}{300(0.857)\,(1/5^2) + 800\,(1.068)\,(1/10^2)} = 273$$

and, through similar calculations, $T_{14}^{(1)} = 227$, $T_{23}^{(1)} = 42$, and $T_{24}^{(1)} = 558$, with all other $T_{ij}^{(1)}$'s, as before, equal to 0. Consequently, in comparing A_j and

$$\sum_{i=1}^{n} T_{ij}^{(1)}$$

we obtain 300 and $273 + 42 = 315$ for zone 3 and 800 and $227 + 558 = 785$ for zone 4.

The new correction coefficients, $b_j^{(2)}$, then are found from

$$b_j^{(2)} = b_j^{(1)} \frac{A_j}{\displaystyle\sum_{i=1}^{n} T_{ij}^{(1)}} \tag{6.10}$$

which, for example, come to

$$b_3^{(2)} = 0.857\,(300)/315 = 0.816$$

$$b_4^{(2)} = 1.068\,(800)/785 = 1.088$$

Using the gravity model as stated in Eq. (6.4), we find that $T_{13}^{(2)} = 265$, $T_{14}^{(2)} = 235$, $T_{23}^{(2)} = 39$, and $T_{24}^{(2)} = 561$. Now, since $T_{13}^{(2)} + T_{23}^{(2)} = 265 + 39 = 304$ and $T_{14}^{(2)} + T_{24}^{(2)} = 235 + 561 = 796$, we have numbers that are reasonably close to the actual values of 300 and 800, so that we can stop our iterations on the A_j's at this point and, at the same time, generalize our modification procedure through the formula

$$b_j^{(c)} = b_j^{(c-1)} \frac{A_j}{\sum\limits_{i=1}^{n} T_{ij}^{(c-1)}} \qquad (6.11)$$

The values of the T_{ij}'s still are not clearly equivalent to the values found through the travel survey (see the circled numbers in Fig. 6.6 again). The forthcoming changes in the F_{ij}'s are intended to alleviate this difficulty. The mechanism for producing these changes involves the utilization of the trip travel time frequency distribution appearing in Fig. 6.7.

The values shown in this frequency distribution are taken from the travel survey figures of the example where, as an illustration, the number of trips 5 min. long are those from zone one to three (200) and two to four (500), giving the total of 700. A necessary condition for the model (estimated T_{ij}'s to equal the survey) found

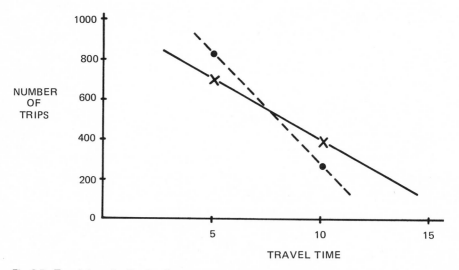

Fig. 6.7 Travel time distribution for example problem in Fig. 6.6.

T_{ij}'s is that the gravity model produce the same trip travel time frequency distribution as that from the survey. Since the F_{ij}'s are related to travel time, by changing them, we concurrently modify the travel time frequency distribution, thus achieving our objective. To help in this direction, let us have a modification formula similar to that in Eq. (6.11). Let

$$F_{ij}^{(d)} = \frac{F_{ij}^{(d-1)} S_{\Delta t}}{G_{\Delta t}^{(d-1)}} \tag{6.12}$$

where $F_{ij}^{(d)}$ = the dth modified value of the travel time factor F_{ij}
$F_{ij}^{(d-1)}$ = the $d-1^{th}$ modified value of the travel time factor F_{ij}
$S_{\Delta t}$ = number of survey trips whose travel time falls into time interval Δt
$G_{\Delta t}^{(d-1)}$ = number of $d-1^{th}$ iteration gravity model trips whose travel time falls into time interval Δt

The $F_{ij}^{(d)}$'s found from Eq. (6.12) then can be employed directly in the gravity model as

$$T_{ij}^{(c,d)} = P_i \frac{A_j b_j^{(c)} F_{ij}^{(d)} K_{ij}}{\displaystyle\sum_{j=1}^{n} A_j b_j^{(c)} F_{ij}^{(d)} K_{ij}} \tag{6.13}$$

where $T_{ij}^{(c,d)}$ represents the T_{ij} obtained in iteration c of the attractions and iteration d of the travel time factors. Returning to the example situation, we previously had determined that $b_3^{(2)} = 0.816$ and $b_4^{(2)} = 1.088$, and these numbers produced suitable values for the sum of the trips attracted to zones 3 and 4. Continuing on from there, we see that the latest value for $G_5^{(0)}$ is $T_{13}^{(2)} + T_{24}^{(2)} = 826$[6] and for $G_{10}^{(0)}$ is $T_{14}^{(2)} + T_{23}^{(2)} = 274$. Moreover, $S_5 = 700$ and $S_{10} = 400$ from Fig. 6.6. Thus

$$F_{13}^{(1)} = F_{24}^{(1)} = (1/5^2)(700/826) = 0.034$$

$$F_{23}^{(1)} = F_{14}^{(1)} = (1/10^2)(400/274) = 0.015$$

Subsequently

$$T_{13}^{(2,1)} = 500 \frac{300(0.816)(0.034)}{300(0.816)(0.034) + 800(1.088)(0.015)} = 195 \text{ trips}$$

[6] To be precise, we should show $G_5^{(0)}$ as $G_4 \cdot^{(0)}5\text{-}5.5$ to indicate that the Δt interval is for 4.5 to 5.5 min. Similar precision is needed for all other G's and S's.

$$T_{14}(2,1) = 500 \frac{800(1.088)(0.015)}{300(0.816)(0.034) + 800(1.088)(0.015)} = 305 \text{ trips}$$

From similar calculations, $T_{23}(2,1) = 66$ and $T_{24}(2,1) = 534$ trips. Juxtaposing these figures with those in Fig. 6.6, we see that $G_5(1) = 195 + 534 = 729$ as compared to $S_5 = 700$ and $G_{10}(1) = 305 + 66 = 371$ as compared to $S_5 = 400$ so that, in one iteration, the estimated travel time frequency distribution now lies much closer to the survey (actual) one.

For the second iteration, the $F_{ij}(2)$'s are

$$F_{13}(2) = F_{24}(2) = 0.034 (700/729) = 0.0326$$

$$F_{23}(2) = F_{14}(2) = 0.015 (400/371) = 0.0162, \text{ thus leading to}$$

$$T_{13}(2,2) = 500 \frac{300(0.816)(0.0326)}{300(0.816)(0.0326) + 800(1.088)(0.0162)} = 181$$

Again through similar computations, $T_{14}(2,2) = 319$, $T_{23}(2,2) = 74$, and $T_{24}(2,2) = 526$. These give $G_5(2) = 181 + 526 = 707$ and $G_{10}(2) = 319 + 74 = 393$, both of which are close to the desired totals of 700 and 400, respectively.

Despite all these calculations, the needed modifications are not yet complete since it turns out that $T_{13}(2,2) + T_{23}(2,2) = 181 + 74 = 255$ which falls short of $A_3 = 300$ and $T_{14}(2,2) + T_{24}(2,2) = 319 + 526 = 845$ which is greater than $A_4 = 800$. Consequently, another iteration of the A_j's must be made with

$$b_3(3) = (0.816)(300/255) = 0.961$$

$$b_4(3) = (1.088)(800/845) = 1.029$$

These two changes produce interzonal trips of 206, 294, 89, and 511 for $T_{13}(3,2)$, $T_{14}(3,2)$, $T_{23}(3,2)$, and $T_{24}(3,2)$, respectively. Since the sum of the trip attractions is now 295 and 805 and since the number of trips in the 5-min interval is 717 and 383 in the 10-min interval, we will consider these values to be close enough to the desired ones that we can terminate the entire iteration procedure. The final gravity model for the example then appears as

$$T_{ij} = P_i \frac{A_j b_j(3) F_{ij}(2) K_{ij}}{\displaystyle\sum_{j=1}^{n} A_j b_j(3) F_{ij}(2) K_{ij}} \tag{6.14}$$

where $b_3{}^{(3)} = 0.961$, $b_4{}^{(3)} = 1.029$, $F_{13}{}^{(2)} = F_{24}{}^{(2)} = 0.0326$, and $F_{23}{}^{(2)} = F_{14}{}^{(2)} = 0.0162$. This is the model that now can be employed for the prediction of future interzonal trips for the example situation.

6.1.5.2 Comments on the gravity model calibration

Several comments should be made on the foregoing gravity model concept and calibration procedure:

1. What appeared to be a rather simple model of the gravitational pull of attracting areas on trip productions becomes, after some serious investigation, a rather complex model which takes great skill to manipulate.

2. The gravity model, through the calibration process, is seen as an extremely malleable model, that is, one which can be twisted to fit a variety of situations. This characteristic is perhaps both the practical beauty and the theoretical bane of the gravity model.

3. The number of calculations required even for the small example used above is quite large. Thus, for any practical application, it becomes necessary to use a digital computer for the arithmetic chores. Programs for the gravity model are described in [6.8].

4. In many situations the gravity model is employed on a trip purpose basis with separate computations being done for each purpose. Several studies in large urban areas have used the following purpose categories [6.8]: (a) home based work, (b) home based shop, (c) home based social-recreation, (d) home based school, (e) home based miscellaneous, (f) nonhome based, (g) truck trips, and (h) taxi trips.

5. The gravity model can be adjusted to replicate situations in which either or both socioeconomic and psychological factors are influential. The former are prevalent when there are significant differences in travel patterns between different types of persons (e.g., high and low income persons). Such factors are handled by means of the K_{ij} coefficients. Psychological factors, such as the "barrier effects" caused by bridges, mountains, large industrial districts, and so forth[7] are handled by changing travel times to be equivalent to those perceived by the traveler.

6.1.5.3 Prediction using a calibrated gravity model

After having developed a fully calibrated model like that in Eq. (6.14), the engineer or planner is in position to make predictions of *future* trip distribution. As an example of the process of prediction involved, let us use the calibrated model from the preceding example and assume that transportation system improvements have been made that result in a lowering of both 10-min travel times to 7.5 min. Future attractions and productions are as shown in Fig. 6.8.

The first step in the prediction phase is to derive travel time factors for the 7.5-min time interval. This usually is done by going to a curve such as in Fig. 6.9 showing the relationship between final calibration phase travel time factors and the

---

[7]People for some reason seem to feel that it will take longer to cross a mountain or a bridge than it really will: thus there is a psychological "barrier effect."

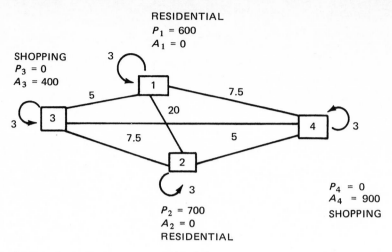

Fig. 6.8 Example future situation for gravity model utilization.

corresponding travel times they represent[8] and then interpolating to find the travel time factor to use for the 7.5-min travel time value. For the example, the resulting F_{ij} to use is 0.0244.

The next step in the prediction phase involves the insertion of the correct productions, attractions, and travel time factors into the calibrated model—with one rather dubious exception: the $b_j^{(c)}$'s found in the calibration phase generally are not included, that is, they are set equal to one. The reason for this move is not apparent, but past experience has shown it to be beneficial, so that we will follow this procedure in order to be consistent. Thus

$$T_{13} = 600 \frac{400(0.0326)}{400(0.0326) + 900(0.0244)} = 218$$

$$T_{14} = 600 \frac{900(0.0244)}{400(0.0326) + 900(0.0244)} = 382$$

$$T_{23} = 700 \frac{400(0.0244)}{400(0.0244) + 900(0.0326)} = 173$$

$$T_{24} = 700 \frac{900(0.0326)}{400(0.0244) + 900(0.0326)} = 527$$

[8] This diagram often is done in log-log form for greater convenience and to obtain smoother curves.

Checking the attractions against the sum attracted, we find that 218 + 173 = 391 which is close to the A_3 of 400, and 382 + 527 = 909 which also is close to its corresponding value of A_j = 900. We therefore will accept these interzonal trip numbers as being final, but it should be noted that if the two corresponding values were not as close as desired, iterations could be made on the A_j's similar to those done in the calibration phase (unless the A_j's are treated as measures of *relative* attractiveness).

6.1.6 Mode Choice

At this point in the travel estimation process we have first predicted the number of trips produced or attracted by each zone in a region and then, through the use of the gravity model, attempted to determine how these generated trips will spread themselves among the zones. The next step, in referring back to Fig. 6.2, is to find the percentage of the inter- and intrazonal trips taking some kind of transit as opposed to those going by private automobile. The Trip Interchange Modal Split Model [6.18] is suitable for this purpose if there are only two major modes of travel (transit and automobile) between each pair of zones.

6.1.6.1 The Trip Interchange Modal Split Model The choice or "split" between two modes is seen in this model as a function of four variables which describe both the transportation alternatives between each pair of zones and the socioeconomic characteristics of the people who avail themselves of the alternatives. These variables are: (1) relative travel time, *TTR;* (2) relative travel cost, *CR;* (3) economic status of the tripmaker, *EC;* and (4) relative travel service, *L*.

Several other variables, such as trip length, population density, employment density, and so forth were investigated for their possible relevance to modal split. However they were found to be correlated highly with the four listed above, so that their influence already was accounted for through the *TTR, CR, EC,* and *L* variables.

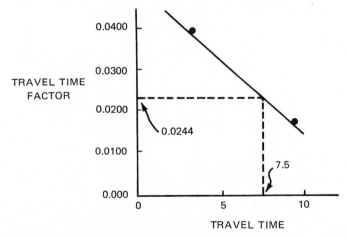

Fig. 6.9 Relationship between final calibration phase travel time factors and travel time.

The first of the four independent variables is defined as follows

$$TTR = \frac{X_1 + X_2 + X_3 + X_4 + X_5}{X_6 + X_7 + X_8} \qquad (6.15)$$

where X_1 = time spent in transit vehicle

X_2 = transfer time between transit vehicles

X_3 = time spent waiting for a transit vehicle

X_4 = walking time to transit vehicle

X_5 = walking time from transit vehicle

X_6 = auto driving time

X_7 = parking delay at destination

X_8 = walking time from parking place to destination

TTR represents the ratio of the *door-to-door* travel time by transit to that by automobile. The effect of TTR on the transit share (percentage) of *work* trips can be seen in Fig. 6.10 where, for the three cities studied, it appears that door-to-door travel by transit must take at least 2.5 times that by auto before the transit share drops below 50 percent.

The second variable is that of relative travel cost CR

$$CR = \frac{X_9}{(X_{10} + X_{11} + 0.5 X_{12})/X_{13}} \qquad (6.16)$$

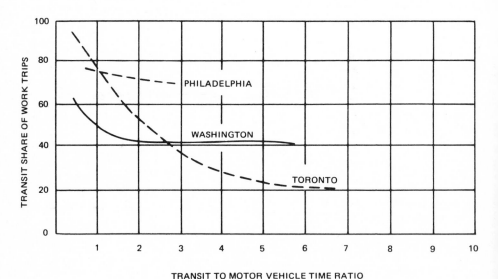

Fig. 6.10 Travel time ratio diversion curve for work trips in peak periods. [6.17, p. 279].

where X_9 = transit fare

X_{10} = cost of gasoline

X_{11} = cost of oil change and lubrication

X_{12} = parking cost at destination

X_{13} = average car occupancy

The significance of the division of the denominator by average car occupancy, X_{13}, and the halving of the parking cost (X_{12}) is that auto costs must be put on a per person per one way trip basis in order to be comparable to the costs for transit. Moreover, the only auto costs considered are those which a *person must take out of his pocket*. The underlying reason for this assumption is that these costs, and not those for such long term items as tires and car insurance are the ones which apparently influence a person's day-to-day decision as to whether or not to take the car to work.

The third variable, the economic status of the tripmaker (EC), is defined strictly in terms of the median income per worker in the zone of trip production. The last variable, travel service (L), is difficult to quantify because it pertains to such intangible factors as the atmosphere within the vehicle, comfort, appearance, ride smoothness, availability of seats, and convenience of transfer. In the Trip Interchange Modal Split Model, L is designated somewhat arbitrarily as the amount of time spent other than in actual travel in the transit vehicle or automobile, giving the relationship

$$L = \frac{X_2 + X_3 + X_4 + X_5}{X_7 + X_8} \tag{6.17}$$

where each of the variables have been defined previously.

Having interpreted these variables in a definite manner, most analysts probably would proceed by utilizing a statistical procedure such as multiple regression to establish a connection between the independent and dependent variables. This was done in a partial manner for the Trip Interchange Modal Split Model, but, for graphic simplicity, the CR, L, and EC variables were divided into discrete stratifications, and then regression equations relating the two variables—transit share of trips, TS, and relative travel time, TTR—were constituted within each stratification. This procedure led to a set of two-dimensional plots as presented in Fig. 6.11. The categories for the three stratified variables in this figure are:

CR_1 = 0.0 to 0.5

CR_2 = 0.5 to 1.0

CR_3 = 1.0 to 1.5

CR_4 = 1.5 and over

EC_1 = \$0 to \$3,100 per annum

EC_2 = \$3,100 to \$4,700 per annum

EC_3 = \$4,700 to \$6,200 per annum

EC_4 = \$6,200 to \$7,500 per annum

EC_5 = \$7,500 per annum and over

L_1 = 0.0 to 1.5

L_2 = 1.5 to 3.5

L_3 = 3.5 to 5.5

L_4 = 5.5 and over

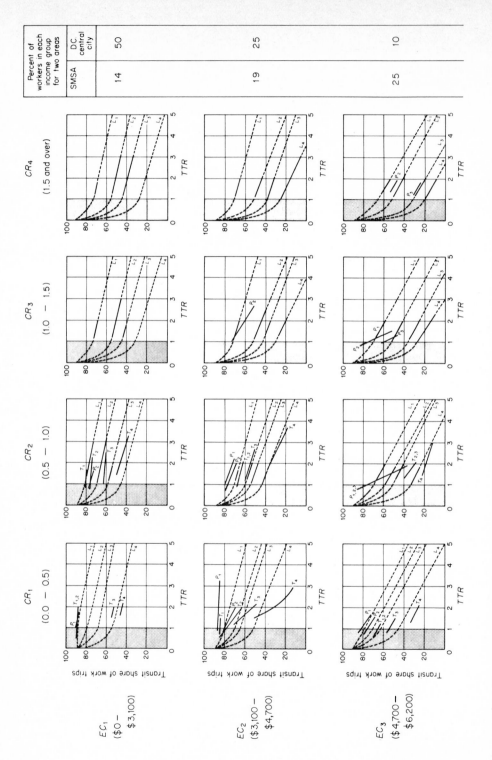

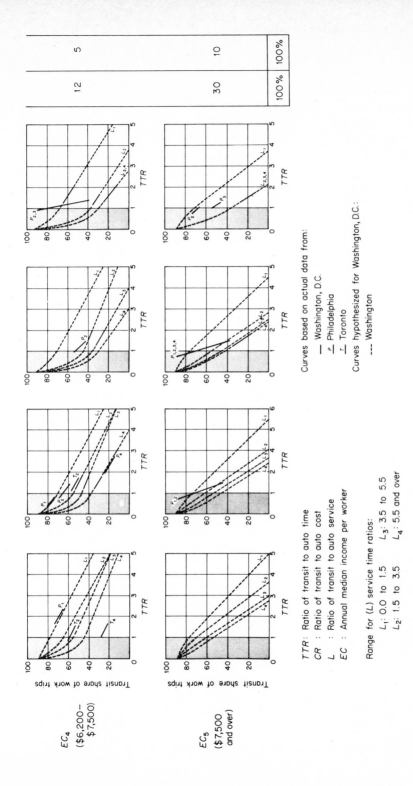

Fig. 6.11 Work-trip modal-split relationships for Washington, D.C., Philadelphia, and Toronto. From Traffic Systems Analysis for Engineers and Planners by M. Wohl and B. V. Martin, copyright (1967, McGraw-Hill Book Co.). Used with permission of McGraw-Hill Book Co.

TTR: Ratio of transit to auto time
CR : Ratio of transit to auto cost
L : Ratio of transit to auto service
EC : Annual median income per worker

Range for (L) service time ratios:
L_1: 0.0 to 1.5 L_3: 3.5 to 5.5
L_2: 1.5 to 3.5 L_4: 5.5 and over

Curves based on actual data from:
— Washington, D.C.
P Philadelphia
τ Toronto

Curves hypothesized for Washington, D.C.:
--- Washington

EC_4
($6,200–
$7,500)

EC_5
($7,500
and over)

Transit share of work trips

Each separate chart in Fig. 6.11 has four curves corresponding to the four stratifications of *L*. Several charts have relationships derived from studies not only in Washington, D.C., but also in Philadelphia and Toronto. The equations are linear except in the shaded portion of each chart where manual adjustments have been made to approximate more closely actual conditions in the study area. Most correlation coefficients for the linear portion of the curves are over 0.85, but should be not accepted injudiciously since they are based on only a small number of data points (a situation which generally leads to higher correlation coefficients).

6.1.6.2 Use of the Trip Interchange Modal Split Model The prediction of the share (percentage) of work trips going by transit at some future point in time would involve the straightforward use of the charts presented in Fig. 6.11. The difficult part of the process, however, would be to forecast the values for each of the 14 factors used to calculate *TTR*, *CR*, *EC*, and *L*. The estimation of future costs of gasoline, oil change and lubrication, and parking would be particularly risky. For the Washington study [6.18], the following assumptions about these factors were made to guide the prediction process:

1. Auto and transit travel times and distances were calculated along minimum time paths.
2. Transit transfer time was taken as half of the time between arrivals of transit vehicles.
3. Walking times to transit stops were established by observation of zone size, transit location, and average walking speeds.
4. Waiting times for transit were equated to half the average time between arrivals of transit vehicles.
5. Parking delay generally was assumed as 1 min.
6. Walking time from parking was taken as 1 min except in downtown areas where 2 to 5 min was used.
7. Parking costs were assumed to be 1.6 times the zonal *average* of all parking costs at the present time.
8. No increases from present zonal median worker incomes were assumed, but at the same time no increases in car operating and transit fare costs were projected, the feeling being that the relative increases in these cost factors would cancel each other out.

In employing the Trip Interchange Modal Split Model in a region other than Washington, D.C., the analyst probably would be wise to recalibrate the regression equations, that is, find new sets of coefficients and constants based on present data. This would be desirable because the variations between Washington, D.C., Philadelphia, and Toronto (shown in Fig. 6.11) are large enough to make us suspect similar differences in other regions. Mode choice relations also should be formulated for trip purposes other than work. In Washington, the three purposes of work, school, and nonwork–nonschool were utilized.

6.1.6.3 Comments on the Trip Interchange Modal Split Model In many studies mode choice relationships are derived through the straightforward use of regression. The Trip Interchange Model goes a step beyond this theoretically by considering a variety of categories of characteristics of users and the transportation system and *then* employing regression. The model has been calibrated with fairly good results in three large urban areas, a fact which gives us an honest basis for comparison. On the negative side, however, we find:

1. Only two "modes" are considered—highway and transit. There is no way to differentiate between bus, streetcar, and commuter rail. This also means that if a new transit technology were introduced (e.g., gravity vacuum tube), it would be difficult if not impossible to determine the proportion of the travel market it would capture.

2. The model is used after all trips have been distributed. It may be that decisions about mode choice are made before the traveler decides where he will go (or even before he decides if he will go).

3. In predicting future mode choice, the model may be employed outside the ranges in which the original variables were measured. This could lead to significant errors.

4. The relationships are all linear, which seems improbable from a theoretical standpoint, and they often are based on a very small number of observations.

6.1.7 Trip Assignment

The final phase of the travel estimation process deals with the assignment of the interzonal, modal trips to the various routes of each mode. Rephrased this means that we are going to be concerned with why tripmakers choose one route over another. The reader also should expect that we will concentrate only on automobile travel since, for the most part, modes other than auto do not provide a multiplicity of routes between zonal pairs.

The question which naturally arises at this point is, "What are the factors that lead people to choose one route over another?" Generally speaking, researchers have identified at least four: (1) travel times, (2) travel costs, (3) comfort, and (4) levels of service (volume/capacity).

While all of these are considered important, the first is used almost exclusively in all models of route choice or trip assignment, the main reason being the relative ease by which travel time as opposed to the other three variables can be measured. In addition, all four variables are somewhat interrelated, so that one often can be used to represent the whole group.

If travel time is utilized as the major factor in trip assignment, a desirable feature in a trip assignment model would be the incorporation of a tradeoff between travel time and trip volume, because, as can be readily observed on any street or highway, the greater the volume of traffic (as compared to the capacity) the greater the travel time of any one vehicle traversing the facility. On the other hand, the greater the travel time, the fewer the number of people who will take the particular route, a fact which indicates that, after a period of time, an equilibrium on a set of routes should be reached in which any person by switching his route could only *increase* his individual travel time. The TRC Trip Assignment Model, to be discussed below, attempts to embody these two tradeoff features through the use of successive iterations between travel time and volume relationships.

6.1.7.1 The TRC trip assignment model This model involves two travel time versus volume relationships used iteratively to arrive at predictions of volumes on up to four separate[9] routes between any two zones. The first equation, utilizing route volume as the dependent variable, was developed from observations from radar detectors mounted at the approaches to eight signalized intersections in Toronto. As seen in Fig. 6.12, 10 separate curves, each composed of two connected linear pieces, have been produced, with each one representing a route with a given speed limit and a given number of signalized intersections per mile. For simplicity it can be assumed that the slope of the low volume linear portions is 0.5 and for the high volume portion 10.0 irrespective of the particular category to which the curve corresponds. In addition to its graphical portrayal, each curve can be represented symbolically as

$$t_r = t_{rc} + \frac{d(V_r - V_{rc})}{V_{rc}} L_r \tag{6.18}$$

where t_r = travel time on route r (minutes)
$\quad\quad V_r$ = volume of traffic on route r (vehicles/hr/lane)
$\quad\quad V_{rc}$ = critical volume[10] for route r (vehicles/hr/lane)
$\quad\quad t_{rc}$ = unit travel time at the critical volume (min/mile)
$\quad\quad L_r$ = length of route r (miles)
$\quad\quad d$ = delay parameter (min/mile)

The parameter d takes on the aforementioned values of 0.5 for $V_r < V_{rc}$ and 10.0 for $V_r \geqslant V_{rc}$.

The second relationship alluded to above is the converse of Eq. (6.18), used for predicting the volume on route r given the travel time

$$V_r = \frac{1/t_r}{\displaystyle\sum_{r=1}^{m} 1/t_r} V \tag{6.19}$$

where V is the total volume of trips from zone i to j on all m routes and V_r and t_r are as in Eq. (6.18). In effect, Eq. (6.19) divides up the volume of trips from zone i to j among the various routes in accordance with the reciprocal of the travel times. A decrease in t_r thus leads to an increase in t_r^{-1} and a corresponding increase in the proportion of the V trips assigned to route r. The value for t_r is found from Eq.

---

[9] A modified Moore's algorithm technique ([6.15] and Appendix) can be utilized to find the second, third, and fourth shortest routes between a pair of zones.

[10] See Fig. 6.12 where the critical volume is that corresponding to the break point between the two linear portions of the curve for each category of street.

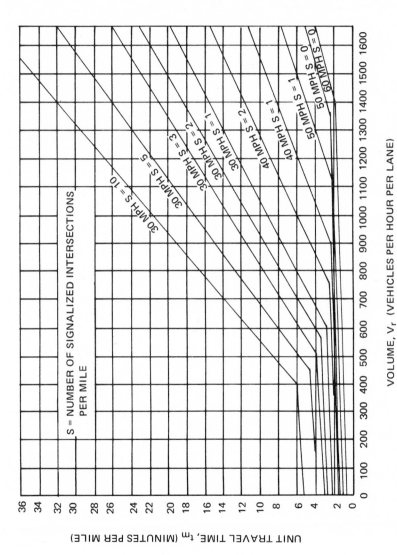

Fig. 6.12 Unit travel time versus volume on various types of roadways. (*E. R. Ruiter, ICES-TRANSNET Procedures Manual, M.I.T., Civil Engineering Dept., Cambridge, Mass., 1968, p. 20*).

217

(6.18), inserted into Eq. (6.19), and the resulting V_r is entered back into Eq. (6.18). This cyclical procedure continues until the changes in volumes or travel times become negligible.

6.1.7.2 Example of the TRC trip assignment model   The interplay between the two TRC Trip Assignment equations can be demonstrated through an example in which a pair of zones is connected by two routes whose characteristics are indicated in Table 6.12. Travel on route 1 is slower, but the route is shorter in distance. Critical volumes, corresponding critical travel times, and travel times when no traffic is on each route (the "ideal" travel times) are found from Fig. 6.12 based on the characteristics presented in Table 6.12.

The assignment procedure starts by using Eq. (6.19) in conjunction with the ideal travel times for the entire length of each route. Thus if no traffic were on route 1, the travel time would equal 2.5 min/mile × 3 miles = 7.5 min, while that for route 2 would be 1.5(4) = 6.0 min, leading to

$$V_1 = \frac{1/7.5}{1/7.5 + 1/6.0} (1,200) = 532 \text{ vph/lane}$$

and

$$V_2 = \frac{1/6.0}{1/7.5 + 1/6.0} (1,200) = 668 \text{ vph/lane}$$

Switching to Eq. (6.18) and using the above values, we find that

$$t_1 = \left[3.0 + \frac{0.5 (532 - 600)}{600} \right] 3 = 8.82 \text{ min}$$

and

$$t_2 = \left[2.0 + \frac{0.5 (668 - 1,100)}{1,100} \right] 4 = 7.20 \text{ min}$$

Table 6.12   Example Route Characteristics

Route no.	No. of lanes	Speed limit	Signals/ mile	Length	Critical volume	Critical travel time	Travel time with no volume
1	1	30 mph	1	3 miles	600 vph/lane	3.0 min/mile	2.5 min/mile
2	1	50 mph	1	4 miles	1100 vph/lane	2.0 min/mile	1.5 min/mile

where in both cases $d = 0.5$ since both route volumes are less than their respective critical volumes. Going back to the previous equations for determining route volumes, and given the above travel times, we obtain

$$V_1 = \frac{1/8.82}{1/8.82 + 1/7.20} \, (1,200) = 536 \text{ vph/lane}$$

and

$$V_2 = \frac{1/7.20}{1/8.82 + 1/7.20} \, (1,200) = 664 \text{ vph/lane}$$

Using these results as inputs to the next set of iterations, we discover that

$$t_1 = \left[3.0 + \frac{0.5 \, (536{-}600)}{600} \right] 3 = 8.85 \text{ min}$$

and

$$t_2 = \left[2.0 + \frac{0.5 \, (664{-}1,100)}{1,100} \right] 4 = 7.18 \text{ min}$$

where, again, $d = 0.5$ because the V_r's are less than their respective V_{rc}'s. The last set of travel times do not differ significantly from the previously calculated ones, so that the procedure can be terminated at this point. The final results are: $V_1 = 536$ vph/lane, $V_2 = 664$ vph/lane, $t_1 = 8.85$ min, and $t_2 = 7.18$ min.

The example calculations closed on the accepted values rather quickly. This may not always be the case, especially if the interzonal volume falls within a range of, say, ±300 vph/lane of the sum of the critical volumes which in this example is $600 + 1,100 = 1,700$ vph/lane. The reason for this statement is that, at the indicated values, the d parameter will jump from 0.5 to 10.0 and back, causing corresponding fluctuations in the related travel times.

Another interesting point to note is that the travel times on the two routes in the example are not equal, although they are fairly close. This circumstance, which is a general situation, may seem to contradict the previously stated concept that a driver cannot improve his travel time by changing his route. However, realistically, most drivers probably do not know exactly what the minimum time path for their trip may be, especially since this path probably changes from moment to moment. Moreover, as brought out before, there are other factors besides travel time which affect route choice, so that a discrepancy in travel times resulting from the use of the two equations, if in the right direction, probably leads to more realistic representations of route choices. As it turns out, tests of the TRC Trip Assignment Model generally have shown it to be fairly reliable.

6.1.8 Peaking Characteristics

With the exception of the trip assignment procedure, all of the foregoing travel models have dealt with 24-hr volumes which for the most part were referenced to the weekday trip. In many situations the specification of a 24-hr volume may be adequate for further analyses and evaluation purposes. But knowledge of the peaks, both within one or over several 24-hr periods often is of vital concern since a transportation facility must be able to handle a high proportion of the peak volumes if it is to be of service to the majority of travelers. This reasoning leads us to a discussion on the variations of tripmaking over time.

6.1.8.1 Peaks within a 24-hr period Probably the most significant temporal variation from the standpoint of design is that within the 24-hr period. In most urban areas the peaks come at two periods—the morning and afternoon rush hours—with a larger volume usually occurring in the latter period. The series of diagrams in Fig. 6.13 to 6.15 show rather clearly the hourly variations which may be anticipated, first by purpose of trip and then by mode. The final figure indicates the variations in the proportion of the p.m. peak hour to daily volume at different locations and for different days in the Nashville urban area. As noted above, the p.m. peak stands out fairly distinctly, representing anywhere from 8 to 14 percent of the total daily traffic. Trips to home comprise most of this peak, with those from work combined with those of family members returning from school, shopping, and personal business visits. Travel by modes other than automobile are particularly peaked, pointing to a major difficulty which faces planners and managers of mass transit systems.

6.1.8.2 Peaks within a week or year It generally is assumed in most transportation planning studies that one day's travel is similar to any other day's. Figure 6.16 bears out this assumption since it shows only minor variations from Monday to Friday of a given week, and, as can be observed, the Saturday and Sunday hourly maximums are not as great, percentage-wise, as those during the week: 8 percent versus approximately 11 percent. In fact, this difference is the basis for the usual planning procedure of concentrating on weekday travel as the major source of traffic problems. Nevertheless, it often turns out that weekend traffic is greater in magnitude than weekday, so that the peaks almost are equivalent in terms of volume, with the added characteristic that little of the weekend travel is by transit. This situation would be particularly noticeable on routes leading to large recreational areas.

Traffic volumes also vary by the month of the year, being higher in the summer months and, as expected, lower during the winter. Again, recreation routes have much greater peaks (Fig. 6.17) than do in-city routes.

The easiest way engineers have found to summarize peaking characteristics is by means of a chart similar to that in Fig. 6.18 where the volumes (taken as a percentage of the annual average daily traffic) in each of the 8,760 hrs in the year are arranged in descending order, with the hour corresponding to the highest hourly volume being called the "first highest hour," the hour corresponding to the second

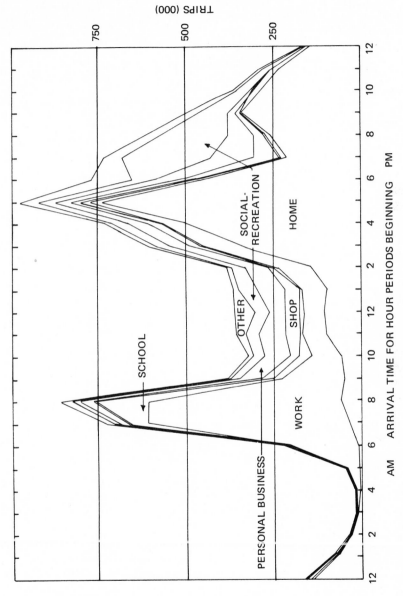

Fig. 6.13 Hourly division of internal person trips by trip purpose. [6.20, p. 35].

221

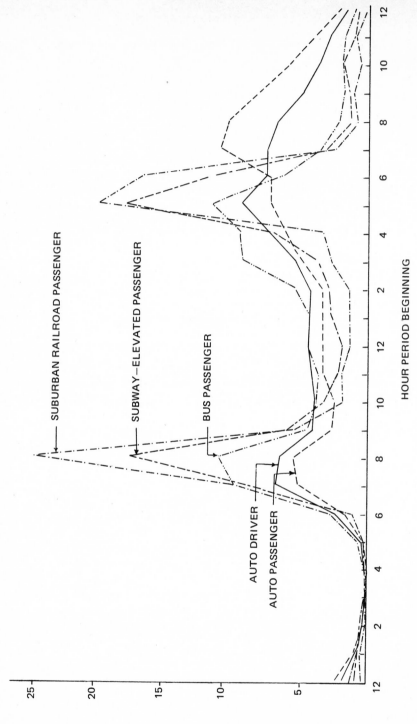

Fig. 6.14 Hourly percentages of total daily trip volume of each model of travel. [6.20, p. 48].

SUBURBAN RAILROAD PASSENGER

SUBWAY–ELEVATED PASSENGER

BUS PASSENGER

AUTO DRIVER

AUTO PASSENGER

HOUR PERIOD BEGINNING

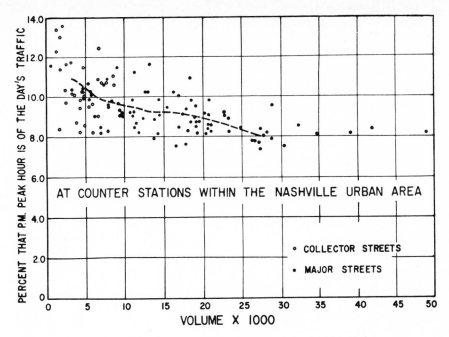

Fig. 6.15 Peak-hour traffic volume as percent of 24-hr volume. [6.3, p. 147].

highest volume called the "second highest hour," and so forth. The 30th and 50th highest hourly volumes are employed extensively in many design considerations, especially in regard to setting the number of lanes and other geometric features. The reason for this, as can be perceived in Fig. 6.18, is that most of the hourly volumes after the 30th or 50th highest hour stay relatively constant (in percentage of AADT), whereas those before rise rather abruptly, thus implying that much more money must be spent to provide adequate capacity for each hour above the 30th or 50th than beyond them. This generally is true, but economy may not be the sole reason for arriving at system modification schemes.

6.1.8.3 Peaking at special generators Certain generators, like the airports, shopping centers, and manufacturing plants discussed earlier in this chapter, are unique in that (1) they have a great influence on travel and congestion in neighboring areas, and (2) they attract trips at times which do not correspond necessarily to the peak periods for the urban area as a whole. Having these two characteristics, they are deservant of further analysis at this point, and, while no elaborate detailing of these characteristics will be presented, at least the reader will become familiar with the general peaking features portrayed in Figs. 6.19 to 6.21.

For airports, perhaps the most important peaking characteristics is that by month of the year. In Fig. 6.19 it can be seen that the variation is quite marked, with increased tripmaking in the summer months and a slow decrease to a low point in February. Hourly trips, on the other hand, follow the same general pattern as overall urban area trips [6.6].

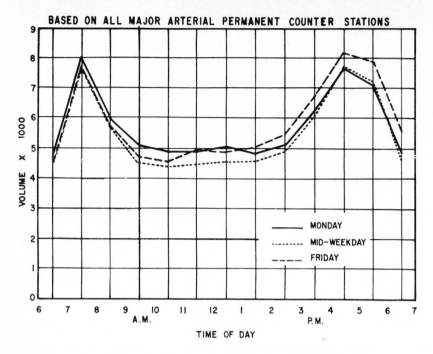

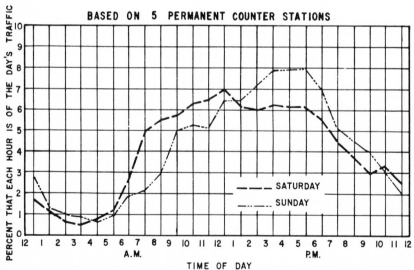

Fig. 6.16 Hourly patterns of traffic-volume variation by day of week. [6.3, p. 146].

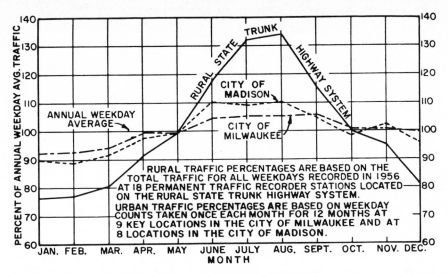

Fig. 6.17   Traffic-volume variation by month of year. [6.2, p. 143].

Shopping center traffic generally peaks during the day at a time different from that of the general morning and afternoon peaks found in most other parts of a city, with the maximum number of arrivals coming around noontime and, for those centers with evening openings, around 7:00 p.m. (Fig. 6.20). Shopping at Christmas time also leads to significant increases in arrivals, with the week after Thanksgiving being the busiest.

As should be expected, work trips, which usually occur in the a.m. rush hour, are the major contributor to travel to manufacturing plants. Consequently, we see in Fig. 6.21 a sharp peak for most plants at about 6:30 a.m. While there is nothing startling about this characteristic, we should be aware that travel in the vicinity of a very large plant may be extremely peaked, thereby requiring additional transportation facility capacity which under usual circumstances would not be necessary.

6.2 TRANSPORTATION SYSTEM IMPACT MODELS

The prediction of transportation system impacts is a difficult and hazardous endeavor. There are many reasons for this situation. First, the impacts are not easy to identify. Transportation is such a basic need in life that almost all aspects of existence can be related to it in some fashion. Transportation can influence such diverse items as levels of communication, preservation of historic buildings, maintenance of bird sanctuaries, and church attendance. Many of these types of impacts cannot be foreseen, much less predicted.

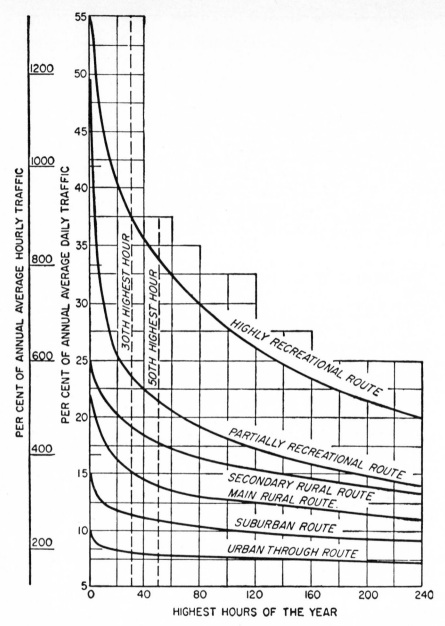

Fig. 6.18 Hourly volumes expressed as percentages of average daily traffic, for typical types of highway. [6.3, p. 15].

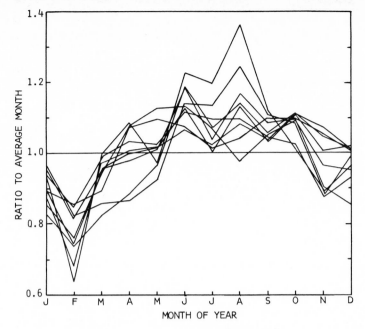

Fig. 6.19 Monthly variation in air passengers. [6.6, p. 10].

A second reason is the often nebulous and undefined (and perhaps undefinable) nature of many impact factors. As everyone knows, "good appearance" is very difficult to define or measure much less predict for some future system and its environment. In the realm of "social factors" clarity usually is equally as difficult to obtain. Do transportation systems increase or reduce the "dignity" of users and impacted nonusers? Does a system provide for more "personal freedom?" Is "community structure" created or destroyed by a highway? These terms have meaning to some people, yet verbalization of these meanings often is impossible. We know, and sometimes can agree, that an *existing* bridge is "beautiful," yet we would be hard pressed to define the totality of components and their interactions that make up the "beauty" of the bridge.

A third reason for difficulty in predicting impacts is the relative lack of research on the subject. Much research has been done, but it is still small in quantity compared to what seems to be needed. As a consequence, there are few detailed models available for use in predicting impacts. Most related research, since it is fairly preliminary and broad in scale, generally ends up being descriptive in nature. This means that relatively few mathematically sophisticated models of transportation impact exist comparable to the travel models presented in the preceding sections of this chapter. At best the planner or engineer usually is left to pursue descriptive studies of past impacts and assume that roughly the same kinds of consequences will result again in the future.

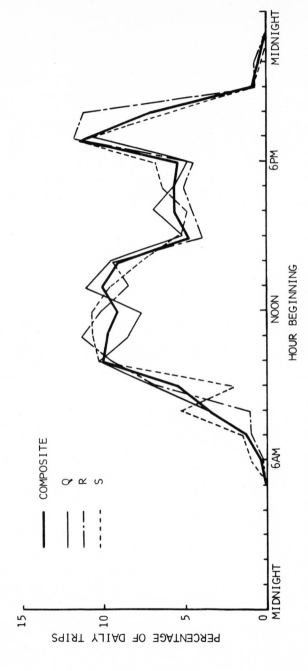

Fig. 6.20 All auto drivers trips to three Miami shopping centers, by arrival hour. [6.6, p. 43].

228

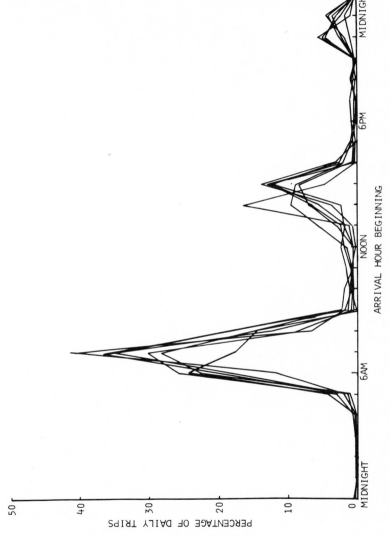

Fig. 6.21 Home interview auto driver trips to work, at selected plants, by employment size groupings. [6.6, p. 71].

A fourth reason for difficulty is the overwhelming complexity of the dynamic metropolitan system. Zettle points out some of these complexities in relation to estimating impacts from the BART system [6.28]:

1. Is BART cause or effect? Did BART cause a preoperation building boom or did business leaders, seeing the need for expansion of their facilities, cause BART to come into being?
2. Did a significant number of people anticipate the advent of BART's operation and choose their residential or job locations ahead of time?
3. Do economic savings to users of BART show up in their disposable income? Or would these savings only show up in increased comfort and convenience?
4. What will banks and other lending institutions do with the estimated $40 million cost in 1975 for service of general obligation bonds? Will this money eventually return to the public? In the San Francisco region? To poor people?
5. If the federal government supplies $100 million to BART, will this lead to an increase in congestion and related impacts *in other cities* across the country that did not receive the funds?
6. Will BART encourage flight to the suburbs, especially by whites?
7. If land values are increased near the BART system, will they also be decreased away from it? Are any land value changes due to BART or to, say, general changes in the regional and national economy?
8. If land values are increased, will this in turn reduce housing opportunities for the poor? Will this in turn cause a greater need for housing subsidies and thus greater taxes?
9. Who gains through transit subsidies and who loses through tax and toll payments? (BART is subsidized by $150 million from retail taxes and $792 million from property taxes, both of which tend to be regressive in nature, that is, bearing more heavily on low income persons).

Finally, we must ask how the "streams" of beneficial and disbeneficial impacts will evolve over time. Will there be a steady positive change in the differential between the two streams? Or will there be cyclical changes? Or will there be steady decreases? The answers to all these questions are difficult if not impossible to provide.

On the other hand, many impacts are extraordinarily easy to predict: The removal of trees will detract from the "naturalness" of surrounding areas and eliminate places where birds can nest; reductions in traffic volumes will result in reductions in noise levels; separation of pedestrians from vehicular traffic will lead to fewer pedestrian fatalities, and so on. Surprisingly, these almost obvious impacts are frequently overlooked, perhaps because of their innate simplicity.

A final reason why impacts are difficult to predict is the influence of many factors beyond the control of transportation planners and designers. If, for example, local transit agencies elect not to provide good connections to BART stations (especially since several of the agencies are in competition with BART), the financial success of the rapid transit system might be in jeopardy. If local water and sewer boards elect to provide service in areas adjacent to BART, land use developments there may be heightened. The extent of impact of most transportation investments thus depends to a great degree on decisions and actions of other major governmental agencies and private enterprises not directly concerned with transportation.

The difficulties elaborated above have been presented to indicate the vastly complex task of determining the impacts of transportation systems. They also have been presented to prepare the reader to expect a much lower level of model sophistication than that found in the beginning of this chapter and in Chap. 5.

In fact, many of the "models" will be nothing more than untested hypotheses based on individual experience. The remainder of this chapter will deal with a brief survey of impacts and four examples of impact "models" and analyses. The examples have been chosen to represent certain types of economic, man-built (land use), social, and environmental impacts and, to a small degree, to demonstrate some analytic techniques involved.

6.2.1 Some Transportation System Impact Controversies

One of the easiest ways to identify and anticipate certain transportation system impacts is to locate relevant articles in a good newspaper. Most of the impacts discussed are negative in nature, yet they still have to be considered. Thomas and Schofer [6.31] have gone through newspaper clippings kept by the Bureau of Public Roads (now the Federal Highway Administration) and have produced a summary of many controversial impacts. This is presented below:

> Highway planners are often tempted to build roads through what often is the only vacant land available—parks and recreation areas. Many groups are legitimately and rightly interested in preserving these open spaces for the use of city dwellers; thus recreation facilities and other natural resources have often become hotly contested issues in transportation disputes. Citizens of Westchester County, N.Y., were concerned about the many acres of wildlife sanctuaries that would be taken in their county during the construction of I-87. In another case, the mayor of Louisville, Ky., in 1966 went to the extreme of blocking construction of I-64 through Seneca and Cherokee parks even though the highway was already under construction on both sides of the parks.
>
> Another example of conflict over park land took place in Minneapolis, Minn. In this case, the Park Board found itself opposed to a local trade union group and the Minneapolis Chamber of Commerce. The downtown businessmen and the union urged the Park Board to agree to the taking of $18\frac{1}{2}$ acres of Parade Park and 15 acres of Minnehaha Park for the upgrading of one highway and building of another. If the park board did not agree to this arrangement, they argued, it would cost a large sum of money to locate the facilities in a residential area and force the taking of 298 structures. Furthermore, the state would lose three years in the rerouting.
>
> This conflict illustrates well the dilemma of planners who attempt to route a highway through an urban area. Frequently, the alternative to building a road through a park is routing it through a residential or business section. This necessitates the taking of privately owned property, however, and is almost certain to arouse protest. In New York City, the Cross-Brooklyn Expressway was protested by the residents of Flatbush because it would displace 1,042 families.

Similarly, the Lower Manhattan Expressway would have displaced 2,000 families and 800 businesses and was consequently rejected by the mayor. Elevated and underground designs were both considered as possible alternatives to this plan. Under the administration of one mayor, the plan was abandoned, only to be revived in the next administration in response to the urging of business and commercial organizations concerned about reducing severe traffic congestion. Most recently, the Board of Estimate took the view of neighborhood associations opposed to the air pollution, blight, and congestion they expected from the planned expressway, and the plans for the expressway have again been dropped.

In Holyoke, Mass., citizens protested the route selected for I-91 on the grounds that the cost of land taking would have been excessive. This was due to the presence of high-priced apartment buildings on the proposed right-of-way. In part because of this protest, another route was eventually selected and the buildings were saved.

In other cases, citizen's groups have protested that land taking would have a deleterious effect on important historical monuments. Local officials and residents of Morristown, N.J., for example, contested the location selected for I-287, because it would be too close to George Washington's Revolutionary War Headquarters. In Philadelphia, the Committee for the Preservation of Philadelphia's Historic Southwark charged that 131 historic homes certified by the Philadelphia Historical Commission would be destroyed unless the route of the Delaware Expressway were changed.

Some cities have attempted to avoid the problem of direct taking of properties for facility construction by building elevated transportation links. This solution usually has not met with unqualified approval either. Protest has usually centered around the question of aesthetics, another aspect of concomitant outputs. Elevated expressways are often considered to be visually unappealing, and the memory of older elevated facilities serves to intensify this feeling. A famous example of this sort of controversy is that of the Riverfront Expressway in New Orleans. The proponents of the plan claimed that elevating the highway would avoid the adverse effect on the economy of the area which taking additional property would produce, and would provide an excellent flood-prevention facility. Opponents countered with the charges that the expressway would be noisy, would shut out light and air, and, most important, would blight and deteriorate the character of the French Quarter, through which it would run.

Citizens' groups and members of the Committee to Preserve Philadelphia's Historic Gateway who protested the construction of an elevated highway through Society Hill were successful in convincing state officials that this section of the Delaware Expressway should be depressed, so that the beauty of the Penn's Landing area might be preserved.

The aesthetic issue of the elevation of transportation facilities also arises in the question of the relative merits of bridges and tunnels. Proponents of tunnels generally argue they they are visually less unattractive than bridges and necessitate less land taking. The Bay View Business Association of Milwaukee protested the construction of a bridge over Milwaukee harbor and advocated building a tunnel which, they said, would not look as bad and would be cheaper to build. Disagreeing with both parts of their statement, however, the County Expressway Commission maintained that a bridge would be beautiful and would cost less to build and maintain.

Some of the most intense recent controversies have been associated with transportation choices where planned facilities were to pass through economically and socially disadvantaged neighborhoods. The principal concern in many of these cases has been the planned destruction of dwelling units and community facilities, although many of the structures were already substandard. The inadequate supply of low cost housing in the affected areas has been more than a contributing factor in these conflicts; it has often been the central problem. The transportation facility, however, has become the focus of controversy, perhaps because of the high visibility of the transportation system and its planning processes. That is, the housing program, if relatively inactive, is not a well-known function that can draw controversy. When transportation plans become known, and when construction begins, considerable attention may result, and the emotions of the community may be directed towards transportation.

6.2.2 Retail Sales and Land Value Impacts

One type of economic impact relates to retail sales and land values. Horwood et al. analyzed a large number of highway impact studies made in the years up to 1964 [6.29]. These studies focused on many items, but retail sales and land values were prominent. Three categories of investigations were identified: (1) bypass studies, (2) urban circumferential studies, and (3) urban radial freeway studies. These will now be discussed in turn.

6.2.2.1 Bypass studies
The bypass studies dealt with sales in highway and nonhighway oriented retail establishments in bypassed towns falling into various population categories. Data were obtained primarily from sales tax information provided by appropriate state agencies. In many cases sales comparisons were made with control areas, that is, towns that with the exception of the bypass were as similar as possible to those of main concern to the particular study. In providing a control area, it was possible to determine in a rough way whether gains or losses in sales were due primarily to the bypassing highway or to general economic conditions prevalent in the region.

A summary of total and highway-oriented retail sales changes in bypassed towns is shown in Table 6.13. As can be seen, only 7 of 36 towns showed a sales revenue loss, 28 had a gain, and one had no change. Towns over 5,000 population showed an average increase over twice that of towns under 5,000. In comparison to the control areas, the overall gain of +8.5 percent turns out to be a slight relative loss of 0.3 percent. In other words, the highway bypasses appear to have almost no relative impact on retail sales for the "average" establishment. Towns of different sizes are not affected equally, however, those under 5,000 population lost 3.5 percent more than their corresponding controls, while those over 5,000 averaged gains of 3.7 percent relative to their controls.

Interestingly, highway-oriented sales for fuel, food, and lodging for transients in bypassed towns increased, and at a greater ratio than for total retail sales—21.0 percent versus 8.5 percent. No control areas were established for these set of studies so it is difficult to tell if the highway-oriented sales actually gained relative to other localities. The apparent gains might be suspect, however, since in a further analysis of 32 impact studies where service station sales were listed separately, Horwood et al. found that the average change in sales was only +2.3 percent and −3.2 percent in comparison to control areas (see Table 6.14).

In addition, restaurant sales decreased an average of 13.0 percent (−6.4 percent relative to controls) and motel and hotel sales decreased an average of 23.1 percent (no controls employed). These latter findings are more in accord with expectations, yet there appears to be much variability in impact. In particular, the largest towns almost always appear to gain significantly while the smaller ones lose equivalently.

Table 6.13 Sales Changes in Bypassed Towns

Population category	Avg. change in retail sales (%)	No. of towns with		Range (%)	Avg. gain (%)	Avg. loss (%)	Control area	No. of towns with	Avg. gain or loss over control (%)
		Gain in sales[a]	Loss in sales[a]					More gain or less loss than control[a]	
(a) Total retail sales									
Under 5,000	+5.6	16/20	3/20	−6.4 to +22.5	+8.2	−6.6	18	6/18	−3.5
Over 5,000	+12.2	12/16	4/16	−13.0 to +49.0	+20.4	−7.5	14	11/14	+3.7
5,000–10,000	+16.9	5/6	1/6	−13.0 to +38.0	+17.7	−13.0	6	4/6	+0.85
10,000–25,000	+7.3	5/7	2/7	−3.1 to +40.5	+12.5	−4.8	7	6/7	+4.1
25,000–50,000	−11.4	0/1	1/1	—	—	−11.4	—	—	—
50,000–100,000	—	—	—	—	—	—	—	—	—
100,000 and over	+22.6	2/2	0/2	+4.3 to +49.0	+22.6	—	1	1/1	+19.0
All towns	+8.5	28/36	7/36	−13.0 to +49.0	+12.9	—	32	17/32	−0.30
(b) Highway-oriented sales									
Under 5,000	+20.8	3/6	3/6	−14.7 to +60.9	+51.8	−10.3			
Over 5,000	+21.2	3/4	1/4	−11.8 to +50.4	+32.3	−11.8			
5,000–10,000	+41.5	1/1	0/1	—	+41.5	—			
10,000–25,000	+50.4	1/1	0/1	—	+50.4	—			
25,000–50,000	−11.8	0/1	1/1	—	—	−11.8			
50,000–100,000	—	—	—	—	—	—			
100,000 and over	+4.9	1/1	0/1	—	+4.9	—			
All towns	+21.0	6/10	4/10	−14.7 to +60.9	+42.5	−10.6			

[a]For example, 16/20 indicates "16 of 20."
Source: [6.29, p. 9].

Table 6.14 Service Station Sales Changes in Bypassed Towns

Population category	Avg. change in retail sales (%)	No. of towns with		Range (%)	Avg. gain (%)	Avg. loss (%)	Control area	No. of towns with	Avg. gain or loss over control (%)
		Gain in sales[a]	Loss in sales[a]					More gain or less loss than control[a]	
Under 5,000	-0.47	8/17	9/17	-33.0 to +39.4	+14.3	-13.6	11	5/11	-0.86
Over 5,000	+5.5	7/15	8/15	-21.0 to +39.0	+20.0	-7.3	10	6/10	-5.75
5,000–10,000	-1.8	2/4	2/4	-21.0 to +17.0	+11.3	-15.0	3	2/3	-20.0
10,000–25,000	-4.2	3/7	4/7	-10.0 to +33.9	+19.1	-7.5	6	3/6	-6.1
25,000–50,000	-4.8	0/2	2/2	-7.0 to -2.5	—	-4.8	—	—	—
50,000–100,000	—	—	—	—	—	—	—	—	—
100,000 and over	+30.3	2/2	0/2	+21.5 to +39.0	+30.3	—	1	1/1	+21.0
All towns	+2.3	15/32	17/32	-33.0 to +39.4	+16.9	-10.6	21	11/21	-3.2

[a]For example, 9/17 indicates "9 of 17."
Source: [6.29, p. 10].

Also, nonhighway-oriented sales changes are better in larger cities. There are gains, nonetheless, over all city sizes (averaging +10.3 percent individually and +5.8 percent relative to control areas).

6.2.2.2 Urban circumferented studies

Only six studies found by Horwood et al. dealt with urban circumferentials. A common feature of several of these studies was relatively rapid and intense land use changes along beltway routes. Commercial and industrial use predominate (in contrast to residential), and land values close by the facility were seen to increase substantially.

Land use changes. Lexington and Louisville, Kentucky, found that total agricultural acreage was reduced 35.7 and 29 percent, respectively, after road construction. Louisville had a 23.6 percent increase in commercial and industrial uses and 3.1 percent increase in institutional uses. Minneapolis–St. Paul showed a 60.5 percent increase in commercial and industrial land uses where little had existed previously.

Land value changes. Commercial lands showed the greatest average increases in values: 53.5 percent in Louisville and 93 percent in Lexington. Older residential areas were more seriously affected than newer ones in both cities. There was an average 5.5 percent decrease for older areas and 2.0 percent for newer ones. In Baltimore the average land value increase near a circumferential was 10.0 percent.

6.2.3.3 Urban radial freeway studies

Four studies of the impacts of urban radial freeways were detailed by Horwood et al. [6.29]. These were for the cities of Dallas, Houston, Atlanta, and San Antonio. Unfortunately, time spans in the studies differed somewhat as did definitions of "land value" and adjustments for inflation and local cost factors. Delineation of study and control areas also varied from area to area. The actions taken to create as much compatibility as possible between studies are summarized in Table 6.15.

Table 6.16 displays a comparison between changes in land use values in the four study areas given the limitations brought out in the preceeding paragraph. The results that seem most prominent are:

1. In most cases, value of land abutting the radial freeway facility exceeded that of land further removed as well as land in control areas.
2. Unimproved or vacant land appears to receive the largest benefit from the freeway, ranging from two to three times the value increases of improved properties.
3. Land values computed with improvement values deducted doubled to tripled for land including improvements.

Another interesting finding is the rapid decline in land values with distance from the radial freeway. For example, band B in Dallas is quite close to the freeway (next to abutting land), yet values there rose less than one-quarter of those in the abutting band. In fact, the rise in band B is slightly less than for the control area (band D). The rapid fall in land values also is quite noticeable on an overall basis. This means that owners of existing facilities in an area should not expect any great

Table 6.15 Definitions and Adjustments for Four Land Value Studies

Delineation of study and control areas.—The study areas for the four reports were delineated as follows:

(a) Houston—   A band, adjacent; B band, removed; C band, affected (nearby on good thoroughfares); and D area, distributed control areas.

(b) Atlanta—   A, B, and C bands were variable-width segments of homogeneous uses roughly parallel to this facility; and D area, one control area supposedly similar to expressway vicinity.

(c) Dallas—   A band, abutting; B band, next two blocks, C band, next two blocks, and D area, dispersed control areas.

(d) San Antonio—A band, expressway fronting; B band, expressway not fronting; C band, main thoroughfare not at expressway; and D area, dispersed control areas not on main thoroughfare or not on expressway.

Adjustment for inflation and local cost factors.—

(a) Houston—   Adjusted for construction costs, inflation, and assessment factor.*

(b) Atlanta—   Adjusted for inflation only.

(c) Dallas—   Variety of adjustment methods, including inflation and construction costs.

(d) San Antonio—No adjustment.

Definitions of values.—

(a) Houston—   Land values with and without improvements, adjusted and unadjusted (four methods).

(b) Atlanta—   Improved land values, vacant land values, and both combined (three methods).

(c) Dallas—   Land less improvements, land and improvements, unimproved land, and tax valuations of land in the 1941 and 1946 annexations (four methods).

(d) San Antonio—Land and improvements, land less improvements, and non-residentially zoned land (three methods).

---

*Assessment factor is defined as "the tax assessment value of improvements (used) as a base for determining the relative values. In 1950 the assessed value ... was 70% of the actual value. In 1955 ... 77%" The assessment factors applied were, therefore, 0.70 and 0.77 for the appropriate years.

Source: [6.29, p. 19].

relative change in land values from a new radial freeway unless they happen to be right next to it.

Owners of vacant and unimproved land are likely to gain substantially, however. Even in band B, increases in land values are up to eight times as great as in the control area. The average is two to four times as great. It would seem, then, that the most return on investment can be obtained by purchasing unused land within an approximate two block strip from the potential location of a radial expressway.

Table 6.16 Changes in Land Values by Locational Relationship to Freeway (Expressway)

| | Average increase over base year (%) | | | | | | | | | | | |
| | Land with improvements | | | | Land without improvements | | | | Unimproved (vacant) land | | | |
Location	Band A	Band B	Band C	Band D	Band A	Band B	Band C	Band D	Band A	Band B	Band C	Band D
Dallas												
1941 Annexation	431	100	139	106	623	123	185	130	518	383	291	166
1946 Annexation	127	26	(22)	31	1027	538	–	104	1179	766	–	136
Houston												
Unadjusted	250	130	50	90	282	150	38	76	–	–	–	–
Adjusted	245	125	(15)	44	190	96	(70)	(12)	–	–	–	–
Atlanta												
West	99	4	11	102	–	–	–	–	197	12	53	148
East	40	18	(35)	102	–	–	–	–	247	35	(58)	148
San Antonio	251	181	71	(2)	377	264	127	30	–	–	–	–
Overall average	206	83	28	68	500	234	70	66	535	299	95	149
Overall range	40– 251	4– 181	†35– 139	–2– 106	100– 1027	96– 538	–70– 185	–12– 130	197– 1179	12– 766	–58– 291	136– 166

Source: [6.29, p. 19].

238

6.2.3 Relocation Impacts

Of all the social impacts of transportation system construction, relocation seems to have been given the most attention. This is probably because it strikes closest to individual citizens and thus exposes many personal problems that otherwise would have laid dormant. Christensen and Jackson express the idea well [6.45, p. 1]:

When expressways run through a major city, large numers of people and many businesses are displaced. Unfortunately, the highways are frequently routed through the least desirable sections of the city, and those who are displaced are the poor, the aged, and those who are least able to take care of themselves, and there is little likelihood that many of them will use the expressway that displaces them . . . .

In theory, relocation assistance is simple. In practice, it is difficult, complicated, and time-consuming. Frequently, successful relocation depends on solving personal problems, both financial and social, in addition to finding replacement property.

The authors go on to portray six examples of the unique types of problems that were faced in relocating some families and businesses in Baltimore [6.45, pp. 4, 5]:

Mr. T, 63, lives with his wife and two college-age children. When first approached, he declined relocation assistance, saying he had already found a home in a good section of town. However, his mortgage application was turned down by one lending institution after another because of his age. Unfortunately mortgage processing took so much time that someone else bought the house. At this point, he turned to relocation, which was able to locate another good house in the same block as the previous one. By diligent work, a cooperative lender was willing to provide a mortgage despite Mr. T's age. The family's living conditions are substantially improved and they are happy with the change.

Mrs. L, 60-year-old widow, lived with her mentally retarded son and daughter, both in their 30's. Conditions were pitiful. The had no furniture and slept on the floor. They had no gas or electricity as these had been shut off in 1960 when they failed to pay a $75 bill. There was no heat. The case looked hopeless when relocation went to work on it. The ideal place for a family of this kind would be public housing, but they refused even to consider it, insisting that they stay in the same general neighborhood. Relocation finally found them a satisfactory apartment nearby at a rent within their welfare allowance. Welfare provided a furniture grant, which was used at Goodwill Industries so as to get the maximum return for each dollar spent. A private charitable organization was found which agreed to pay the back-due gas and electric bill. Finally, relocation provided transportation for the few goods owned, and assisted them in paying the rent deposit. The family is now warm and comfortable, much better than they have been for years.

Mr. B, a 90-year-old man, lived with his 70-year-old widowed daughter. He had owned the property for many years, but had lost it two years before it was acquired by the city. As the new owner permitted him to stay there and did not collect rent, Mr. B could not realize that he was no longer the owner of the property. The daughter was little better, for she was a mental problem. Relocation sought help from medical sources, and from social agencies but these provided no solution. After several weeks of effort, no progress had been made, and the problem seemed almost insoluble, when Mr. B died. It was then possible to work with a granddaughter who lived elsewhere in the city. The granddaughter was unable to take the mother into her home, but cooperated in every way possible. Relocation found a new apartment, which the granddaughter inspected and approved. Then the granddaughter took her mother by the hand to the new location while Relocation completed the move.

The situation is not the most ideal, but this woman seems to have adjusted well to her new surroundings, and is content.

Mrs. A, a 45-year-old recluse, also has mental problems. Relocation showed her numerous possible locations, yet she refused to move. Because of her very limited income, a charitable landlord was found who agreed to reduce rent to a price she could pay. Still she refused to move. Something had to be done, as the remainder of the block was vacant, and it was dangerous for her to stay in her apartment any longer. Her brother was contacted and asked to assist, but he was unable to change her mind. Finally, with the brother's cooperation, eviction was arranged on court order. As her furniture was moved out of the apartment and onto the sidewalk, her brother arrived with a truck to take her to a new location which he had approved. Mrs. A calls occasionally. It is hard to say whether she is content in her new location or not. Sometimes she says she would like to move, but by the time Relocation reaches her apartment, she has changed her mind and decided that she will stay where she is. Probably this should be rated as a failure, because she had to be evicted; yet she is without any serious problems at her new location, other than those she had before.

Mr. R moved out of a house without telling Relocation. He was traced and visited at his new location which was found to be substandard. He was offered further assistance but refused the offer saying he was satisfied with the new place and would not move again. He had lost ground as a result of his move.

Mr. S operated a small two-chair barber shop. He suffered from cancer and had had a laryngectomy, which left him virtually unable to speak. His attempts to find a new location were met with failure. Even when he finally found a place he thought he could use, his application for a zoning exception was turned down. He was bitter and depressed. Finally, he turned to Relocation, which found him a new location, assisted in processing an application for a permit, assisted him in obtaining credit, and finally arranged for a SBA loan. He is proud of his new, greatly improved shop, and is getting along fine.

These types of problems, although handled here successfully for the most part, are compounded by the size of the relocation program. In Baltimore, the current expressway program is expected to displace 3,800 families (about 15,000 people). Only 20 percent of these families are white; less than 40 percent own their homes; their median income is $4,500. Nearly three-quarters have incomes so low that they qualify neither for public housing nor for other government subsidized housing programs. A large number are elderly, and many have large families. Some 500 businesses also are expected to be displaced, varying in size from the small neighborhood grocery or barber shop to multi-million dollar factories [6.45]. On the national level, the federal-state highway program will be responsible for about 50,000 displacements annually for the next several years [6.46].

The question now arises as to how the relocatees have fared in general. Were there any groups that were more or less successful than others? What was the overall reaction of relocatees to their forced move? The answers to these questions are not readily available, as relatively little intensive research has been done on the subject of relocation. In addition, the extent of some impacts seems to have been altered significantly after passage of some important federal and state laws. Prior to the Federal-Aid Highway Act of 1962, for example, no payments to families, individuals, and businesses for moving expenses or for loss of personal property were authorizied to be included within the project cost to be financed in part by federal funds [6.42]. This meant, in effect, that relocatees were reimbursed only for the "fair market value" of their property, which usually was not sufficient to reestablish a home or business.

The 1968 Federal-Aid Highway Act upgraded the relocation program considerably. Many of the far-reaching provisions of that act were [6.46, p. 13]:

1. New declaration of legislative policy with respect to highway relocation assistance.
2. Provision for assurances to be given by the state highway departments in connection with specific project proposals.
3. Increase in the level of all moving cost payments without a ceiling but with certain limitations.
4. Provision for 100 percent federal share of the first $25,000 of such payments to any person until July 1, 1970.
5. Authorization for an additive to fair market value of property acquired in the form of a replacement housing payment up to $5,000.
6. Provision for a similar additive in the form of a rent supplement for tenants up to $1,500.
7. Sanction of the payment of expenses to the property owner incidental to the transfer of his property to the state.
8. Requirement for an expanded level of relocation assistance services to displacees.
9. Definition of several real property acquisition policies that are mandatory on all federal-aid highway acquisitions.

The primary effect of this act was to place a significant burden on highway departments and other state and local agencies to find "decent, safe, and sanitary" housing for those families displaced by highway facilities.

Some statistical information on the impacts of relocation before the 1968 Act are presented by House [6.43]. She studied displacement caused by the North–South Freeway in Milwaukee, which bisected the city's Negro area, and concluded that, in general: (*a*) living conditions were improved for a majority of families, (*b*) changes in housing induced positive psychological attitudes, (*c*) housing costs increased, and (*d*) the concentration of Negroes was increased in a predominantly Negro area.

The area bisected by the freeway was 70 percent Negro, had below average housing conditions but comparatively high home ownership, and a rent to income ratio of about 0.13. After the move, the proportion of these families living in poor housing dropped from 39 percent to 14 percent. Housing was *perceived* as better by 62 percent of the relocatees and worse by only 23 percent. Home ownership increased from 59 to 70 percent, but average rents increased 12 percent from $67 to $75 per month and monthly mortgage payments increased substantially, from $45 to $72. This latter result apparently came about because many older families who already had paid for their houses were forced to resume mortgage commitments for their new residences. In balance, as can be seen in Tables 6.17 and 6.18, the overall impact of relocation seemed to be beneficial.

**Table 6.17 Comparisons of Residential
Characteristics for Areas Occupied
before and after Relocation**

Characteristics	Before	After
Housing quality		
% sound	60.5	85.0
% deteriorating	34.4	12.6
% dilapidated	5.1	1.5
Overcrowding		
% dwellings with		
1.01 + persons	14.0	8.5
Housing costs		
Average house value	$9,681	$12,312
Average monthly rent	60	72
Occupancy structure		
% owner-occupied	44.0	41.0
% renter-occupied	56.0	59.0

Source: U.S. Census of Housing, 1960, [6.43, p. 76].

**Table 6.18 Comparisons of Individual
Housing Characteristics before and
after Relocation**

Characteristics	Before	After
Housing quality		
% good/fair	60.5	86.0
% poor	39.5	14.0
Overcrowding/living space		
% more space after		62.0
% no change		29.0
% less space after		9.0
Housing costs		
Average monthly mortgage		
payment	$67	$75
Average monthly rent	$45	$72
Occupancy structure		
% owner-occupied	50.0	70.0
% renter-occupied	41.0	30.0

Source: [6.43, p. 76].

The impact on certain individuals and groups was not as beneficial, however. In particular, most of the families (25 percent of the total) whose main wage earner was retired, and whose families therefore were living on generally low, fixed incomes, were forced out of houses which they owned and into less desirable rental facilities. Moreover, segregation was increased, as most of the Negro displacees moved to closeby neighborhoods where, in 75 percent of the cases, Negroes already lived on the block.

The findings brought out above are repeated in other relocation situations across the country. In a 1965 survey done by the U.S. Advisory Council on Intergovernmental Relations [6.42], of the 31,000 residential units from which families were relocated by highways, 30 percent had an estimated value under $6,000 or rented for less than $60 per month. The poor thus seem to be relocated out of proportion to their number.

In the Milwaukee situation there seemed to be adequate housing available on the open market for those displaced. Such is not always the case, however. Housing stocks for the poor, black, and those with large families often are limited. Added to this problem is that of income and racial segregation, which prevents some families from moving into available housing units [6.41].

Another result, found to a small degree in Milwaukee, is that housing prices and rents in a tight market usually go up, and in some instances a family must pay more for a unit that is inferior to that which they had before. Of course some households can be moved to public housing when it is available and if it suits the particular household. Even then, the very poorest people often are not eligible for public housing because they cannot even pay the minimal rent required [6.42].

Business relocation also can be quite traumatic, especially for the marginal and submarginal "family" businesses such as grocery stores and barber shops run generally by older people. Their success as an enterprise depends heavily on people in the immediate neighborhood, and if they are displaced, sales naturally decline. These losses come about primarily because of the "wet blanket" affect that relocation (which may be several years off) has on purchases and land values in the community. Losses occur also in moving and starting up anew elsewhere (if the business is not terminated). In addition, obtaining a license (e.g., for a bar) in a new location can be a difficult problem [6.42].

Mental and psychological problems also abound. While in many cases the relocated family or business eventually adjusts to its new surroundings (and even is benefited by them), there are other cases where a longing for the old neighborhood remains. This is particularly true in neighborhoods in which families (and possibly generations) have lived for many years. Contacts with former friends and relatives is difficult since they are scattered. Churches that have been the center of many lives often cannot be attended any more. Many times those who lived within walking distance of the CBD now must ride the bus, if they can afford it [6.41].

Interestingly, many people move themselves and do not require or make use of advisory services. This seems to result for three reasons:

1. The general mobility of families in the United States (roughly 13 million families move every year anyway [6.42].
2. The general desire not to live in a neighborhood that is running down.
3. The lack of any advisory relocation assistance.

The last reason is particularly disturbing. As an illustration, in one New York City urban renewal project reported by Niebanck a set of volunteer workers (local citizens and some Peace Corps people) found [6.41, p. 60]:

> ... major deficiencies in the amounts of aid being received by persons who were fully eligible for and in need of such aid. These gaps existed both in the immediate relocation program with which the project was primarily concerned and in city welfare programs generally. The deficiencies stemmed from many factors: inadequate regulations; poor administrative procedures; unnecessarily rigid policies originating at the top of the official hierarchy; poor communications between office personnel and field workers; and indifferent or incompetent people in either the office or the field.

On the other hand, one of the nicer aspects of this and other relocation projects was the friendliness of caseworkers toward the relocatees, particularly the elderly. Many older people had known only loneliness, lack of care, and insecurity until caseworkers and volunteers (sometimes church groups and neighborhood house workers) approached them concerning the expected moves. Relations were built up, particularly with other, elderly relocatees, that lasted past the movement period [6.41].

6.2.3.1 Comments on relocation impacts

The effects of relocation for highway purposes generally have been favorable, especially in terms of physical well-being. Often relocation housing, although somewhat more expensive, has induced positive psychological attitudes. Yet there are some problems:

1. Segregation might be increased.
2. The elderly generally are uprooted from long-standing social and religious contacts.
3. Many marginal businesses are forced to terminate.
4. Relocation services often are not readily available, meaning that many relocatees do not get equitable treatment.

In theory everyone affected by a highway system change should be compensated so that he is no worse off then he was before the change was created and perhaps he is better off. Yet, according to Christensen and Jackson, the sad practice seems to be that [6.45, p. 2]: "... practically every person and every business which must move is injured far beyond any benefit which they may derive from the new road."

6.2.4 Visual Impacts

Another set of impacts that are very difficult to measure and predict are those concerned with the visual impact of a transportation facility. Relatively little has been written about appearance *of* facilities, while somewhat more has been reported about appearance *from* facilities, especially from the point of view of the highway driver. Thus, while the concern in this section is primarily for nonuser impacts, we will have to draw primarily from research related to the user.

Two points should be made initially:

1. Good appearance is not solely a result of "cosmetics," that is, changes in the visible surface of an object. It usually is an intricate part of the overall building effort.
2. Good appearance varies according to the viewer, that is, "beauty is in the eye of the beholder."

Lynch emphasizes these points heavily. In regard to the first, he says [6.38, p. 250]:

> City design is the technical core of the process of city planning, and its concerns are equally broad. Design does not focus solely on appearance, nor indeed on any single factor which is affected by form. The immediate sensuous quality of an environment—the way it looks, smells, sounds, feels—is one consequence of the way it is put together. . . .

In connection with the second point, he states further [6.38, p. 251]:

> Current campaigns for "beautification" are a reflection of middle and upper middle class taste, with its emphasis on tidiness, appropriateness, and camouflage. The junkyard, abhorrent to the garden club, is a rich mine of form for the sculptor. A lower class citizen may be attracted by visible signs of security, durability, newness, or upward mobility, and take pleasure in forms which to an upper class observer seem coarse, hard, and vulgar.

6.2.4.1 Visual impact criteria With these points in mind, and working primarily from conscious experience rather than from detailed scientific experiments, Lynch and other researchers have developed sets of perceptual criteria that give some indication of the likely acceptability of appearance of various urban forms, including highways. Lynch divides these criteria into six major statements [6.38]:

1. Sensations should be within the range of comfort.
2. Within the range of comfort, diversity of sensation and setting are to be desired.
3. Places in the environment should have a clear perceptual identity: recognizable, memorable, vivid.
4. The identifiable parts should be arranged so that the observer can mentally relate them to one another and understand their pattern in time and space.
5. The environment should be perceived as meaningful. Identifiable parts should be related to other aspects of life.
6. The environment should play a role in fostering the intellectual, emotional, and physical development of the individual by encouraging attention and exploration.

Perhaps the greatest sources of discomfort induced by the visual environment are those scenes which portray large-scale complexity, undertones of risk and uncertainty, and culturally unacceptable sites. Most people feel uneasy, for example, when faced with a bewildering and complex array of signs, signals and symbols. As Appleyard et al. state [6.35, p. 11]:

> Finding a way through the intricacies of a modern city is a demanding performance, and one cannot depend entirely upon such conventional aids as directional signs, at least not without some emotional insecurity.

It thus appears that when the complexity of a scene is great, the viewer is likely to be stressed emotionally and will not consider the appearance to be of the highest quality. Further, if the viewer is distressed by some scenes that obviously are not culturally acceptable, such as borrow pits, strip mines, or sanitary fills through which or by which a transportation facility must pass, he naturally will respond negatively to the scene.

Diversification appears to be a significant feature of good visual impact. Human beings seem to have an appetite for novelty and variety. Moreover, it is such change that gives them choice and helps them develop their perceptual and cognitive system. These statements have particular significance for the driver or passenger viewing the road and its surroundings as they appear and pass by. Appleyard, Lynch, and Myer allude to this when the say [6.35, p. 4]:

> The sense of spatial sequence (in views from the road) is like that of large scale architecture; the continuity and insistent temporal flow are akin to music and the cinema. The kinesthetic sensations are like those of the dance or the amusement park, although rarely so violent.

Lack of diversity in the driving experience is found in the long trips over the unchanging, featureless plains of the Midwest. The result is a monotony that in many cases leads to drowsiness and even sleep. It may be important, in fact, to make sharp changes in the otherwise smooth-flowing alignments of most roads to joust the driver out of his monotony.

Of course the amount of diversification in a view differs according to the newness of the scene to the driver and his speed. A tourist obviously sees the landscape with a fresh eye and attaches relatively few personal meanings to it. He generally is engaged in orienting himself to the large and outstanding features in it. The habitual commuter, on the other hand, probably ignores large landscape features in favor of new and unique events: construction activities, new buildings or roadway appurtenances, moving trains and airplanes nearby, and so on.

Naturally all these events cannot be seen and absorbed if the speed of the vehicle is high. In this situation the driver can only experience those views positioned almost directly ahead of him. At 25 mph his total horizontal angle of vision is about $50°$ to either side, and the eyes focus at a point about 600 ft ahead. At 60 mph, the focus may be nearly 2,000 ft ahead while the angle of vision has shrunk to less than $20°$ [6.36]. These findings indicate that it is better if the driver of high speed roads has long, straight-ahead views of large scale features (e.g., city skylines), while the driver of slower roads has views of more detailed and widely spaced objects.

Another way in which diversity is enhanced is through accentuated features of unique sites such as historical monuments, towers, bridges, and rock outcroppings. In addition, the masking and subsequent revelation of a prominent feature and the confinement, rotation, feinting, jogging, swerving, and sliding past of objects in the foreground all add to the diversity of the driving experience. In terms of nondriving experiences, some important variations people might seek are [6.38, p. 252]:

The range from lonely to gregarious places, for example; or from highly defined and structured surroundings to ones which are free and loose; from calm, simple, slow worlds to rapid, complex, and stimulating ones. . . . A secluded garden opening on a busy street is one example.

While variety is important, so also is identity. Many of those who have studied the visual form of the city feel that there is a constant search by people for a "sense of place." As Lynch remarks [6.38, p. 253]:

If the setting is vividly identifiable, the observer has a concrete basis for a sense of belonging. He can begin to make relations; he can savor the uniqueness of places and people; he can learn to *see* (or to listen or to smell).

Every street should not look like every other street.

The question now becomes that of determining what makes a setting unique. Certainly many of the features that contribute to diversity also are unique: historical monuments, bridges, cuts and other tunnel-like confinements in the roadway, and prominent natural features. Another set of situations that are dramatic and therefore create a "sense of place" are the gateway views of many large cities. Pittsburgh's freeway approach to the Golden Triangle, the view of Manhattan from the Brooklyn-Queens Expressway, or of San Francisco from the Golden Gate Bridge are examples of the spectacular possibilities. Such experiences should not be accidental.

The legible structure in space and time of these and other less imposing but still unique settings is also an important aspect of good visual impact. People seem to need the emotional security of knowing where they are and how they are going to get to where they want to go. In terms of the automobile driver, he is caught up in a sequential and unfolding flow of images that must be related in some way. In this regard, the alignment of transportation guideways is important since it is through the geometric layout that the driver sets his future movement patterns and predicts their success. Sharp changes in alignment thus are not encouraged unless the intent is to provide some drama to overcome monotony. Perhaps also of importance is the creation of a "beat" or "rhythm" for the traveler. If unique objects such as light poles or abutments pass by too infrequently, temporal relationships become indistinct. The same appears to be true, however, if the objects go by so quickly that their passage is blurred in the traveler's mind.

On a larger scale, the strength of the relationships between areas of the city can be increased through emphasis on contrasting features of different neighborhoods, through more and better informational signing, and, more simply, through making the outstanding objects in the city more visible from transportation facilities. In a temporal view, clues of time can be made by exposing the scars of history and the signs of future intentions, and more attention might be paid to clarifying cyclical times in the environment (day/night, winter/summer, holiday/workday).

The next step in improving visual impact is to attempt to relate visible parts meaningfully to other aspects of life: the nature site and its ecology, functional activity, social structure, economic and political patterns, and so on [6.38].

Appleyard et al. point out that the transportation guideway actually should be a kind of linear exposition [6.35, p. 17]:

> ...running by the vital centers, exposing the working parts, picking out the symbols and the historical landmarks. Signs might be used for something more than giving directions or pressing a sale. They could point out the meaning of the scene: what is produced there, who lives there, how it grew, what it stands for.

The view, in other words, should become an extension of one's self.

There are many ways in which this extension might take place. One is through more intimate contact with the environs. This could be accomplished, for example, by splitting lanes so that the driver is not quite as overwhelmed with his smallness in relation to the mass of people flowing in and out of the city. Another method is to create a succession of "goals" for the driver to achieve. These "goals" would be a series of major landmarks that could be passed after short time intervals, thus giving the driver a sense of accomplishment. It is important that all major landmarks on the horizon eventually be achieved, that is, that the road not stop short of the landmark. Otherwise, there will be a feeling of frustration on the part of the driver.

The final criterion related to the visual impact is that the visual environment should play a role in fostering intellectual, emotional, and physical development of the viewer. This criterion is not easy to demonstrate, but certainly the negative effects of a highly impoverished environment have been shown over the years. Moreover, development of the types alluded to above can come as a result of many of the other perceptual criteria previously explored: diversity, legibility, and meaning. As one example, we might think of drawing attention to the more thought-provoking elements of a scene—unique manufacturing plants, railroad yards, recreational sites (such as for rowing and sailing)—and so on. This would be done by tipping and pointing the guideway so that drivers and passengers could view the scenes with little additional effort. Or, as pointed out by the Urban Advisors to the Federal Highway Administration, these sort of developments could also be achieved by creating an appropriate foreground and enframement of the feature as viewed from the road [6.39, p. 42]. The alternatives are many and as yet hardly explored.

6.2.4.2 Comments on visual impact As might be expected, discussion of the visual impact of a transportation system is difficult. Little of a concrete nature is known except that visual impact is significant. The preceding discussion thus has focused on six criteria for indicating the major points to be considered in analyzing visual impacts. These criteria are, in a sense, very general social-psychological models with a wide range of uncertainty. Still, despite the large variations, the generalities hopefully will provide adequate estimates for the likely acceptability of the visual features of a transportation system and its environs.

6.2.5 Noise Impacts

Before a study can be initiated on noise impacts, we must first identify the nature and types of noise. Figure 6.22 portrays various noise sources and factors influencing the emission levels of these sources. Surveys have indicated that urban

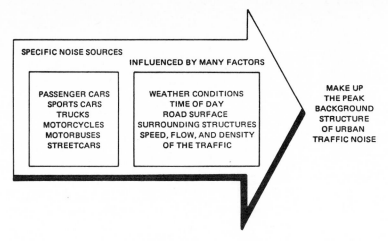

Fig. 6.22   The composition of urban traffic noise. [6.52, p. 24].

traffic is by far the greatest contributor to noise pollution [6.50]. Increasing flow and density of traffic are major reasons for this situation. The following parts of this section are concerned with measurement of noise, the comparison of noise levels of different transportation systems, and the known effects of noise pollution on health.

6.2.5.1 Measurement of noise   The unit or standard utilized in measuring noise or its intensity is the decibel, which is a logarithmic function of sound pressure. There are several decibel scales, and two of the most widely used in urban traffic noise analysis are the A-Weighted Scale (dBA) and the Perceived Noise Level Scale (PNdB).

The dBA scale, illustrated in Fig. 6.23, relates various sources of noise to subjective human response. A New York subway, for example, generates about 95 dBA, which has been found to be very annoying and, if continued for an extended period of time, would lead to hearing damage. This figure does not lend itself conveniently to comparing different transportation systems, however. It is also difficult to visualize how sound levels decrease as the distance from the source increases. Figure 6.24 gives a graphical representation of this additional information. As can be seen, there is a natural decline in dBA levels with distance.

The PNdB scale in Figs. 6.25 and 6.26 adapts well to graphical representation for comparing transportation systems and modes. The main difference between the dBA and PNdB scales is the manner by which calculations are made in plotting the curves. A comparative PNdB value can be found by adding approximately 13 dB to the dBA scale. It is important to note that when comparing noise levels one should not expect to find strict decibel equivalents for each transportation system. The results of noise surveys will vary since the manner in which they are performed and the factors affecting noise sources are not standard in all cases, but may vary according to weather conditions, road surface, and so on (see Fig. 6.22).

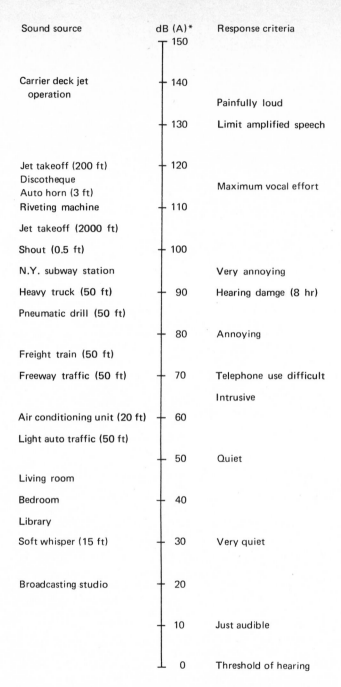

Sound source	dB (A)*	Response criteria
	150	
Carrier deck jet operation	140	
		Painfully loud
	130	Limit amplified speech
Jet takeoff (200 ft)	120	
Discotheque		Maximum vocal effort
Auto horn (3 ft)		
Riveting machine	110	
Jet takeoff (2000 ft)		
Shout (0.5 ft)	100	
N.Y. subway station		Very annoying
Heavy truck (50 ft)	90	Hearing damge (8 hr)
Pneumatic drill (50 ft)		
	80	Annoying
Freight train (50 ft)		
Freeway traffic (50 ft)	70	Telephone use difficult
		Intrusive
Air conditioning unit (20 ft)	60	
Light auto traffic (50 ft)		
	50	Quiet
Living room		
Bedroom	40	
Library		
Soft whisper (15 ft)	30	Very quiet
Broadcasting studio	20	
	10	Just audible
	0	Threshold of hearing

*Typical A—Weighted sound levels taken with a sound-level meter and expressed as decibels on the scale. The "A" scale approximates the frequency response of the human ear.

Fig. 6.23 Weighted sound levels and human responses. [6.54, p. 62–63].

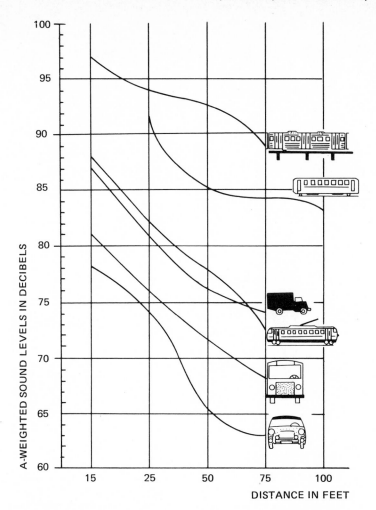

Fig. 6.24 Distance as a factor in noise intensity: Survey of specific noise sources. [6.49, p. 115].

6.2.5.2 Comparison of noise levels from various transportation systems The chart in Fig. 6.23 was developed by the Council on Environmental Quality and provides a standard by which to compare the dBA noise levels emitted by transportation systems to subjective human response. The 60 dB level is considered the normal conversation level while 80 dB or higher levels over continuous periods can produce loss of hearing [6.49].

A close look at Figs. 6.24 and 6.25 reveals that railroad systems and urban interstate systems produce noise in the 70- to 110-dB range within 1,000 ft or less from the source. The chart in Fig. 6.24 shows the elevated rail system as the noisiest ground transportation system. Railroad systems are second, and bus systems also ranked high on the decibel scale. Generally all of the ground

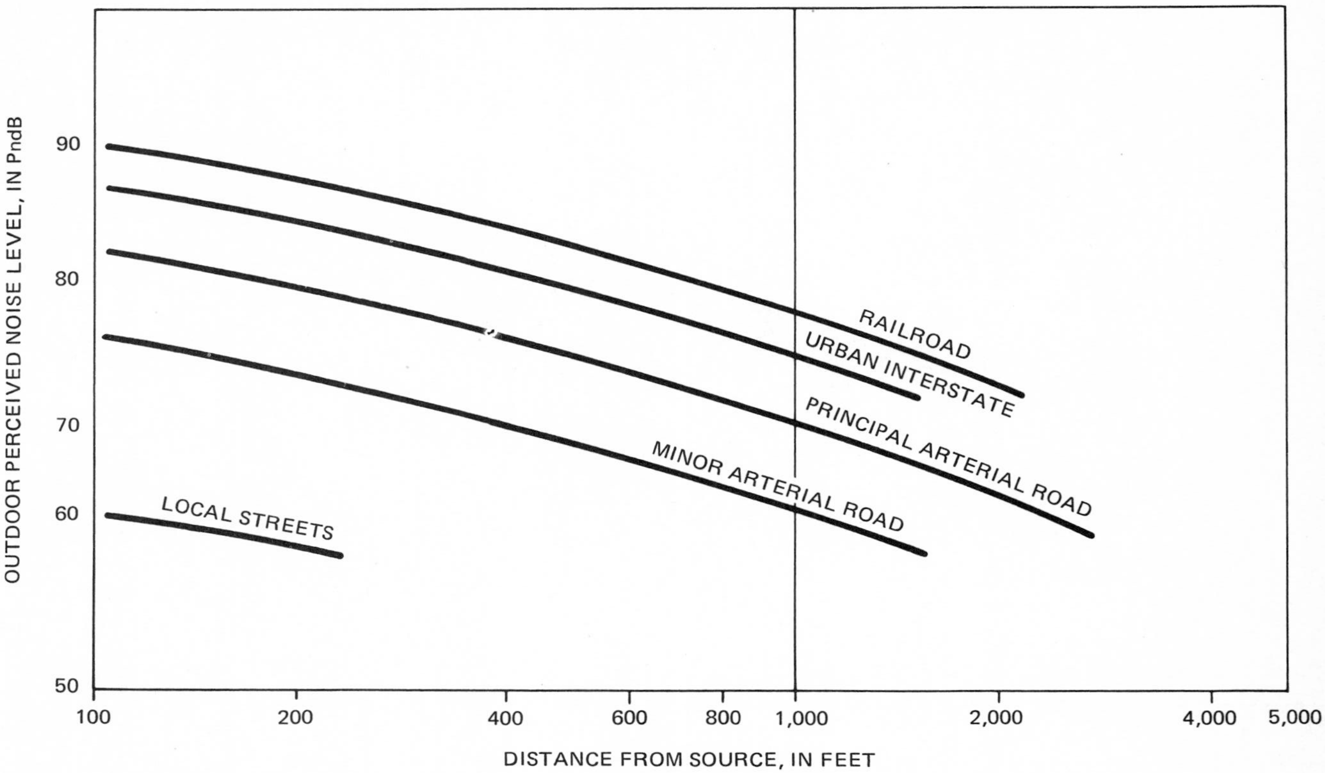

Fig. 6.25 Typical continuous noise produced by surface ground transportation modes. [6.54].

X-axis: DISTANCE FROM SOURCE, IN FEET

Y-axis: OUTDOOR PERCEIVED NOISE LEVEL, IN PNdB

Curve labels: RAILROAD, URBAN INTERSTATE, PRINCIPAL ARTERIAL ROAD, MINOR ARTERIAL ROAD, LOCAL STREETS

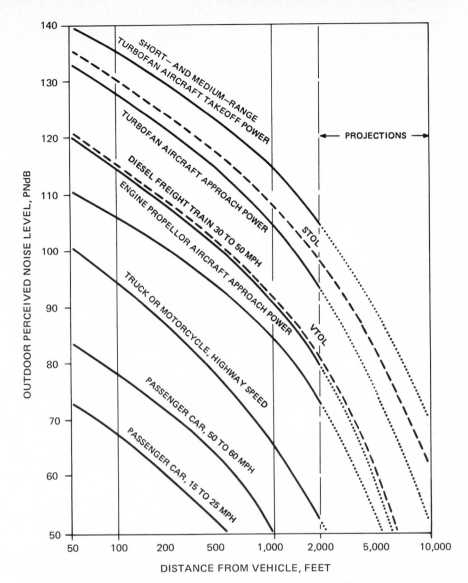

Fig. 6.26 Typical PNdB values for vehicles noises heard at a distance. [6.54, p. c2-18].

transportation systems rank in the annoying and danger areas of the decibel scale. The charts used in this discussion are not necessarily comparable in terms of factors present during the noise surveys (e.g., speed, flow, and density of traffic). The results, therefore, should be interpreted only in a very general way.

Noise produced by Interstate or other highway systems is present constantly, with minor variations during peak periods. People living close to these facilities are being subjected continuously to high noise levels and are in most cases unaware of the consequences. On the other hand, transit systems, such as rail and bus, are not constant producers of noise, yet they do rank higher on the noise level scale than do highways. People are subjected to harmful noise levels only intermittently, with much less lasting damaging effect on hearing. However, people are more aware of the noise level inflections produced by transit systems. This causes these systems to be more apparent, and they are thereby subjected to more public criticism.

6.2.5.3 Effects of noise pollution on health The preceding general comparisons are important in considering the rising health and nuisance effects of noise pollution from transportation sources. Such effects are becoming more and more evident as the number of automobiles and highways increase. Unfortunately, there is very little in the literature of noise and its control that meets the needs of the general public [6.47]. The following are a few major health hazards caused by noise pollution:

Loss of hearing. One theory is that the cumulative effect of prolonged exposure to noise below the levels produced by the Chicago and New York subway system can cause deafness. Another theory for the cause of hearing loss is that the constant pressure of intense noise does physical damage to the nerve endings in the inner ear. Noise even has its effects on the ears of the totally deaf. Research has shown that the totally deaf felt vibrations and tickles, and experienced warmth, pain, and dizziness when subjected to loud noises. Thus noise not only effects their inner ear structure, but also their bodies [6.47].

Stress. The Benox Report conducted by the University of Chicago in 1953 noted that "excessive fatigue, occasional nausea, and loss of libido are common complaints of men working in noise" [6.48]. Research has also indicated that noises cause headaches, migrain headaches, tense muscles, and an increase in the blood pressure [6.47].

Cardiovascular system. Stress has been noted as being a primary cause for increase in cholesterol changes which contribute to the thickening of the arterial walls. "When noise exerts an unfavorable influence over these factors, there is presumptive evidence that noise contributes in some degree to the chain of events leading to heart disease and to an eventual attack" [6.47].

These are just a few of the consequences that noise has upon the human body as documented from various research studies. Further detailed discussion is not within the realm of this book, but the following list identifies other effects of noise as mentioned in various medical research publications: (1) vasoconstriction, (2) incipient peptic ulcers, (3) enlarged pupil size, (4) reduced heartbeat stroke, (5) trigger of epileptic seizures, and (6) lowered biological resistance to disease.

6.2.5.4 Comments on noise impacts Noise pollution caused by urban traffic appears to be steadily increasing as the number of automobiles, trucks, and other modes of transport increase in number and usage. Methods of measuring such pollution vary, but the A-Weighted Decibel Scale (dBA) and the Perceived Noise Level Scale (PNdB) have been utilized frequently for this purpose. Noise levels from highways and streets generally hold fairly constant and thus do not make the same impression as the more intense but less frequent noises from, say, rail transit.

Unfortunately, relatively little is known from a health standpoint about the effects from such noise sources, yet some studies have shown a variety of consequences, ranging from incipient peptic ulcers to lowered biological resistance to disease. There is little doubt, however, that loss of hearing is one consequence of continued exposure to noise levels above 80 dBA.

6.3 SUMMARY

This chapter has been divided into two major sections, one dealing with travel on transportation systems and the other with the impacts of the systems. In the first section some fairly sophisticated mathematical models were displayed. These were used to forecast travel demands in a four stage sequence: (1) trip generation, (2) trip distribution, (3) mode choice, and (4) trip assignment (route choice).

In the trip generation stage, such factors as auto ownership, household income, distance from the central business district, and square feet of floor area were employed to estimate the future number of trips produced in or attracted to a given zone. In the trip distribution stage, these trip productions and attractions were allocated from each zone to all other zones based on the inverse of travel times to those zones and their "relative attractiveness."

In the mode choice stage, the trips distributed between the zones were divided according to use by auto or transit. This division was based on such factors as comparative travel times, costs, and excess times between the modes and on the income and car ownership characteristics of potential users. In the fourth stage, those trips going by auto were "assigned" to the various highway routes between each pair of zones. This was done in an iterative fashion, utilizing relations between traffic volumes and travel times. The final result of the travel prediction process was a forecast of the peak number of trips going between each pair of zones on each mode and each highway route.

The second section of the chapter dealt with transportation system impacts. Such impacts cover a broad spectrum, all the way from the destruction of historic markers to the economic development of the entire metropolitan area. Most of the models discussed were much less sophisticated than those presented in the travel forecasting section. This is not to imply that they are less important, however.

Considered in this section were the specific matters of: (1) retail sales and land values, (2) relocation, (3) visual impacts, and (4) noise.

Retail sales and land values both have been affected by freeways, but most of the greater increases go to vacant land right next to new highway facilities. Relocation was shown to be an often traumatic experience, especially for older and handicapped persons, yet in most cases the effects of relocation, especially on the physical quality of housing for the relocatees, has been positive.

Visual impacts were treated from the viewpoint of the user since relatively little is known about impacts on nonusers. Six criteria were explored: (1) sensual ranges of comfort, (2) diversity, (3) perceptual identity, (4) mental relationships in space and time, (5) meaningful environment, and (6) encouragement of attention and exploration.

Transportation systems were shown to generate a significant amount of noise. The primary impact, in addition to annoyance, is loss of hearing under extended exposure. Other health impacts included lowered biological resistance to disease.

Impacts of the type described here plus forecasts of travel are employed in the evaluation stage in making decisions as to the best transportation system alternatives. Previous to that, however, specific information must be collected. This is the subject of the chapter to be presented next.

BIBLIOGRAPHY

6.1   Overgaard, K. R.: *Traffic Estimation in Urban Transportation Planning*, Acta Polytechnica Scandinavica, No. Ci 37, Copenhagen, 1966.

6.2   Martin, B. V., F. W. Memmott, and A. J. Bone: *Principles and Techniques for Predicting Future Demand for Urban Area Transportation*, M.I.T., Department of Civil Engineering, Cambridge, Mass., January, 1963.

6.3   Baerwald, J. E. (ed.): *Traffic Engineering Handbook*, (3d ed.), Institute of Traffic Engineers, Washington, D.C., 1965.

6.4   Ridley, T. M.: *General Methods of Calculating Traffic Distribution and Assignment*, Information Circular No. 39, ITTE, Univ. of Calif., Berkeley, February, 1968.

6.5   U.S. Department of Transportation, Federal Highway Administration, Bureau of Public Roads: *Guidelines for Trip Generation Analysis*, U.S. Government Printing Office, Washington, D.C., June, 1967.

6.6   Keefer, L. E.: *Urban Travel Patterns for Airports, Shopping Centers, and Industrial Plants*, NCHRP Report 24, Highway Research Board, Washington, D.C., 1966.

6.7   Systems Analysis and Research Corp.: *Demand for Intercity Travel in The Washington-Boston Corridor*, Federal Clearinghouse, PB 166 884, Springfield, Va., 1963.

6.8   U.S. Department of Commerce, Bureau of Public Roads: *Calibrating and Testing a Gravity Model for Any Size Urban Area*, U.S. Government Printing Office, Washington, D.C., October, 1965.

6.9   Ruiter, E. R.: "Improvements in Understanding, Calibrating, and Applying the Opportunity Model," *Highway Research Record* 165, 1967.

6.10 Meyer, J. R., J. F. Kain, and M. Wohl: *The Urban Transportation Problem*, Harvard Press, Cambridge, Mass., 1965.

6.11 Fratar, T. J.: "Vehicular Trip Distribution by Successive Approximations," *Traffic Quarterly*, vol. 8, no. 1, January, 1954.

6.12 U.S. Department of Commerce, Bureau of Public Roads, Urban Planning Division: *Traffic Assignment Manual*, U.S. Government Printing Office, Washington, D.C., June, 1964.

6.13 Irwin, N. A., and H. G. VonCube: "Capacity Restraint in Multi-Travel Mode Assignment Programs," *Highway Research Board Bulletin* 345, 1962.

6.14 Schneider, M.: "Direct Estimation of Traffic Volume at a Point," *Highway Research Board Record* 165, 1967.

6.15 Dreyfus, S. E.: *An Appraisal of Some Shortest Path Algorithms*, Memorandum RM-5433-PR, The Rand Corporation, Santa Monica, Calif., October, 1967.

6.16 Worrall, R. D.: *Monitoring Urban Travel*, Unpublished Ph.D. Dissertation, Department of Civil Engineering, Northwestern Univ., Evanston, Ill., 1966.

6.17 U.S. Department of Commerce, Bureau of Public Roads, Office of Planning: *Modal Split*, U.S. Government Printing Office, Washington, D.C., December, 1966.

6.18 Hill, D. M., and H. G. VonCube: "Development of a Model for Forecasting Travel Mode Choice in Urban Areas," *Highway Research Record* 38, 1963.

6.19 Quandt, R. E., and W. J. Baumol: "The Demand for Abstract Transport Modes: Theory and Measurement," *Journal of Regional Science*, vol. 6, no. 2, Winter, 1966.

6.20 Chicago Area Transportation Study: Vol. I, *Survey Findings*, Chicago, December, 1959.

6.21 Kolifrath, M., and P. Shuldiner: "Covariance Analysis of Manufacturing Trip Generation," *Highway Research Record* 165, 1967.

6.22 Shuldiner, P. W.: "Land Use, Activity and Non-Residential Trip Generation," *Highway Research Record* 141, 1966.

6.23 Tomazinis, A. R.: "A New Method of Trip Distribution in an Urban Area," *Highway Research Board Bulletin* 347, 1962.

6.24 Grecco, W. L., and S. M. Breuning: "Application of Systems Engineering Methods to Traffic Forecasting," *Highway Research Board Bulletin* 347, 1962.

6.25 Moore, E. F.: "The Shortest Path Through a Maze," *Proceedings*, International Symposium on the Theory of Switching, Harvard Univ., Cambridge, Mass., April 2–5, 1957.

6.26 Wohl, M., and B. V. Martin: *Traffic System Analysis for Engineers and Planners*, McGraw-Hill, New York, 1967.

6.27 Kanwit, E. L., C. A. Steele, and T. R. Todd: "Need We Fail in Forecasting?", *Highway Research Board Bulletin* 257, 1960.

6.28 Zettel, R. M.: "On Studying the Impact of Rapid Transit in the San Francisco Bay Area," *Highway Research Board Special Report* 111, Washington, D.C., 1970.

6.29 Horwood, E. M., et al.: *Community Consequences of Highway Improvement*, National Cooperative Highway Research Program Report 18, Highway Research Board, Washington, D.C., 1965.

6.30 Banfield, E. C.: *The Unheavenly City*, Little, Brown and Co., Boston, 1968.

6.31 Thomas, E. N., and J. L. Schofer: *Strategies for Evaluation of Alternative Transportation Plans*, National Cooperative Highway Research Program Report 96, Highway Research Board, Washington, D.C., 1970.

6.32 Barton-Aschman Associates: *The Impact of Transportation Staging on Metropolitan Growth*, Metropolitan Planning Council, Boston, Mass., February, 1970.

6.33 Kresge, D. T., and P. O. Roberts: *Systems Analysis and Simulation Models* vol. 2 of *Techniques of Transport Planning*, J. R. Meyer, (ed.), The Brookings Institution, Washington, D.C., 1971.

6.34 Lamm, R. D., and S. K. Yasimow: "The Highway Beautificiation Act of 1965: A Case Study in Legislative Frustration," *Denver Law Journal*, vol. 46, no. 3, Summer, 1969.

6.35 Appleyard, D., K. Lynch, and J. R. Myer: *The View from the Road*, The M.I.T. Press, Cambridge, Mass., 1964.

6.36 Cron, F. W.: "The Act of Fitting the Highway to the Landscape," in W. B. Snow (ed.), *The Highway and the Landscape*, Rutgers Univ. Press, New Brunswick, N.J., 1959.

6.37 Lynch, K.: *The Image of the City*, The M.I.T. Press and Harvard Univ. Press, Cambridge, Mass., 1960.

6.38 Lynch, K.: "City Design and City Appearance," in W. I. Goodman and E. C. Freund (eds.), *Principles and Practice in Urban Planning*, International City Managers Association, Washington, D.C., 1968.

6.39 The Urban Advisors to the Federal Highway Administrator: *The Freeway in the City*, U.S. Government Printing Office, Washington, D.C., 1968.

6.40 Hartman, G. W.: "Current Research Relating to Relocation of Families and Businesses," in *Relocation: Social and Economic Aspects*, Special Report 110, Highway Research Board, Washington, D.C., 1970.

6.41 Niebanck, P. L.: *Relocation in Urban Planning: From Obstacle to Opportunity*, Univ. of Pennsylvania Press, Philadelphia, 1968.

6.42 U.S. Advisory Commission on Intergovernmental Relations: *Relocation: Unequal Treatment of People and Businesses Displaced by Government*, Washington, D.C., January, 1965.

6.43 House, P.: "Relocation of Families Displaced by Expressway Development: Milwaukee Case Study," *Land Economics*, vol. 46, no. 1, February, 1970.

6.44 Mill, S. L.: "Century Freeway (Watts)," in *Joint Development and Multiple Use of Transportation Rights-of-Way*, Highway Research Board Special Report 104, Washington, D.C., 1969.

6.45 Christensen, A. G., and A. N. Jackson: "Problems of Relocation in a Major City: Activities and Achievements in Baltimore, Maryland," *Highway Research Record* 277, Washington, D.C., 1969.

6.46 Levin, D. R.: "Displacement and Relocation Needs for Present and Future Highway Programs," in *Relocation: Social and Economic Aspects*, Special Report 110, Highway Research Board, Washington, D.C., 1970.

6.47 Baron, R. A.: *The Tyranny of Noise*, St. Martin's Press, New York, 1970.

6.48 Berland, T.: *The Fight for Quiet*, Prentice-Hall, Englewood Cliffs, N.J., 1970.

6.49 Bragdon, C. R.: *Noise Pollution*, Univ. of Pennsylvania Press, Philadelphia, 1971.

6.50 Bolt, Beranek, and Newman, Inc.: *Noise in Urban and Suburban Areas*, Literature Search Report No. 1460, Boston, Mass., January, 1967.

6.51 Turk, A., T. Jonathan, and J. T. Wittes: *Ecology, Pollution, Environment*, W. B. Saunders, Philadelphia, 1972.

6.52 Consultation Group on Transportation Research: *Urban Traffic Noise*, Organization for Economic Co-operation and Development (OECD), Paris, 1971.

6.53 Resource Management Corp.: *External Costs and Benefits Analyses*, NECTP, Bethesda, Md., December, 1969.

6.54 U.S. Department of Transportation: *Recommendations for Northeast Corridor Transportation, Final Report*, vol. 1 and 3, National Technical Information Service, Springfield, Va., September, 1971.

7 Transportation Information Systems

The information system idea is one of the great synthesizing concepts of our time. It denotes the purposeful organization of information. It may encompass either, or both, qualititative and quantitative data. Transportation information systems may involve information collection, processing, storage and retrieval for planning, construction, maintenance, and operation.

This chapter, reflecting the assumed needs of the reader, is devoted primarily to management of quantitative data. This emphasis should be put in perspective by noting the growing recognition being given to qualitative info-systems, such as special libraries and professional communication networks. Both types of info-systems are fundamental to sophisticated approaches to complex urban problems that utilize professional experience and judgment, as well as empirical fact-gathering and analysis. Throughout this book the emphasis is on a combined inductive-deductive, quantitative-qualitative approach.

In practice, quantitative information systems are in the ascendancy, and it is in this area that metropolitan transportation planning has made its unique contribution. Here we can justifiably talk about the "spectacular breakthroughs" of the 1960s. Thanks to efforts like the Chicago Area Transportation Study (1956–62) and the leadership of the U.S. Bureau of Public Roads, among many other persons and organizations, the basic concepts and technology for information systems for urban transportation planning were developed and put into practice in every U.S. metropolitan area in the short span of 15 years (see Chap. 11).

These urban transportation planning studies have contributed a major prototype and reservoir of experience to the development of more advanced and inclusive urban information systems. It is this contribution that this chapter will cover, and the term "information system" will refer particularly to the quantitative type.

An information system is a collection of technical people, procedures, computer hardware, computer software, and a data base organized to develop the information required to support the functions of the parent organization and/or allied organizations. It is important to note that "information system" and "data processing system" have quite different denotations. Data processing system refers specifically to the computer hardware and software (e.g., computer programs). Information system includes not only a data processing system, but also the data base and complete personnel organization for a particular information function. Our focus here will be on the particular data base needed for urban transportation planning; more general readings on data processing and information systems can readily be found elsewhere [7.9].

The data base plays a vital role in transportation planning. Such public confidence that urban transportation planning enjoys is based in part on its demonstrated ability to simulate urban systems in the computer. Such demonstrations require vast quantities of measurements of land use, human travel behavior, and other urban characteristics. These measurements cost money—which is a second reason for the importance attached to the data base. In a typical metropolitan transportation study during the 1960s, 60–70 percent of the budget went into collecting and organizing data for subsequent analysis. In an area of 1 million people, where the overall transportation study costs about $1.50 per capita, this would mean an investment of $1,000,000 in data. Obviously, both the purposes and magnitude of the task demand careful professional attention to this phase of planning.

7.1 PROBLEMS WITH INFORMATION SYSTEMS

Generally speaking there are two distinct concepts of quantitative information systems—the "data bank" and the "management information system." Information systems for urban transportation planning have characteristics of both types. The data bank, or data library, offers a common data base to a number of different users. For continuous transportation planning this concept has strong appeals: (1) With data so expensive, its use by a number of agencies helps to justify its cost. (2) Use of a common data base by different agencies and for different planning purposes removes one of the causes of lack of planning coordination; put positively, it facilitates coordination.

The multiple-use idea may not have as much appeal in initial transportation studies which are often so hard pressed to whip data into shape for their own purposes that the needs of other agencies for the data take second priority. For this and for other reasons noted below the viable ideal of a data bank is not easily achieved.

The second type, the management information system (MIS), also has its appeal and its problems. The appeal is that of operations research—that through computer simulation of real world problems and alternate solutions the best decision can be determined. For many types of transportation decisions this has been at least partially realized. The OR-type models described in other chapters utilize basic land use and travel data to advise decision makers which of several alternate metropolitan transportation systems would be least expensive, safest, or require the least travel time. For the freeway design engineer these models aid decisions regarding the number of lanes and the location and design of ramps. For rapid transit planners the forecasts of ridership make possible informed decisions regarding the economic feasibility of a proposed system or line extension.

However, here too, our present capabilities fall far short of the ideal, especially since the term "management information system" (MIS) connotes to many people a system that supports *all* functions of urban management. It brings to mind a command post in which managers who are fed from "real time" sensors can make decisions that control urban processes. But in only a few narrow sectors of management—such as control of rapid transit trains, regulation of freeway access to maintain traffic capacity, and disposition of police and fire-fighting units—are we approaching "on-line, real time," command-and-control systems.

For both on-line and off-line the state-of-the-art in management information systems is still far from the ideal. "Our understanding of the urban processes is poor; the use of quantitative methods of analysis, such as mathematical modeling, is embryonic; planning is heuristic and (most) factors in the urban environment—housing, employment, education, health, welfare—are not accessible to automatic control as is, for example, the flow of traffic."[1] In sum, the picture we try to paint here is one of cautious optimism: while the ideal MIS is still far off, we have emerging capabilities in many transportation applications.

The need for caution is underscored by the experience of transportation studies during the last decade. A few of the pitfalls and problems encountered, and the lessons learned, are summarized below.

Over-optimism and over-ambition. Experience shows that it is too easy to be carried away by the exciting vistas of system concepts—and to promise too much too soon. It is better to proceed incrementally, accomplishing a series of limited objectives that lead toward the goal of a more complete information system.

Error. The nature of urban planning requires data with a high degree of accuracy. But gathering the data usually depends on a small army of previously inexperienced and very human people. As a result, some studies have been near disasters; most have had some trouble. The moral is clear: Data collection demands careful recruitment, selection, training, and supervision of personnel, and quality control.

[1] See Ref. 7.9.

Precision. Precision problems are generally not as serious as those involving error, but over-precision is wasteful of money and under-precision affects the validity of results. Among the problems that require attention are zone size, sample size, and area measurement.

Incompatible data. When data are gathered in different surveys, at different times, incompatibilities are likely to crop up. Some of the most common problems are delineation of blocks (e.g., study blocks versus census blocks) and analysis areas (traffic zones versus census tracts), and definitions of parcel (assessors versus planners) and household. Not all compatibility problems can be avoided, but preventing them requires continuing vigilance and resolving them, statistical ingenuity.

Administrative files. Records of local agencies which would be valuable for transportation planning, even if computerized, are often formulated in ways that are unsatisfactory for planning. Common examples are assessor's records, building permits, traffic accident reports, and fire calls. Since these records are satisfactory to the agency paying for them and a change would require effort, building a common information system is often frustrated.

Random invention. A real demon! In the absence of an adequately preplanned data system with well-understood conventions and procedures, ad hoc arrangements will prevail. This kind of unwelcome innovation can occur when a member of a field crew experiences an unanticipated situation; or it can come from a top manager acting decisively but in ignorance of the operating system. There are no substitutes for (1) pretesting the system to anticipate problems and questions and (2) thorough training of all personnel.

Computer system support. Many transportation planning information systems fail or falter because of the inadequacies of computer services. They may not have their own computer and are using a remote installation. They may be dependent on a local government installation that is already overloaded with accounting and other administrative applications and does not have the systems and programming personnel competence to handle their "scientific" jobs. In some localities computer personnel competent for scientific applications are hard to find and even the study's own installation may be inadequately staffed.

7.2 GEOCODING

A system of geographic controls is indispensible in any urban study involving the handling of data that is spatially disaggregated finer than metroplitan-wide totals. Geographic controls—or "geocoding," as the subject is more popularly called—are especially needed in metropolitan transportation studies, where data is highly disaggregated. Land use and tripmaking by their nature are usually located by parcel number and/or street address. For use in transportation models these data must be aggregated to traffic zones and/or census tracts. Similarly, specific locations such as intersections in the transportation network must be fixed in space. In addition, computer mapping, which can present the results of surveys or computer simulation model runs almost instantly rather than taking hours or days of a draftsman's time, requires a method for positioning the computer printer or plotter so as to replicate the actual locations of urban phenomena. Consequently, transportation studies by the mid 1960s had developed a rather sophisticated system of geocoding.

The function of geographic controls in a metropolitan study is to provide a system for locating the distribution of various data in geographic space. The data can be of any type that can be converted to metric or other computer-readable form and are of a sufficiently fine detail that they can be geographically fixed. A system of geographic controls is, of course, separate from and by and large independent of the particular data files controlled by it. The data are coded, stored, and retrieved according to the geocoding system. However, the geocoding system itself produces a sizable set of computer records, known as the "geographic base file" (GBF).

The antecedents of an urban geocoding system are familiar to all planners and most layman. The most common is street address, which in all cities follows some system of street names and house numbers. Another familiar concept is the "block"—the two sides of a street between intersections. The U.S. Census has popularized another meaning of the term "block"—that of an area bounded typically on all sides by streets (the definition used herein). The Census aggregates blocks into Census tracts. Planners and other urban statisticians have always used Census tracts and other subareas as handy devices for aggregating and disaggregating data.

However, none of these traditional geocoding systems were by themselves adequate for the requirements of metropolitan transportation planning. To a very large extent, the development of high-speed, high capacity computers, about 1960, made possible the handling of the mass of geographically disaggregated data involved in metropolitan subarea analyses. Existent geocontrol systems, like street addresses and traffic zones, assumed new importance. Block and parcel data, which previously could only be handled by cumbersome manual methods, came into much wider use. The possibilities of computer mapping and graphics spurred the use of grid coordinates.

The geographic control system that emerged in the 1960s consisted of means of relating the various geocoding subsystems so that data could be disaggregated or aggregated to the appropriate scale. There is correspondingly a rough scale of size in these subsystems, rising from a point in space to larger zone systems, as follows:

Point in urban space	Census tract
House number	Traffic zone
Assessor's parcel	Zone, ring, sector, district
Block face	Political jurisdiction
Block (census)	(minicipality, county,
Grid unit	township, etc.)

A bit of elaboration may be in order for some of these geocoding subsystems. Points in urban space can be described in numeric characters through the use of an X-Y coordinate system. Typically, any point can be fixed precisely enough with three X digits for its "easting" location and three Y digits for its "northing" location relative to some southwest point of origin ($X = 0$, $Y = 0$). "Digitization" of a point in space is a prerequisite for modern transportation and land use planning since computer mapping and other operations are dependent on this means of simulating urban activities in space. The three common map coordinate systems shown in Fig. 7.1 are discussed further below. Figure 7.2 illustrates the importance of the point or node in describing other features.

The house number or street address is the most familiar geocoding system. Since a parcel may have many dwellings or businesses, it may be that its weakness as such lies in identifying locations where there are no buildings with "house" numbers: vacant or undeveloped land, parks, cemeteries, large institutions, etc.

The assessor's parcel is the unit of record for the local tax assessor. Typically, it is contiguous land under a single ownership. Since this generally corresponds to the way the land is used, planners have found the parcel a convenient unit for recording land use. In addition, if the assessor's records are computerized and can be accessed, valuable data for urban analysis and planning can be gained.

The block face (Fig. 7.3, shown later) is important as the interface between street address and the (Census) block. It is one side of a block and demarked typically by intersections.

The block, illustrated in Fig. 7.2, is usually bounded on all sides by streets. Occasionally a block boundary will be a river, railroad, city limit, or other feature.

The grid unit is a geographic subarea that in the last decade or so has come from obscurity to perform valuable services. Figure 7.1 illustrates three different sets of grid units or cells derived from three different map projections. Within the same projection, grid units may be hierarchical, e.g., square mile and quarter-square mile. Grid units are very useful as a means of computer mapping, since a certain number of characters on the computer printer will form a square to represent the real world phenomena within the grid unit. Grid units are also useful when analysis subareas having equal area (or approximately equal area, as we will see below) are desired.

Census tracts (Fig. 7.2) are groups of blocks. Tract boundaries are generally stable from Census to Census and are widely used. Tracts are therefore often a useful subarea for analysis.

Traffic zones are tailored to the particular needs of transportation planning. They are formed to keep the zone size roughly equal in numbers of trips generated and somewhat homogeneous as to the kind of trip. Zone size correlates with the precision of simulations and forecasts of urban travel. In some trip generation models zone homogeneity facilitates forecasting of tripmaking by type of trip, e.g., commercial. Often traffic zones are modifications of Census tracts, but smaller than tracts in areas of high trip generation, such as the central business district (CBD). Tract boundaries might also be modified in order to place a regional shopping center in a single zone. An alternative to modified Census tracts, usable with the

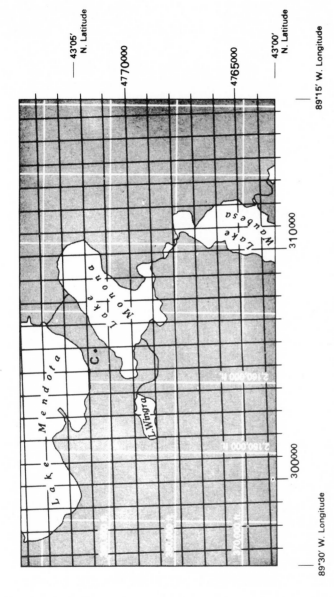

Fig. 7.1 Three systems of coordinates: The bordering ticks show longitude and latitude, the dashed lines show the Wisconsin Coordinate System, and the solid lines show the Universal Transverse Mercator (UTM) grid. [Arthur N. Robinson and Randall D. Sale, "Elements of Cartography," New York: John Wiley & Sons, Inc., 1969, p. 29.]

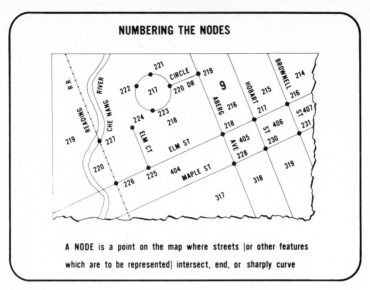

Fig. 7.2 Example of sequential node numbering and block description by node (Census Tract No. 9). [*Bob Totschek, Vlad Almendinger, Ken Needham, "A Geographic Base File for Urban Data Systems," Santa Monica, Calif.: Systems Development Corporation, 1969.*]

opportunity trip distribution model, is to create traffic zones from combinations of grid units. For example, in the Niagara Frontier Transportation Study, zones varied from a quarter-square mile in the Buffalo CBD up to 6 and 8 square miles in rural areas, [7.2].

7.2.1 Developing a Geocoding System

This section will describe the general steps and principles for developing a geocoding system that were evolved in urban transportation studies during the 1960s. The next section identifies the further refinement of this system formulated to enable the *1970 Census* to function as the core of a multipurpose urban information system.

Prior to the *1970 Census* it was necessary to develop an information system, including geocoding, that was independent of the Census. Now that some of these steps have been incorporated into Census procedures, it is not necessary to repeat them. However, it is still helpful to be familiar with the more traditional (1960s) method of preparing a geocoding system, as follows:

1. Inventory map resources
2. Design geocoding system
3. Delineate Census blocks and tracts
4. Grid base map
5. Number blocks
6. Delineate zones, sectors, rings, and districts

7. Code and list blocks
8. Keypunch and check blocks
9. Verify in field and correct geocoding file
10. Prepare address coding guide (ACG)

7.2.1.1 Map resource list A first step in creating or updating a comprehensive geocoding system for a region is a search for all available maps and aerial photography, at appropriate scales.

The acquisition of good maps is particularly critical. They provide the geographic data for (1) digitizing locations and calculating distances and areas. Equally important, they provide necessary information on (2) geodetic accuracy (used for determining the accuracy of calculations of distance and area), (3) streets and street numbering systems, (4) landmark buildings and major traffic generators, (5) administrative boundaries, and (6) geographic-related information (especially public utilities). Significantly, much of this information can only be found in map form.

A variety of types and scales of maps must be collected. Zoning, assessor's, utility, topographic, insurance, and land use maps are necessary, but especially important are those maps produced by the U.S. Geological Survey, including their standard 7.5- and 15-min. topographic maps and those issued by the Census Bureau, particularly their Metropolitan Map Series (MMS). The topographic maps, at the 1:24,000 and 1:75,000 scale, are used for scale control; the MMS defines the geographic base for the areas used to collect, tabulate, and publish statistical information by the Census Bureau. Scales range from 1 in. = 200 ft for engineering-type data to 1:75,000 for regional data. Maps at intermediate scales are sometimes useful for community zonal studies.

The use of aerial photography can be an effective technique for updating and correcting information from maps. It can be used to discern new streets, street extensions, "paper streets" (dedicated but not improved or opened) and any other land developments that may have occurred in the period between the preparation of the map and the taking of the aerial photography. Nor are its uses limited to these. Depending on the scale and displacement of the photography (from the vertical), it can be used as a source of initial information on prominent land use features, topography and drainage. It can also be used to recognize areas of new development, to locate the pattern and intensity of traffic flow, and to confirm the information derived from other sources.

The photo-interpretation approach to data update is, of course, not entirely trouble-free. Many of the same difficulties resulting from poor record-keeping practices which currently complicate the updating will remain.

Nevertheless, this approach does hold promise because it obviates the need for costly and time-consuming field visits. It eliminates the troublesome "paper street" problem, and it insures that the alignment of new street features is accurately recorded on the master coding map.

7.2.1.2 Geocoding system design Design of the geocoding system, generally part of overall study design (work program), must address basic questions of geocoding procedure. Specifically, it must (1) develop a generalized framework for data analysis, (2) establish the general procedures for data management for such an analysis, (3) identify possible areas of difficulty, and (4) make an initial assessment of the time, money, and personnel resources necessary for geocoding. Without this preparation, errors of omission and substance can be expected. Critical to system design, and suggestive of the questions that must be considered, are the following:

(a) Can existing base maps be used or must new base maps be drafted? The quality of existing maps must be weighed against the time and cost of constructing new maps.

(b) Can the spatial framework of an Address Coding Guide (ACG) or Dual Independent Map Encoding (DIME) system be used, thus saving both time and cost and building a common information system?

(c) What analysis areas will be needed or will existing subareas suffice? Transportation study traffic zones are usually based on adaptations of census tracts or grid units. To develop new subareas more reflective of behavioral characteristics would require a significant expenditure of time and money. Whether the old areas are used, new areas developed, or some hierarchical combination used will depend on the precision of data needed and the desirability of using subareas compatible with those of other studies.

(d) Finally, which grid coordinate system shoud be used? The State Plane Coordinate system is the most often used for this purpose. However, the Universal Transverse Mercator (UTM) projection is also growing in use, especially as more states think in terms of statewide transportation planning. Many states have two or more plane coordinate zones, which makes statewide plotting and other analyses of coordinate-based data extremely difficult when this projection is used. Both projections lend themselves to the use of Cartesian coordinates because X and Y distances (scale factors) are equal, thus simplifying many types of calculations.

In both of these equirectangular projections the X and Y lines are usually not exactly east-west and north-south due to the representation of the earth's spherical surface as a plane. This is illustrated in Fig. 7.1 which shows three systems of coordinates which generally appear on the United States Geological Survey (U.S.G.S.) quadrangles, the most popular source of grids for transportation studies. This figure is drawn from the Madison (Wisconsin) Quadrangle, at a scale of 1:62,500. The boarder ticks show the graticule, that is, the net formed by meridians of longitude and parallels of latitude, and the Wisconsin Coordinate System, South Zone. The other lines show the UTM grid. Only in latitude and longitude are the grid lines true north and south.

Locations in coordinates are given by a series of digits, the first half of which is the X location and the second half the Y location. Thus, on Fig. 7.1 the reference 0571 would locate point C (the capitol) with a 1,000-m square and 058716 would locate it within a 100-m square, these designations being the coordinates of the southwest corners of the squares. Additional digits would add greater precision in locating point *C*, but this would have to be done on more accurate, larger scale maps. The decision on the coordinate system to be used will depend largely on the desirability of coordinating transportation study data collection with other existing or potential information systems.

7.2.1.3 Census tracts and blocks Blocks are usually the basic units for control of field data collection. Their boundaries must be defined (delineated) explicitly. In turn, block boundaries are followed exactly in delineating the boundaries of the traffic zones on the master coding map. This is done to preserve the character of the original data.

Block boundaries are usually acquired from Census blocks. Departures from Census block definitions may be made when (1) new streets have not yet been reflected by the Census and (2) large Census blocks, usually in rural locations, are inappropriate for small-area analysis. In the latter case, the large "blocks" are rather arbitrarily divided into "pseudo-blocks" for statistical convenience. Departures may also be necessary should bodies of water such as lakes, rivers, and wide streams fall within the coding area. These water bodies must be incorporated into existent blocks or must themselves be construed as blocks for the purpose of coding shoreline features.

7.2.1.4 Grid base map As noted earlier a grid coordinate system provides "location identifiers" to which data can be referenced. Once the coordinate system is selected, it can be operationalized in a three-step process.

First a "grid map" is prepared. Grid ticks given on the sides of U.S.G.S. maps are connected to one another to form a kind of matrix (Fig. 7.1). Second, to use the grid to determine the location of intersections, street curves, and other features, it is usually necessary to transfer the coordinate system to a larger scale map. Usually sectionalized maps are used for this purpose. Such sectional maps provide controls for disaggregated data at the block, parcel, or dwelling-unit level. Regional maps control aggregated data. The hierarchical character of the coordinate system is therefore critical, since data are frequently shifted from one level to another in analysis.

Third, a "grid template" is drafted on transparent milar or plastic. It divides the larger grid units on the base map into smaller units. When the template is superimposed over the base map, the coordinate location of intersections and other features can be determined. By dropping superfluous higher and lower digits, six-digits, three *X* and three *Y*, are all that is needed to locate a point to the nearest 100 ft. Data can then be coded to such locations.

7.2.1.5 Block numbers Blocks must be defined and numbered for geographic reference (see Figs. 7.2 and 7.3). Files in the geographic base system are referenced to such identifiers, which provide the key to (1) data aggregation about geographic nodes (e.g., block or zone centroids) and to (2) the display of spatial data within the coded region. A variety of identifiers may be used. Sometimes the grid coordinate of the block centroid or its southwest corner suffices to give the block a unique name. At other times, blocks may be numbered serially within grid units or Census tracts.

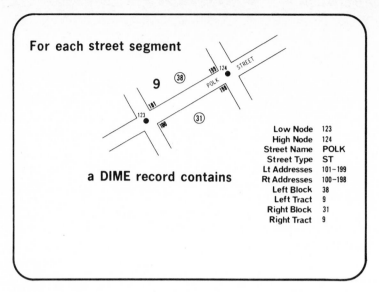

For each street segment

a DIME record contains

Low Node	123
High Node	124
Street Name	POLK
Street Type	ST
Lt Addresses	101–199
Rt Addresses	100–198
Left Block	38
Left Tract	9
Right Block	31
Right Tract	9

Fig. 7.3 Dual independent map encoding (DIME) system. [*Bob Totschek, Vlad Almendinger, Ken Needham, "A Geographic Base File for Urban Data Systems," Santa Monica, Calif.: Systems Development Corporation, 1969.*]

7.2.1.6   Zones, sectors, rings, and districts   Traffic analysis requires that data be aggregated from census block to traffic zones in order to form meaningful transportation-land use relationships. These zones are often further aggregated into districts for metropolitan-level studies. Traffic districts are organized into a ring-sector system by which the spatial location of districts can be readily visualized. Each district has a two digit name, the first representing its ring location and the second its sector location. The 10 sectors start at 12 o'clock and run clockwise. Thus each district has a geographic location which can be visualized without the aid of a map, a unique value of the ring-sector system.

7.2.1.7   Code and list blocks   Once blocks, zones, and districts have been defined, geographic control data for each block are recorded on a Block Index Coding Sheet. Such data include (1) Census tract and block numbers; (2) study block numbers; (3) grid location of block centroid; (4) jurisdictional codes, zone, ring, sector, and district numbers, and tax assessor block number. Blocks are usually the largest common unit in such diverse geographic units as Census tracts, traffic zones, grid units, and election wards.

The block number therefore provides a control key by which the computer can aggregate and disaggregate block data into each of these diverse units. The Block Index then performs two important functions: (1) control of data in aggregation and disaggregation, and (2) a check for missing blocks when data are subsequently automated.

7.2.1.8 Keypunch and check blocks The block index number, together with accompanying transportation data, must then be keypunched. Verification of the index number is accomplished by computer, which sorts through a listing of such numbers to locate the given identifier. Verification of certain alphanumeric data may also be done by computer, although much descriptive information must be checked manually by reading from a printout.

7.2.1.9 Verify in the field and correct file Field work is necessary at this point unless the requisite information is already available (e.g., a Census DIME file). Actual, on-the-ground inspection is needed to provide (1) the high and low street addresses on each block face (Fig. 7.4) and (2) verification that block boundaries can actually be identified in the field. In transportation studies this field work may be combined with that for the land use inventory, discussed later in this chapter.

7.2.1.10 Prepare address coding guide An Address Coding Guide (ACG) is a device that permits conversion of locations identified by street address to locations identified by block number, Census tract, traffic zone, grid unit, political jurisdiction, etc. This is done by "address matching" of the input records against the high-low address ranges for each block face in the ACG (Fig. 7.4). While address matching can be done as a manual look-up, the geographic coding of large files, such as trip origins and destinations compiled from home interviews, is usually done by computer. A common synonym for the Address Coding Guide in transportation studies is "Dictionary," since streets are alphabetically ordered.

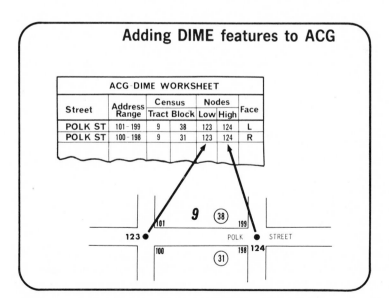

Fig. 7.4 Coding of a DIME file. [*Bob Totschek, Vlad Almendinger, Ken Needham, "A Geographic Base File for Urban Data Systems," Santa Monica, Calif.: Systems Development Corporation, 1969.*]

7.2.2 Geocoding with Census Files

The *1970 Census* instituted a new computerized procedure that incorporated many of the advances developed in the transportation studies during the 1960s, just as the studies had previously incorporated Census blocks, tracts and data into their information systems. The new Census procedures should prove very helpful to continuing transportation planning, not only in simplifying geocoding preparations, but in facilitating the coordination of interactions between the transportation system and other urban systems.

The major geocoding innovation in the *1970 Census* is DIME—Dual Independent Map Encoding. DIME incorporates most of the useful geocoding components just discussed, especially the grid coordinates, the parcel/block inventory system, and the ACG. A DIME geographic base file is essentially a description of block boundaries defined by its nodes (points such as intersections and other turns in boundaries). Figure 7.4 illustrates this technique. The term "Dual Independent" refers to the fact that each boundary segment is described by specifying its two end nodes and its right and left blocks (Fig. 7.3).

7.2.2.1 Steps in Census geocoding Transportation-related coding may now more readily use Census data and coding maps as a basic analytic framework. Many of the steps in the traditional geocoding process are eliminated by (1) the use of specially prepared master coding maps and by (2) the keying of Census files to coding maps through geographic identifiers. The construction of noded maps, map resource lists, block numbering schemes, field work, ACG preparation, and several keypunching operations may be unnecessary. Master coding maps with geographic identifiers at street intersections are available for most SMSA's. These depict most street features and are sufficiently detailed to read street address ranges and major nonstreet features. Keyed to the DIME maps, which exist in computer form, are ACG (Address Coding Guide) files; these contain street address ranges by blockface and are referenced to the DIME system through grid coordinates at street intersections.

Use of standardized DIME/ACG files entails (1) the construction of the arterial network in the DIME system, (2) the reconstruction of Census data to fit traffic zones, and (3) the addition of local transportation and land-use files to the modified DIME Census file

7.2.2.2 Constituting the arterial network from DIME A DIME file must be adjusted for transportation system applications. Data needed can be selected by developing a dictionary of required streets (e.g., arterials), comparing this to the DIME file, and creating a new network file for only the required streets. It is also possible to add data on traffic direction, capacity, pavement width, etc., to a DIME file [7.7, p. 20].

7.2.2.3 Reconstruction of Census data To obtain Census data by traffic zones, it is necessary to provide a table of equivalents between Census areas (e.g., blocks) and traffic zones. Given a table of equivalents the Census Bureau will aggregate data not otherwise available to traffic zones. The form in which these equivalents will be provided has not yet been determined, but they will probably be in machine-readable form. The Bureau provides lists and formats of the various data which will be available in this program.

7.2.2.4 Adding local codes to the DIME file The addition of local codes allows use of the DIME file in the analysis of local and Census data as they relate to local areas. Examples of local areas for which codes can be added to geographic base files include planning districts, police precincts, poverty neighborhoods, health districts, and, most importantly, traffic zones. Local area codes facilitate the interrelating of Census and local data either for the areas originally coded in the DIME file, such as Census tracts, or for local areas, such as land use files or traffic records. Transportation studies would probably use both, in order to evaluate the effect of transportation modifications and to calibrate models.

Local codes may be added to a DIME file by means of a dictionary or correspondence table of local codes for each Census area. There are two relatively simple methods which can be employed. The primary method is to plot the local areas on a Census Bureau metropolitan map and then manually prepare a corresponding list of local area codes for each individual or series of Census codes comparable to the local areas. The Census codes necessary for areal units are Census tract and block. Once a dictionary or correspondence table is prepared, it is keypunched and the file processed to add the local codes to the DIME records.

The variant method of creating a dictionary utilizes the DIME file as the source for the dictionary records and is described in Census publications [e.g., Ref. 7.7, p. 15].

7.2.3 Computer Mapping and Analysis

The addition of coordinates to a DIME file permits computer mapping of numeric data. Several "levels" of mapping are feasible. The simple aggregating of data to grid units by use of the Block Index previously discussed permits mapping of data by grid units. Since mapping by grid units can be done by the computer printer, no special plotting hardware is needed. The grid unit is a particularly handy unit for mapping since its square shape can be related to a certain number of horizontal and vertical characters on the printer.

Similar computer-made maps by Census tracts, police precincts, traffic zones, or other areas in the Block Index can be accomplished by adding the centroids of the areas to the Index. Block centroids are often added to enable computer mapping of data by blocks.

Network maps (Sec. 7.4.4) require a pen plotter, such as the widely used Calcomp. Coordinates of block boundary nodes are often added to the DIME file to enable the entire street network to be plotted. This plot serves as an outline map of blocks and provides one way of checking the accuracy of the DIME file. Data in files, such as street pavement or ROW width, pavement condition, or parking regulation can be added to the plot.

Ability to plot the arterial network is a near essential feature of transportation studies. Computer maps verify the accuracy of the network file, depict volume/capacity relationships, compare assigned to actual volumes, and display other important characteristics. Since the arterial network is much more limited than the street network, arterial plots are a correspondingly less ambitious task.

Digitization of coordinates is the process of converting locations into numeric characters and adding them to geographic base files. Digitization can be accomplished manually by using templates (Sec. 7.2.1.4). However this task has been automated through the use of machines called digitizers. Since digitization jobs are usually sizable, they are usually accomplished under contracts or through lease or purchase of a digitizer.

7.3 LAND USE INVENTORY

A review of other chapters reveals the vast and varied data requirements of transportation models and planning. There are, however, three basic transportation surveys that frequently take two-thirds of a study's budget and have specialized requirements. The remainder of this chapter is devoted to these three inventories— land use, travel, and transportation facilities.

Land is a limited community resource, and it will become even less available in future years as the urban population increases and as the population places increasingly varied demands upon it. Not only is land itself valuable, but the way it is used is critical, since certain combinations of land uses tend to be compatible and reinforcing, others less so, and still others noncompatible and conflicting. For these reasons, the land use survey, which attempts to identify and classify land uses in a systematic fashion, has been of great value to community planning. It should become even more valuable in coming years.

The types of surveys that have been used in the past have varied widely in function, but most transportation-oriented land use surveys have tried to serve four basic objectives, all of which remain valid:

1. To provide a land use base from which trip generation factors and trip generation forecasts can be derived
2. To provide necessary data for coordinating transportation facilities with other uses
3. To provide a "universe" of dwelling units from which a sample can be drawn for the home interview phase of the travel survey
4. To provide data useful for the day-to-day planning activities of city, county, and state government

7.3.1 Types of Land Surveys

Planning agencies conduct a wide range of land use studies to acquire basic data on land characteristics and the activities that occupy land. These data are used in evaluating current patterns of land use and in formulating the land related aspects of the transportation plan. Chapin, in *Urban Land Use Planning* [7.1], describes nine basic studies of this type:

1. Land use survey
2. Vacant land survey
3. Flood damage prevention survey
4. Structural and environmental survey
5. Cost-revenue studies
6. Land value studies
7. Studies of the aesthetic features of the urban area
8. Studies of public attitudes and preferences regarding land use
9. Studies of activity systems

7.3.2 Classification of Land Uses

In the past, land use data have been collected for one purpose and then collected again in another format for another purpose. This led to an undue duplication of effort and a lack of uniformity in results. To a very large degree these and other deficiencies have been rectified by the publication of the *Standard Land Use Coding Manual* in 1965 by the U.S. Urban Renewal Agency and the U.S. Bureau of Roads [7.11]. One of the main advantages of the *Manual's* approach is the ease with which data can be used for a variety of purposes once they are coded. Other advantages include the amenity of coded data to automated data processing techniques and the facility with which data collected at different times and in different cities can be compared. Use of this coding scheme has become increasingly common in the years since its publication and its continued use should go far toward facilitating the analysis and interchange of statistical information and research findings.

The *Manual's* standard coding system provides four levels of detail on land use activity. Further, each level is subdivided into categories: there are 9 one-digit categories, 67 two-digit categories, 294 three-digit categories, and 772 four-digit categories. The first two levels are illustrated in Table 7.1. The categories at the one-digit level identify land use activities of a general nature, and categories at the two-, three-, and four-digit level, activities of a more specialized type. The structure of this classification system stresses, then, the activity aspect of land and permits that level of detail to be selected that is most appropriate to the analysis and presentation of data.

The coding scheme also permits a very rough correlation with the Standard Industrial Classification (SIC); insofar as possible, it uses the SIC category titles and that system's description of manufacturing activities. It does not, however, identify the four-digit land use categories by the same code numbers as the comparable categories in the SIC, nor does it use similar criteria to code activities. For these and other reasons, the land use data collected and coded under the standard coding scheme is not entirely compatible with the economic data collected using SIC specifications. Data obtained from the two systems to be used together must, therefore, be screened to determine the actual areas of differences and appropriate procedures developed for reconciling their statistical categories [7.11].

Table 7.1   A Standard System for Identifying and Coding Land Use Activities—One- and Two-digit Levels

Code	Category	Code	Category
1	Residential	11	Household units
		12	Group quarters
		13	Residential hotels
		14	Mobile home parks or courts
		15	Transient lodgings
		19	Other residential, NEC*
2	Manufacturing	21	Food and kindred products—manufacturing
		22	Textile mill products—manufacturing
		23	Apparel and other finished products made from fabrics, leather, and similar materials—manufacturing
		24	Lumber and wood products (except furniture)—manufacturing
		25	Furniture and fixtures—manufacturing
		26	Paper and allied products—manufacturing
		27	Printing, publishing, and allied industries
		28	Chemicals and allied products—manufacturing
		29	Petroleum refining and related industries
3	Manufacturing (continued)	31	Rubber and miscellaneous plastic products—manufacturing
		32	Stone, clay, and glass products—manufacturing
		33	Primary metal industries
		34	Fabricated metal products—manufacturing
		35	Professional, scientific, and controlling instruments; photographic and optical goods; watches and clocks—manufacturing
		39	Miscellaneous manufacturing, NEC*
4	Transportation, communication, and utilities	41	Railroad, rapid rail transit, and street railway transportation
		42	Motor vehicle transportation
		43	Aircraft transportation
		44	Marine craft transportation
		45	Highway and street right-of-way
		46	Automobile parking
		47	Communication
		48	Utilities
		49	Other transportation, communication, and utilities, NEC*
5	Trade	51	Wholesale trade
		52	Retail trade—building materials, hardware, and farm equipment
		53	Retail trade—general merchandise
		54	Retail trade—food

Table 7.1   A Standard System for Identifying and Coding Land Use Activities—One- and Two-digit Levels (*Continued*)

Code	Category	Code	Category
		55	Retail trade—automotive, marine craft, aircraft, and accessories
		56	Retail trade—apparel and accessories
		57	Retail trade—furniture, home furnishings, and equipment
		58	Retail trade—eating and drinking
		59	Other retail trade, NEC*
6	Services	61	Finance, insurance, and real estate services
		62	Personal services
		63	Business services
		64	Repair services
		65	Professional services
		66	Contract construction services
		67	Governmental services
		68	Educational services
		69	Miscellaneous services
7	Cultural, entertainment, and recreational	71	Cultural activities and nature exhibitions
		72	Public assembly
		73	Amusements
		74	Recreational activities
		75	Resorts and group camps
		76	Parks
		79	Other cultural, entertainment, and recreational, NEC*
8	Resource production and extraction	81	Agriculture
		82	Agricultural related activities
		83	Forestry activities and related services
		84	Fishing activities and related services
		85	Mining activities and related services
		89	Other resource production and extraction, NEC*
9	Undeveloped land and water areas	91	Undeveloped and unused land area (excluding noncommercial forest development)
		92	Noncommercial forest development
		93	Water areas
		94	Vacant floor area
		95	Under construction
		99	Other undeveloped land and water areas, NEC*

*NEC = not elsewhere coded.
Source: [7.11, pp. 29–31].

7.3.3 Types of Land Use Surveys

Once a classification system has been adopted—preferably the standard coding scheme just described or a variant thereof—the task of planning and carrying out the land use inventory can begin. The decision as to the type of survey will be based on its purpose or purposes, and on the resources available. Land use surveys are classified in several ways: First by whether or not dwellings and other places must be entered, and, second, by whether or not the data must be computer readable.

The first classification regarding building entry offers two types of land use surveys, which Chapin calls the "inspection" type and the "combined inspection interview" type. The former is the most economical and is used whenever the survey purposes can be satisfied by inspection of the exterior of buildings. Such inventories are often termed "windshield surveys."

The combined inspection-interview survey is used when exterior inspection does not yield enough information. One such instance is when the land use inventory is combined with another survey purpose, such as a taxable property inventory or school census, generally in cooperation with other agencies. In this way the cost to the planning agency is kept within acceptable limits. Other reasons for building entry is to collect data on space use by floor area or to determine the number of dwelling units. Still another reason is to determine the condition of the structure. Obviously, the inspection-interview type of inventory is more elaborate and expensive than the exterior inspection type.

The second classification relates to the way the land use data are recorded in the field. The older method is to record the data directly on maps or airphotos. During the last decade, especially in the large scale transportation-land use studies, there has been increased use of a method known as "field listing." The use of either format is predicated on the purposes and amount of data to be acquired and the methods to be employed in storing and retrieving data. In general, the former is best suited to a map storage system, and the latter to a punch card storage system.

The map-record type of land use inventory is the simplest. It is more frequently employed in the small town or city, or where a new planning program needs quick data, or a new planner wants to get the "feel of the area," or where the only data required are simple classifications of use. Sometimes blue line prints or airphotos at 1 in. = 400 ft or larger scale are used as field sheets on which the land use information is annotated.

"Field listing" of land use is the near-universal method for transportation planning, and is growing in popularity for general comprehensive planning purposes. A separate field list form is usually reserved for each block and a line is filled out for each parcel or land use and dwelling unit. In certain situations it has advantages over map-recorded surveys. First, it lends itself to computerized records and analyses. Computerized land use is especially suited to large metropolitan areas where statistical analyses are more used than conventional land use maps. Second, it permits automated and integrated record systems encompassing property assessment, land use, building permit and inspection, and other parcel-based records.

Third, it must be used when the land use survey provides the universe of dwelling units from which the home interview sample is drawn. Finally, it must be used when the amount of information to be included exceeds that which can be recorded on a map. Field lists can be used either for hand preparation of conventional colored land use maps, or keypunched for computer-made maps and analyses. The field listing procedure is described in more detail below.

7.3.4 Preparation for Field Work

Once the type and scope of the survey has been determined, the unit of data collection must be decided upon. Often ownership parcel is chosen, particularly when a common unit record with the tax assessor and building inspector is desired. Otherwise, larger area units, called "use areas," are employed. A parcel is simply a contiguous land unit under a single ownership. It may be a factory, a house, an apartment house or several different uses in an office building. In the latter cases, a finer record unit may be used. A line on the field list form is then devoted to each land use or dwelling within the parcel. Data on the number of parcels, and the area, boundaries, and property and land values of individual parcels, when necessary to a land use inventory, may be derived from the assessor's and city engineer's offices, and the files of the planning agency, and aerial photographs.

"Use areas," as an alternative to parcels as collection units, are contiguous land areas in a single use. For example, if an entire block were in single family residential use with 18 houses, it would be recorded as a one use area, that is, as a single record indicating 18 dwelling units.

An important question to face in design of the field listing is the manner in which the lines on the forms will subsequently be matched with the parcel or use area boundaries on maps in the office. Since land uses are usually identified in the field by street address, if the office parcel map also shows street addresses of parcels, the match is usually easy. Likewise, the match is easy when a large-scale (e.g., 1 in. = 400 ft) airphoto is used by the field lister to key in his line entries.

Numbers are assigned to uniquely identify each parcel or use area. Occasionally, the assessor's parcel numbers are suitable, but more often than not parcels are identified by (*a*) house or building number and (*b*) their location in the field listing sequence. This is the procedure that is required by the sample form, Fig. 7.5. If, however, use areas are employed as the data collection unit, the use of a parcel map is optional and identifying numbers are assigned in some type of sequence in the field.

Finally, all field procedures must be set down in a memorandum, a "Manual of Standard Field Procedures." This aspect of advance planning is essential in large cities where large crews of field workers must be trained and is especially critical in inspection-interview surveys. The manual must be pretested in order to identify and clear up any problems of ambiguity and to eliminate or modify those items which present difficulties in coding in the field. Test surveys are also helpful in improving manual definitions and collection procedures. After the manual is issued in final form, short test surveys must be made to acquaint the field workers with the

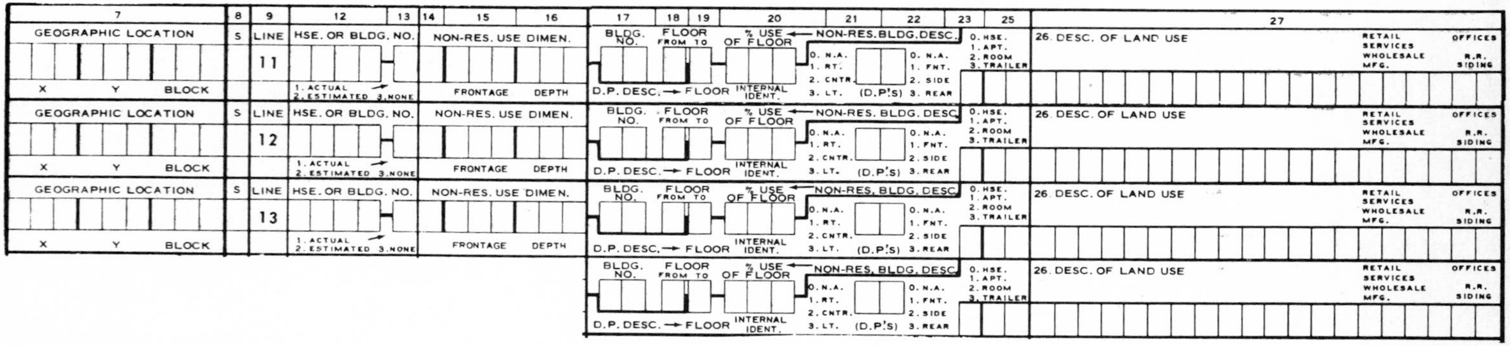

280

Fig. 7.5 Land use filed listing form (rural areas). [*New York State Department of Transportation, Albany, New York.*]

collection process and the results analyzed to remedy any difficulties that may have arisen. The purpose of these preparations is to minimize the error due to interpretation of instructions and to ensure the greatest possible uniformity in those procedures that require subjective interpretation.

7.3.5 Conducting the Field Work

Field survey procedures differ according to whether the data are to be stored on punch cards or in map form. Both types are discussed.

To indicate the general nature of the land use survey that is designed to lead into machine methods of analysis, a simple type of inspection survey—uncomplicated by joint tax assessment, housing quality, or health surveys—will be examined. Punch cards are assumed as the storage medium.

This type of land use survey is usually organized into two parts—one for built-up areas and one for rural areas—and slightly different forms used for each. Figure 7.5 illustrates the basic form for "field listing" land uses. This form is designed to serve both the field form and the coding form from which the computer cards are key punched. Combining the forms saves the time of transcribing as well as eliminating the errors that would occur. The field form therefore reflects the standard 80-column punchcard.

On the form a separate line is used for each parcel and for each separate dwelling unit or space use on the parcel. Thus every use in a multi-use building is listed separately. Field list forms for rural and urban areas differ because of the large size of rural parcels and blocks. This dictates that for efficiency the field lists in rural areas list both sides of a road on one form. Thus in the rural form, Fig. 7.5, the "Street Face Number" appears at the top of the form and the minidigit block number for each use goes in field 8 (geographic location, X, Y, block) at the left side of the form.

In urban areas the reverse is true. The field lister lists only parcels in a single block on each sheet. Hence, the block number would appear at the top of the form and the street name where field 7 is in Fig. 7.5. Since this is the only difference, a sample form for urban areas is not shown. In both areas the hierarchical relationships of uses within parcels, within blocks, within grid units (see Sec. 7.2 on geographic controls) are preserved.

Whether in rural or urban areas the lister travels in a predetermined and regular pattern so that the order of listing can be subsequently retraced on maps by official personnel. In an urban area this usually means starting at the northwest corner of a block and proceeding clockwise. Most areas can be covered by a two-man team in a car. However, where structures must be entered or traffic conditions will not allow the use of cars, the field listing is on foot.

As the field lister proceeds on his route, he lists successive parcels by entering in field 7 the block number (9 digits) in rural areas or the street name in urban. Field 12, the house or building number (i.e., the address) is entered in either case. Column 13 is filled with code 1, 2, or 3 to show, respectively, (1) an observed house or building number, (2) an estimated or interpolated number, as for a vacant lot, or (3) neither.

Column 8 is used subsequently in the office to check dwelling places selected for home interviews. If a 20 percent sample were desired, every fifth dwelling would be checked. Column 8 would be used only if this is done "by hand"; usually sampling is done more accurately and less expensively by computer after keypunching, but the time required to complete the land use survey before keypunching does not always permit this.

Fields 14–16 "use dimensions" are also filled out in the office from parcel and building maps; the code in column 14 indicates whether the dimensions are land or floor space.

For nonresidential uses, field 17 receives the building number where there are several buildings at the same address. Columns 18 and 19 show the floors containing the use and field 20 the percentage of the floor in that use. The actual floor space can later be computer calculated from fields 14–16.

For residential uses, fields 19 through 22 are used. Internal identification receives the aparment number, where appropriate. Where no number is evident, the apartment still must be uniquely and positively identified for sampling purposes. Fields 21 and 22 are used to do this with the following codes

Field 21:	Field 22:
0—Not applicable	1—Front
1—Right side	2—Side
2—Center	3—Rear
3—Left side	

Column 23 records the type of dwelling—house, apartment, room or trailer. Fields 25, 26, and 27 are used for land (or space) use classification (if other than a dwelling). In field 26 the field lister writes a complete description of the use, circling one of the major categories—retail, services, wholesale, manufacturing, or offices—as may be appropriate, on the right. Positive identification of these major categories is thus forced in the field, eliminating a major source of error. For example, a description "home appliances" in field 26 could mean any of the categories.

The lister letters into the coding squares of field 27 the actual name of a nonresidential establishment. This field may also be used for the name of a dwelling occupant when no other means exist to identify uniquely the dwelling for sampling.

7.3.6 Office Procedures

From the information in fields 26 and 27 the use is subsequently coded in the office and entered in field 25. This is best done in the office since, for accuracy, it requires a look-up in the coding manual. This is especially needed in cases where the four-digit, 772 classification system of the *Standard Land Use Coding Manual* [7.11] is used.

After the field lister completes a "batch" of forms they are logged in at the office, edited for completeness of coverage, checked for accuracy, sometimes spot checked against other sources or in the field, and the areas and use codes determined. The field lists forms are then keypunched. Once the cards are punched, machine contingency checks are made to screen out errors in coding, transcription, and keypunching. After they clear this check, various machine runs are made to see that parcel area totals equal block areas, and that maps made by the computer printer conform to known retail, industrial, and residential areas. Lastly, summary punch cards derived from summary machine runs are prepared for the basic geographic unit (block, zone, grid unit, etc.) to be used in land or building space analysis.

7.3.7 Map-Record Surveys

Those land use surveys that use maps as the basic means of storing data follow many of the steps just described. They, too, divide the area to be surveyed into sections to be covered by foot and by automobile; outlying sections are covered by automobile, the more densely built-up areas by foot, with field investigators being assigned individual blocks in the latter.

The techniques in this type of survey vary with city size and study objectives, but there is some degree of uniformity in the essential of field plotting. Generally, each field worker is given a sectional base map showing in schematic form the outlines of structures, property lines, and streets. This map is compiled in the office. Land use data are then annotated onto this base, using a predetermined system of field notations. Concomitantly, new structures are added to this base, use lines are related to property lines, and where discrepancies occur, these are noted for later checking against property maps and other office records. The memorandum or manual of instructions specifies the standard symbols and other types of notation to be used in the field.

7.3.8 Presentation of Land Use Data

The results of the land use survey may be summarized in either map form or statistically. Traditionally, land use data have been presented in the form of the land use map. This shows land use by general category of use, that is, residential, commercial, industrial, institutional, parks and recreation, transportation and utilities, agriculture, and water. Ordinarily, these categories are shown in color in order to provide visual differentiation to the various uses, and since this type of presentation is more effective in conveying information and in appealing to the public. A standard color scheme is nearly always adopted, the type varying with the diversity and types of uses and with the purpose of the survey.

In recent years, however, land use maps have increasingly been based on printouts of data processed on a grid-cell basis by computer. These only require that a draftsman prepare an overlay of principal streets for orientation; hence, they eliminate the time-consuming task of transcribing from the data base to the overlay.

The statistical summary of land use is typically prepared to show the total land area devoted to each category of use employed in the survey, with an added entry to summarize the area that is vacant or in nonurban use. This information is usually broken down into subunits of the inventory area. These may be Census tracts, traffic zones, well-defined neighborhoods, ring-sector districts, or other areas delineated for analytical purposes. The amount of land given over to urban uses is frequently summarized in terms of percentages for the developed part of the city, the fringe areas, and the planning area of the survey. This format provides a meaningful summary for intercity comparisons or for comparisons between existing land use and proposed land use as set forth in a land development plan.

7.4 TRAVEL FACILITIES INVENTORY

Inventories of the networks of transportation facilities—both road and mass transportation facilities—serve three basic objectives. They (1) measure the capacity for and quality of service, (2) locate trouble spots, and (3) make possible simulation of existing and future travel. The last is especially important since it is used to devise and evaluate transportation plans.

7.4.1 Types of Facilities

Generically, transportation facilities consist of four components: the guideway, vehicle, terminal, and control system. Each is an important element of the circulatory system of a city, and in combination they provide the means by which goods and people move freely throughout the city and through which the various systems of social and economic interdependencies are created and maintained. In the discussion to follow, the control system will be included with the guideway.

1. *The guideway.* Movement on a transportation system takes place over permanent pathways; these include streets of all types and, in larger cities, separate rights-of-way for railroads and other types of mass transportation facilities. The guideway is the main structural element of any city, accounting for 30 to 40 percent of the total land area. In smaller cities, they may take up even more than this amount. The different types of facilities—local, collector, and arterial streets, freeways, and mass transit rights-of-way—are the components of this system.

2. *Vehicles.* Automobiles, buses, trucks, and rapid transit cars are the types of vehicles used on today's circulatory system; each has its own special function and efficiency in transporting goods and people. As might be expected, the automobile is by far the most important of these in terms of use and accounts for some 85 to 90 percent of total person trips in most urban areas; trucks are responsible for much of the remaining travel. Except for the 15 largest metropolitan areas in the U.S., the amount of travel by mass transportation is relatively small. For example, in a medium-sized city having only bus transportation, it is unusual to find that more than 10 percent of residents' personal trips are made by bus.

3. *Terminal facilities.* A terminal is any facility providing for the delivery and temporary storage of freight, the embarcation or disembarcation of passengers, or the temporary storage of vehicles. It includes such things as off-street parking, garages, railroad yards, bus stations, truck terminals, and docks.

Each of these subsystems is equally important to the proper functioning of a city's transportation and each must be thoroughly understood before effective planning can take place. The planner may directly influence the circulatory system and its terminal facilities. The forms and procedures to be described hereafter focus on only the first of these, the circulatory system.

7.4.2 Functional Classification of Guideways

Road component. The road or "private" component of the guideway system is subdivided into an arterial and nonarterial subsystem. In turn, the arterial subsystem consists of freeways and arterials. In transportation engineering parlance, freeways are divided roadways having no direct land access and no intersections with other streets at grade. Their prime function is to move traffic quickly, easily, and with a high measure of safety. By way of contrast, arterials have a dual function: to move traffic and to provide access to land uses, especially the high trip generating commercial activities. Arterials are the main channels of movement within an urban area, and they comprise nearly 27 percent of all street mileage in a large city; in contrast, freeways constitute only 0.6 percent of total street mileage. Together arterials and freeways carry more than 80 percent of all traffic in large cities.

The nonarterial subsystem is composed of local streets and collectors. The prinicpal function of local streets is to provide access to land and primarily to residential land. While they occupy nearly 70 percent of total street mileage, they carry only 10 to 17 percent of all traffic. For this reason, local streets have no real significance at the scale of metropolitan transportation planning, and transportation network analysis and evaluation can reasonably focus on the smaller number of large facilities with little attendant loss in accuracy. The collector is primarily a street which filters traffic from local streets and conducts it to arterials or to local traffic generators such as shopping centers, schools, or parks. In commericial areas, traffic volumes often mount too quickly for the effective use of collectors; but they are sometimes used in large industrial areas. For most collectors, land access is an important function.

Transit component. There are two types of public transit: local transportation and rapid transit. The difference between the two stems in part from the type of vehicles they use but more precisely from the type of right-of-way they operate upon.

Local transit generally operates on a public street right-of-way. As such, the mass transportation vehicle—be it bus, street car, or cable car—shares the right-of-way with automobile and truck traffic. The speed of the vehicle depends, then, on the speed of the traffic streams as well as on the number of stops per run and the distance between stations.

Contrarily, rapid transit operates on a right-of-way reserved solely for its use. Because of this, it provides faster, more efficient service than most transportation facilities, especially over long distances. Suburban railroads in Chicago, for instance, attain mean journey speeds of just under 15 mph; whereas, buses in that city average only 6.2 mph. But even with its greater speed, rapid transit is rarely available in American cities; since it requires high passenger thresholds to maintain its profitable operation, it is confined to metropolitan areas, and even there its use is restricted to the high density radial corridors focusing on the central business district.

There are several types of rapid transit. One is the suburban railroad: it operates at relatively high speeds with intervals of .5 mile or more between stations. Another is the subway-elevated: it uses lighter, self-propelled cars with an ability to accelerate and decelerate relatively quickly, permitting more frequent stops. A third type is the bus system on its own right-of-way; an example of this is under operation on the Shirley Highway (I-95 freeway) serving the District of Columbia and northern Virginia.

To be tangible, yet avoid repetition, the procedure described below describes the road subsystem of guideways. The procedures for the inventory of public transportation facilities are similar.

7.4.3 Levels of Planning

There are two levels of transportation facilities planning: the system level and the route level. The first applies to the planning of overall transport networks at the city or regional scale and the second to individual components and subunits of the system. Transportation systems planning may be conceived as a first stage in a transportation planning process. Its output is a recommended "best" system (or network) of guideways identified only in general locations or "corridors." The second stage, preliminary location and design, determines the exact alinement of each route previously designated as a corridor. The third stage, final location and design, provides working drawings and specifications ready for construction contract letting. The inventories described in this chapter, while serving all three stages, are primarily associated with area-wide systems planning.

7.4.4 Network Coding Concept

Until very recently, transportation studies were unable to represent an entire transportation system within a computer. Lacking this, they were unable to readily construct minimum time paths through the network or to simulate vehicle flows over the system. As a consequence, the quality and comprehensiveness of their findings suffered noticeably.

A procedure developed during the Chicago Area Transportation Study in 1956–61 did much to correct these deficiencies, and thereby vastly improved the sophistication and quality of on-going transportation studies. This breakthrough was supplied by a very simple numbering system which enabled all the links of a transportation system to be identified and interconnected numerically, just as they are interconnected physically on the ground. The system is described thusly:

1. The entire metropolitan area is divided into zones, and each zone receives a three-digit number.
2. Each intersection between links in the street network is identified by a five-digit number, the first three digits being the number of the zone in

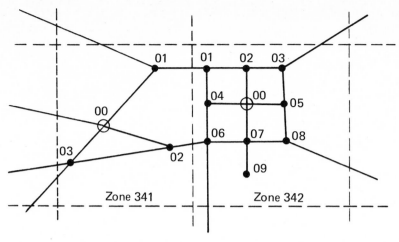

Fig. 7.6 Method of coding transportation networks. Arterials are identified by their numbers within zones and/or by their x-y coordinate locations [7.2].

which the intersection is located, and the last two digits identifying intersections within the zone.

3. Each link of the street system is identified by the number of the intersection at its beginning and end.

An illustration, Fig. 7.6, shows how this numbering system works in practice, as it did in the Chicago Transportation Study. Other studies use variants of this system [7.2].

7.4.5   Steps in Travel Facilities Inventory

7.4.5.1   Arterial network survey The inventory process itself consists of locating and describing each link of the transportation system in the manner just noted. The description of each link includes a measure of both the present capacity and use of a specific link and a statement of its performance characteristics. The acquisition of this data follows a number of sequential, predetermined steps.

Among the first things to be done is that of determining which of the many streets in a circulatory network are freeways and which are arterials, sorting these from collectors and local streets. The freeways are relatively easy to determine. But arterials are not as easily defined, since it is not always possible to determine just what streets are the major channels of movement within a city, nor what streets provide the main means of access to commercial activities. This can be and often is a subjective interpretation. It is not unusual, for example, for some streets to be classified as arterials that have a lower traffic volume than streets that are not so classified. Generally, though, roads that carry more than 2,000 vehicles per day and that are continuous in length are considered to be arterials; in any case, that is the criteria suggested here.

The second step is to prepare an arterial survey manual. Similar to the land use survey manual in purpose and objective, this is a listing of procedures and criteria. The importance of determining just how the results of the survey are to be used in advance of the field survey cannot be overemphasized. Unless the specific use is known well in advance, the inventory of uses and the kinds of data to be gathered are apt to be ill-defined and often inappropriate to the real needs of the study. A careful examination of existing sources of data should also be made at this time in order to avoid unnecessary duplication of effort.

Next the location of each arterial is identified, preferably in the digital coding format suggested previously. By identifying the terminus of each arterial link in this manner, not only is data reduction and processing facilitated, but the spatial interconnections of the network can be fully described and the geometry of the system mapped in computer form. The process of digitizing itself can be done by hand using maps or geodetically controlled photomosaics overlayed by a cartesian grid.

But more commonly, in order to avoid the time and inaccuracies inherent to this method, electronic graphic devices are used to digitize the system. Although an expensive device to use, it is relatively easy to operate and involves nothing more than positioning the cusor of the digitizer over the intersection to be mapped. The intersection number and map reference number is then recorded onto a machine-readable record along with X, Y, coordinates calculated by the digitizer.

The digital coordinates are then keypunched, if the information is not processed by the machine. After this, contingency checks are made of the keypunched material; usually this takes the form of mapping the computer data against the known locations of network arterials. As errors are uncovered the digitized materials must be revised and reentered into the system.

An important second phase to the arterial network survey is the inventory of physical and control data, largely in the field. At the minimum, this inventory includes the length, pavement width, right-of-way width, number of signals, signal timing, number of lanes, and parking control. Additional information on transit facilities, speed limits, type of street, traffic movement, and type of surrounding land use is sometimes collected. Figures 7.7 and 7.8 suggest the diversity and depth of the data often required in a road network survey. Much of this information is used to determine arterial traffic capacity.

After the Intersection Inventory Form and the Street Inventory Form, Figs. 7.7 and 7.8, have been completed, those data are then coded according to the format prescribed by the arterial survey manual. Any number of formats can be used. One commonly followed is the *Transportation System Inventory Coding Manual* published by the Chicago Area Transportation Study. Coded data, it should be noted, can be linked to the network coding scheme simply by adding fields of digits to the link identification number. This procedure has the merit of linking the geographic location of arterials with their traffic capacity, thereby integrating network interconnection with network traffic capacity. The data are then keypunched and contingency checked in the same way that coded arterial data were.

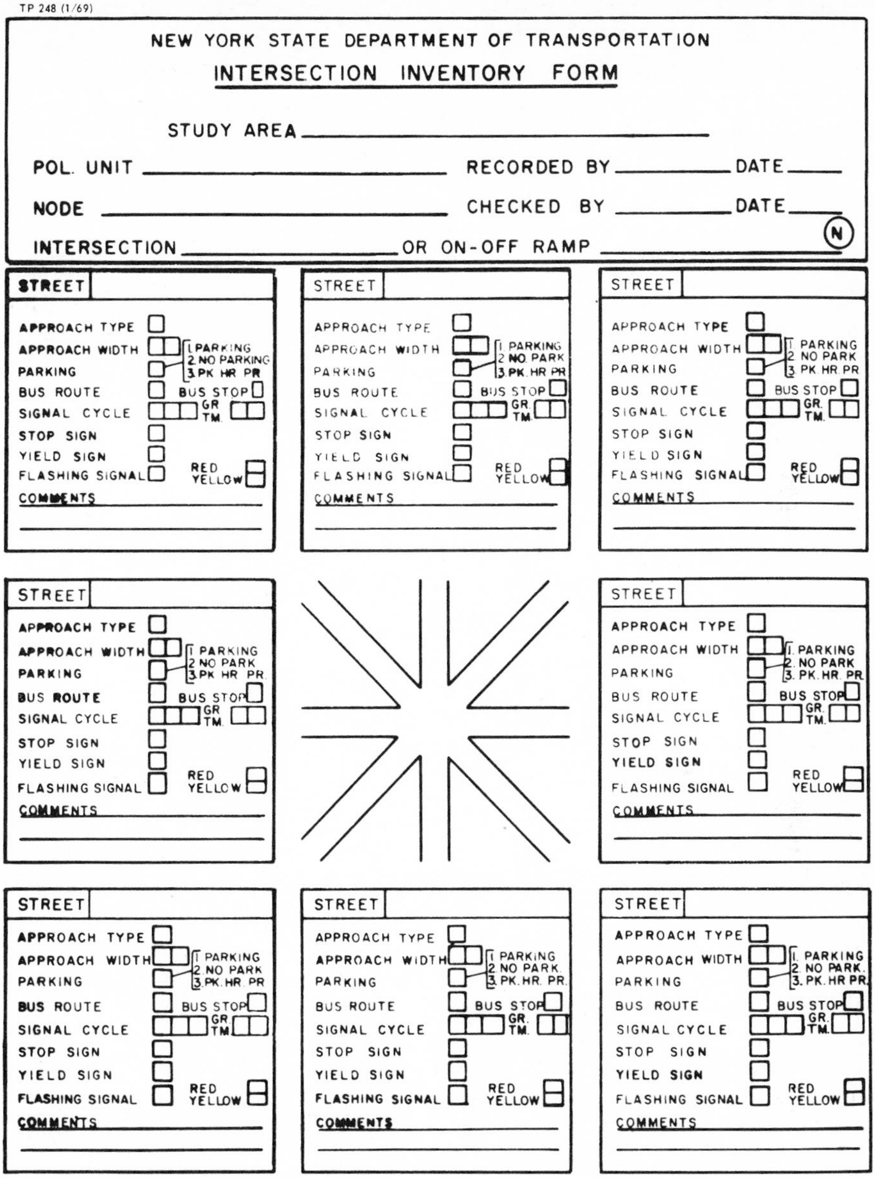

TP 248 (1/69)

Fig. 7.7 Intersection inventory form. [*New York State Department of Transportation, Albany, New York.*]

Finally, a road network report is issued. It describes the design characteristics of the arterials, their traffic capacities, and, in map form, the spatial pattern of the arterial system. It does not, however, suggest plans nor advocate modification of the existing system.

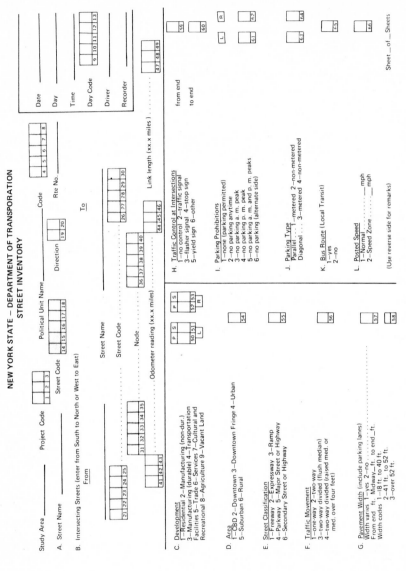

Fig. 7.8 Street inventory form. [*New York State Department of Transportation, Albany, New York.*]

7.4.5.2 Facilities usage survey The function of this survey is to sample the traffic volume carried by individual links of a road network so that areas of congestion can be defined. It is also used—in an important function—to measure the accuracy of computer simulation models. This type of survey is often called the vehicles miles of travel survey (VMT).

The basic procedure for conducting the route usage inventory has been suggested by Creighton [7.2, pp. 155–156]. First the network of roads in an urban area must be mapped and classified into convenient categories such as freeways and parkways; major and secondary arterials; collector and local streets. These streets are then sampled, the sample rate depending on the volume carried by each class of street. "Limited access roads may be sampled at a rate running between 30 and 100 percent of all links. Arterials may be sampled at rates between 20 and 25 percent." Very small samples are taken of local streets; these range between 1 and 5 percent since they carry such small volumes of traffic that great reliability is not required. The samples are selected on a random basis by computer.

The techniques used to measure traffic-flow vary by type of street. On freeways, counts are generally taken with portable machine counters for 24 hr or more. Arterial streets may be counted in the same way, or they may be counted manually for short periods of time (usually 2 hr) and the count expanded to reflect a 24-hr period. A volume count intersection form is used to manually record traffic flow. In similar fashion, local streets may be counted manually for 2-hr periods (Fig. 7.9) and this amount factored to represent 24-hr traffic volumes. Volume counts can be made at intersections or midblock on both arterial and local streets, and on links of freeways.

Finally, the volume data is coded, keypunched, and contingency checked. The sample volumes are then applied to other streets of similar type in the study area. The volume count for each street is multiplied by the length of the link. This produces the estimate of vehicle miles of travel, which can be presented in map or statistical form.

7.5 ORIGIN AND DESTINATION SURVEYS

The origin and destination travel survey provides data on the origin and destination of all trips, the purpose, travel time, and length of trip, the mode of travel, and the land use at the points of origin and destination. This information then serves as the basis for predicting the demand levels and flow patterns of future travel.

7.5.1 Types of Trips

The origin-destination survey measures a representative sample of the trips that originate within or pass through an urban area. The vehicular and person trips that occur in an area are composed of three types: those made by persons and commercial vehicles from outside the area (external trips); those made by commercial vehicles within the area (internal commercial); and those made by

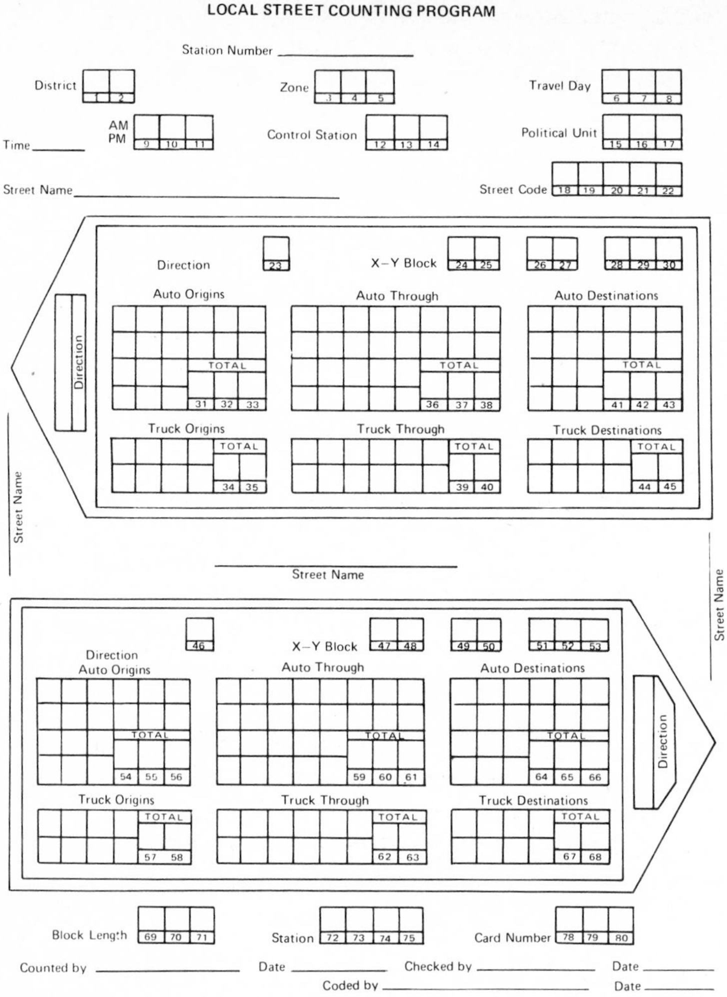

LOCAL STREET COUNTING PROGRAM

Station Number _____

District | 1 | 2 | Zone | 3 | 4 | 5 | Travel Day | 6 | 7 | 8 |

Time _____ AM PM | 9 | 10 | 11 | Control Station | 12 | 13 | 14 | Political Unit | 15 | 16 | 17 |

Street Name _____   Street Code | 18 | 19 | 20 | 21 | 22 |

Direction | 23 | X–Y Block | 24 | 25 | | 26 | 27 | | 28 | 29 | 30 |

Auto Origins   Auto Through   Auto Destinations

TOTAL | 31 | 32 | 33 | TOTAL | 36 | 37 | 38 | TOTAL | 41 | 42 | 43 |

Truck Origins TOTAL | 34 | 35 | Truck Through TOTAL | 39 | 40 | Truck Destinations TOTAL | 44 | 45 |

Street Name

Direction | 46 | X–Y Block | 47 | 48 | | 49 | 50 | | 51 | 52 | 53 |

Auto Origins   Auto Through   Auto Destinations

TOTAL | 54 | 55 | 56 | TOTAL | 59 | 60 | 61 | TOTAL | 64 | 65 | 66 |

Truck Origins TOTAL | 57 | 58 | Truck Through TOTAL | 62 | 63 | Truck Destinations TOTAL | 67 | 68 |

Block Length | 69 | 70 | 71 | Station | 72 | 73 | 74 | 75 | Card Number | 78 | 79 | 80 |

Counted by _____ Date _____ Checked by _____ Date _____
Coded by _____ Date _____

Fig. 7.9 Local street counting program. [*New York State Department of Transportation, Albany, New York.*]

persons who reside in the area (internal residential). Each of these requires a different type of sampling, interview technique, and listing.

7.5.2 Types of Travel Surveys

7.5.2.1 Cordon survey The cordon survey is used to inventory external travel. As the first step in this survey, a cordon line is drawn about the study area. The line itself is located some distance from the built-up portion of the study area, where the density of roads is not too great. All roads which cross the cordon line are listed and traffic volumes on these roads counted by portable mechanical counters.

After these roads have been counted, they are arrayed in order from largest to smallest. The most heavily traveled roads are interviewed for a 24 hr period, less heavily traveled roads for 16 hr, and minor roads for some 8 to 12 hr. Generally a sufficient volume must pass through the interviewing stations to equal about 90 to 95 percent of the total average daily traffic crossing into the study area. Only a representative sample of the vehicles (perhaps 20 to 35 percent) that cross through the cordon line need be interviewed for trip data.

Vehicles are stopped at the interviewing station and the drivers questioned as to their origin, destination, trip purpose, land use at origin and destination, and number of occupants inside the vehicle. Trucks are similarly interviewed, but buses and emergency vehicles are not stopped.

7.5.2.2 Truck-taxi survey This survey gauges the amount of commercial traffic within the urban area. Trucks and taxis can be sampled from lists of registrations obtained from the state government or from municipal tax lists if they are licensed by the municipality. The sample is made on a random basis, and each selected registration is interviewed either by telephone, mail, or by personal visit. The personal visit is the most expensive of the three types of interviews, but is unquestionably a more thorough and trustworthy technique. The data to be derived from these interviews include the purpose of the trip, the origin and destination of each trip, the number of passengers in the vehicle, and, in the case of trucks, the industry of ownership and truck loading. The sample rate may vary between 5 and 20 percent, and is based on city size, interview technique, and needed accuracy.

7.5.2.3 Home interview survey The home interview survey measures the largest form of movement within an urban area, internal residential based travel, which composes about 85 percent of all trips.

The sample in this survey is often a difficult technical problem requiring a knowledge of statistics, administrative costs, data processing techniques, and use of data. Usually the sample is obtained through field listings, or from the Bureau of the Census, directories, or utility lists. Choice of source hinges on such factors as budget, reliability and currency of existing sources, and whether the source can be used to generate other types of data. Once the source has been chosen, the sample is then selected, usually so that there is an even distribution of interviews for each day of the work week over the entire metropolitan area. The sample rate may vary between 1 and 25 percent, depending on city size. Because of recent advances in sampling procedures, the sample population in these surveys has tended to decline, with a great savings in cost.

Data collected in a home interview include both characteristics of the household as well as information on trips made by members of the household. Characteristics of the household that are determined include such things as number and ages of residents, occupation, car ownership, and sometimes income. Travel data include origin and destination of trips, trip purpose, mode of travel, time of day, car loading, and land use at origin and destination. Travel data are obtained for every person 5 years of age or older. Children under 5 are considered as accompanying adults. Figure 7.10 shows portions of a typical form. The data from

Fig. 7.10 Dwelling place inventory form. [*New York State Department of Transportation, Albany, New York.*]

the three travel surveys are then expanded to reflect the entire "universe" of trips in the urban area. Using this format, tripmaking can be related to land use and then forecast as a function of land use type and intensity.

7.6 SUMMARY

The four activities described in this chapter—geocoding, and inventories of land use, travel, and the transportation system—constitute the minimum components of a transportation study information system. Completion of these four data collection activities would create the core data bank from which information could be "withdrawn" for a large variety of transportation and other purposes.

Other chapters in this book discuss uses of the information system. A few examples will suffice here: Land use data is the primary source of trip generation data for the base year. It is also the major input into planned or forecast future land use from which future trip generation is derived. Travel surveys provide data on current actual trip making. Among other uses of trip data is calculation of trip generation factors for travel forecasts. The existing transportation network is a basic input to computer simulation of current travel behavior. The present network is also usually a "given" in preparation of proposed future networks.

An elemental geocoding system is a prerequisite for handling any spatially disaggregated data. In modern transportation studies the extensive use of the grid coordinate system has made possible operations research simulations of complex urban travel behavior and the testing of alternate proposed networks. Decision makers are thus given objective measures of the effectiveness of the alternatives in achieving the goals of the transportation system.

The use of coordinates also provides another requisite of an ideal management information system. Computer mapping, based on the coordinates, displays results of analyses, forecasts, simulations, and tests to decision makers in ways that are timely and comprehendible.

The basic transportation information system described in this chapter is of course evolving rapidly. There is, and will be, more attention to goals, including the values placed on various goals by different groups. Similarly data required for measuring and forecasting the socioeconomic interactions between transportation and other urban systems is a major concern. Means of making data available to all responsible agencies and affected groups are being explored and developed. These trends indicate that the information systems and models described in this book are the precursors of more objective and democratic future decision systems.

BIBLIOGRAPHY

7.1 Chapin, S. F.: *Urban Land Use Planning*, 2d ed., Univ. of Illinois Press, Champaign–Urbana, Ill., 1970.

7.2 Creighton, R. L.: *Urban Transportation Planning*, Univ. of Illinois Press, Champaign–Urbana, Ill., 1970.

7.3   Memmott, F.: "Transportation Planning," in W. Goodman and E. C. Freund (eds.), *Principles and Practice of Urban Planning*, International City Managers Association, Chicago, 1968.

7.4   Southern California Regional Information Study: *An Interim, ACG-DIME Updating System, SCRIS Report No. 4, Census Use Study*, Southern California Assoc. of Governments and U.S. Bureau of Census, Los Angeles, 1970.

7.5   Southern California Regional Information Study: *The Long Beach California Experience, ACG-DIME Updating System, SCRIS Report No. 8, Census Use Study*, Southern California Association of Governments and U.S. Bureau of Census, Los Angeles, 1970.

7.6   System Development Corporation: *A Geographic Base File for Urban Data Systems*, Systems Development Corporation, Santa Monica, Calif., 1969.

7.7   U.S. Department of Commerce, Bureau of the Census: *The DIME Geocoding System, Report No. 4, Census Use Study*, Government Printing Office, Washington, D.C., 1970.

7.8   U.S. Department of Commerce, Bureau of the Census: *Use of Address Coding Guides in Geographic Coding, Proceedings to the 1970 Conference at Wichita, Kansas, Nov. 19-20*, Government Printing Office, Washington, D.C., 1971.

7.9   U.S. Department of Housing and Urban Development: *Urban and Regional Information Systems*, Superintendant of Documents, Washington, D.C., undated, c. 1968.

7.10 Urban and Regional Information Systems Association: *Geocoding-71; Papers from the Working Session on Geographic Base File Developments at the Ninth Annual Conference, Sept. 8-10, 1971*, Urban Data Processing, Inc., Cambridge, Mass., 1971.

7.11 Urban Renewal Administration and Bureau of Public Roads: *Standard Land Use Coding Manual*, Government Printing Office, Washington, D.C., 1965.

7.12 Weiss, S.: "Land Use Analysis," in W. Goodman and E. C. Freund (eds.), *Principles and Practice of Urban Planning*, International City Managers Association, Chicago, 1968.

8 Transportation Evaluation and Decision Making

The need to evaluate proposed alternatives and make decisions among them is one of the most pressing yet difficult requirements in the transportation planning process. When one considers the beneficial and disbeneficial impacts which transportation systems can have—among them the development of access to employment opportunities, the movement of valuable natural resources to places where they can be utilized more effectively and, on the other side of the ledger, the creation of hazardous and unsafe conditions for both users and nonusers of the system—he surely must have some feelings of uneasiness about the manner in which decisions affecting these important aspects of life might be made. He certainly would want to ensure that all possible avenues of approach had been explored so that the alternative providing the maximum benefits for the required financial outlays would be both detected and chosen.

The difficulties inherent in the evaluation and decision-making process are many and, unfortunately, of great consequence. While these will not be covered in depth now, it should be pointed out that the problems of making adequate predictions of the consequences of alternatives and of determining the relative importance of these consequences have made the responsibility of decision making a heavy burden to public officials.

Who, for example, could have foreseen years ago that the automobile would take the place of the front porch swing, that it would change building design to allow for drive-in banks and restaurants, or that it would help to create the spread of suburbia? Who can determine with any assurance that the value of a life saved from an automobile accident is $34,000, that a dollar spent on the appearance of subways is equally as beneficial as a dollar spent for added speed, or that private ownership of transit facilities is to be preferred by the public to governmental ownership or control? These are several of the many vexing problems which face the planner, engineer, and public official.

This chapter is divided roughly into three sections. First, the general theory of the benefit-cost evaluation technique is presented, followed by a detailed discussion and an example taken from the American Association of State Highway Officials (AASHO) *Road User Benefit Analyses for Highway Improvements* [8.1].[1] This presentation forms a basis for an evaluation of the advantages and limitations of evaluation techniques and leads into the more general approach of cost-effectiveness. Finally, having shown how decisions theoretically *should be* made, we proceed to discuss how some decisions *are* made and who makes them.

8.1 A FRAMEWORK FOR EVALUATING BENEFITS AND COSTS

Economists and others concerned with the benefits and costs of various alternative policies and actions long have worked with the "willingness to pay" idea summarized by Wohl and Martin [8.5, pp. 183–84]:

> For the case of public projects . . . all factors or elements of concern and value to the owning public and for which value the public would willingly pay to gain, or to keep from losing, will be included. . . . Generally, then, social or political factors enter the analysis only in those instances where society would be willing to forego financial or *other resources of value* in their stead. This assumption is made, first, since most tangible and so-called intangible objects of concern have a history of experience and have been valued at the marketplace (at least implicitly). . . . Second, this assumption is made to point out that factors of *presumed* concern to the owning public and for which they are *not* willing to forego something else of value (which *must* be foregone to achieve the object of concern) are just that—presumed rather than real.
>
> Also, it must be emphasized that lack of willingness to pay for some social objective (or at least to forego something else of value in order to achieve that goal) suggests the lack of real value associated with the objective.

The idea of "willingness to pay" is brought into reality through the "demand curve" which shows what quantity of a given product people are willing to purchase at a given unit cost for the product.[2] In the case of highways, the product that is offered is "trips" of a given type, while the unit cost is composed of such items as

---

[1] Because of its long title and red cover, this document usually is referred to as the "Red Book." This shortened title will be the one utilized throughout the remainder of this text.

[2] Most demand curves show the relationship between quantity and *price*, not cost. But most economists view "price" as something which evolves through a market interaction. But, since there is not explicit market interaction to establish a price for highway service, we prefer to use the word "cost" in this connection rather than "price."

vehicle operating and maintenance costs, tax payments, parking fees, and the time of the driver and his passengers.

As a basis for an example of a demand curve for a highway, consider the overly simplified situation presented in Fig. 8.1. Trips are made between cities A and B

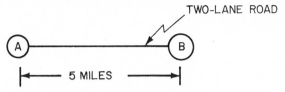

Fig. 8.1 A simple example of a roadway connecting cities A and B.

over a two-lane road which presently is 5 miles long. These trips, made during a given 1 year period, are all for the same purpose, are all done at one time of day, are all made by people of a similar socioeconomic background, and so forth. Under these conditions, and using procedures for travel prediction similar to those in Chap. 6, it is possible to construct a curve, such as that in Fig. 8.2, showing the number of trips made if the unit cost per mile of each trip were as indicated. Generally, it can be expected that as the unit cost per mile of each trip gets higher, there will be few yearly trips made over the road: thus the reason for the negative slope in the demand curve in Fig. 8.2.

In Fig. 8.2 it also can be seen that if the unit cost of travel were C_1, there would be v_1 yearly trips made. Further, it can be seen that some people would be willing to pay *more than* C_1, but would not be required to do so. For instance, v_2 trips would be made even if the cost were C_2 which is greater than C_1. As a consequence, there is a surplus (known as the "consumer surplus") which accrues to the people who are willing to pay more: they can take the money they are willing to pay but do not have to $(C_2 - C_1)$ and use it for some other purpose. This consumer surplus thus can be thought of as a benefit arising from tripmaking, and the summation of these benfits for all trips which are made gives the total benefit on yearly trips made by travelers.[3]

At this juncture, it should be noted that demand curves often are difficult to establish in practice. The correlation coefficients for trip generation presented in Chap. 6 certainly verify this statement. Of particular difficulty is the establishment of the end points in Fig. 8.2. It is a rare occurence when travel is either free or is so expensive that none is made. Because of these uncommon situations, observations at the extremes have been lacking, and no firm commitment can be made of exact

---

[3] The usual definition of benefits as proposed by economists includes the entire area between the demand curve and abscissa, whereas the definition employed in the Red Book follows that presented above. The distinction between the two concepts is not a crucial one for purposes of the exposition in this book, and so the Red Book definition will be adopted here. Economists usually denote the total consumer surplus as the "net benefits."

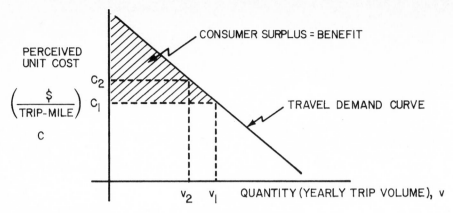

Fig. 8.2 Travel demand curve showing consumer surplus.

locations.[4] The result is that consumer surplus measurements also have been difficult to make.

Laying these problems aside temporarily, we can continue to develop the theoretical framework and at least determine what would be *desirable* insofar as an evaluation technique is concerned. The next step after establishing the demand curve would be to construct its counterpart—the supply curve. To do this, it is necessary to consider the short run elements of perceived cost associated with each mile driven on the example two-lane highway. Following the example of Wohl and Martin [8.5], the first of these costs might be for tax payments on gasoline, tires, and so forth. These would not be expected to vary greatly with the number of yearly trips made on the highway, so that an almost horizontal curve in Fig. 8.3 probably would be realistic.

[4] For an elaboration of this point see [8.21].

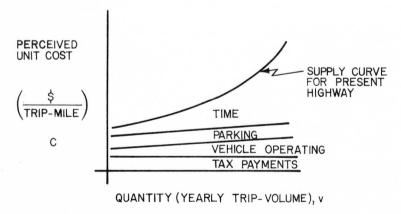

Fig. 8.3 Supply curve for travel.

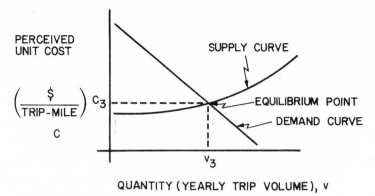

PERCEIVED
UNIT COST

$$\left(\frac{\$}{\text{TRIP-MILE}}\right) c_3$$

c

SUPPLY CURVE

EQUILIBRIUM POINT

DEMAND CURVE

v_3

QUANTITY (YEARLY TRIP VOLUME), v

Fig. 8.4 Equilibrium of demand for and supply of travel.

In addition to tax payments, there would be the perceived unit vehicle operating costs to consider. A reasonable assumption would be that these would rise somewhat with increases in travel volumes since more traffic would mean more delays, more idling of engines, longer times on the road (and thus more gas consumption), and so forth. These prices, when added to those for tax payments, would bring the total unit costs *up to* the second lowest curve in Fig. 8.3. Following a similar line of reasoning, we would anticipate that parking costs would not vary significantly with volume but that travel time costs, the fourth and final type, might increase rather sharply with volume as congestion on the highway slows traffic and increases the time for each trip. The sum total of these four unit costs,[5] calculated for each yearly tripmaking level, is represented by the topmost line in Fig. 8.3. It should be remembered that this line is indicative only of the particular highway used in the example, and depicts the perceived cost to *supply* or handle the given number of yearly trips by that existing facility.

The combination of the supply curve for the example highway in Fig. 8.3 and the demand curve in Fig. 8.2 is diagrammed in Fig. 8.4. The crossing of the two curves forms an equilibrium point (v_3, C_3), which can be interpreted as follows:

No amount of trips greater than v_3 will be made since, after a period of time, some people will find that the cost of making the additional trips is greater than they are willing to pay (the supply curve lies about the demand curve). Similarly, no amount of trips less than v_3 will be made since, after a period of time, some people will realize that the cost of making a trip is less than that which they are willing to pay (the supply curve lies below the demand curve). Thus, additional trips will be made until the unit costs equals that which the travelers are willing to pay.

The equilibrium point (v_3, C_3) therefore indicates the volume (v_3) of traffic that will use the example highway and the cost per trip mile (C_3) that the travelers

[5] It is not intended that these four costs represent an exhaustive set, but the general feeling seems to persist among transportation planners that these are the major costs which the automobile driver *perceives* as being significant. Other costs, such as car depreciation and insurance, do not appear to be important to the driver in determining whether to make *additional* trips.

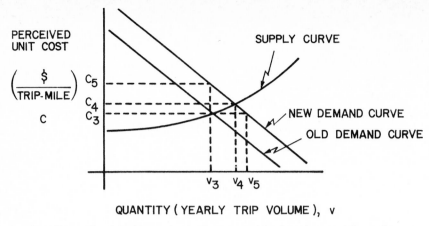

Fig. 8.5 Changes in tripmaking and unit trip cost resulting from increased demand.

will pay for making their trips. This cost then can be employed to calculate total benefits in a manner similar to that outlined in connection with Fig. 8.2.

The supply and demand curve concepts can be enlarged to take into account the consequences both of changes in demand and proposals for possible alternative highway improvements. By way of introduction to the first case, it has generally been true in the United States that overall income levels are rising,[6] and these increases usually lead to corresponding increases in the willingness of people to pay for certain goods or services. Thus, in referring back to Fig. 8.4, it can be seen that the perceived unit cost for a given number of trips, say v_3, will tend to increase over time or, stated another way, greater number of yearly trips will be made for a given cost. This type of change is indicated in Fig. 8.5, which also incorporates the demand curve from Fig. 8.2 and the supply curve from Fig. 8.3. The "new" demand curve rises above the "old" one for the reasons cited above.

One important point to notice in Fig. 8.5 is that a new equilibrium point (v_4, C_4), results from the establishment of the new demand curve. Interestingly enough, both the amount of money paid for travel and the number of trips increases the former from C_3 to C_4, the latter from v_3 to v_4. This situation implies that rising economic levels lead to increases in travel and explains to some extent why many transportation facilities are used to their capacity long before expected. These increases are part of what is known as "induced traffic."

Figure 8.6 shows the effect of a proposed new highway on the unit trip cost, number of trips, and benefits as regards travel between A and B. It is assumed that the new highway will be an "improvement" over the old one (which, for purposes of this example, will be eliminated after the new one is opened) in that there will be fewer and flatter curves, slighter grades, dual lanes in each direction, and so forth. With these conditions, it then follows that the new highway most likely will lead to

[6] For some relevant data, see Table 3.14 in Chap. 3.

a reduction in both the operating and travel time costs that help to make up the short run supply curve in Fig. 8.3.

The former costs would be lower primarily because of decreases in motor fuel needs brought about by the straightening of horizontal curves, the smoothing of vertical curves, and, in general, the creation of a more direct route between A and B, whereas the latter costs would be lower because of the ease of passing associated with the dual laning and, in general, the increased capacity of the new facility. The result of these effects, displayed in Fig. 8.6, would be a new short run supply curve associated with the new highway and lying below that for the present facility.

Also resulting from these travel cost reductions would be an increase in yearly tripmaking. By building a highway with a lower unit cost of travel, we can anticipate that more people would be willing to travel, and this is the case since at the new equilibrium point (v_6, C_6), the cost has been reduced from C_4 to C_6 while the number of trips has gone up from v_4 to v_6. This increase is another major component of "induced traffic."

Another result of a reduced cost of travel usually (and in this particular example) is an increase in benefits (as defined in Fig. 8.1). Looking at Fig. 8.7, which summarizes most of the information from the previous diagrams in this chapter, we can see that the benefits, B_p, of the present facility at the present time (old demand curve)[7] are

$$B_p = \tfrac{1}{2}(C_7 - C_3)(v_3 - 0) \tag{8.1}$$

Similarly, the future benefits (new demand curve) that would result if the present highway were not replaced by the proposed one, would be

[7] For simplicity, and to follow the general procedure in the Red Book, a linear demand curve is assumed in the calculations to follow.

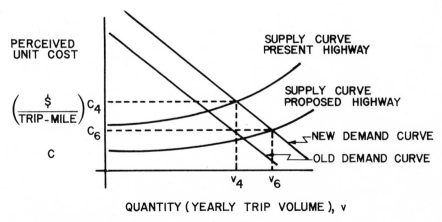

Fig. 8.6 Changes in tripmaking and unit trip cost resulting from a new highway facility.

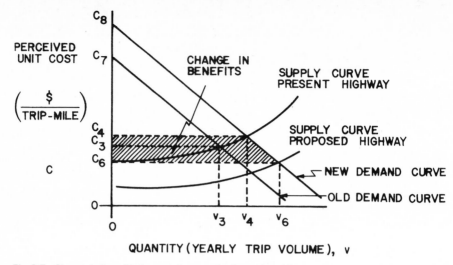

Fig. 8.7 Change in benefits from an increase in demand and from a proposed highway.

$$B_0 = \tfrac{1}{2} (C_8 - C_4) (v_4 - 0) \tag{8.2}$$

Finally, if the new highway were constructed and the old one eliminated, the benefits, B_n, would be

$$B_n = \tfrac{1}{2} (C_8 - C_6) (v_6 - 0) \tag{8.3}$$

The increase in future benefits attributed to the new highway thus could be calculated via

$$B_n - B_0 = \tfrac{1}{2} (C_8 - C_6) (v_6 - 0) - \tfrac{1}{2} (C_8 - C_4) (v_4 - 0) \tag{8.4}$$

which can be reduced to

$$B_n - B_0 = \tfrac{1}{2} [C_8 (v_6 - v_4) - C_6 v_6 + C_4 v_4] \tag{8.5}$$

Under the assumption of linearity and with a slope of $-(C_4 - C_6)/(v_6 - v_4)$ and an intercept of C_8, the general equation of the demand curve is

$$C = - \frac{C_4 - C_6}{v_6 - v_4} v + C_8 \tag{8.6}$$

Since the point (v_4, C_4) falls on the line, we obtain

$$C_4 = - \frac{C_4 - C_6}{v_6 - v_4} v_4 + C_8 \tag{8.7}$$

or

$$C_8 = C_4 + \frac{C_4 - C_6}{v_6 - v_4} v_4 \qquad (8.8)$$

Substituting this into Eq. (8.5) results in

$$B_n - B_0 = \frac{1}{2} \left[\left(C_4 + \frac{C_4 - C_6}{v_6 - v_4} v_4 \right) (v_6 - v_4) - C_6 v_6 + C_4 v_4 \right] \qquad (8.9)$$

which, after algebraic manipulation, becomes

$$B_n - B_0 = \frac{1}{2} (C_4 - C_6)(v_6 + v_4) \qquad (8.10)$$

which is also the formula for the area of the shaded trapezoidal section in Fig. 8.7.

A point to be stressed at this time is that some benefits (or disbenefits) may accrue even if the proposed improvement is not built. In the example presented here, the change in benefits over time caused by the increase in demand is

$$B_0 - B_p = \frac{1}{2} (C_8 - C_4)(v_4 - 0) - \frac{1}{2} (C_7 - C_3)(v_3 - 0) \qquad (8.11)$$

This quantity may or may not be positive, depending on the magnitude of each of the unit costs and volumes. However, there most likely will be a change in benefits even if nothing were done. This situation implies that the "do nothing" alternative is one that has to be considered in its own right: it has an impact that may be significant. In fact, the existence of this alternative is one of the main reasons why the evaluation stage has been placed before the solution generation stage in the transportation planning process outlined in Chap. 2. It is imperative that the consequences of *not changing* from the present state be evaluated before any solutions are proposed. Otherwise, the planner or engineer has no basis by which to *compare* the benefits which may arise from various "improvement" schemes.

8.1.1 Accounting for Capital and Maintenance Costs

After the analysis of benefits is completed, it is necessary to look on the other side of the ledger—on the facility cost side. The primary component costs to be considered are those for right-of-way (land), grading and drainage, major structures, pavement, and, in a slightly different category, those for maintenance. The former set of costs, known as capital costs, generally are the most extensive, yet maintenance costs also can be significant. In either case, the objective at this point is to compare the benefits that will accrue from the expenditure of funds for the construction and maintenance of alternate highway facilities.

It should be noted at this juncture that the "benefits" calculated by means of Eq. (8.10) are stated in dollar terms just as the capital and maintenance costs are.

Each of the unit costs is expressed in dollars per mile per trip and volume of trips, of course, is expressed in "trips/year." Therefore, since in each equation we have the unit cost multiplied by the number of trips, we get ($/trip-mile) × (trips/year) = ($/mile/year) as the units for benefits. Benefits and costs thus are commensurate, that is, measurable in the same units. Commensurability naturally is desirable in an evaluation procedure since we do not, as the expression goes, want to "mix apples and oranges."

Another consideration which must be taken into account at this stage is that the benefits and costs associated with a transportation facility vary over time. Referring to the hypothetical curves in Fig. 8.8, we can see that if a new highway facility were constructed, the benefits would not start until its completion and probably would build over time as travel increased. The costs, on the other hand, would be extremely high at the beginning when the full amount of capital had to be expended, then would decrease sharply, followed by a slight increase over time as the facility started to approach the end of its service life and subsequently require more maintenance.

It would be quite cumbersome to calculate the area between the two curves in Fig. 8.8 to get the total difference between benefits and costs. As a consequence, most analysts will calculate average (over time) benefits and costs and use these for comparison purposes. The averages for the hypothetical curves in Fig. 8.8 also are presented in that diagram. The assumption of this procedure, at least insofar as cost to the agency responsible for evaluating the facility is concerned, is that the *initial* cost is not as important as the average long run cost. This assumption may not always be the correct one.

8.1.1.1 Interest rates   A final consideration to be brought out before the comparison of benefits and costs can be made is that funds for capital costs often must be borrowed, and, of course, there are interest payments to be made if borrowing is necessary. Even if borrowing were not necessary, we should take into

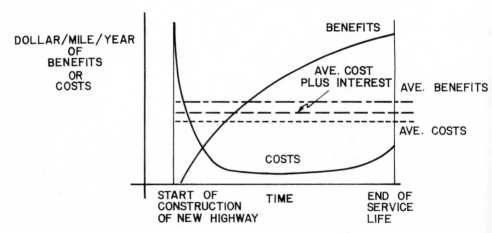

Fig. 8.8 Hypothetical changes in benefits and costs over time.

account the time value of money, which can also be represented by the interest rate. To understand this point one has only to remember that if an investment in a transportation facility cannot create monetary returns of at least, say, 3 percent per year (simple interest),[8] then the investor, be it a city, state, or federal government, or a private firm, would be better off financially by putting its funds into a savings account at a local bank. In other words, we would expect that all funds should be allocated in such a manner that they will have a return that compares favorably with any other of their possible uses: a 3 percent return is "no return" in the sense that most other investments would give back at least this amount. In conclusion, then, the benefits from a proposed or existing transportation facility should exceed the costs plus interest in order for it to be a worthwhile investment. The "average costs plus interest" curve has been superimposed in Fig. 8.8 to demonstrate this point.

What interest rate to use in a given situation is a matter of some debate. Of course, if funds are being borrowed, the actual interest rate can be employed. If not, then some other means must be found for making such a determination. Wohl and Martin [8.5] go into a considerable discussion on this issue and their book should be consulted for further information. While they come to no firm conclusions, they do appear to agree with quoted statements which set the rate at not lower than 4 percent and, hopefully, greater than 10 percent. We do not make any further recommendations except that the line of thinking of Wohl and Martin be followed in each case under study.

8.1.1.2 Calculating yearly costs With the adoption of an interest rate, it is then possible to calculate the average yearly payments for capital and interest together. This is accomplished through the use of the capital recovery factor $(CRF_{i,N})$, which shows the percentage (expressed as a decimal) of the capital costs which must be paid each year with a given interest rate (i) and service life (N). The equation[9] for $CRF_{i,N}$ is

$$CRF_{i,N} = \frac{i(1+i)^N}{(1+i)^N - 1} \tag{8.12}$$

Table 8.1, taken from the AASHO Red Book, allows for the $CRF_{i,N}$ to be read directly.

A common example of the utilization of the capital recovery factor is found in house payments. Suppose a mortgage (loan) of $20,000 at 6 percent interest rate for 20 years is made on a house. What percentage of the $20,000 must be paid each year?[10] To begin, let us note that if no interest were involved, the yearly payment would be $20,000/20 years = $1,000/year. This corresponds to a yearly percentage of $1,000/$20,000 = 5 percent. Thus, with interest involved, the percentage

---

[8] This figure has been chosen to represent a probable lower bound on the interest rate.

[9] This equation is not correct when $i = 0$. In that special case, $CRF_{0,N} = 1/N$.

[10] House payments generally are on a monthly basis, but this example is intended to have carryover to transportation facilities payments which usually are made annually.

Table 8.1 Capital Recovery Factors

N Years	\multicolumn{11}{c}{Rate of interest, in percent (i)}										
	1.0	1.5	2.0	2.5	3.0	3.5	4.0	4.5	5.0	5.5	6.0
1	1.0100	1.0150	1.0200	1.0250	1.0300	1.0350	1.0400	1.0450	1.0500	1.0550	1.0600
2	0.5075	0.5113	0.5150	0.5188	0.5226	0.5264	0.5302	0.5340	0.5378	0.5416	0.5454
3	0.3400	0.3484	0.3467	0.3501	0.3535	0.3569	0.3603	0.3638	0.3672	0.3707	0.3741
4	0.2563	0.2594	0.2626	0.2658	0.2690	0.2723	0.2755	0.2787	0.2820	0.2853	0.2886
5	0.2060	0.2091	0.2121	0.2152	0.2183	0.2215	0.2246	0.2278	0.2310	0.2342	0.2374
6	0.1725	0.1755	0.1785	0.1815	0.1846	0.1877	0.1908	0.1939	0.1970	0.2002	0.2034
7	0.1486	0.1515	0.1545	0.1575	0.1605	0.1635	0.1666	0.1697	0.1728	0.1760	0.1791
8	0.1307	0.1336	0.1365	0.1395	0.1425	0.1455	0.1485	0.1516	0.1547	0.1579	0.1610
9	0.1167	0.1196	0.1225	0.1255	0.1284	0.1314	0.1345	0.1376	0.1407	0.1438	0.1470
10	0.1056	0.1084	0.1113	0.1143	0.1172	0.1202	0.1233	0.1234	0.1295	0.1327	0.1359
11	0.0965	0.0993	0.1022	0.1051	0.1081	0.1111	0.1141	0.1172	0.1204	0.1236	0.1268
12	0.0888	0.0917	0.0945	0.0975	0.1005	0.1035	0.1065	0.1097	0.1128	0.1160	0.1193
13	0.0824	0.0852	0.0881	0.0910	0.0940	0.0971	0.1001	0.1033	0.1065	0.1097	0.1130
14	0.0769	0.0797	0.0826	0.0855	0.0885	0.0916	0.0947	0.0978	0.1010	0.1043	0.1076
15	0.0721	0.0749	0.0778	0.0808	0.0838	0.0868	0.0899	0.0931	0.0963	0.0996	0.1030
16	0.0679	0.0708	0.0737	0.0766	0.0796	0.0827	0.0858	0.0890	0.0923	0.0956	0.0989
17	0.0643	0.0671	0.0700	0.0729	0.0759	0.0790	0.0820	0.0854	0.0887	0.0920	0.0954
18	0.0610	0.0688	0.0667	0.0697	0.0727	0.0758	0.0790	0.0822	0.0855	0.0889	0.0923
19	0.0581	0.0609	0.0638	0.0688	0.0698	0.0729	0.0761	0.0794	0.0827	0.0861	0.0896
20	0.0554	0.0582	0.0611	0.0641	0.0672	0.0704	0.0736	0.0769	0.0802	0.0837	0.0872
21	0.0530	0.0559	0.0588	0.0618	0.0649	0.0680	0.0713	0.0746	0.0780	0.0815	0.0850
22	0.0509	0.0537	0.0566	0.0596	0.0627	0.0659	0.0692	0.0725	0.0760	0.0795	0.0830
23	0.0489	0.0517	0.0547	0.0577	0.0608	0.0640	0.0673	0.0707	0.0741	0.0777	0.0813
24	0.0471	0.0499	0.0529	0.0559	0.0590	0.0623	0.0656	0.0690	0.0725	0.0760	0.0797
25	0.0454	0.0483	0.0512	0.0543	0.0574	0.0607	0.0640	0.0674	0.0709	0.0745	0.0782

26	0.0439	0.0467	0.0497	0.0528	0.0559	0.0592	0.0626	0.0660	0.0696	0.0732	0.0769
27	0.0424	0.0453	0.0483	0.0514	0.0546	0.0579	0.0612	0.0647	0.0683	0.0719	0.0757
28	0.0411	0.0440	0.0470	0.0501	0.0533	0.0566	0.0600	0.0635	0.0671	0.0708	0.0746
29	0.0399	0.0428	0.0458	0.0489	0.0521	0.0554	0.0589	0.0624	0.0660	0.0698	0.0736
30	0.0387	0.0416	0.0446	0.0478	0.0510	0.0544	0.0578	0.0614	0.0651	0.0688	0.0726
31	0.0377	0.0406	0.0436	0.0467	0.0500	0.0534	0.0569	0.0604	0.0641	0.0679	0.0718
32	0.0367	0.0396	0.0426	0.0458	0.0490	0.0524	0.0559	0.0596	0.0633	0.0671	0.0710
33	0.0357	0.0386	0.0417	0.0449	0.0481	0.0516	0.0551	0.0587	0.0625	0.0663	0.0703
34	0.0348	0.0378	0.0408	0.0440	0.0473	0.0507	0.0543	0.0580	0.0617	0.0656	0.0696
35	0.0340	0.0369	0.0400	0.0432	0.0465	0.0500	0.0536	0.0573	0.0611	0.0650	0.0690
36	0.0332	0.0361	0.0392	0.0425	0.0458	0.0493	0.0529	0.0566	0.0604	0.0644	0.0684
37	0.0325	0.0354	0.0385	0.0417	0.0451	0.0486	0.0522	0.0560	0.0598	0.0638	0.0679
38	0.0318	0.0347	0.0378	0.0411	0.0445	0.0480	0.0516	0.0554	0.0593	0.0633	0.0673
39	0.0311	0.0341	0.0372	0.0404	0.0438	0.0474	0.0511	0.0549	0.0588	0.0628	0.0669
40	0.0305	0.0334	0.0365	0.0398	0.0433	0.0468	0.0505	0.0543	0.0583	0.0623	0.0665
41	0.0229	0.0328	0.0360	0.0393	0.0427	0.0463	0.0500	0.0539	0.0578	0.0619	0.0661
42	0.0293	0.0323	0.0354	0.0387	0.0422	0.0458	0.0495	0.0534	0.0574	0.0615	0.0657
43	0.0287	0.0317	0.0349	0.0382	0.0417	0.0453	0.0491	0.0530	0.0570	0.0611	0.0653
44	0.0282	0.0312	0.0344	0.0377	0.0412	0.0449	0.0487	0.0526	0.0566	0.0608	0.0650
45	0.0277	0.0307	0.0339	0.0373	0.0408	0.0445	0.0483	0.0522	0.0563	0.0604	0.0647
46	0.0272	0.0303	0.0335	0.0368	0.0404	0.0441	0.0479	0.0518	0.0559	0.0601	0.0644
47	0.0268	0.0298	0.0330	0.0364	0.0400	0.0437	0.0475	0.0515	0.0556	0.0598	0.0641
48	0.0263	0.0294	0.0326	0.0360	0.0396	0.0433	0.0472	0.0512	0.0553	0.0595	0.0639
49	0.0259	0.0290	0.0322	0.0356	0.0392	0.0430	0.0469	0.0509	0.0550	0.0593	0.0637
50	0.0255	0.0286	0.0318	0.0353	0.0389	0.0426	0.0465	0.0506	0.0548	0.0591	0.0634
60	0.0222	0.0254	0.0288	0.0324	0.0361	0.0401	0.0442	0.0485	0.0528	0.0573	0.0619
70	0.0199	0.0232	0.0267	0.0304	0.0343	0.0385	0.0427	0.0472	0.0517	0.0563	0.0610
80	0.0182	0.0215	0.0252	0.0291	0.0331	0.0374	0.0418	0.0464	0.0510	0.0558	0.0606
90	0.0169	0.0203	0.0240	0.0280	0.0323	0.0367	0.0412	0.0459	0.0506	0.0554	0.0603
100	0.0159	0.0194	0.0232	0.0273	0.0316	0.0362	0.0408	0.0456	0.0504	0.0553	0.0602

Source: [8.1, p. 150].

naturally will be higher. Using Table 8.1 we obtain a $CRF = 0.0872$ or 8.72 percent. Consequently, in each year (0.0872) $($\$$20,000) = $\$$1,744$ must be paid.[11]

Similar examples could be generated in regard to transportation facilities with the CRF used in the determination of average yearly costs. A CRF usually is not calculated for benefits. Instead, the benefits are appraised for a year which lies in the middle of the time span between construction and the end of the service life. This procedure is based on the assumption that the change in benefits over time is approximately linear.

8.1.2 Comparison of Benefits and Costs

By using the capital recovery factor and the assumption of a linear change in benefits over time, we are capable of making a direct comparison of dollar benefits and costs from a new facility. This is usually done in the form of a ratio known as the benefit-cost ratio. If reference is again made to the example used up to this point in the chapter, it will be remembered that the difference in future benefits between the old highway from cities A to B (Fig. 8.1) and the new one is $B_n - B_o = \Delta B$. The corresponding difference in costs can be calculated as follows:

Let K_n = the total capital costs for constructing the new facility;

    M_n = the average yearly maintenance cost of the new facility; and

    M_o = the average yearly maintenance cost of the old facility.

Then the difference in average yearly costs is

$$\Delta C = (CRF_{i,N})K_n + M_n - M_o \tag{8.13}$$

The comparison of benefits and costs thus becomes

$$\frac{\Delta B}{\Delta C} = \frac{B_n - B_o}{(CRF_{i,N})K_n + M_n - M_o} \tag{8.14}$$

Naturally, it is desirable that the change in benefits associated with the new highway (in comparison to the old one) be large enough to cover the costs (plus interest) involved, so that the ratio in Eq. (8.14) should be greater than or equal to one. If it is not, the change in costs would exceed the change in benefits and would make the project of dubious value.

If more than one new facility were being proposed, we would have to evaluate each one separately but in relation to the present facility. The one with the greatest $\Delta B/\Delta C$ ratio theoretically should be the one to be built. However, there is another aspect to consider when evaluating multiple projects. It may turn out that a low cost facility may have a high $\Delta B/\Delta C$ ratio whereas a high cost facility may not. At

---

[11] The concerned student should note that interest payments in this case amount to about 75 percent of the capital costs. Thus, the magnitude of interest payments can be a relatively important consideration in transportation planning.

the same time, it may be possible that the difference in cost for the more expensive facility over the less expensive one may be matched or even exceeded by the increase in benefits of the former over the latter. The conclusion then would be that, if the budget permits, it would be better to build the more expensive facility since the extra investment still would bring a return exceeding the costs involved. In other words, an investor should continue to invest as long as he can get a return greater than he can get any place else.

To make the indicated comparison among acceptable $(\Delta B/\Delta C \geqslant 1.00)$ alternatives, all that one does is to use the lowest cost alternative as a base and calculate a benefit-cost ratio in a manner similar to that done in Eq. (8.14). The only difference in this case would be that there would be a capital cost, associated with the low cost alternative, that would have to be included along with its corresponding maintenance cost in the denominator of Eq. (8.14).[12] An example of this procedure along with that of the entire benefit-cost concept will be given as part of the next section of this chapter.

8.1.3 Example of the Benefit-Cost Approach: The AASHO Procedure

The foregoing discussion has set the theoretical framework for the evaluation of alternative proposals using the benefit-cost technique. It has been employed for many years, and, in particular has formed the framework for the much used procedure outlined by the American Association of State Highway Officials in the Red Book. The material in this section has been taken almost verbatim from that publication and demonstrates a rather detailed application of the technique. This application also provides a basis for a succeeding discussion of the many limitations and problems associated with benefit-cost evaluation.

A road user benefit analysis for highway improvements is a comparison of annual costs of alternates. For each alternate the annual road user costs and the annual cost of improving, maintaining, and operating that portion of the highway are determined for a selected period of time. Then the alternates are compared arithmetically to express a benefit-cost ratio, or quotient of the differences, similar to that in Eq. (8.14).

The annual road user cost is the total of a computed vehicle operating cost and annual time cost. The highway improvement is divided into as many sections as there are significant variations in the major analysis elements. Summation of these sectional vehicle operating and time costs give the annual road user cost for that highway alternate. Road user costs include all traffic directly involved or affected by the improvement. One alternate may include road user costs for vehicles operating on a new or improved route and also those continuing to operate on one or more parallel or connecting routes on which the traffic flow is affected by the improvement.

---

[12] There generally is no capital cost associated with the present highway, of course.

The annual highway cost is the total of the annual capital cost and the annual cost for maintenance and operation of the highway and its appurtenances. The annual capital cost is the annual amount required to amortize the total highway improvement cost plus interest. Usually separate average life values are used for right-of-way, grading and drainage, pavement, and major structures. The annual road maintenance and operations costs are estimated by study of actual costs for similar highways and conditions.

8.1.3.1 Calculation of road user costs for continuous operation

Charts presented in this section give combined unit vehicle operating and time costs in terms of the running speed and other condition variables. For any alternate considered in an evaluation, the annual vehicle operating and time benefit, B, is calculated using a version of Eq. (8.10) revised to take into account the lengths of the sections under consideration and the use of a *daily* volume, V, instead of yearly volume (v). The revised equation is

$$B_n - B_o = \tfrac{1}{2} (C_o l_o - C_n l_n) (V_n + V_o) (365) \tag{8.15}$$

The n subscript denotes the new facility and the o the old. Each unit cost, expressed in dollars per vehicle mile of travel, is multiplied by the length of the section in miles to get the cost for each vehicle trip over the entire highway. The V's, which are annual average daily volumes for the period of evaluation (a period in which reasonable accuracy can be expected in the estimation of future traffic), are multiplied by 365 days per year to get the yearly volume. The incorporation of these two changes allows for the calculations of future yearly benefits accruing for the entire facility.

If more than one section for a facility is involved (with a different unit cost), the product of C and l for each section is summed to get the total cost of a trip over the facility. If there are different travel volumes on each section, the calculations become quite complex and Eq. (8.15) cannot be utilized directly. The reader is referred to the AASHO Red Book for examples of procedures in these two kinds of situations.

8.1.3.2 Value of V

Three steps are necessary to determine the value of V for each alternative in an evaluation:

1. Estimate the annual average daily traffic that will use the facility upon its completion;
2. Determine the number of years for which the analysis is to be made and the expansion factor for traffic on the facility during this period; and
3. Calculate an expanded annual average daily traffic volume that is a representative or average value for the period of analysis. This is the V value in Eq. (8.15).

Current traffic data are essential for any road user benefit evaluation. Those basic traffic data must be of a form to permit separation of the volumes operating on each section used in the analysis. Also, studies as to the expansion of traffic are necessary to determine the expanded traffic volumes for this period of time used in the analysis. This period of time should not be greater than that for which traffic can be estimated with reasonable accuracy. Many administrators believe a time period of 15 to 25 years to be a maximum for which they can estimate traffic with desired accuracy. The traffic forecast period is independent of the average life values used for calculating annual capital cost, as explained under the section on calculation of highway costs.

In most instances it will be necessary to separate the traffic data by vehicle types, since different unit road user costs must be used for each. Light trucks, such as pickups, delivery wagons, etc., that have the general size, weight, and performance characteristics of passengers cars should be included in the latter class. All heavier and larger trucks and buses should be considered separately. For practical purposes trucks and buses with manufacturers' rating for gross vehicle weight of 9,000 pounds or more can be considered in the truck and bus class. Where capacity is the basis of rating, a capacity of 1.5 tons or more should be considered in the truck or bus class. A rule of thumb that may be used without appreciable error is to consider all vehicles with dual-tired driving wheels in the truck and bus class.

8.1.3.3 Value of *I*   For purposes of road user benefit analysis the highway route should be divided into sections of convenient length. As a first control, there should be a separate section for each significant variation in traffic volume. As a second control, there should be a separate section for each variation in the major analysis elements. The latter are of two types: (a) the physical changes such as number of lanes, profile conditions, or type of surfacing, and (b) the vehicle operational changes as determined jointly by the highway conditions and volumes.

In general, short sections should be avoided. Sections need not be established unless their separation serves to increase the practical accuracy of the analysis as a whole. Sections of considerable length can be used if the conditions throughout are nearly the same.

8.1.3.4 Value of *C*   Figures 8.9 through 8.12 show values for combined unit vehicle operating and time costs for tangent (straight section) roadways, as based on national average current prices. They are in a form for direct use in Eq. (8.15). The proper *C* value for any section is read from the appropriate figure after the following conditions are established for that section, usually in the order listed:

    a. Number and arrangement of lanes (type of highway).
    b. Type of surface; with (a) above this determines which of Figs. 8.9 to 8.12 is applicable.
    c. Grade of profile type (gradient class); determines which curve or group of curves in the figure is applicable.
    d. Running speed; determines where to enter the group of curves on the lower axis.
    e. Type of operation; determines which curve or group of curves is applicable.
    f. Alignment features; determines correction factor (Fig. 8.12) applied to tangent alinement costs obtained from Figs. 8.9 to 8.12.

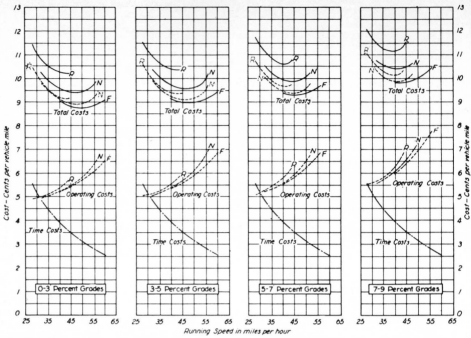

Fig. 8.9 Unit road user costs versus running speed for passenger cars in rural areas on tangent divided highways with pavements in good condition. [8.1, p. 20].

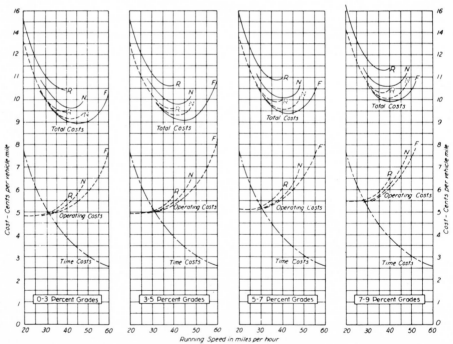

Fig. 8.10 Unit road user costs versus running speed for passenger cars in rural areas on tangent two-lane highways with pavements in good condition. [8.1, p. 21].

314

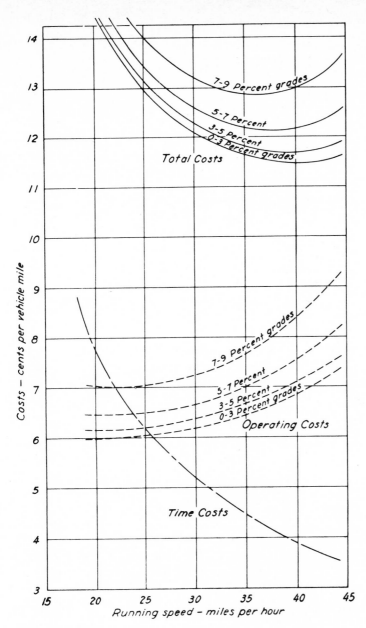

Fig. 8.11 Unit road user costs versus running speed for passenger cars in rural areas on tangent, loose surface highways in good condition. [8.1, p. 22].

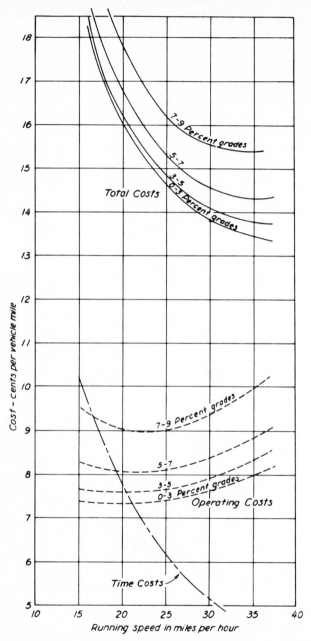

Fig. 8.12 Unit road user costs versus running speed for passenger cars in rural areas on tangent, unsurfaced roads. [8.1, p. 23].

The unit costs obtained from Figs. 8.9 to 8.12 include the combined effects of all the above variables except alinement.

a. Number and arrangement of lanes. For the same terrain and geometric design details a somewhat different effect from other variables can be expected on a divided highway than on a two-lane highway with pavements in good condition. Unit cost values for these two types of rural highways are shown separately in Figs. 8.9 and 8.10. Running speeds on three-lane highways and on four-lane undivided highways are about equal to or only slightly greater than on two-lane highways for comparable conditions, and the effects of other variables are only slightly different.

Accordingly, the preparation of separate charts for unit costs on these types of highways is not warranted. Unit costs on three-lane highways can be assumed to be nearly the same as those on two-lane highways and unit costs on undivided highways of four or more lanes can be approximated as values between those for two-lane and divided highways. The differences are small and of little consequence for running speeds of 40 mph or less.

b. Type of surface. Regardless of geometric design, the type of surface has pronounced effects on unit costs. Unit road user costs are separated for three types: (i) paved surfaces, either rigid or flexible, (ii) loose surfaces, primarily all-weather gravel, and (iii) unsurfaced. Each analysis section can be classified accordingly. The data for paved and loose surfaces are representative for surfaces in good condition. Unit costs for paved surfaces in fair to poor condition can be obtained by interpolation between the "paved" and "loose" values. Likewise, values for gravel surfaces in poor condition can be estimated by interpolation between "loose" and "unsurfaced."

c. Grade of profile type. Running speeds and resultant unit costs are affected by the profile type and gradients involved. The unit cost data are separated for four gradient classes: 0 to 3 percent, 3 to 5 percent, 5 to 7 percent, and 7 to 9 percent. These classes indicate an average grade along the highway and the unit cost values for them include the momentum effect for operation in rolling terrain. The gradient class must be determined for each analysis section. This determination can be made from profile data by any one of several methods without significant error in the resulting unit cost.

A simple method, conforming closely to the source cost data, is the calculation of average gradient for the analysis section by summation of actual grades for each 100-foot section or at every other 100-foot section and dividing by the number of sections in the summation or by dividing the total rise and fall by the length. Where the profile varies considerably in the length of an otherwise suitable analysis section, the section should be divided into two or more subsections each of a different gradient class. Such precision usually is necessary on long sections only.

d. Running speed. The running speed must be representative for the whole length of the analysis section, for all vehicles of the type to which it applied, and for the whole of the period used in the analysis. Running speed is lower than the typical "average" speed, which is a spot speed determined on an open section of the highway. The running speed must be representative of the terrain, curvature, gradient, sight distance, traffic volume, and other affecting conditions on the section. Where comparable highway conditions exist, it is most conveniently determined by dividing the total length by the total running time for representative operation. To be fully representative, the running speed so determined should be adjusted to include dark as well as daylight hours, typical inclement weather conditions, and anticipated future operations.

Where comparable measurement is not possible, an estimate for running speed on two-lane highways can be made from design speed and traffic volume data.

e. Type of operation. The traffic volume operating on a certain section of highway will decidedly affect the running speed and consequently the unit cost. While data are not complete enough to permit positive accuracy, they are sufficient to establish the effect of type of operation on operating cost. The general combined effects of terrain, type of highway, control of access, and traffic volume are grouped into three types of operation: (a) free, (b) normal, and (c) restricted, each determined by a relation of the 30th highest hourly traffic volume of the year to the volume at level of service D.[13] While these operating conditions are relative rather than precise, they serve as a practical means of distinguishing a complex combination of factors. For this method of analysis it is necessary to rate the operating conditions as being in one of these three classes:

Type of operation	Ratio of the 30th highest hourly traffic volume to volume at level of service D
Restricted	Greater than 1.25
Normal	0.75 to 1.25
Free	Less than 0.75

f. Alignment features. The values in Figs. 8.9 to 8.12 are prepared for open or high type alignment. For conditions of curved alignment a correction is made by increasing tangent costs in accordance with the percentage obtained from Fig. 8.13. To use Fig. 8.13 it is necessary to determine both the sharpness and the percent of length of significant curvature. Little error results in using the average degree of curvature and average superelevation (banking) for the section being analyzed, weighted on the basis of length.

Upon determination of the above six factors, the proper value of C is selected for each section from Fig. 8.9 to Fig. 8.13.

The unit cost values given herein are representative on a nationwide basis.[14] They were established by use of the following cost factors:

Gasoline	32 cents/gallon
Oil	45 cents/quart

---

[13] The phrase "practical capacity" was used in the AASHO Red Book; however, this phrase no longer is employed and we have chosen the words "volume at level of service D." See Chap. 5, Sec. 5.2.5 for an elaboration of the "level of service" concept.

[14] These figures are 1959 costs and should be updated accordingly for present conditions.

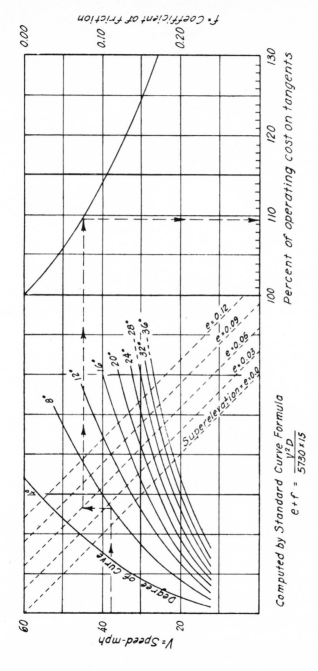

Computed by Standard Curve Formula

$$e + f = \frac{V^2 D}{5730 \times 15}$$

Example : Assume 38 mph operation on 8° curve, 0.06 superelevation. Follow arrows and read 109.50 % as the factor to apply to correct the tangent road user cost values.

Fig. 8.13 Relation between operating costs on curves and on tangents. [8.1, p. 24].

Tires	$100 initial cost per set
Car repairs	When operating on good pavements: 1.2 cents/ vehicle mile
	On loose surfaces: 1.8 cents/vehicle mile
	On unimproved surfaces: 2.4 cents/vehicle mile
Car depreciation	1.5 cents/vehicle mile
Time	$1.55 per hour
Comfort and convenience	Paved highways: 1.0 cents/vehicle mile for restricted operation, 0.5 cents for normal operation, and 0.0 cents for free operation
	Loose surfaced highways: 0.75 cents/vehicle mile
	Unsurfaced highways: 1.0 cents/vehicle mile

8.1.3.5 Calculation of highway costs   The total highway cost for road user benefit evaluation is the sum of the capital costs expressed on an annual basis and the annual cost of maintenance. The total cost for an improvement usually is obtained from an engineer's estimate based on preliminary plans. As necessary, the total capital cost of each highway alternate may be separated into the costs for (1) right-of-way, (2) grading, drainage, and minor structures, (3) major structures, and (4) pavement and appurtenances. The total annual highway cost is calculated as follows:

$$C = CRF_{i,N}K^{(1)} + CRF_{i,N}K^{(2)} + CRF_{i,N}K^{(3)} + CRF_{i,N}K^{(4)} + M \qquad (8.16)$$

where C is the total annual highway cost; $K^{(1)}$, $K^{(2)}$, $K^{(3)}$, and $K^{(4)}$ are the capital costs of the items above enumerated; $CRF_{i,N}$ are the capital recovery factors for a known rate of interest, i, and amortization of total cost of each of the above items based on its average life, N; and M is the annual cost for maintenance of the improved highway.

The computation of total annual capital costs based on the summation of the annual costs of the individual items of improvement is the "proper and accurate method" (AASHO wording), but, for quick analysis and for projects with similar ratios of costs of individual items to total costs, an estimate of total overall cost and overall life provides adequate accuracy. In this case the formula would be reduced to $C = CRF_{i,N}(K) + M$ in which K is the total cost of all the items of improvement and N is the overall estimated average life of the improvement.

In most cases, the capital costs, $K^{(1)}$, $K^{(2)}$, $K^{(3)}$, $K^{(4)}$, of the separate items of improvement, or, if satisfactory, the overall capital cost (K), can be calculated directly for the entire length of a highway alternate being analyzed without dividing it into sections as may be needed for the computation of road user costs. To weigh the advantages of sections of the improvement for stage construction, it will be necessary to estimate the sectional costs.

In most cases of main highways the average life period for each of the four major items of capital cost (or a representative composite) will be greater than the period used for traffic forecasting. For road user benefit evaluations it is not necessary that these periods be the same. Use of the shorter traffic forecast period as the basis for the analysis makes the resulting benefit-cost ratio correct insofar as the traffic data can be established.

At the end of the analysis period, the improvement still has value, the complete capital cost items not yet being amortized. Expression of the capital cost as a summation of the annual costs of construction and maintenance gives a proper value for any period of time. For analysis of a low type highway where the surface life may be less than the usual traffic forecast period, the shorter period would be used for the traffic estimate and analysis.

The factor M is the annual cost to cover all work necessary to keep the improved highway in good condition and the other operating charges as for striping, signs, lighting, etc. Suitable current average costs per mile per year generally can be obtained or estimated. These must be adjusted to include all costs anticipated within the weighted average life of the improvement, such as resurfacing work a number of years hence. The product of the adjusted annual cost per mile and the total length gives the desired annual cost for maintenance and operation of the highway.

8.1.3.6 Calculation of benefit-cost ratio The general equation for calculating the benefit-cost ratio now can be expressed as

$$\frac{\Delta B}{\Delta C} = \frac{B_n - B_o}{C_n - C_o} \tag{8.17}$$

where C_o is the annual cost (usually for maintenance, M_o, only) of the old facility. With substitutions from Eq. (8.15) and the shortened version of Eq. (8.16), the above equation becomes

$$\frac{\Delta B}{\Delta C} = \frac{\frac{1}{2}\left(p_o l_o - p_n l_n\right)\left(V_n + V_o\right)(365)}{CRF_{i,N}\left(K_n\right) + M_n - M_o} \tag{8.18}$$

The same formula is used for a second alternate by designating the total annual road user benefits from that alternate as B_{n2} and the total annual facility costs as C_{n2}. Similar benefit ratios are calculated for all other alternatives, each compared with the basic condition. By so doing, the several ratios can be compared directly as to their relative value. A benefit-cost ratio less than one indicates that in a road user benefit sense the basic condition is to be preferred over the alternate improvement.

8.1.3.7 Numerical example Assume a relocation project where by heavy grading work on new alignment it is possible to reduce the length between two points on an existing highway. The existing highway is to be abandoned if the new alignment proves economical. Present traffic on the existing route is 1,500 vpd, and it is estimated that the average traffic for the next 20 years, the analysis period, will approximate 2,500 vpd on the new route and 2,000 vpd on the

Table 8.2   Data for Example Problem

		Existing sections		Proposed sections	
		1	2	1	2
1.	Future volume (vpd)	2,000	2,000	2,500	2,300
2.	30 HHV (vph)	375	375	450	425
3.	Service volume, level D (vpd)	450	450	715	700
4.	Ratio	0.83	0.83	0.63	0.61
5.	Type of operation	Normal	Normal	Free	Free
6.	Design speed (mph)	50	50	60	60
7.	Running speed (mph)	37	34	42	44
8.	No. lanes	2	2	2	2
9.	Length (miles)	2.0	0.4	1.5	1.5
10.	Grade class (%)	0–3	3–5	0–3	5–7
11.	Surface and condition	Paved–Good	Paved–Good	Paved–Good	Paved–Good
12.	Curvature	50% –4°	50% –4°	Negligible	Negligible
13.	Unit cost (¢/veh-mile)	10.24	10.24	9.01	10.18
14.	Estimated pavement life (yr)	—	—	20.00	20.00
15.	Estimated R.O.W. life (yr)	—	—	60.00	60.00
16.	Estimated life, other (yr)	—	—	40.00	40.00
17.	Pavement cost ($)	—	—	66,000	10,000
18.	R.O.W. cost ($)	—	—	33,000	5,000
19.	Other cost ($)	—	—	451,000	300,000
20.	Annual pavement cost ($)	—	—	5,290	5,600
21.	Annual R.O.W. cost ($)	—	—	1,740	260
22.	Annual other cost ($)	—	—	26,290	17,500
23.	Total annual capital cost ($)	—	—	33,320	23,360
24.	Maintenance cost ($/mile)	1,100	1,100	880	880

Note: vph = vehicles per day, HHV = highest hourly volume, mph = miles per hour, R.O.W. = right-of-way (land and buildings).

old.[15] This traffic is composed of passenger cars with a very small proportion of trucks. Due to the character of the trucks, a distinction between them and the passenger cars is not considered necessary. Assignment of type of operation is made on the basis of the indicated ratios of 30th highest hourly traffic volume to the volume at level of service D. The proposed facility contemplates a pavement width of 20 feet compared with 18 feet on the existing facility. This factor, together with improved alignment and grades, permits distinction between a free and normal operation, respectively. Table 8.2 shows the data used to arrive at this differentiation.

The curvature proposed on the new facility is generally flat, with a minor portion approaching the design speed limit. This is to be properly superelevated (banked), so a correction for curvature can be ignored. However, the existing

[15] Most of the examples given in the Red Book assume equal volumes of future traffic on both the old and new route. This type of occurence is highly improbable, of course.

highway has a large number of curves approaching the maximum for a 50 mph design speed. It is estimated that 50 percent of its length will have an average curvature of about four degrees with superelevation negligible. From Fig. 8.13 a correction of between 7 and 8 percent is read for the speeds considered. Since only one-half of the roadway is curved, the correction is halved to 4 percent and applied for the whole of the route to the values from Fig. 8.10. The calculated unit cost can be found in the thirteenth row of Table 8.2.

From Eq. (8.15) the average annual road user benefits are calculated as follows:

$$B_n - B_o = \tfrac{1}{2} [(2.0)(0.1024) + 0.4(0.1061)$$
$$- 1.5(0.0901)](2{,}500 + 2{,}000)(365) = \$92{,}000$$

The average annual unit maintenance cost on the existing route is estimated to be $1,100 per mile or a total of 2.4 (1,100) = $2,640, and that of the proposed route to be $880 per mile or a total of 1.5 ($880) = $1,320.

The total estimated cost of the proposed improvement is $550,000 and the prevailing local interest rate is 5 percent. This interest rate is applied with reference to the cost and life expectancy of the individual items of improvement to compute the annual cost. Capital recovery factors, $CRF_{i,N}$, are selected from Table 8.1 and turn out to be 0.0802, 0.0528, and 0.0583 for each capital item respectively. With these, the total annual capital cost of the new alignment comes out to be $33,320.

The benefit-cost ratio for the proposed improvement is computed from Eq. (8.17) as follows:

$$\frac{\Delta B}{\Delta C} = \frac{\$92{,}000}{\$33{,}320 + \$1{,}320 - \$2{,}640} = 2.88$$

The analysis indicates that the annual benefits are almost three times the annual project costs. From this it appears to be a worthwhile project as far as road user benefits are concerned and one that should be slated for early construction.

Suppose now, that as another example, a second project is proposed. This new alignment is generally the same as the first one proposed except for volume, grades, and several other items shown in the right hand column in Table 8.2. Proceeding in a manner similar to that done for the previous proposal, we can determine the benefit-cost ratio through the following steps:

1. Calculate unit cost: Fig. 8.10 gives 10.18¢/veh-mile
2. Calculate benefits: Eq. (8.15) gives

$$B_n - B_o = \tfrac{1}{2}[(2.0)(0.1024) + 0.4(0.1061)$$
$$- 1.5(0.1018)](2{,}300 + 2{,}000)(365) = \$12{,}000$$

3. Calculate annual capital costs: (same $CRF_{i,N}$'s as in previous case)

$$C_n = 0.0802(70{,}000) + 0.0528(5{,}000) + 0.0583(300{,}000) = \$23{,}360$$

4. Calculate $\Delta B / \Delta C$ ratio

$$\frac{\Delta B}{\Delta C} = \frac{\$72,000}{\$23,360 + \$1,320 - \$2,640} = 3.28$$

The benefit-cost ratio from the last calculation seems to indicate that the second proposal will create high economic returns, even higher than those for the first alternative. However, it is at this point that the statements made in section 8.14 should be emphasized. The second alternative has a lower capital cost than the first: $23,360 versus $33,320; but it also brings fewer dollars of benefits, $72,000 versus $92,000. The question then arises as to whether it would not be wise to build the first alternative in spite of its relatively low benefit-cost ratio. After all, if the additional funds required for the first project can bring in an equivalent or greater amount of benefits, then why not build it?

To determine if the extra expense for first alternative is in fact worthwhile, it is necessary to calculate a benefit-cost ratio between proposal one and two. Thus, if $n1$ is used to designate proposal one and $n2$, two, then

$$B_{n1} - B_{n2} = \tfrac{1}{2}[1.5\,(0.1018) - 1.5\,(9.01)]\,(2,500 + 2,300)\,(365) = \$15,400$$

$$C_{n1} - C_{n2} = \$33,320 + \$1,320 - \$23,360 - \$1,320 = \$9,960$$

$$\frac{\Delta B}{\Delta C} = \frac{\$15,400}{\$9,960} = 1.55$$

From these figures it can indeed be concluded that the extra expenditure for the more costly proposal will give a return 55 percent greater than the outlay. Therefore, any wise investor who had the necessary funds would be more than willing to put them into the first alternative, evaluating it as the most desirable one. Likewise, public officials and decision makers should find the first alternative "best" from an economic investment standpoint.

8.2 COMMENTS ON THE BENEFIT–COST APPROACH TO EVALUATION

Benefit-cost approaches to evaluation and decision making have been used extensively in the past by many different agencies and companies. The technique offers the distinct advantage of neutrality: the numbers used as inputs lead to an exact determination of the alternative which is best, and there can be no inference made that the evaluation process has been interfered with for personal or political reasons.

In this light, the benefit-cost technique is extremely valuable in that, if the theory behind it is agreeable to everyone, the outputs which come from it also must be accepted. In general, it gives the appearance of a certain mathematical purity—a purity that cannot be tampered with and is instrumental in providing the decision maker with results unbiased by emotional factors.

The benefit-cost approach does have many difficulties nevertheless. Some are technical in nature, while others stem directly from its failure to take into account many "human factors." Each of these types of difficulties will be discussed in turn in succeeding paragraphs.

8.2.1 System Effects

One of the foremost difficulties that arises in the utilization of the benefit-cost approach in any real world situation is that proposed alternatives generally are part of a system and do not stand by themselves as in the previous example problem. A change in a route alignment between two points or a decrease in travel time between two points often affects travel not only on that route but on many other nearby routes.

After construction of a new facility from D to C, people traveling from A to C and presently using the section of highway from B to C, may rearrange their route, going to A to D to C instead of from A to B to C. The result is that the number of trips on the sections from A to B and B to C is reduced *because* of the change in the route from D to C. The effects of improvements on one route thus permeate over other routes and present the evaluator with a difficult problem in accounting for *all* the benefits.

8.2.2 Unequal Alternatives

Alternatives, by definition, are different ways for accomplishing the same objective or solving the same problem. Quite obviously, we would not treat proposals for rapid transit either in Los Angeles or in Atlanta as alternates for the present mass transit situation in Minneapolis. The former two do not serve the same populations or the same travelers nor would they necessarily result in the same type of physical system as in Minneapolis. But do any transportation alternatives ever serve the same purpose?

Referring back to the example problem used for benefit-cost calculations, we see that the three facilities (including the existing one) really do not serve the "same" population of travelers, the major difference being in the *number* served. There are 2,000, 2,500, and 2,300 vph, respectively, for each alternative. Thus, the construction of either of the two new facilities changes the travel situation and, in effect, produces a new problem to be solved. The main point to be made here, however, is that benefit-cost ratios developed for evaluating alternatives rarely compare "equal" situations because the problem under study usually is modified by the alternatives proposed.[16]

---

[16] The creation of unequal alternatives is not a difficulty related to the benefit-cost technique per se, but is common to almost every evaluation procedure.

8.2.3 Risk and Uncertainty

Inherent in all evaluation techniques, including the benefit-cost approach, are problems of risk and uncertainty. Wohl and Martin [8.5, p. 223] make the distinction between these two entities as follows:

1. Problems of *risk* are those whereby the future outcomes or consequences have a known probability of occurrence; thus while the chances of a particular outcome may be known, no assurance can be given about which particular outcome will take place.
2. Problems of *uncertainty* are those whereby even the probabilities of the future outcomes or consequences are unknown and whereby the probabilities can be determined only subjectively.

The determination of whether an outcome is subject to risk or uncertainty is a difficult matter. Yet, what is important here is that almost all of the entities used in a benefit-cost calculation—the unit costs, the travel volumes, the interest rates, the service lives, and the capital and maintenance costs—have to be predicted for the future and therefore fall prey to inaccuracy.

Capital costs, for example, usually are thought of as being easily predictable, but factors such as inflation and unanticipated expenses resulting, perhaps, from the discovery of rock to be excavated or, in another situation, from the need for funds for drawn out legal cases, make even cost predictions hazardous. As a consequence, if the uncertainty (or risk) is anticipated to be great, the evaluator should take this feature into account, either by weighing each outcome by its probability of occurrence or, as is done in many cases, by increasing the interest rate so that the investor gets a larger and quicker return to make up for the riskier situation. Such techniques can be incorporated as part of benefit-cost procedure, but are rather cumbersome and data consuming.[17]

8.2.4 Inclusion of Various Benefits and Costs

The benefit-cost approach demands that the set of benefits and costs to be included be identified explicitly. This is desirable, yet the problem arises as to how to make an accounting of *all* benefits and costs. How about disbenefits or diseconomies resulting from increases in noise and air pollution levels? How about engineering, planning, and administration costs? The first question is more difficult to answer, mainly because we often are not sure of the extent of the effect of transportation on the two entities.

It may be, for instance, that air pollution in a certain sector of a city is created mostly by an industrial plant there and not by automobiles, trucks, buses and so forth, so that air pollution should not be counted as a disbenefit of transportation. Even a prominent item like travel is not caused by the transportation system alone, but is a function of land use and other factors.[18] From these example situations we

[17] For more information on handling risk and uncertainty, see [8.11] and [8.22].
[18] See Chap. 5.

can conclude that an accounting of benefits should include only those attributable to the particular alternative under study but that such an approach would require the identification of cause and effect relationships about which, in many cases, little is known.

Another aspect of the benefit and cost identification problem is that of the inclusion or noninclusion of benefits or costs passed from one level of government to another. Wohl and Martin [8.5, p. 181] pose an interesting example of such a situation:

> Should a state highway agency, in deciding among various highway projects (including the null alternative), consider only the consequences to the state highway users or those to the entire state populace or should it adopt a broader national point of view? Also, should the state highway agency consider the economic feasibility of only the *state* expenditures on construction, maintenance, and administration, or should it be concerned with the feasibility of total outlays, whether federal, state, or local?

Most people would argue for the national point of view, but the vote would be far from unanimous.

8.2.5 Measurement of Benefit Factors

If, for purposes of evaluation, an attempt were made to list all of the factors affected by a given transportation alternative, a major difficulty to be faced would be that of measuring (or actually defining) the factors. Of course, travel time and number of trips are two entities which are fairly easy to measure, but, as the time-worn argument goes, beauty is not easy to gauge.

We might try to utilize such individual measures as color (wavelength), hue, contrast, brightness, and so forth[19] in combination, but to date no one has originated a single, mutually satisfactory measure of beauty. The problem which this situation creates for the evaluator is that, without an acceptable definition of beauty, he cannot predict whether an alternative transportation system will in fact add or detract from the appearance of the setting into which it is thrust, and, as a consequence, he cannot predict some of the system's benefits (or disbenefits). Lack of a measurement device thereby implies a possible miscalculation of benefits (and sometimes also costs).

8.2.6 Commensuration

Earlier in this chapter the problem of "mixing apples and oranges" was presented in the context of putting benefits in dollar terms. Assigning a "value" to travel time is a good example of this problem. The AASHO Red Book uses $1.55 per vehicle hour, or roughly $1.00 for each hour of a person's time, as the value. Haney [8.9], in a survey of the studies made before 1961, found assumed dollar values of time up to $2.74/person/hr.

---

[19] That these factors are somewhat related to beauty is demonstrated by the presence of knobs for their control on color television sets.

By far and away the most cogent example of an attempt to put benefits in dollar terms is that found in a National Safety Council memo and adopted for the *Traffic Engineering Handbook*. There [8.23, p. 249], the statement is made that:

> The calculable costs of motor vehicle accidents are wage loss, medical expense, overhead cost of insurance and property damage. In 1964, these costs for all accidents (fatal, nonfatal, injury, and property damage) averaged about $175,000 per death. This "per death" total includes the cost of one death, 36 injuries, and 235 property damage accidents. The unit costs are:
>
> Death $34,000
> Nonfatal injury 1,800
> Property damage accident 310

Obviously, any attempt to put all benefits, such as reduction in deaths, on a common monetary basis will attract the label of "mercenariness," and, to some extent, this charge rings true. Nevertheless, if the evaluator does not endeavor to make all benefits commensurate, either in terms of dollars or "utiles" of utility or with some other unit, he runs the risk of *implicitly* assigning a value way out of proportion to its actual worth. If, for example, a highway costing $10 million and resulting in five deaths during its lifetime is chosen over a mass transit facility costing $2,000,000 and resulting in one death in the same period, then, all other factors being equivalent, the price of four deaths (five minus one) has been implicitly set at $8 million ($10 million minus $2 million), or at $2 million per life. This value, most people would agree, is too high. But the point is that many transportation planners and decision makers are faced directly with the unenviable task of deciding on the relative worth of the life of each citizen in the population.

Another interesting aspect related to attempts at commensuration is that values associated with a given item often vary according to the quantity of the item and the kind and amount of substitutes available. As an example of the first case, if 1 hour of travel time were saved from use of a new transportation system, it may be worth only $1 (per hour) to the traveler. Yet, if 2 hours were saved, they may be worth $4 total, or $2 per hour. As an example of the second case, suppose that in the previous illustration a second transportation system were built which also saved the traveler 2 hours. Because there now can be a choice in route of travel and because of the corresponding increase in dependability (if one route is closed, the other can be taken), the travelers may devalue the importance he attaches to travel time to, say, $1.50 per hour. These, then, are some of the considerations which make commensuration a difficult task.

8.2.7 Perceived versus Actual Benefits and Costs

A very perplexing decision to be made in most evaluation procedures is that of whether to use actual benefits and costs which accrue as a result of transportation systems or the ones *perceived* by the people affected by the system. Travel time again provides an interesting example. Suppose that, through verifiable calculations or empirical studies, the engineer or planner determines that 50 minutes are saved on a given journey over a new transportation system. The user, however, feels that he is saving less time,[20] say, 40 minutes and judges the worth of the system using this figure. Which figure should the evaluator use?

On the cost side of the picture, there also might be significant differences between actual and perceived costs. In fact, these differences are used to advantage by many business operations through the use of the charge account. The lesson is all too clear: it is much less agonizing to charge a $10 item than to pay for it in cash. The perceived cost of a cash payment is much higher.

It is important at this point to note the *significance* of the differences between perceived and actual costs and benefits. If a comparison were made between highway and mass transit facilities, for example, we probably would find that vehicle purchase costs generally are *not* considered as part of travel costs (prices) by the highway user[21] but that vehicle costs for transit would be important since they must be included in the fare, which is all too prominent. Because automobile travel *appears* less expensive, more tripmaking is done by that mode and less by transit, a situation which naturally affects the stability of transit service.

8.2.8 Discounting of Benefits and Costs

When considering the capital and maintenance costs associated with a transportation system, we described briefly the role of the interest rate in economic evaluations. Its purpose, generally speaking, is to indicate that with all other factors being equivalent, the expenditure of funds for present projects must be greater than that for future projects since money is worth more now than in the future. Similarly, benefits are worth more now than in the future. Almost everyone, when given the choice, would take $1,000 now instead of, say, $1,300 ten years from now.

It is the *unevenness* over time of the streams of benefits and costs that causes most practical discounting difficulties. The amoritization of costs over time may be fairly uniform and end after a period of 40 to 50 years, and amoritization costs, of course, would continue as long as the facility existed. But, on the other side of the ledger, benefits may continue to accrue way into the future, perhaps even at an increasing rate (Fig. 8.8).

An interesting example of this type of situation is the famous Appian Way (Appia Antica). Opened by Claudius Appius in 312 B.C. and running outside the ancient walls of Rome, this facility still is providing service benfits to travelers after some 2,300 years of use.[22] The prolonged nature of this service brings to the fore the question of how to compare in a correct manner the different time-sequenced and widely divergent streams of benefits and costs.

---

[20] In most cases, those affected by a transportation system do not have the opportunity to determine *exactly* how they are being affected.

[21] The mode choice model presented in Chap. 6 indicates this clearly. Automobile and insurance costs are *not* shown to have an effect on choice of mode of travel.

[22] Information taken from A. Storti, *Rome: A Practical Guide*, E. A. Storti, Venice, Italy, 1965.

The difficulty in the AASHO approach to benefit and cost comparison is this: if the period of benefit analysis is chosen to be relatively short, say 20 years, then the probability exists that a large amount of benefits will be ignored. Suppose, for example, that people value a dollar's worth of benefits today at 94¢ a year from now. Under this circumstance, it turns out the benefits 20 years from now are still worth 31¢. Thus, despite difficulties in estimating benefits at such a future date, it appears to be important not to overlook them since they are significant from an absolute standpoint (because of the probable increase in benefits over time) as well as from a percentage standpoint. Discounting of benefits and costs to their present worth, as done by most economists, is one possible solution to this problem.

8.2.9 Double Counting of Benefits and Costs

Another perplexing problem facing the evaluator or decision maker is that of the possible double counting of benefits and costs. It would not be correct, for instance, to include both the service station charged price for gasoline *and* the tax on gasoline as components of the unit cost of operating an automobile on the highway. This would be an obvious case of double counting since the tax already is incorporated in the service station price. Other opportunities for double counting are not quite as obvious, however, and stem basically from the transfer of benefits[23] from one person or group of persons to another. Mohring and Harwitz [8.8, p. 12] give the following example of a transfer:

> ... completion of an expressway which reduces the time and dollar costs of travel to the center of an urban area may enable a suburban apartment house owner to charge higher rents to his commuting tenants than would otherwise have been possible. To the extent that he is able to do this, he has, in effect, extracted some of the highway benefits initially received by these tenants. He has, that is to say, forced them to transfer some or all of their highway benefits to him.

The conclusion to be drawn from this example is that it would be improper from an accounting standpoint to include both decreases in travel costs and increases in apartment rents (and thus in land values) as benefits from the expressway. They are "two sides of the same coin." Likewise, it would be improper to count any benefit or disbenefit until it has been shown to be a separate and distinct entity from any of the others under consideration. To make the distinction, however, is extremely difficult.

8.2.10 Determining Who Benefits

Perhaps the most critical comment that can be made of benefit-cost and similar approaches to evaluation is that they do not indicate who is receiving the calculated benefits. The benefits are totaled but nothing is said about their distribution among the poor or the rich; the young or the old; the user or the nonuser; the truckers or the railroads or the airlines; the whites or the blacks; those who live in one part of

---

[23] To be discussed in more detail in Sec. 8.2.12.

the city or region or those who live in another; or others. Needless to say, the question of who benefits is an important one. As John A. Volpe, President Nixon's original Secretary of Transportation, has stated:

> I would submit to this group (the Greater Dallas Planning Council) tonight—as I have done before the President and before my Cabinet colleagues—that all the job training centers, employment opportunities, health facilities, educational institutions, recreational areas and housing projects—all things that are needed in virtually all of our cities—will never be fully utilized if the people cannot get to them inexpensively, safely, and efficiently.
>
> We must have a new mobility in this nation if we are to fulfill our pledges to the disadvantaged, the young, the poor, the elderly, and the physically handicapped.[24]

In regard to evaluation involving various groups of persons, one observation which must be made and given strong emphasis is that by *not* looking at the types of groups affected by a given change in a transportation system, that is, by taking the attitude of "letting the chips fall where they may," the evaluator may *inadvertently* (and disproportionately) benefit one group at the expense of another.

An example of such a situation may be that of comparative highway benefits for the poor and rich in, say, Virginia's cities. *The U.S. Census of Housing: 1960* [8.29, Table 16] shows that the percentage of those occupied city housing units not having an automobile available ranges from 15.5 percent in Hampton to 38.5 percent in Richmond. And in the District of Columbia the percentage is 47.3! The meaning of these figures is fairly clear: if family members do not have access to an automobile (and most of the poor would fall in this category), they would have difficulty benefiting from any highway improvement, at least as compared to the gains they would receive from a mass transit improvement. As a consequence, any plan which, either by design or indifference, stresses highway construction and not mass transit can be expected to produce more benfits for the wealthier elements of society than for their poorer counterparts. The question of who gains or loses thus has great social significance, yet is rarely encountered in benefit-cost studies.

8.2.11 Criterion Form

If the engineer and planner are in fact concerned over the welfare of certain individuals or groups in society, then they cannot be interested solely in the amount of benefits, but also in their distribution. Winch [8.10, p. 33] is particularly critical of benefit-cost analysis for just this reason; he even goes so far to say that

> ... unless we make some assumption about interpersonal comparisons, economics can offer no help in problems of policy such as that of highway planning. Our assumption is simply that if one person derives a benefit of $10 and another of $15 between them they are $25 better off; and that this situation is preferable to one which would make two other people $20 better off between them. It cannot be proven that from the standpoint of the community as a whole it is better to make one group of people $25 better off rather than another group $20 better off, since community welfare depends on the distribution of

---

[24] Remarks prepared for delivery by Secretary of Transportation John A. Volpe before the Greater Dallas Planning Council, Tuesday, September 9, 1969, Dallas, Texas.

wealth as well as its total. It might well be better to have a smaller cake fairly divided than a larger cake unfairly divided.

The form of the criterion or objective function used in evaluation thus is of extreme importance.

Other forms of objective functions besides the maximization of the benefit-cost ratio certainly are available. Hitch and McKean, [8.2], for example, in their analysis of military evaluation discuss those of (1) maximizing the *difference* between gains (benefits) and costs, (2) maximizing gains with cost fixed, (3) minimizing costs with gains fixed, and (4) maximizing the minimum gains. Most of these and other functions have their analogs in the highway evaluation field,[25] but the choice as to which one to use appears to have been extremely subjective in the past. The point is that this *subjective* decision between criterion forms has a significant effect upon the evaluative decisions that come out of the *objective* technique (such as benefit-cost) and consequently cast some doubt on the supposed objectivity of the entire procedure.

8.2.12 Transfer of Benefits and Costs

Assume for the moment that we have settled on a particular criterion form and have, in effect, identified those individual groups whom we would like to see benefit from or pay for a new transportation system. How can we insure that they will, in fact, be the ones who receive the benefits or make the payments? The problem is that on the surface it may appear that certain groups are assimilating benefits (or costs), but that in actuality they are forced (or are able) to transfer them to some other group.

Suppose, for instance, that in the Mohring and Harwitz example presented earlier, it had been decided to attempt to direct as many of the benefits as possible to the expressway user. This attempt would have resulted in failure. The users are the *first* recipients of the benefits of reduced operating and travel time costs, but are forced to pay equivalently higher rents in order to live close enough to the expressway to get the travel benefits. In the end, the user has no actual gain in capital, services, or land to show for himself. Instead, the landlord has made the gain (assuming that he also is not forced to pass it on).

Quite obviously, this transference of benefits and costs creates a perplexing situation for the evaluator and, to make matters worse, there really has not been enough research to provide a basis for predicting the ultimate recipients and their shares of such transfers.

8.2.13 Multiplier Effects

Besides being perplexing, the transfer of benefits (and costs) performs a possibly valuable function: it allows for the multiplication of benefits. Many studies have shown that investments in transportation facilities, especially highways, do

---

[25] Examples are the annual cost method, the rate of return method, and others.

have this multiplier effect.[26] Decreased travel costs associated with a new transportation system allow the user to take the money saved and invest it elsewhere at a profit greater than the total of the reduced travel costs. Then this profit is invested in another, more profitable venture, and so the cycle goes. This creation of new benefits (or possibly disbenefits) is one of the major reasons why many people are interested in having new transportation systems in their region—their benefits generally permeate the whole area and grow rather significantly at the same time. Unfortunately, the benefit-cost approach to evaluation does not, in its present form, take into account multiplier effects.

8.2.14 Conformance with Goals

The final problem with benefit-cost and similar techniques for evaluation is one which is somewhat representative of the underlying nature of most of the problems discussed in this section. It has to do with conformity to goals. If we were to return to Chap. 4, we would see that a considerable amount of energy was expended in an attempt to develop goals for transportation not only for direct service factors but also for other factors external to the system but still affected by it. The effect was seen to be both broad and pervasive, playing a role in changing such diverse factors as ecology, business sales, and even church attendance in some cases. As a consequence, goals had to be set up for these and many other factors to insure that the impact of transportation "improvement" was guided in the most advantageous directions. Viewed in the light of this wide scope of intent for transportation, the benefit-cost approach as currently employed seems to have an extremely short range of concern.

To highlight some of the differences between factors taken into account in the AASHO benefit-cost approach and factors relating to likely transportation goal sets, we have developed ten goals of probable general importance to transportation (see Table 8.3). Along side each of these is a subjective assessment of whether or not the goal is recognized in the AASHO approach. Naturally, there can be difference of opinion over each assessment, but the point is that many goals are not covered. For example, the rather significant goal of safety, for both the user and nonuser (goal 9) alike, is not considered at all in the AASHO benefit-cost procedure, nor is the goal of reduced air pollution (goal 10); and other goals are given only partial recognition. Moreover, as has been emphasized throughout the discussions in previous sections, we must not be concerned only with the *extent* of the benefits but also with such matters as the time at which they accrue, the amount by which they are multiplied in passing from one person to another, and finally, and perhaps most important, the nature of the ultimate recipients of the benefits (and costs).

Of course, the amount of effort involved in the type of evaluation implied above should be recognized. It would require gathering data and making predictions for an extremely wide range of factors, much wider than has usually been the case. In fact, one of the main reasons why techniques such as benefit-cost have been

---

[26] See, in particular, the summary by Isard [8.14].

Table 8.3 Extent of Consideration in AASHO Benefit–Cost Procedure of Goals of Probable General Importance to Transportation

Goals	Taken into account in AASHO benefit-cost procedure?
Goals for direct transportation service factors	
Provide a transportation system that will:	
1. Offer low door-to-door travel time (with emphasis on low waiting and transfer time).	Yes
2. Have a low door-to-door travel fare and/or cost of operation (if user owned).	Yes
3. Offer adaptability and flexibility in routes, schedules, types of goals hauled, etc., to meet variations in demand of different sorts.	Partially
4. Be dependable in all weather, traffic conditions, etc.	Partially
5. Enable the greatest returns on investments.	Yes
Goals for factors affected by transportation	
Provide a transportation system that will:	
6. Better the economic position of each and every individual.	Partially
7. Cause the development of more and better activities and facilities.	No
8. Offer a reduced need for land of various types.	Partially
9. Offer a high level of safety to those in contact with the system.	No
10. Not add to air pollution or give off toxic gases externally.	No

utilized so much in the past has been the *relative* ease of data collection and prediction. But the present procedure of collecting land use, travel, and transportation system data still is a fairly time and money consuming one, and it appears that, in relation to the overall pervasiveness of transportation, only a limited set of the effects associated with desired goals have been gauged.

8.3 THE COST-EFFECTIVENESS EVALUATION TECHNIQUE

In reviewing the preceding comments and criticisms on benefit-cost and similar evaluation procedures, one has to be somewhat dismayed with the seemingly overwhelming complexities facing the decision maker. One also gains some appreciation for the position of the politician or manager who must react to and give solutions for these types of problems every day. The question, then, is what, if anything, can be done to improve decision-making procedures as they exist today? A partial answer lies in the cost-effectiveness technique developed originally to aid the military in making their extremely important decisions.

The cost-effectiveness technique actually is a much less sophisticated procedure than one might at first suppose. It works on the basic premise that better decisions will arise if clearer and more relevant data are supplied to the decision maker. No specific attempt is made to put all benefits and costs in common units such as the dollar. As Thomas and Schofer [8.4, p. 218] remark on the cost-effectiveness approach:

> Because many of the consequences and outputs from the transportation system are intangible and otherwise difficult to value in some common metric, the decisions regarding the conversion to a single dimension—and hence the plan selection decisions—are necessarily subjective in nature, at least at the present time. . . .
>
> What might be more useful at this time is a technique for providing the kind of informational support for the selection of alternative plans which recognizes the complex nature of these transportation decisions. Such a decision supporting framework would not attempt to *make* decisions, but instead *would structure the information required for making a subjective but systematically enlightened choice* (our underlining). At the same time, however, the framework . . . must be sufficiently flexible to permit the adoption of more sophisticated techniques, such as analytic methods for realistically implementing benefit-cost analysis or ranking schemes, when such techniques are appropriate.

In conjunction with these remarks, Thomas and Schofer specify three criteria which any framework for evaluation should satisfy:

1. It should be capable of assimilating benefit-cost and similar methodological results *in addition* to other informational requirements.
2. It should have a strong orientation toward a system of values, goals, and objectives.
3. It should allow for the clear comparison of *tradeoffs* or compromises between objectives by making explicit the relative gains and losses from various alternatives.

These criteria also can be inferred from the criticisms in the preceding section of this chapter and tend to reinforce the needs brought out there. The cost-effectiveness approach, as a later example will show, seems to satisfy all three of the criteria.

8.3.1 Description of Cost-Effectiveness Framework

In the application of cost-effectiveness analysis, the attributes of the alternative relevant to the decision are separated into two classes—costs and indicators of effectiveness. Costs are defined as the monetary outlays necessary to procure all of the resources for the construction or purchase, operation, maintenance, and so forth of the facility during its useful life cycle. Of course, this assumes that the pricing mechanism operates so that all items expended on the project can be valued in terms of dollar prices. Where this is not possible, it may be necessary (and entirely realistic) to consider costs in other units of measure, such as hours of labors and tons of steel, as well. This approach to costing is contrary to that in most present evaluation schemes and allows for a certain flexibility in cost analysis.

Effectiveness is defined as the degree to which an alternate achieves its objectives. The definition, by itself, helps to overcome one of the major objectives to the benefit-cost approach in that goals are specified explicitly and are not covered by an all encompassing "benefit" term. In the AASHO case, for example, "benefits" are related to reductions in user operation costs, user time, tax payments and so forth, but in a particular situation these factors may be of only minor concern. The objectives to be met may be akin to an entirely different set of factors.

Information regarding the costs and effectiveness of the alternatives is presented to the decision maker who, in turn, makes the subjective choice of the one which seems best to him. While the planner and engineer may provide all the supporting data and estimates from these data, and may even suggest what alternative appears best to them, the ultimate choice is left to the duly appointed decision maker(s). No hard and fast decision rules, such as those inherent in the benefit-cost approach, are permitted to make the selection "automatically." It is quite permissible, of course, to provide the decision maker with information concerning the benefit-cost ratio and the like; however, these are and should be kept from being the sole determinants of choices among alternatives.

The value of the cost-effectiveness approach lies in several areas:

a. It stimulates, to some extent, the process by which actual decisions are made.
b. It allows for the clearer delegation of responsibilities between analyst and decision maker.
c. It makes it easier to provide the type of relevant information, structured in an understandable form, so that the choice process is simplified.

8.3.2 Cost-Effectiveness: An Example

The example of the cost-effectiveness approach that follows is based on an article by Millar and Dean [8.30] describing one part of the *Manchester (England) Rapid Transit Study*. While the article itself did not deal directly with cost-effectiveness as an evaluative technique, it did seem to fit very neatly into the framework described in the preceding section.

The government agencies concerned with the transit problem in Manchester made several recommendations to the study group before a detailed investigation was initiated. As quoted from Millar and Dean [8.30, p. 155]:

> The Ministry of Transport recognized that this study would not only be of value in the context of providing a *well-balanced* and *economical* overall transport system for Manchester, but would also yield information of wider application and interest.

Moreover:

> It was stipulated that this evaluation should investigate the characteristics of any system which could be *built by 1972;* that the *quality of service* which each could give should be assessed; that the likely *environmental effects* be explored; and that reliable estimates should be provided of the *capital and operating costs.* (emphasis ours)

The underlined statements can be thought of as general goals toward which the decision regarding a rapid transit system should be directed. Thus, in a general sense, the evaluation was goal oriented, as is desired in a cost-effectiveness approach.

After preliminary elimination of some candidate transit systems (mainly because they could not be built by 1972), the study group settled on four possible alternatives: (1) Safege monorail, (2) Electric railway (duorail), (3) Westinghouse skybus, and (4) Alweg monorail. These systems are pictured collectively in Fig. 8.14. We will not detail their technical characteristics here.

Data were gathered on each system. The first items collected were responses to direct questions. Could the system be built by 1972? Did the system have a route capacity of 7,500 persons per hour (pph)? Would the system fit in with the present British Rail system? As seen in Table 8.4, the answers to the first two questions were "yes" for all alternatives. However, only the duorail system would be compatible with British Rail.

(a)

(b)

Fig. 8.14 Four transit system alternatives: (a) Safege monorail, (b) Electric railway or duorail. (*Continued*)

(c)

(d)

Fig. 8.14 (*Continued*) Four transit system alternatives: (c) Westinghouse skybus, and (d) Alweg monorail.

Table 8.4 Effectiveness and Cost Characteristics for Four Possible Rapid Transit Systems for Manchester

Effectiveness measures	Safeage monorail	Duorail	Westinghouse skybus	Alweg monorail
Could be built by 1972?	yes	yes	yes	yes
Route capacity of at least 7,500 mph	yes	yes	yes	yes
Compatible with existing British rail system	no	yes	no	no
Maximum speed (mph)	50	60	40	50
Mean acceleration rate (mph/sec)	3.3	3.0	2.3–3.0	2.7
Car capacity (person)	173	279	120	360
Height of guideway above ground (ft)	over 16.5	16.5	16.5	16.5
Beam span (ft)	104	60	60	65
Width of elevated span (ft)	30.3	27.5	19.8	15.5
Use at ground level	Suspended	On ground	On ground	On ground
Tunnel diameter (ft)	17.0	15.6	14.0	18.3
Switching	Slow	Fast	Undeveloped (?)	Slow
Noise level (internal) dB(A) over drive unit	68	71	*	81
Noise level (external) dB(A) 25 ft away	81	88	*	80
Total car requirements for				
10,000 pph	72	44	110	70
20,000 pph	144	88	220	135
30,000 pph	216	132	330	204
Train headway (min) at				
10,000 pph	2.65	2.84	2.87	3.64
20,000 pph	2.65	2.84	2.87	2.76
30,000 pph	2.65	2.84	2.87	2.44
Costs				
Total capital costs (£) (at 30,000 design hour cap.)	81,110,000	61,090,000	66,240,000	66,920,000
Annual operation and maintenance costs (£) (at 30,000 design hour cap.)	2,040,000	1,410,000	1,800,000	1,760,000
Tota annual cost (£)	7,350,000	5,330,000	6,130,000	6,090,000

*Information not available.

The second set of data dealt with performance characteristics and structural dimensions. The main differences between systems appear to be that
a.   The skybus has a slightly lower maximum speed and mean acceleration rate.
b.   The Safege monorail, hanging below the guideway, would require a taller structure and would also need a major structure on ground level.
c.   Switching would be easiest for the duorail.
d.   The duorail and the skybus require the least diameter tunnel.
e.   The Safege monorail could have the longest elevated beam span but also the widest.

Other characteristics did not seem to differ significantly.

Environmental considerations were reduced to two factors: noise levels and visual intrusion. The duorail was found to be somewhat louder than the others. No information was available at the time on noise levels from the skybus. (Note that evaluative decisions still must be made even in cases where some relevant information cannot be obtained). Visual intrusion, being a fairly subjective matter, was judged on the basis of reaction to a set of photomontages (Figs. 8.15 and 8.16) where mockups of the guideways of the four systems were superimposed over pictures of buildings and streets along the proposed route. The planners and designers felt there was no significant visual difference between systems based on these photomontages.[27]

The final set of data was the capital and operating costs for the four systems. On a total annual cost basis the duorail system was estimated to be least expensive, about 15 percent lower than that for the next lower system—the Alweg monorail. Capital costs for the duorail would be approximately £20 million (about $50 million) less than for the Safege monorail—the most expensive system.

The study group, in looking over the tradeoffs between different system characteristics apparently felt that, except for costs and adaptability to the British Rail system, all alternatives were essentially equal. The duorail, because it dominated the other systems on the two exceptional characteristics thus was chosen for recommendation for adoption.

8.3.3   Comments on the Cost-Effectiveness Technique

The preceding example has illustrated that an important characteristic of the cost-effectiveness technique is the manner in which information is presented to clarify relationships between alternatives and to outline tradeoffs or compromises that must be made to choose one alternative over the others. The cost-effectiveness framework does not indicate which system to select. It illustrates tradeoffs between alternatives, and it identifies dominated systems. It clearly lays out the expected accomplishment of each system and the related costs.

Whether the cost of additional effectiveness makes one alternative more worthwhile than another is a subjective matter and is therefore left to the decision

---

[27] This visual elevation was only of the structures, not the vehicles.

Fig. 8.15 Mockups of the guideways of the four systems superimposed over pictures of residential buildings and streets, at 25 and 50 feet. *Source:* DeLeuw Cather O hEoche, Manchester, England.

makers. It can be argued that leaving this decision on a subjective level is not helpful and that what is needed is an approach which will determine the worth of additional effectiveness. However, it is just such information that cannot be provided, particularly in the evaluation of more complex transportation plans. To obtain such worth measurements involves much greater capabilities for working with large sets of interrelated objectives than is presently available. In the cost-effectiveness model, the decision makers just need to be sensitive to these issues and can then secure information indicating the cost and consequences of meeting a particular goal.

Fig. 8.16 Mockups of the guideways of the four systems super-imposed over pictures of residential buildings and streets at 100 and 150 feet. *Source:* DeLeuw Cather O hEoche, Manchester, England.

The choice itself, if there are no other factors to consider, is made when the decision makers determine which of the alternatives results in a relation of cost to effectiveness acceptable to them. It is the decision makers, through the choice itself, who establish the relationship between cost and effectiveness, thus placing a boundary value on the measure of effectiveness.

In other words, if the duorail alternative were eventually chosen, the given level of effectiveness would be worth *at least* that particular cost. The duorail system is thus termed "cost-effective," for it provides decision makers with a level of effectiveness they deem satisfactory at what they consider to be a fair price. The value of that level of effectiveness is merely bounded in that the decision makers might be willing to pay more than the cost of the duorail system for the same level of effectiveness. This amounts to a subjective consideration of the criterion of efficiency. The duorail results in sufficient returns on its resource costs to the decision makers at one point in time.

In many cases there will be other factors to consider, of course. For example, there may be a *required* level of effectiveness which must be achieved. When such a requirement is set in advance, it remains only to select the alternative which meets it at the lowest cost. Similarly, there may be a budget constraint which cannot be violated. In this case, the decision makers might try to achieve the highest level of effectiveness while staying within the budget constraint.

There are several aspects of the cost-effectiveness technique which are extremely valuable and should be presented briefly at this time. First, all forms of information, regardless of degree of sophistication of description, are admissible in the framework. Pictures, diagrams, and even sound tapes can be entered in the tally. Second, estimates of the extent of effectiveness factors and costs at various points of time in the future can be presented in a series of charts, thereby giving a much needed time orientation to benefits and costs and allowing for the all important weighting of effectiveness and cost according to time of occurence. Another important possibility is the breakdown according to different accounting schemes, that is, into different cost classifications. For example, the commonly used industry cost schedule might include such breakdowns as (1) research and development costs, (2) capital investments or fixed facility costs, and (3) variable or operating costs.

Costs classifications might also be developed whereby each individual outlay for various components of an alternative transportation plan is treated separately. For example, in the explanation of benefit-cost earlier in this chapter the categories were (1) right-of-way costs, (2) grading, drainage, and minor structure costs, (3) major structure costs, and (4) pavement and appurtenances costs.

An additional advantage of the cost-effectiveness technique is that, if desired, separate impact calculations for individuals or various groups of interest can be developed. A good example is found in a National Academy of Engineering report on *Technology Assessment* [8.31], which dealt with five alternatives for reducing noise at airports (see Table 8.5). Impacts were judged for airline passengers, airline operators, local taxpayers, and so on. Obviously, impacts will vary for different groups and, especially for implementation purposes, it may be useful in a cost-effectiveness application to determine who is being affected and to what extent.

Perhaps, the greatest advantage of the cost-effectiveness technique is that it is complimentary to the "values-goals-objectives-standards" format presented in Chap. 5. Looking back at Table 8.4, we see that the measures (or criteria) presented for evaluation of the Manchester rapid transit systems all flowed directly from the preliminary goals set up by the Ministry of Transport and others. Thus, the cost-effectiveness technique is a natural extension of attempts to plan using goals and objectives.

Table 8.5   A Characterization of the Impacts of Strategies 1 through 5 on the Set of Affected Parties

Affected parties	1 Continue methods used in 1967–1968	2 Relocate airports	3 Create a buffer zone around airports	4 Sound-proof residences	5 Modify aircraft hardware and flight profiles
Airline passengers					(±)
Airline operators	+	±	(±)		−
Airport operators	−	−	(+)	+	+
Airport and engine manufacturers	+	±	(+)		(+)
Airport neighbors	−	+	−	(−)	+
Local taxpayers		±	−	−	+
Local business	±	−	−	+	+
Local government	−	−	−	±	+
Federal government	+	±	−	±	−

Note: + or − represents favorable or unfavorable impacts, respectively; ( ) indicate that the impacts are judged to be uncertain even though they have been characterized; ± indicates favorable as well as unfavorable impacts. No entry is made where the impact is believed to be negligible or where no impact has been identified.
Source: [8.31, p. 84].

The major difficulty with the cost-effectiveness approach, and one which affects almost any evaluation technique, is that of overwhelming data requirements. This problem has been discussed earlier, but its importance cannot be overstressed. Many current transportation studies have found themselves inundated with data and subsequently unable to perform even some of the simple analyses required of them. This type of situation naturally is not desirable and requires extra effort on the part of analysts and decision makers to identify and extract only those factors of relevance to the evaluation.

8.4   ACTUAL TRANSPORTATION DECISION MAKING

Techniques such as cost-effectiveness have been found to be extremely helpful in guiding the decision making process. Yet any practitioner knows that there is a great difference between how decisions *are* made and how they *should be* made. Moreover, there surely is a significant difference between who actually makes and enforces decisions and who should be doing such. The purpose of this section is to present a brief exploration into several studies of real world decision making situations in order to highlight the differences mentioned above. Particular emphasis will be given to the actors and factors involved in urban transportation decisions.

8.4.1 BART: A Case Study Example

The San Francisco Bay Area Rapid Transit System (BART) became operational in 1972, but preliminary discussion on similar ideas began as far back as the Second World War. A unique and certainly provocative outlook on decision making relative to BART is presented by Beagle, Haber, and Wellman [8.32], who contend that its real purpose is to serve downtown banking and insurance interests:

> The second element in the [corporate metropolitan] strategy is the creation of a rapid transit network which will connect the central city to the outlying consumer markets and labor pools.
>
> The push for a rapid transit system in the Bay Area began in the early fifties with Carl Wente (chairman of the board of the Bank of America), Kendric Morrish (a Wells Fargo director) and Mortimer Fleishhacker (a Crocker Citizens Bank director connected with both BAC and the Blyth-Zellerbach Committee, a corporate group supporting urban renewal). These men initiated feasibility studies for what was to become the Bay Area Rapid Transit District (BART). In 1962 voters approved an initial bond issue for the construction of a high speed transit system embracing San Francisco, Contra Costa and Alameda counties and, ultimately, San Mateo and Marin.
>
> The first chairman of the BART board of directors was Adrian Falk, a retired vice-president of S&W Fine Foods and past president of the California Chamber of Commerce. According to Falk, BART's basic function was to make possible the centralization of certain executive functions in downtown San Francisco. "It's the only practical way," he told a local newspaperman. "Certain financial, banking, and industrial companies want to be centralized, want to have everyone near each other. They don't want to have to go one day to Oakland, the next day to San Jose, the next day to San Francisco."
>
> The major contributors to the public relations fund during the 1962 bond election were the three downtown banks plus a large number of companies which stood to benefit directly from construction contracts: Westinghouse, Kaiser, Bethlehem, Bechtel and the Downtown Property Owners and Builders. Bank of America's Carl Wente was head of the finance committee. BART was sold to the electorate as a crusade against the auto lobby. In fact, it ran into little trouble from this direction. The construction of thirty-two additional freeway lanes is projected for this area in the next ten years (there are forty-eight now). From the outset, BART was conceived of more as a commuter railroad than a true public transit system. It makes no pretense at carrying the great bulk of local traffic. Traffic on the Oakland–San Francisco Bay Bridge is still expected to reach the point of absolute capacity by 1975.
>
> BART will have many consequences: first, it will greatly encourage downtown congestion and density. It has already stimulated a substantial building boom. Almost immediately after construction began, the three major banks put up high-rise headquarters buildings downtown, and increasingly the downtown San Francisco landscape is spotted with new BART-oriented construction sites. According to the Chamber of Commerce, a "direct dividend" of BART's construction will be the new "Embarcadero Center," a Rockefeller venture of great ugliness. The Embarcadero Center will involve three high-rise buildings on the waterfront, and gradually plans are being announced for redevelopment of the entire waterfront area.
>
> More important, though, BART will guarantee the growth and renewed prosperity of downtown business. Essentially, it expands many times over the labor market area and the marketing area for goods and services. The "best workers" can be recruited for downtown jobs, choosing from the whole three-county area. And likewise, the richest, most discriminating consumers are given easy access to the prestige retailers of the downtown complex and the professional services in which it specializes.

Also, property values all along the transit route will soar. In Toronto, they increased up to tenfold adjacent to the new subway line. And BART officials expect a comparable rise in their domain. Millions of dollars will be made by the public-spirited businessmen who pushed the plan and then made their services available to construct it. And the taxpayers will be stuck with paying off the bond issues and debts of $2 billion or more. That BART will actually be profitable, that it will contribute significantly to the retirement of its debt, is highly unlikely. BART has already run into financial troubles, spending far more than its initial capitalization. The public is about to pay for these profits, inefficiencies and costs of inflation out of a special hike in the sales tax.

But the problem is not that business will make money off the construction and financing of public services; nor even that business will do a bad job and end up providing uncomfortable, ugly, and congested services. The problem is that it serves the rich and is paid for by the poor. By increasing the public debt and tax burden and by raising property values along the route, BART insures an increased squeeze on those least able to pay. Its effect on housing is obvious. Rents will be forced up as tax costs are passed on, and homeowners will be deprived of their property as the costs of ownership increase.

BART doesn't even have the saving grace of helping workers from the black and brown ghettos get to industrial jobs outside the city. The trains do run both ways. But the routes link the central city with the rich suburbs, not the industrial hinterland. And the trains will pass through ghettos only incidentally: Hunters Point is not on the route, and there are no stations in the Oakland ghettos. BART will make little contribution to an anti-poverty policy of connecting poorer workers with jobs and a wider employment area.

"The end result of BART is that San Francisco will be just like Manhattan," according to an influential insurance broker. "It's not a question of whether it's desirable," he continued, "but what's the practical matter. As a practical matter you can't have eighteen different banking and insurance centers. You have to concentrate them with all the various services around them. The people who run these centers want all their services—the people they work with—advertisers, attorneys, accountants—around them. It's a complete part of the way we do business in this country."

While we do not necessarily agree in total with the above statement, it certainly does indicate that decisions relative to transportation can be made at levels substantially different from those assumed, say, in the benefit-cost approach.

8.4.2 Actors and Factors in a Variety of Urban Transportation Decisions

The quote in the preceding section brought out some interesting aspects of urban transportation decision making in one situation. In this section we will attempt to broaden the outlook to include decisions made in urban areas throughout the United States.

Dickey and Stuart [8.33] surveyed 151 urban transportation decisions across the country. Their objective was to determine which actors and factors were predominant in these decisions. Eight hundred city planners, traffic engineers, public works officials, transit operators, and mayors were asked to report on a transportation project or problem of interest to them and to answer a series of questions about that situation. Biases in the questionnaires could not be avoided, of course, particularly since it was not possible to talk personally with each of the many respondents. The results of the study thus are subject to considerable ranges in interpretations. Nonetheless, the findings are presented here primarily to give some basic insight concerning the actors and factors most likely to be involved in urban transportation decisions.

The first set of analyses in the study concerned the actors in the various decision cases. These actors were divided into two classes: "professionals" and "participants." The former class consisted of planners, lawyers, engineers, and so on while the latter consisted of various governmental and nongovernmental agencies and people at different organizational levels. Governmental agencies included those on federal, state, metropolitan, county, and city levels. Examples of governmental personnel singled out were governors, national legislators, mayors, and city and county managers. Nongovernment groups included civic organizations, newspapers, and television and radio stations.

The mean number of *professional* types involved was surprisingly small, averaging only a little over three in each case. The number of all participants was much larger, with a mean near 14. This difference suggests that many non-professionals or similar professionals in different governmental agencies were heavily involved. We thus can conclude that with so many participants involved in each decision, a variety of roles will be taken and a certain amount of time will be needed to resolve the inevitable conflicts that arise. Urban transportation decison making therefore can not occur "instantaneously" (as is assumed in many evaluation techniques), but over an extended time period.

More information about the role of the actors in the various transportation problems cases is found in Table 8.6 and 8.7. The first table shows the number of cases, out of 151, in which different professionals were involved. Planners and traffic engineers dominate in their participation, but this was to be expected because they were the ones responding most often to the questionnaire. Moreover, they usually represent operating agencies most likely to be contacted in regard to urban transportation problems. Lawyers play a role in many cases, possibly indicating the increased use being made of the courts to help settle the more complex problems of relocation reimbursements, environmental damage, and so forth. Housing and renewal officals were engaged in as many as 28 of the 151 cases, perhaps showing the large incidence of joint development projects.

Table 8.6 Number of Urban Transportation Decision Cases in Which Each Professional Was Involved

Professional type	Cases	Professional type	Cases
Planner	117	Transit engineer	24
Lawyer	46	Traffic engineer	115
Educator	5	Other engineer	66
Architect	20	Housing or renewal	
City manager	47	official	28
Transit manager	30	Welfare official	3

Note: Total number of cases is 151.
Source: [8.33].

Table 8.7 Number of Urban Transportation Decision Cases in Which Each Participant Was Thought to Be Influential

Participant type	Cases	Participant type	Cases
Federal level		City level	
Bureau of Public Roads	72	Council/legislative	105
Urban Renewal Administration	28	Mayor	97
Other	12	Manager	53
		Traffic engineering	103
State level		Other engineering/works	75
Governor	16	Planning	113
Legislator	20	Renewal	35
Highway department	100	Health	2
Planning agency	24	Welfare	3
Other	17	School	19
		Police	28
Metropolitan level		Other	21
Transit operations	31		
Special district	4	Nongovernmental	
Regional planning, COG	57	Civic groups	79
Transportation planning	58	Trade groups	41
Other	7	Business/industry	53
		Newspaper	73
County level		TV/Radio	55
Commissioners-legislative	29	Individual citizen	73
Administrator	17	Other	16
Traffic engineering	32		
Other engineering/works	30	Other	5
Planning	42		
Health	2		
Welfare	2		
School	5		
Other	5		

Note: Total number of cases is 151.
Source: [8.33].

In Table 8.7 we find transportation agencies represented heavily at each level of the governmental hierarchy: the Bureau of Public Roads (now the Federal Highway Administration) in 72 cases, the state highway agency in 100, the metropolitan transportation planning agency in 58, the county traffic engineer in 32, and the city traffic engineer in 103. At present, then, there would seem to be almost equal representation from all levels.

Table 8.7 also seems to show the influence of many groups other than those directly responsible for transportation systems. At the federal level, the Urban Renewal Administration of the Department of Housing and Urban Development was connected with 28 of the 151 cases. The "other" federal agencies listed included the Urban Mass Transportation Administration and such diverse organiza-

organizations as the Forest and Park Services, the Army Corps of Engineers, and the Department of Agriculture. At the state level and below, planning agencies start to make their impact felt. Moreover, at the lowest level (and the one generally closest to the citizen) there is an increase in the number of agency types to include schools, police, and public works as well as planning, renewal, and traffic engineering. It is also at this level that elected officials—mayors, city managers, and council members—are most responsive to the problems and influential in decision making regarding them.

The fact that the elected officials were so involved might indicate that transportation problems are of some concern to them and thus are not always left in the hands of the delegated agency. Many nongovernmental groups—civic, trade, business, newspaper, and TV/Radio—also were heavily involved at the local level, and individual citizens were influential in almost half (73/151) of the cases. It would seem that the voices of at least some nongovernmental actors were being heard directly and with about as much influence as various city agencies.

In the second part of the questionnaire, a list of factors of possible concern in urban transportation problems was presented to each respondent. These factors were divided into four classes: user-related, neighborhood impact, area-wide impact, and transportation management and planning. Room was left to add other factors not listed. Respondents were asked to determine whether each particular factor was (a) not considered, (b) considered but not important (i.e., "just considered"), or (c) important in the transportation decision being reported. A total of 39 factors were listed. Nine others were recognized in the answers added to the survey form.

The name of each factor and the number of times it was "just considered" or was important are displayed in Table 8.8. The nine additional factors are listed at the bottom. The distribution of factors in the four major categories was about equal, thereby indicating that *nonuser* considerations both on a neighborhood and area-wide level and management factors are of about equal concern as user factors.

The user factors taken into account in most transportation planning studies still were prominent, however. Travel time, user safety, and "presence of different modes of travel" all were just considered or important in a large number of cases. At the neighborhood impact level "local traffic circulation" rated highest in concern. "Access to economic activities" similarly rated high on the area-wide impact level, although this might be another indication of direct transportation needs. Another factor which often entered into the transportation decision making situation was that of facility appearance, "just considered" in 69 cases and important in 6 more. Noise, taxes, land values, and centralization and decentralization all were considered frequently. On the management side, costs were significant along with capacity. Interestingly, agency coordination was a matter of some concern, rating consideration in 69 cases and importance in 14. If this finding is representative, it would appear that many new problems are being generated for governmental organizations as they attempt to deal with the large numbers of factors listed in Table 8.8.

Table 8.8 Number of Urban Transportation Decision Cases in Which Each Factor Was Considered or Important

Factor	Cases just considered	Cases important	Factor	Cases just considered	Cases important
User related			Nonuser-areawide impact		
Travel time	76	14	Access to economic activities	96	33
User safety	77	13	New economic activities	51	12
Relief foot travel	20	1	Access to social, cultural, educational activities	77	9
Vehicle comfort	34	0	New social, cultural, educational activities	28	5
Weather protection	15	0	Centralization-decentralization	42	3
Signs, information	32	1	Natural features	32	0
Dependability	19	1	Other	21	0
Fares	22	3			
Variety, novelty	17	0	Transportation management and planning		
Parking	39	5	Costs	92	21
No. of travel modes	54	8	Capacity	83	19
Other	53	1	Funding	47	22
			Legal consideration	49	1
Nonuser-neighborhood impact			Agency coordination	69	14
Nonuser safety	54	6	Political feasibility	53	20
Facility appearance	69	6	Type of management	31	5
Air pollution	25	1	Other	11	0
Noise	44	5			
Taxes	37	1	Added factors		
Relocation	39	21	Emergency service	1	0
Local traffic circulation	100	19	View from facility	1	0
Unusable land	33	1	Service frequency	2	1
Geographical boundaries	41	4	Historical preservation	4	8
Land values	67	5	Temporary service	1	0
Multiple use	36	1	Removal	1	0
Other	31	1	Vandalism, crime	1	0
			Natural disorder	1	0
			Psychological value	1	0

Note: Total number of cases is 151.
Source: [8.33].

Factors not included in the questionnaire but added by respondents involved such matters as services during emergencies, view from the facility, frequency of service, and preservation of historical and cultural sites. The only one of these that evoked consideration in more than three cases was the latter one.

8.5 SUMMARY

The broad aim of the chapter has been to present views on the manner in which metropolitan transportation system evaluation and decision making should be and are made. In the first section a fairly detailed presentation of the AASHO benefit-cost technique was given. Despite the fact that this technique is now losing favor as a *sole* decision making tool, it undoubtedly will continue to play a significant role in most future evaluation endeavors. The more subjective cost-effectiveness technique (Sec. 8.3), for example, is fashioned to accept benefit-cost ratios in the evaluative process. In addition, the cost-effectiveness approach overcomes many of the associated disadvantages of benefit-cost methodology (Sec. 8.2), especially that of the assignment of artificial weightings of importance to decision factors.

Actual decision making does not necessarily adhere to any particular methodology, however, although such actions are simulated to a degree by the cost-effectiveness technique. Benefit-cost ratios have been used heavily in the past and can be found in many reports. Yet in Sec. 8.4 it is suggested that at least some larger decisions (like for BART) are made by major business interests primarily for their own advantage and that benefit-cost ratios are simply unimportant afterthoughts. Whatever the situation, it does appear that in the many urban transportation decisions made across the country, many actors are participants and a great many factors in addition to user satisfaction are taken into account.

BIBLIOGRAPHY

8.1   American Association of State Highway Officials: *Road User Benefit Analyses for Highway Improvements*, Washington, D.C., 1960.

8.2   Hitch, G. H., and R. N. McKean: *The Economics of Defense in the Nuclear Age*, Atheneum Press, New York, 1966.

8.3   Kuhn, T. E.: *Public Enterprise Economics and Transport Problems*, Univ. of California Press, Berkeley, 1962.

8.4   Thomas, E. N., and J. L. Schofer: *Strategies for Evaluation of Alternate Transportation Plans*, Two Part Report, The Transportation Center, Northwestern Univ. Evanston, Ill., 1967.

8.5   Wohl, M., and B. V. Martin: *Traffic Systems Analysis for Engineers and Planners*, McGraw-Hill, New York, 1967.

8.6   Chapin, F. S., Jr. and S. F. Weiss (ed.): *Urban Growth Dynamics in a Regional Cluster of Cities*, Wiley, New York, 1962.

8.7   Meyer, J. R., J. F. Kain, and M. Wohl: *The Urban Transportation Problem*, Harvard Univ. Press, Cambridge, 1965.

8.8   Mohring, H. and M. Harwitz: *Highway Benefits: An Analytical Framework*, Northwestern Univ. Press, Evanston, Ill., 1962.

8.9 Haney, D. G.: *The Value of Time for Passenger Cars: A Theoretical Analysis and Description of Preliminary Experiments*, Final Report, vol. I, Stanford Research Institute, Menlo Park, Calif., May 1967.

8.10 Winch, D. M.: *The Economics of Highway Planning*, University of Toronto Press, Toronto, 1963.

8.11 Chernoff, H., and L. Moses: *Elementary Decision Theory*, Wiley, New York, 1959.

8.12 Jessiman, W. et al.: "A Rational Decision Making Technique for Transportation Planning," *Highway Research Board Record* 180, Washington, D.C., 1967.

8.13 Fishburn, P. C.: *Decision and Value Theory*, Wiley, New York, 1964.

8.14 Isard, W.: *Methods of Regional Analysis*, M.I.T. Press, Cambridge, 1963.

8.15 Bos, H. C., and L. M. Koych: "The Appraisal of Road Construction Projects," *Review of Economics and Statistics*, vol. 43, February, 1961.

8.16 Eckstein, O.: *Water Resource Development*, Harvard Univ. Press, Cambridge, Mass., 1958.

8.17 Galbraith, J. K.: *The Affluent Society*, Houghton-Mifflin, Boston, 1958.

8.18 Grant, E. L., and W. G. Ireson: *Principles of Engineering Economy*, (4th ed.), Ronald Press, New York, 1960.

8.19 Rothenberg, J.: *The Measurement of Social Welfare*, Prentice-Hall, Englewood Cliffs, N.J., 1961.

8.20 Ritter, L. F., Jr. and R. J. Paquette: *Highway Engineering*, (3d ed.), Ronald Press, New York, 1967.

8.21 Little, I. M. D.: *A Critique of Welfare Economics*, Oxford University Press, London, 1958.

8.22 Luce, D. R., and H. Raiffa: *Games and Decision*, Wiley, New York, 1957.

8.23 Baerwald, J. E. (ed.): *Traffic Engineering Handbook*, Institute of Traffic Engineers, Washington, D.C., 1965.

8.24 The Rand Corporation: *Measurement and Evaluation of Transportation System Effectiveness*, Federal Clearinghouse, PB-185 772, Springfield, Va., 1969.

8.25 Dodson, E. N.: "Cost-Effectiveness in Urban Transportation," *Operations Research*, vol. 17, no. 3, May–June, 1969.

8.26 Dorfman, R. (ed.): *Measuring Benefits of Governmental Investments*, The Brookings Insitution, Washington, D.C., 1965.

8.27 English, J. M. (ed.): *Cost-Effectiveness, the Economic Evaluation of Engineered Systems*, Wiley, New York, 1969.

8.28 Winfrey, R.: *Economic Analysis for Highways*, International, Scranton, Pa., 1969.

8.29 Bureau of the Census: *U.S. Census of Housing: 1960, Vol. 1, Virginia*, Washington, D.C., 1962.

8.30 Millar, J., and J. Dean: "Practical Considerations of Rapid Transit—A Summary of the Manchester Study," *Journal of the Town Planning Institute*, vol. 54, no. 4, April, 1968.

8.31 National Academy of Engineering: *A Study of Technology Assessment*, U.S. Government Printing Office, Washington, D.C., July, 1969.

8.32 Beagle, D., A. Haber, and D. Wellman: "Turf Power and the Tax Man," *Leviathan*, vol. 1, no. 2, 1969.

8.33 Dickey, J. W., and R. C. Stuart: "Actors and Factors in Urban Transportation Decisions," Presented to the Operations Research Society of America Meeting, Disneyland, Anaheim Calif., October, 1971.

9 Generation of Alternate Solutions

In using the phrase *generation of alternate solutions* we are attempting to portray a situation in which components such as vehicles, networks, terminals, and controls are brought together to form a complete system. Hopefully, when this system is evaluated it will be worthwhile or, in the most promising case, optimal in some sense. The objective of this chapter is to present some examples of the ways in which transportation solutions have been formulated or "synthesized."

The first section will deal with the general idea of creativity. The second section contains a discussion of different transportation technologies and their performance characteristics. This is followed by two sections in which more detailed descriptions of the processes by which actual transportation systems have been generated are presented. One section deals with a pedestrian mover system for a central city, the other with a metropolitan-wide system. In the last two sections, alternate approaches to the "using transportation to solve transportation problems" syndrome are discussed. In one approach, land use arrangements are altered to reduce the *need* for travel (and corresponding transportation systems). In the second, transportation is employed to create beneficial impacts on other types of development, in this case the mixing of families of different income types throughout a region.

No attempt will be made in this chapter to discuss all of the many ways in which transportation systems can be developed, simply because the variety and breadth of transportation problems would make such a discussion lengthy and arduous. Instead, we will try to display an assortment of both techniques and application situations through a set of representative examples.

9.1 CREATIVITY

It is usually through the creative process that many valuable solutions to problems are obtained. Consequently, any effort spent in exploring this process probably will result in better plans. Harrisberger [9.10, p. 34] says this about creativity:

> The creative ability of man could easily be regarded as our greatest natural resource and, no doubt, our greatest *underdeveloped* natural resource. It is this human quality that makes the impossible real, anticipates the future, and extrapolates reality. It is the principle source of our progress, man's most distinguishing ability—a noble attribute of the human mind.

If creativity has this much significance, what can be said about it that will allow us to find it more readily? To answer this, we first will need a definition:

> It's a spontaneous, irrational, intuitive process of imagination—a mysterious mixing of previous experiences and combinations that are totally new [9.10, p. 36].

> It's the manifestation of a fundamental ability to relate previously unrelated things [9.10, p. 35].

The latter definition has interesting ramifications in the field of transportation. Until the period of 1955–1960, urban transportation was an area of endeavor in which the store of knowledge was fairly fixed or at least expanding at a relatively slow rate. But then many researchers and practitioners began to *identify connections* with other subject areas such as systems analysis, operations research, economics, sociology, and urban and regional planning. The result was a vast array of new ideas on many aspects of transportation,[1] as exemplified by the new technologies pictured later in this chapter.

While the defining of creativity gives us a direction in which to search for better solutions, we still lack techniques by which to proceed. How do we become more creative or obtain more creative solutions? McPherson [9.11] and Langemann [9.21] give one answer to the first part of the question by providing a list (see Table 9.1) of characteristics of the highly creative persons they have examined. The highly creative person in his childhood is, among other things, quick and persistent, toys with ideas, accepts disorder, and is playful, with tremendous energy. The highly creative person, among other things, seeks privacy, is aggressive in goals sought, is intelligent (but not a genius), and likes regimentation, although he can accept chaos and change. To become more creative, a person obviously must concentrate on achieving the attributes presented in Table 9.1.

---

[1] Including the idea of the metropolitan transportation planning process itself.

Table 9.1   The Highly Creative Person

Childhood characteristics

Persistent, purposeful	Lags in verbal ability
Quickly thinks of alternatives	Attracted to the mysterious
Sees gaps, finds hidden meanings	Playfull, spirited in disagreement
Self-winding, self-feeling	Emotionally sensitive
Toys with ideas	Finds fault
Accepts disorder	Courageous, adventurous
Tremendous energy	Takes risks

Adult characteristics

Seeks autonomy and privacy	Accepts chaos and change, antisymmetry
Dedicated to problem-solving tasks	Insensitive to others' feelings
Aggressive in goals sought	Likes to explore ideas
Relentless worker, great zeal	Nonconformist, enjoys nonconformity
Does not value job security	Independent, observant, says what he thinks
Likes to clown around, childish play	Gullible, open to experience
Unimpressed by status symbols	Can easily accept failure
Rejects theological arguments	Needs continual reinforcement, and understanding listener
Good sense of humor	
Intelligent (IQ: 100–140)	
Likes supervision and regimentation	

Source: From *Engineermanship: A Philosophy of Design*, by L. Harrisberger. © 1966 by Wadsworth Publishing Co., Inc. Reprinted by permission of the publisher, Brooks/Cole Publishing Company, Monterey, California.

In response to the second part of the question, that of obtaining more creative solutions, Harrisberger [9.10] has summarized several possible procedures, two of which will be discussed here. The first one, the *checklist technique*, ". . . serves to remind you of other ways of looking at the problem so that new imagination stimuli can be introduced into the 'ideation' process" [9.10, p. 37]. The checklist is shown in Table 9.2. One interesting possibility for the *modify* contrast and perhaps also for the *change places* inversion in a transportation-oriented situation would be that of having people live and have other activities on bridges, as has been done since early times on the Ponte Vecchio in Florence, Italy.

A second creativity-producing procedure is that of brainstorming, the objective of which is to bring out inspirations and reactions on a spontaneous basis in hopes that each idea will trigger another and another until eventually a unique and valuable solution evolves. The rules for a useful brainstorming session, according to Harrisberger, [9.10, p. 64], are:

1. Use a group of not more than six or eight individuals who are conversant with the field but not necessarily expert or even acquainted with the problem.
2. The person with the problem acts as moderator to define the situation and provide new interpretations of the problem when there is a lag in inspiration.
3. Record everything that's said.

Table 9.2 Checklist for Creating New Solutions

Put to other uses?
Adapt? (like, suggest, copy, parallel, etc.)
Modify? (change, color, motion, order, taste, shapes, etc.)
Magnify? (stronger, higher, longer, add, extra, exaggerate, etc.)
Minify? (subtract, condense, lower, shrink, cut off, etc.)
Substitute? (what else, other, replace, etc.)
Rearrange? (interchange, alter sequence, scramble, etc.)
Reverse? (opposite, backward, upside down, inside out, etc.)
Combine? (blend, assortment, hookup with, etc.)

Source: Reprinted from *Applied Imaginations* by Alex F. Osborn by permission of Charles Scribner's Sons. Copyright© 1963 Charles Scribner's Sons.

4. Maintain a light humorous atmosphere. Encourage members to think freely and bring out wild ideas.
5. Caution every member to refrain from judging each idea. This is very important.
6. Stop the session when the group begins to tire (usually after 30 to 40 min).

It would be difficult to say how many valuable solutions in the transportation field have arisen through *individual* efforts using, implicitly or explicitly, something similar to the checklist technique as opposed to *group* approaches exemplified by brainstorming. Yet there is little doubt that one person's ideas can trigger another's, with the subsequent outputs being modified to create what may be appreciable improvements. The advertising industry provides a good example of such success. Brainstorming (in addition to individual efforts) thus could be a useful approach for obtaining new and beneficial ideas and solutions for transportation problems.

9.2 TRANSPORTATION TECHNOLOGIES

An important part of any potential solution to transportation problems involves "technology," which in this context refers primarily to a "hardware" system. Naturally there are many types of transportation technologies, from the more mundane—motor buses, highways, traffic signals and signs, parking lots, subway trains, and the like—to the more esoteric—air cushion vehicles, linear induction motors, pneumatic tube trains, and the like. In recent years the number of technologies potentially applicable in urban transportation situations has increased markedly, especially as attempts have been made to alleviate such annoying problems as air and noise pollution, lack of comfort and privacy in mass transit, and high operating and travel costs.

It is difficult in a text of this nature to describe all of the technologies that may be available and applicable in various transportation situations. Consequently, we first will outline the main elements of a transportation system so that different technologies can be classified and put in their proper role, and then we will describe 14 representative technologies. These have been chosen to display a wide spectrum of possibilities and to indicate the types of functional characteristics that should be of some consequence in the assessment of technologies for potential application in a particular situation. For information on other technologies, the reader is referred to [9.52].

9.2.1 Taxonomy of a Transportation System

Transportation is a complex set of objects and events which are difficult to summarize in a simple fashion, yet the need to synthesize and operate systems requires an articulation of the elements which form the entity known as transportation. Many classifications or taxonomies have been proposed, and the one in Table 9.3 is a condensation of those ideas.

Perhaps the easiest way to understand the makeup of this taxonomy is to envision a situation in which a consultant is called in by the developers of a potential new town site presently having little or no transportation system. Since they are interested in an almost totally new system, the consultant is asked to describe all of the elements which might go into a complete transportation "package" which could be used in the new town.

Inevitably this "package" would contain, in some form, a network composed of individual links, nodes, and perhaps tangible surface (traveled way) on which trips could be made. Moreover, the consultant might specify a vehicle or set of different vehicles having certain propulsion, suspension, braking, and communication systems and, of course, a compartment of some sort in which passengers could ride. There also would have to be terminals for the concentrated loading, unloading, and storage and maintenance of these vehicles as well as a control mechanism for

Table 9.3   A Transportation System Taxonomy

1. Network
   a. Links
   b. Nodes (switching or loading points)
   c. Physical traveled way (if any)

2. Vehicle
   a. Passenger and cargo space
   b. Suspension system
   c. Propulsion system
   d. Braking system
   e. Communication system

3. Terminals
   a. Loading and unloading area and systems
   b. Storage area
   c. Maintenance area and system

4. Control system
   a. Physical
   b. Legal and governmental
   c. Managerial—policy and budget

overseeing and directing the operation of the whole system. This, briefly, would be the contents of the "package" presented to the new town developers.

As in most classification schemes, there are items which do not fit neatly into one category or the other: what is the "vehicle" in the cases of the moving sidewalk or pipeline? What are the "links" for a craft which hovers on a cushion of air, allowing it to travel almost anywhere? What is the traveled way or the control system for a vehicle running in a tube under the force of gravity? Obviously, these questions cannot be answered simply, but the circumstances to which they pertain are exceptions rather than general situations. The taxonomy displayed in Table 9.3 thus is a useful one under most circumstances.

9.2.2 Examples of Transportation Technologies

As mentioned previously, fourteen different technologies will be described here. The discussion will focus on their functional characteristics. Pictures of the described technologies are found throughout the discussion.

Automated highway. The automated highway involves a specially designed roadway with control cables buried in the pavement. Usually there would be two unidirectional lanes and a third reversible lane under control, with additional outside lanes for transition. Each vehicle using the automated highway would have

Interior of an experimental vehicle for an automated highway. Side-mounted control stick located on seat. (*Department of Electrical Engineering, Ohio State University*)

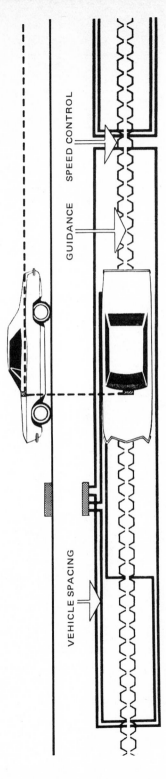

Cars will be guided, controlled and spaced by an electronic control system embedded in the highway

VEHICLE SPACING

GUIDANCE   SPEED CONTROL

Electronic guideway configuration for an automated highway. (*General Motors Research Laboratories*)

1 A motorist traveling in a normal lane but wanting to enter the Autoline lane would move into the transition lane and signal his desire to enter the Autoline.

2 By putting his car on automatic control, his speed and position would be monitored and adjusted.

3 The car would be automatically guided into position at the end of the first available group on the Autoline lane.

4 To leave the Autoline lane, the motorist would first signal his intention to the system.

5 His car would move automatically into the transition lane at the first safe opportunity.

6 He would return his car to manual control and then move into a normal lane.

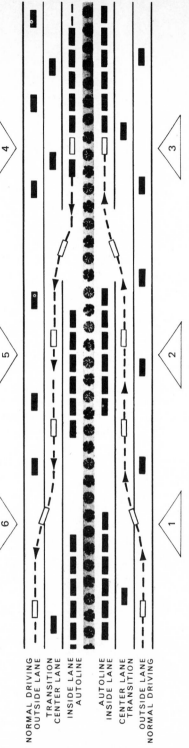

NORMAL DRIVING
OUTSIDE LANE

TRANSITION
CENTER LANE

INSIDE LANE
AUTOLINE

AUTOLINE
INSIDE LANE

CENTER LANE
TRANSITION

OUTSIDE LANE
NORMAL DRIVING

Concept for transition from a regular to an automated highway. (*General Motors Research Laboratories*)

to be equipped with a special electro-mechanical package for control of speed, spacing, and lateral placement. These controls would be activated by a computer located at some central point. Information signals would be transmitted via the buried cables and then induced into the vehicle.

The special "add on" control package for the vehicle would cost about $140, while the guideway cost is anticipated to be about $3,843,000 per lane mile. Operating costs for the vehicle and system would run about $0.105/passenger mile [9.23 and 9.24].

The automated highway would appear to be much safer than a regular highway, and the passenger, relieved of the driving task, would be able to move at an average trip speed of 58 mph. With maximum vehicular speeds of 70 mph, the automated highway would be capable of accommodating 9,000 vehicles/hr/lane. Access points or terminals would be at minimum intervals of 2 miles [9.23 and 9.24].

Alweg Monorail. The Alweg Monorail was developed initially by the Swedish industrialist Axel Wenner-Gren. It consists of an automatically controlled vehicle riding on top of a single rail. Currently there are Alweg Monorail installations in Tokyo, Disneyland (Anaheim, California), Disneyworld (Orlando, Florida), and Seattle. The first full scale operation was the Japanese one, placed in service in 1964. Since then more than 77 million passengers have been transported on the line, with the monthly figure reaching 2 million.

The average cost of an installation varies from $1.8 million to $3.2 million per mile. A double-track line requires 24 ft 10 in. of right-of-way [9.27 and 9.28]. The track usually is constructed 17 ft 9 in. above the ground surface to allow for passage underneath of trucks and other vehicles.

A monorail system of this type can accommodate 45,000 passengers per hour in one direction if access points are at a minimum of 0.4 mile. The operation of the

Alweg Monorail vehicle and guideway. (*Rapid Transport Development Company Limited*)

Interior view of Alweg Monorail. (*Rapid Transport Development Company Limited*)

system above ground creates relatively little disturbance to existing transportation modes. However, it does have at least one undesirable characteristic: because the vehicle rides on top of the track, it is subject to interference from ice, snow, and related weather conditions as well as from physical objects such as rocks and tree branches.

Much of the monorail's appeal has been due to such technological features as the use of modern structural design techniques and lightweight rolling stock with rubber tire wheels, features which are readily applicable to conventional rail systems [9.53]. It also is electrically powered, which cuts down on local air pollution and noise.

Safege Monorail. The Safege Monorail, unlike the Alweg Monorail, hangs underneath the rail. It has been licensed by the General Electric Company, and a system has been in operation on a 1-mile track at Chateauneuf-sur-Loire, France, since 1964 [9.27] and on a 5-mile single lane track in Kamakura, Japan, since 1970 [9.59].

The guideway for the Safege Monorail costs from $2.7 million to $5.0 million/mile/lane, with the cost of operation being $0.035 to $0.040/passenger mile. A minimum right-of-way of 30 ft 3 in. is required for two-way operation. The vehicle has a top speed of 75 mph, with a maximum capacity on the guideway of 57,000 passengers/hr/lane. A minimum headway of 90 seconds can be achieved if access points are located at average intervals of 0.5 mile [9.27 to 9.29].

At a rail clearance of 32 ft above the ground the Safege Monorail can operate with little disturbance from existing systems and haul passengers or materials on grades up to 20 percent [9.27]. This system also offers some theoretical speed advantages on curved sections due to the self-banking resulting from the pendulum

Safege Monorail vehicle and guideway. (*Safege—Transport*)

motion of the hanging vehicle. Again, as with the Alweg Monorail, air pollution and noise levels are reduced, and the system has a natural aesthetic appeal.

StaRR-car. This is a small dual mode vehicle which can operate independently with a storage battery as a source of power or automatically on a specially powered track. It has been developed by Alden Self-Transit Systems in Westboro, Mass.

The Alden StaRR-car vehicle on a test track in Bedford, Mass. (*Alden Self-Transit Systems Corporation*)

The manually operated StaRR-car can accommodate either two or four passengers while the automatic car, if used exclusively in this mode, could seat six passengers. With an average station spacing of 1,600 ft, the automatic system would have a capacity of 27,900 passengers/hr [9.30 to 9.34]. For the automatic network, the vehicle cost would be about $670, and the guideway would require 8 ft of right-of-way for each lane [9.25 and 9.28].

The StaRR-car system probably would be operated with the cars owned by a company or the city and rented to the users. The automatic car would have the unique ability of offering privacy to "captive" passengers, that is, those forced to take some form of transit because they are incapable (too young, old, poor, or handicapped) of driving an automobile. However, the manually operated system also would allow physically and legally able people to drive a vehicle, thereby giving them the freedom of movement usually associated with the private automobile. If this system were to become popular, it would provide the additional advantage of reduced parking requirements in various areas, especially in central business districts. Unencumbered vehicles could be sent to remote areas for temporary storage.

Aerotrain. Developed by the Société De L'Aerotrain in France, the aerotrain, has a fuselage resembling an aircraft and has two gas turbine engines with a propellor at the top rear of the vehicle. It is of light alloy construction and moves on a thin cushion of air along a T-shaped guideway made of prestressed concrete. This system has been tested on an 11.2-mile track near Orleans since 1969.

The guideway for the aerotrain would cost about $800,000/mile for a double track above ground. The vehicle, seating 180 passengers, would cost $500,000 to $600,000, while operating costs would run about $0.026/passenger mile [9.33 and 9.29]. The top speed of the vehicle appears to be 250 mph, with minimum headways between vehicles usually ranging from 25 to 75 seconds. Under these conditions the guideway would have a capacity between 4,000 and 11,500 passengers/hr [9.34].

This type of system, substituting a thin layer of air for wheel-to-rail support, eliminates rolling resistance while operating more quietly at higher speeds. Care

The aerotrain interurban vehicle on its test track. (*Société De L'Aerotrain*)

would have to be taken under high wind and snow conditions, however, and large obstructions on the track could prove dangerous.

Gravity-Vacuum Transit (Mark IV B/15 urban version). The Gravity-Vacuum Transit System, developed by Tube Transit Corporation in California, employs a long, cylindrical vehicle in an air-evacuated tube. The tube would run underground to considerable depths, with the vehicle operating under the force of gravity somewhat like a pendulum.

The guideway for such a system probably would cost about $15 million/mile. The average speed of travel, with 3 miles between stops and a delay of 20 seconds at each stop, would be around 93 mph. Each vehicle, seating 64 passengers, would have a total capacity of 128 passengers, thereby allowing the guideway to accommodate 46,000 passengers/hr [9.36 and 9.27].

This technology appears to be capable of operating in urban areas on grades of 15 percent and at depths as great as 900 ft. The fact that the system operates completely beneath ground is advantageous in that it is not subject to surface congestion conditions. It appears to be costly this way, although the developers claimed lower costs, due to the small tunnel section, than for comparable subways. In addition, emergency procedures would present a problem if the vehicle stopped at the bottom of the tube.

The control of gravity-vacuum transit trains would be accomplished externally through variation of pneumatic pressure in front and back of the trains. A computer would be required to process real-time data concerning the progress of each train and to issue commands to the various control elements. Energy requirements would seem to be relatively low for this system since "gravity" would

Gravity-Vacuum Transit System. (*L. K. Edwards, Tube Transit Corporation*)

be doing most of the propulsion and braking. However, no full scale prototype has been developed yet to test the technology in a real world situation.

Minirail. The minirail, developed by Habegger Maschinen Fabrik in Switzerland and Universal Mobility, Inc., of Salt Lake City, Utah, is comprised of a series of small cars joined into trains that run on top of a small rail. It has seen service as a transportation system in the Swiss Exhibition at Lausanne in 1964, at Expo in Montreal in 1967, in Charlotte, North Carolina, and elsewhere.

The minirail has a top speed of 28 mph when stations are spaced at approximately 0.3-mile intervals. Each car accommodates up to 12 seated passengers, with a train usually being made up of 9 cars. Under these conditions, the guideway would have a capacity of 6,000 passengers/hr in each direction [9.41 and 9.32].

The minirail is suitable as a distribution system in central business districts, at airports, and other areas of intense activity, accommodating many trips normally made on foot. The system has been designed to run through buildings.

Major advantages of this technology are the relatively low costs of construction and operation (an automatic version would require no on-board operating personnel), unobtrusive appearance, and relatively clean, quiet operation. One disadvantage it shares with other pneumatically tired vehicle systems (e.g., automobiles) is its particular susceptibility to snow and ice.

Unimobil/Habegger monorail (minirail) system. (*Universal Mobility, Inc.*)

Dial-a-bus. The dial-a-bus sytem, a taxicab-type service using a small bus to collect a number of callers individually, is in use in several cities and rural areas around the world. It is designed so that a potential user calls a special telephone number, giving his origin and destination. A dispatcher aided by a computer then combines the origin-destination pair for the caller with those of others to form a group whose travel would comprise a reasonably direct route for the bus.

Haddonfield, New Jersey, dial-a-ride bus. (*New Jersey Department of Transportation*)

Interior and appurtenances, Haddonfield, New Jersey, dial-a-ride bus. (*New Jersey Department of Transportation*)

The estimated cost of 1,500 of these buses is about $27,096,000, with the operational cost averaging about $0.096/passenger mile. The top speed of the bus is 60 mph, but average trip speeds would be about 16 mph. The proposed buses have a capacity of 20 passengers [9.42 and 9.43].

A network of this type would be most effective in low-density areas, offering passengers a mode of door-to-door transit presently not available. Travel times would be slightly higher than for the private automobile, and, because of the additional labor costs, fares would need to be somewhere between that for the usual transit service and that for a taxi. Many people thus would be unable to afford dial-a-bus service.

Multi-Modal Capsule Systems.   The Multi-Modal Capsule System, developed by General Motors, is comprised of a group of small passenger capsules transported by special highway vehicles similar to flat bed trucks. This system is designed to be in operation in 1975 [9.44].

The guideway is estimated to cost about $630,000/mile and create an associated operating cost of about $0.032/passenger mile. The top speed for the Multi-Modal Capsule is intended to be 65 mph, with an average trip speed (including waiting time) of 22.1 mph. Following the design employed in test applications, the actual guideway probably will have access points spaced at approximately 5-mile intervals. Each capsule would have a capacity of two passengers, permitting unusual privacy for a mass transit system [9.24].

Multi-modal Capsules. (*General Motors Research Laboratories*)

Duo-rail subway system: Le Metro.   Le Metro is the subway system in Montreal. It was planned to give efficient service along principal arteries of the city, following closely the main streams of traffic. Use has been made of streets adjacent to the major arteries in order to prevent traffic congestion and interference with

Montreal (duo-rail) subway vehicle. (*Montreal Urban Community Transit Commission*)

local business. Work began on the network in May, 1962 with the system put into service in October, 1966. The guideway cost $250/linear ft in rock, $900/linear ft in earth, and $600 to $1,000/linear ft in open cut areas [9.44].

Average trip speed on the system is 22 mph, with headways between trains in peak periods of 130 seconds. The 15.5-mile network is serviced by 26 stations. A nine-car train has a capacity of 1,500 passengers, giving a capacity of 60,000 passengers/hr/lane in each direction. The use of pneumatic tires on the vehicles, and concrete rails, as compared to steel wheels and rails on most subways, results in a smoother ride, a substantial decrease in noise [9.44], and greater acceleration and deceleration.

Dashaveyor. Developed by the Dashaveyor Company of California and the Bendix Corporation, the Dashaveyor is a system which can be used to transport people or material on any grade (or even upside down, if so desired). A 5.5-mile facility currently is in operation for transporting copper ore in a copper mine in Michigan.

A Dashaveyor system for transporting people would be designed for a top speed of 30 mph, with the module seating 12 passengers and having a total capacity of 30 passengers [9.31]. The Dashaveyor utilizes computerized command with the control systems located on the wayside. Under these conditions it would give a fairly high capacity and low cost of operation. It also would be pollution-free and fairly quiet. Its primary use would be in major activity centers.

Motor bus (urban). The typical motor bus employed in urban areas in the United States carries 50 seated and up to 25 standing passengers, usually according to a fixed schedule along a fixed route. It costs about $31,200, with the cost of operation and maintenance being approximately $0.65/vehicle mile. A bus can be either gasoline, diesel, or propane powered [9.46 and 9.53].

Dashaveyor vehicle. (*U.S. Department of Transportation, Urban Mass Transportation Administration*)

Since the motor bus can operate on existing streets and highways, it does not require a special guideway, although exclusive bus lanes have been constructed in more than 20 regions, such as in the Los Angeles, Dallas, Chicago, San Francisco, and Northern Virginia areas.

The motor bus operating on the regular highway network is one of the most economical modes of mass transportation because an exclusive guideway does not have to be constructed and maintained. In addition, bus routes can be changed at relatively little cost, bus service usually is very reliable (e.g., in bad weather), and, of course, does not require passenger operation or maintenance. These latter two advantages are particularly significant to those who cannot afford or are not able to employ a private automobile. As for disadvantages, many buses are old, smelly, and dirty. Vandalism has caused many bus companies to go to hard seats and visually

Urban motor bus. (*General Motors Corporation, Truck and Coach Division*)

unattractive decor. Passengers who stand are subject to sudden and uncomfortable lurches. Privacy is lacking.

Exclusive bus lanes: Shirley Highway. One "technology" that seems to have a lot of promise is that of exclusive bus lanes being set aside on expressways. The idea of installing such lanes on the Shirley Highway in the northern Virginia suburbs of Washington, D.C. was conceived by the U.S. Department of Transportation, the Virginia Department of Highways, and the Washington Metropolitan Area Council of Governments. This experimental project, which will be completed in 1974, consists of 9 miles of exclusive express bus lanes. The first section was opened in September, 1969, with the entire project open in April, 1971 [9.50]. The buses employed seat 47 passengers, which means that the express lanes are capable of accommodating about 1,200 buses, or 60,000 passengers/hr.

A facility of this type should result in time savings for both the transit users and the auto drivers, and also should relieve some of the downtown parking requirements. Costs of construction are much lower than would be the case for a mass transit guideway by itself. Another advantage is that the lanes can be switched to alternate uses if demands change.

Shirley Highway exclusive bus lanes. (*U.S. Department of Transportation, Federal Highway Administration*)

Hovercraft. Developed in Britain and manufactured there by organizations such as the British Hovercraft Corporation Ltd., Hovermarine Transport Ltd., and Vosper Thornycroft Ltd., the hovercraft is a vehicle gaining support over land or water by means of an air cushion. Various designs of craft exist: amphibious, semiamphibious, and sidewall. Only the amphibious craft can travel over a variety of surfaces apart from water and retain no contact with the surface other than the skirt. Hovercraft may operate at a "hover height" of up to 8 ft above water level for the largest craft, SR.N4, for example, although for most craft it is usually 2 or 3 ft.

SR.N4 hovercraft. (*British Hovercraft Corporation*)

The "Mountbatten"-class SR.N4 hovercraft is the largest in the world and weighs almost 200 tons. It measures 130 ft long, 78 ft wide, and when hovering is 45 ft high. Five craft have been constructed and all are engaged in ferry operations between England and France across the Dover Straits. Each craft can carry up to 280 passengers and 37 cars and operates at speeds of up to 70 knots. Normally crossings take 30 to 40 minutes. Almost 1.5 million passengers and 250,000 vehicles are carried annually by these hovercraft services, which began on August 1, 1968.

This type of transport is particularly useful for traversing water in areas where bridges or other fixed links are not possible, and where shallow water prevents ships from taking shorter, more direct routes between landmasses or across rivers. It is also possible to take advantage of the craft's amphibious qualities to site new terminals outside existing port or city areas and usually only simple slipways need be used. The hovercraft's faster speed and ability to take shorter routes may mean that service capacity can be better tailored to traffic demand as well as offering more frequent timings [9.48 and 9.49].

9.2.3 Summary of Characteristics of Various Technologies

The preceding discussion necessarily has been short and not too inclusive. Table 9.4 provides a more exhaustive description of the characteristics of some of the technologies discussed here as well as some additional ones. It should be noted that measurements or estimates of some characteristics may not exactly equal those presented in the previous section. This is due primarily to the use of different references and to latter developments of the corresponding technologies.

9.3 FORMULATION OF A PEDESTRIAN AID TRANSIT SYSTEM

A good example of a fairly creative attempt to develop a new transportation system is that by the Working Party on the Introduction of a New Mode of Transport in Central London. In their publication *An Aid to Pedestrian Movement* [9.13], they go into detail on the stages in the synthesis process, the factors and constraints considered in each stage, and the guidelines developed as a result. In the interest of displaying these components of the synthesis process, we will summarize the study here.

9.3.1 The Working Party Study

The investigation was divided into twelve major sections:

1. The "transport gap"
2. Route principles
3. Effect on developments
4. Possible routes
5. Potential demand
6. System concepts and journey times
7. Flexibility and reliability
8. Capacity
9. Stations and depots
10. Comfort
11. Environmental impact
12. Costs and revenues

This classification itself might prove useful in creating a new system since the planner must identify at the start the kinds of elements for which he must have a concern (see Chap. 4 for goals, objectives, and constraints and this chapter for transportation system components). Also, as part of the planning endeavor, it usually is necessary to state some generally accepted objectives. In this study they seemed to be:

1. A maximum walking distance of 3 min (690 ft) should be observed.
2. The system should serve as many high activity zones as possible.
3. There should be minimum initial provision of track.
4. Room for extension should be allowed.
5. Connections should be made to present transport stations (suburban rail, subway, car parks).
6. Visitors to London should be considered.

The final and perhaps most important objective was to fill the so-called "transport gap." This relates to travel ranging in length from about 0.25 to 1.5 miles.[2] Shorter trips can be done by foot, longer ones by automobile (or taxi, bus, subway, and so on). In between lies a gap where it is inconvenient to go by any of these modes.

---

[2] Generally 50 percent of all urban travel is less than 3.0 miles in length [9.14, p. 31].

Table 9.4   Characteristics of Selected Mass Transit Systems

| Characteristic | Conventional systems for low- | |
	Automobile	Bus (city streets)
Mode of operation	—	—
Developer	—	—
Status	—	—
All-weather system	No	No
Restricted-access right-of-way	No	No
Average wait for service, peak hour (min)	None	1–2.5
Ride quality	Fair–good	Poor
Average wait for service, off-peak hour (min)	None	7.5
Noise to passengers	Fair	Poor
Adaptability to load	Good	Fair
Maximum total capacity (passengers/hr)	2,930/lane	6,000/lane
Maximum seated capacity (passengers/hr)	2,930/lane	4,000/lane
Grades (percent)	10	10
Fire hazard	Yes	Yes
Turn radius (ft)	20	40
Installation flexibility	Poor	Poor
Adaptability to short haul	Good	Good
Service reliability	Fair–good	Poor
Maintenance	Fair	Fair–good
Horsepower/passenger seat	10–30	4
Operating cost/passenger-mile (¢)	10	6–8
Right-of-way width, one-way traffic (ft)	12	12
Right-of-way cross section, one-way traffic (sq ft)	96	120
Right-of-way volume/mile/peak hour, seated passenger (cu ft)	173	158
Right-of-way area/mile/peak hour, seated passenger (sq ft)	21.6	15.8
Parking problem	Yes	No
Adaptability to automation	Poor	Poor
Adaptability to automatic structures fare collection	n.a.	Poor
Air pollution	Yes	Yes
Vibration to host community	Good	Fair
Noise to host community	Fair	Poor
Cleanliness for host community	Poor	Poor
Safety from criminal acts	Good	Good
Regulation and control	Poor	Poor
Privacy	Yes	No

density areas	Proposed systems for nonstop service				
Bus (freeways)	Fichter system	StaRR-car	Teletrans	Transdrive	Uniflow
—	Automatic small car	Dual-mode, small car	Automatic tram-like vehicle	Dual-mode automobile	Small car in pneumatic tube
—	Donn Fichter	Alden Self-transit systems	Teletrans	Transdrive	North star R&D institute
—	Concept	Prototype vehicle; short length of track built	Prototype vehicle; short length of track built	Concept	Small-scale car built
No	No	No	Yes	No	Yes
No	Yes	No	Yes	Yes	Yes
1–2.5	Minimal	Minimal	Minimal	*	Minimal
Fair	None	None	None	None	None
7.5	Poor–fair	Fair–good	Fair–good	Poor–fair	Good
Poor	Fair	Fair–good	Good	Fair	Good
Fair	Good	Good	Good	Good	Good
13,500/lane	5,140	37,200	30,200	17,600	31,700
9,000/lane	5,140	37,200	30,200	17,600	31,700
10	10	10	100	8	3
Yes	No	No	No	Yes	No
40	50	350	350	350	350
Poor	Good	Good	Good	Good	Good
Poor–fair	Good	Good	Good	Poor	Good
Poor	Good	Fair–good	Good	Fair–good	Good
Fair–good	Poor	Poor–fair	Fair	Fair	Good
4	3.75	3.33	n.a.	n.a.	2.35
5–7	2.6	1.3–2.6	1–4	3.85	1.6–4.6
12	3.5	8	5	7	5
120	26	56	40	90	50
70.4	26.7	7.96	7.0	27	8.33
7.04	3.6	1.14	0.88	2.1	0.83
No	No	Yes	No	Yes	No
Poor	Fair	Fair	Good	Fair	Good
Poor	Good	Good	Good	Good	Good
Yes	No	No	No	No	No
Fair	Good	Good	Good	Fair–good	Good
Fair	Fair–good	Good	Good	Fair–good	Good
Poor	Fair	Poor	Good	Poor	Good
Good	Poor–fair	Good	Good	Good	Good
Poor	Good	Poor	Good	Good	Good
No	Yes	Yes	Yes	Yes	Semi

Table 9.4   Characteristics of Selected Mass Transit Systems (*Continued*)

	Proposed systems	
Characteristic	Articulated train system	Bingham system
Mode of operation	Small cars on moving belt	Automatic bus-like vehicle
Developer	E. G. Knolle	S. H. Bingham Assoc.
Status	Small-scale model built	Concept
All-weather system	Yes	No
Restricted-access right-of-way	Yes	No
Average wait for service, peak hour (min)	None	0.75
Ride quality	None	15
Average wait for service, off-peak hour (min)	Poor	Fair–good
Noise to passengers	Fair	Fair
Adaptability to load	Poor	Poor
Maximum total capacity (passengers/hr)	20,000	60,000
Maximum seated capacity (passengers/hr)	20,000	30,000
Grades (percent)	10	8
Fire hazard	No	No
Turn radius (ft)	350	200
Installation flexibility	Fair–good	Poor
Adaptability to short haul	Good	Poor
Service reliability	Good	Good
Maintenance	Poor	Fair
Horsepower/passenger seat	n.a.	4
Operating cost/passenger-mile (¢)	Very high	2–3
Right-of-way width, one-way traffic (ft)	5	14
Right-of-way cross section, one-way traffic (sq ft)	25	168
Right-of-way volume/mile/peak hour, seated passenger (cu ft)	6.6	29.5
Right-of-way area/mile/peak hour, seated passenger (sq ft)	1.32	2.46
Parking problem	No	No
Adaptability to automation	Good	Fair
Adaptability to automatic structures fare collection	Poor	Poor
Air pollution	No	No
Vibration to host community	Fair	Poor
Noise to host community	Fair	Poor
Cleanliness for host community	Good	Fair
Safety from criminal acts	Good	Poor
Regulation and control	Good	Fair
Privacy	Yes	No

for multistop service

Carveyor	Horizontal elevator	Monocab	Mono tri rail	Pneumatic tube
Passive cars on conveyor belt	Elevator monorail combination	Cars on monorail	High-speed elevated train	Large vehicles in tube
Stephens-Adamson Mfg.	Goodell Monorail, Inc.	E. O. Halton	R. M. Galsoe	H. C. Hickman
Engineering design;	Development	Full-scale cab built	Concept	Concept
No	No	Yes	No	Yes
Yes	Yes	Yes	Yes	Yes
None	0.5	*	0.75	2
None	5	None	7.5	15
Fair–good	Fair	Poor–fair	Fair–good	Fair
Fair	Fair	Fair	Fair	Good
Poor	Fair	Good	Fair	Poor
14,000	5,600	37,200	21,000	24,000
7,000	2,800	37,200	14,000	12,000
10	10	10	10	10
No	Yes	No	No	No
80	80	25–150	150	786
Good	Fair	Good	Fair	Poor
Good	Fair	Good	Poor–fair	Poor
Good	Fair	Good	Fair	Good
Fair	Poor–fair	Fair	Poor–fair	Poor
1.7	n.a.	n.a.	10	n.a.
1.5–2.5	5	3–4	4–5	Very high
6	10	7	12	15
72	160	60	144	247
54.3	302	8.5	54.3	108.7
4.53	18.9	0.995	4.52	6.6
No	No	No	No	No
Good	Good	Good	Fair	Good
Poor	Poor	Poor	Poor	Poor
No	Yes	No	No	No
Good	Fair	Good	Fair	Fair–good
Fair	Fair	Good	Fair	Good
Fair	Fair	Poor–fair	Fair	Good
Poor	Poor	Fair	Good	Poor
Good	Fair	Good	Fair	Fair
Semi	No	Semi	No	No

Table 9.4 Characteristics of Selected Mass Transit Systems (*Continued*)

	Proposed systems	
Characteristic	Safege monorail	Scherer monobeam
Mode of operation	Monorail at New York World's Fair	High-speed elevated train
Developer	American Machine and Foundry	Scherer Monobeam
Status	Operating in Paris; U.S. licensee is General Electric	Model built
All-weather system	Yes	No
Restricted-access right-of-way	Yes	Yes
Average wait for service, peak hour (min)	0.75	0.75
Ride quality	7.5	7.5
Average wait for service, off-peak hour (min)	Fair	Fair–good
Noise to passengers	Fair–good	Fair
Adaptability to load	Poor	Poor
Maximum total capacity (passengers/hr)	60,000	60,000
Maximum seated capacity (passengers/hr)	30,000	30,000
Grades (percent)	12	8
Fire hazard	No	No
Turn radius (ft)	100	100
Installation flexibility	Fair	Fair
Adaptability to short haul	Poor	Poor
Service reliability	Fair	Fair
Maintenance	Poor–fair	Poor–fair
Horsepower/passenger seat	n.a.	2.14
Operating cost/passenger-mile (¢)	3.5–4	4–5
Right-of-way width, one-way traffic (ft)	10	11
Right-of-way cross section, one-way traffic (sq ft)	120	120
Right-of-way volume/mile/peak hour, seated passenger (cu ft)	21.1	21.1
Right-of-way area/mile/peak hour, seated passenger (sq ft)	1.76	1.94
Parking problem	No	No
Adaptability to automation	Fair	Fair
Adaptability to automatic structures fare collection	Poor	Poor
Air pollution	No	No
Vibration to host community	Fair	Fair
Noise to host community	Fair	Fair
Cleanliness for host community	Fair	Fair
Safety from criminal acts	Good	Poor
Regulation and control	Fair	Fair
Privacy	No	No

*Unpredictable.
Source: [9.28].

for multistop service

Skylift	Standard rail (elevated)	Tex train	Transit Expressway
Automatic small cars	—	Automatic platform trains	Automatic bus-like vehicle
Lockheed Aircraft Service	—	S. H. Seidman	Westinghouse Electric
Concept	—	Concept	Demonstrated
Yes	No	Yes	No
Yes	No	Yes	Yes
*	0.75	None	2
None	7.5	None	2
Good	Fair	Fair	Fair–good
Fair	Fair	Good	Fair–good
Good	Poor	Fair	Fair
9,400	60,000	38,400	6,300
9,400	15,000	38,400	2,520
3.3	8	10	10
No	No	No	No
60	150	350	150
Good	Poor	Fair	Fair
Good	Fair	Good	Poor–fair
Good	Fair–good	Good	Good
Fair	Fair	Good	Fair
1.5	n.a.	n.a.	4.29
4–6	3.2	1.5–2.5	2–3
6	13	9	11
48	150	135	110
27	52.8	18.5	69.1
3.37	4.58	1.24	6.91
No	No	No	No
Good	Fair	Good	Good
Poor	Poor	Poor	Poor
No	No	No	No
Good	Poor	Good	Good
Good	Poor	Good	Good
Poor–fair	Poor	Good	Fair
Fair	Poor	Fair–good	Poor
Good	Fair	Good	Fair
Semi	No	Semi	No

Based on these objectives (not stated specifically as such in the report), eight "route principles" were developed. These are quoted in full here since they provide useful guidelines for the synthesis endeavor.

1. In any attempt to install a new transport system in the existing fabric of central London serious limitations on space would apply at street level because of the dense vehicular and pedestrian traffic which is already carried and the network of utility services which exists just below ground level. To install a segregated system at ground level would mean that conventional traffic would have to be re-routed at intersections and frequent pedestrian ways constructed from one side of the street to the other, either by bridge or subway. On the other hand an elevated system would need to provide the minimum statutory headroom of 5.03 m (16 ft 6 in.) over the highway so as to give clearance to buses and other large vehicles, and the supporting columns would need to occupy positions in which they did not obstruct either vehicular or pedestrian traffic significantly. Provision would also need to be made for stations.

2. A further consideration which would have to be borne in mind is the existence of conservation areas in the central area. Although these areas are not necessarily "hard" in planning terms, their penetration by any new transport system would have to be considered in relation to the character of the area concerned and the physical characteristics of the system under consideration.

3. Although the likelihood of installing a new system within the existing fabric need not be completely ruled out, particularly now that much lighter transport systems can be envisaged, in the light of the foregoing any new system should be regarded basically as one which could be integrated successfully into the framework of major redevelopments, that is, having regard to the location of such areas, to the necessity to avoid routing through the existing fabric, and to the anticipated time sequence of the redevelopment of central London.

4. Within these areas of redevelopment it might be possible for the buildings and shopping malls to be designed around a system so that it played an important part in their functioning. Stations could be situated either within or behind the new buildings but the route could emerge into the main pedestrian areas between stations so that passengers would be able to see and enjoy the surrounding environment, and be brought into contact with the shops, restaurants, theatres, hotels, and other amenities situated along the route. It is clear in these circumstances that the possibility of suspending a system below the pedestrian deck could be disregarded, and that in order to provide this flexibility of routing, and also so that it would be able to skirt existing "hard" development where necessary, a comparatively tight turning circle might be required.

5. With a new transport system designed basically to integrate satisfactorily within redevelopments, the question would also arise as to whether it

should be at pedestrian level or placed overhead. The prime advantage of a system at pedestrian level would be its ease of accessibility for intending passengers. On the other hand, it would have the disadvantage of dividing the pedestrian areas through which it passed. An overhead system might overcome this difficulty and avoid any vehicle/pedestrian conflict while at the same time taking up less space at pedestrian level. It might also be possible to move the structures so that alterations could be made to short lengths of the route because of such things as redevelopments with the minimum of interference to pedestrian movement. On balance, therefore, the indications are that an overhead system might be preferable to one at pedestrian level.

6. Use of an overhead system would necessitate careful investigation being made into the siting of stations. Should a system be brought down to pedestrian deck level at stations or should intending passengers be taken up? The provision of stations at pedestrian level could give rise to considerable technical and operational problems, particularly if standing passengers were carried. For example, additional stress would be placed on braking systems and power units in having to overcome gradients when entering and leaving stations. Journey times could be longer, and the continual rising and falling at stations could provide an unpleasant journey for passengers. Furthermore, where stations are situated within redevelopments, the cost of the extra space required to accommodate the track gradients into and out of stations could prove prohibitive. Elevated stations might overcome these difficulties and although it could be argued that ideally stations should be sited at pedestrian level, in all probability the great majority of stations might have to be situated at mode level. In some circumstances, however, as for example where there were natural changes of level, it might prove possible to site stations at pedestrian level.

7. On the question of stations generally, in view of the probably high capital cost involved, including land costs, station sizes would have to be kept to the minimum practicable.

8. If it can be accepted that an opportunity appears to exist for the introduction of a new mode of transport capable of complimenting existing modes in circumstances where they might be inadequate or unable to penetrate, the next step would be to select in broad principles the areas through which it might operate. Rights-of-way would need to be protected, and it would be important that firm guidance was given as early as possible to architects involved in redevelopments through which a system might pass so that these rights-of-way could be protected and the financial implications evaluated. It would be essential that no major redevelopments were carried out in such a way that they blocked the best routes, unless a system and the buildings were so designed that the system could pass through the building. In such circumstances, limitations on the size of the envelope of the system immediately become apparent.

A significant point to be noted about these principles is the attention given initially (and somewhat predominantly) to land use and environmental concerns. The Working Party apparently recognized from the beginning that synthesis could not be accomplished by first determining where routes ought to go to save the *users* the most inconvenience. The solution resulting from this approach probably would have required much relocation of buildings, significant visual intrusion, and, in general, a level of inconvenience to the nonuser that probably would not have been tolerated. Instead, an immediate effort was made to locate routes in redevelopment areas *in the general vicinity* of the optimum user routes. In these areas, the impacts would not be as crucial and in some cases would have a positive effect.

The Working Party also appeared to anticipate that with such a great emphasis on the use of redevelopment areas, there would be a heavy dependency on developers, especially insofar as their reactions to potential plans and timetables for improvements were concerned. The next part of the synthesis process thus dealt with potential difficulties that could arise in these areas. First, there were land costs. An effort had to be made to encourage developers to absorb most of these costs based on the incentives of increased land values and commercial sales and improved appearance.

Timetables were especially difficult to judge. Often developments are not built on schedule (if at all), and a transportation system tied into such potential developments obviously would be subject to the same uncertainties. To allow for these possibilities, the Working Party looked at several alternate locations for routes.

The next two steps in the synthesis process were those of specifying route locations in more detail, then estimating the potential demand for the services provided. It was thought that a pilot study would be needed initially because of the uncertainty about demands, costs, impacts, and the progress of future redevelopment plans. If successful, the pilot project could be expanded in coordination with redevelopment efforts. Several full scale route plans were tested, however. The primary factors considered in the location of routes were:

    a. Connection with rail and subway stations,
    b. Closeness to a major arts complex,
    c. Avoidance of areas with architectural character,
    d. Possible installation problems,
    e. Possible areas of redevelopment,
    f. Availability of alternate crossing of the Thames,
    g. Access to theaters, movies, major shopping and tourist areas, and
    h. Possibility of later extensions of routes.

Of course, potential ridership also was a major factor in route location. Estimating this ridership proved to be a difficult task. It was necessary to predict the number of passengers on the proposed system who previously would have been pedestrians or bus, taxi, auto, subway, or rail riders. Moreover, there was the possibility of people (especially tourists) being *induced* to make more trips because of the increased transport service. Unfortunately no well-tested and reliable models existed to predict mode choice and induced traffic for the situation being studied, so most predictions were made under somewhat arbitrary assumptions. For example, it was assumed that all passengers on bus trips wholly within the limits of the network would transfer to the new system.

After having specified possible route locations and corresponding traffic volumes, the Working Group evaluated several possible technologies to be used on the route. These included low speed belts, continuous trains, and independent vehicular systems. The first two were eliminated from consideration. The moving belt proved to be slow (2 mph) and had serious limitations on curvature (500 ft minimum when superelevated) while the continuous train was felt to require acceleration/deceleration structures that were too large. The operation of the independent vehicle system then was simulated under various conditions of network switching capabilities, and corresponding journey times were calculated.

The next step was to consider various vehicle types and sizes and the resulting capacities under different headway and station stopping time conditions. It was felt that, at least during rush hours, some people had to stand, otherwise the system could not possibly support itself financially. With standing, the turning radii would have to be 25 ft at a minimum (for passenger comfort). Actual capacities were taken to be 66 percent of predicted, theoretical capacities because of daily variations in demand, station stopping times, weather conditions, accidents, and so on. Three car trains were anticipated, although it had yet to be determined if they would cause a visual intrusion or would fit into the stations.

Stations were preliminarily designed so as to fit within new buildings at mode level. Consideration was given to ways of loading and unloading trains, safety zones and capacity, passenger information systems, revenue collection, and need for attendants to repair breakdowns and reduce vandalism. Thought was also given to a process by which potential passengers could be monitored, then metered, so that stations (and the system as a whole) would not get overcrowded.

User comfort was judged on the basis of four major factors:

1. Acceleration, deceleration, and jerk rates both laterally and longitudinally;
2. Degree of body support;
3. Heating; and
4. Ease of entry and exit from the vehicle.

One result of this part of the study was that the lateral acceleration rate was limited to 8 ft/sec^2, a not uncomfortable level for most people. Heating was felt to be a difficult problem in vehicles with large doors that were opening constantly.

The final two sections of the study dealt with the environmental impact of the system and its expected costs and revenues. In the environmental impact section, such items as noise, visual intrusion, vibration (external), and fumes and dirt were taken into account. A vehicle with electrical propulsion and air or pneumatic tire suspension was assumed, so that most of the potential environmental problems would be eliminated. Visual intrusion (and over-shadowing) were checked by taking pictures at critical points on the proposed system routes and making sketches from the pictures with the system overlayed.

The cost and revenue balance appeared to be somewhat unhealthy. Using two proposed pricing schemes, the Working Group found that in both cases traffic receipts would not even cover operating costs much less capital costs. In addition, there was an unfavorable impact on London Transport services, so that the overall effect on public transport finance was sizably negative. Of course the estimates of ridership could be quite conservative, but it is doubtful that the new transit system would ever pay for itself entirely.

9.3.2   Comments on the Working Group Study

The preceding discussion has been an attempt to summarize the main points of the Working Group Study for a "people-mover" system in Central London. It is difficult in an actual study to separate the setting-of-objectives stage from the evaluation stage or from the transportation synthesis stage, which is of concern here. Subsequently, there may be some confusion as to what constitutes the solution generation or *synthesis* stage. In the study outlined above, synthesis was shown primarily through the process by which the various transportation system elements were brought together and through the identification of factors of primary concern in each stage of the process.

Looking first at the factors, we find that consideration was given to such diverse items as structural weight of the guideway, scheduling of redevelopment plans, land value increases, and effect on other transport systems. Quite obviously, a useful synthesis of transportation elements can be much enhanced by taking into account a wide variety of factors that would appear to be important to different citizens and citizen groups. From these considerations then comes a set of general principles (e.g., the route principles) that can be used as guides in the planning endeavor.

The nature and sequencing of stages in the synthesis process also is of importance. The stages correspond roughly to the general elements of the transportation system (vehicles, guideways, terminals, controls—Sec. 9.1) and to the general types of objectives (transportation service and impact). The sequencing of these stages in the study proceeds something as follows:

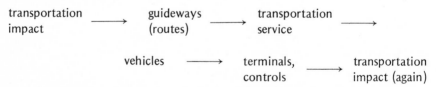

As was brought out earlier, the first stage in the process was not directed primarily to the servicing of traffic. Instead thought was given to possible acceptable locations (e.g., redevelopment areas) of routes somewhere in the vicinity of the best user service locations. In the next stage, attention was given to the possible reactions of renewal area developers. Then (and only then) was consideration given to more precise locations of routes for the users and to the travel produced as a result. Also of interest is the fact that the routes and general guideway configurations were chosen before the vehicle type was specified. Subsequently, the vehicle type was used to dictate in large measure the type of stations and controls needed. Finally, environmental impacts and revenues and costs were estimated (note also that pricing schemes were considered almost last in the process).

In conclusion, we have found in the Working Group's study one type of process for combining transportation elements to form a system having certain service characteristics and impacts. This process may serve as a guide for future endeavors of a similar nature.

9.4 GENERATION OF SOLUTIONS AT THE METROPOLITAN LEVEL

An approach to system generation at the metropolitan level must respond to the demands placed on the transportation planner, especially at this juncture of the planning process. The goal of the generation phase can be stated as the creation of alternative plans (or courses of action) that satisfy as best possible the goals of the project.

The phrase *satisfy as best as possible the goals* needs to be fully understood as it applies to public planning. Transportation planning, like other public planning, often must be conducted in a "goldfish bowl" where it is observed intently by many groups—public agencies, elected officials, special interests, civic associations, businesses and families—affected actually or potentially by the planning effort. Each group has its sets of goals and attitudes—often conflicting with those of other groups—which it tries to impose on the planners. The complexity of transportation planning problems is greatly compounded by the range of goals to be served, the vitalness of the goals to the groups holding them, and the conflicts between these goals. While it is the function of the political system to resolve conflicts between groups, the planner cannot escape pressures to create solutions that will bridge the conflicts, or at least to maintain credibility with the different groups. Every reasonable effort must be made to serve their goals.

9.4.1 Special Requirements for Solution Generation

In any case the demands of complex transportation problems place certain special requirements for creativity, relevance, political credibility and economy, and effectiveness of effort on the planner or engineer in the synthesis phase. Seven such requirements are identified here:

1. Clear definition of project goals, including some resolution of goal conflicts (Chap. 4).
2. A *strategy* to balance the conflicting demands for (a) consideration of broad range of relevant factors within (b) the constraints of time, staff, and money.
3. An *information system* of all relevant and available information, including the necessary analyses and forecasts (Chaps. 5, 6, and 7).

4. Organization and presentation of this information in a form meaningful and "instantly" available for the planmaking task.
5. Design of alternatives relative to the goals.
6. Documentation of design decisions.
7. An effective feedback relationship between the plan synthesis phase and the plan testing and evaluation phases.

As noted previously several of these requirements are discussed in some depth elsewhere in this text. In this section they are related specifically to the metropolitan synthesis stage, with examples drawn from several transportation systems planning endeavors.

The first three requirements, relating to goals, strategy, and information, would largely be fulfilled in preceding stages of the transportation planning or problem solving process. The requirement of goal definition and resolution corresponds to the situation noted above that most complex transportation problems involve multiple, conflicting goals. A solution that satisfies one goal may adversely affect another. This dilemma is not always easily resolved when faced by a single individual and is compounded when multiple public groups are also involved.

Technical devices for resolving goal conflicts through combining, ranking, or weighing goals are dicussed in Chap. 4 and [9.14 and 9.54]. Sometimes these devices are ignored and goals are deliberately blurred and ambiguous. Often, and we hope increasingly, however, both real and political solutions are served by precise, operational definitions of goals (i.e., criteria that permit measurement of the effectiveness of each alternative in achieving the goals). The sharpening of tensions on the planner or engineer often enhances the possibility of creative solutions that bridge conflicts.

Without goals so sharpened and confirmed with the decision-making body, the planner cannot effectively and efficiently structure the data collection, modeling, plan making, testing, or evaluation phases. Among the devices used to do this in metropolitan transportation systems planning are the following:

1. Combine all goals to the extent they can be measured in dollars into a single cost/benefit ratio (Chap. 8). This device was extensively used until the early 1960's but generally is no longer acceptable [9.55].
2. Use one goal as a decision rule to select the best plan from among those that meet minimum standards with respect to other goals [9.14].
3. Develop effectiveness measures for all goals and set weights as to the importance to be attached to each goal [9.54].
4. Develop effectiveness measures for all goals and rank the goals (See Chap. 4).

The second requirement relates to the strategy needed in part to cope with the major dilemma of complex planning problems. The horns of the dilemma are relevance and feasibility. On the one hand, the numerous relevant goals seem to require use of an overwhelming amount of information. On the other hand, resources of calendar time, staff time and skills, and money are too scarce to permit consideration of all relevant factors. To be effective, the strategy must be set during an initial policy and study design stage to make best use of staff in the data collection stage (where often 70 percent of the budget goes in metropolitan transportation studies) and in the modeling stage so as to provide the best preparation possible for the generation, model use, and evaluation stages.

In several typical studies [9.56, 9.57, 9.58], the dilemma between relevance, complexity, and incommensurate calendar time was resolved basically by this strategy:

1. Assume continuation of existing land use trends and policies of local government (i.e., no exploration of greenbelts, new towns, etc.)
2. Use least cost as a decision rule and minimum standards in respect to other goals (i.e., device 2 above).
3. Concentrate first on developing and evaluating a system of *expressway* corridors. Then do subsequent work on the transit system, the arterial system, and construction scheduling. Leave route location and specification to be accomplished incrementally as scheduled.
4. Use optimum spacing of expressways in relation to future trip density to zero in on the scale of network needed.
5. Test all system and route proposals economically and rapidly by combining them into a "composite network" of corridors.

Requirement three, the need for a data base for systems synthesis, is probably the most obvious. In metropolitan-wide synthesis this means, at a minimum, completion of data collection and usually also of modeling. The latter is desirable for greatest efficiency, as it is important to have as precise a picture as possible of future travel demand before starting preparation of alternate plans. In the Chicago (CATS) and Niagara Frontier Studies this was accomplished by analysis of optimum spacing of urban freeways in relation to anticipated future trip density [9.14].

This optimum spacing analysis usually is carried out as follows. An attempt is made to balance costs of travel against costs of construction of facilities, both freeways and major arterials. Clearly, if it were desired to minimize costs just for travelers, freeways would have to be built at extremely close intervals (e.g., one block apart). On the other hand, if it were desired to minimize construction costs, no freeways or arterials would be built, since the least expensive streets are local ones. The optimum balance between these two, that is, the balance that minimizes the sum of both costs, has been found to be

$$X = 2.24 \sqrt{\frac{C_z}{KDV_{yz}P_s}} \tag{9.1}$$

where X = optimum freeway spacing in miles,
C_z = construction and right-of-way cost of freeways in dollars per mile,
K = a constant capitalizing the value of time, and
D = number of trip destinations per square mile.

Also

$$V_{yz} = \frac{1}{V_y} - \frac{1}{V_z} \tag{9.2}$$

where V_y and V_z are the speeds on arterials and freeways, respectively, (in miles per hour).

In addition

$$P_s = \sum_{i=b}^{n} F_i \tag{9.3}$$

where P_s is the proportion of trips whose length is greater than b, which is the length where trips start to use freeways for some portion of their journeys; F_i is the frequency (proportion) of trips in time internal i.

When the optimum spacing formula was applied in Chicago for 1980 trips, the results, as indicated in Table 9.5, gave spacings of from 2.7 to 7.0 miles [9.14]. When the formula was examined carefully [9.14, pp. 222, 227], it was possible to develop the following generalizations about spacing:

1. If the construction cost per mile of expressways rises, expressways should be spaced farther apart.
2. If the cost of travel increases (for example, if people's time becomes worth more), then it is better to build expressways closer together.
3. Where the densities of vehicular tripmaking are high, expressways should be spaced closer together.
4. If trips become longer on the average, expressways should be built closer together.
5. If the speed of travel on arterial streets is increased (for example, through superior traffic management), then expressways should be built farther apart.

Table 9.5   Minimum Cost Spacing Determinants and Results, Chicago Area, 1980

Ring	Mean distance from loop (miles)	Vehicle trip destinations per square mile (thousands)	Expressway speed (mph)	Arterial speed (mph)	Expressway cost per mile (millions)	Minimum cost spacings for expressways (miles)
2	3.5	28.7	45	15	$11	2.7
3	5.5	25.3	45	15	10	2.8
4	8.5	19.6	50	15	8	2.9
5	11.5	13.4	50	20	6	4.0
6	16.0	9.0	50	25	5	6.3
7	24.0	6.2	50	25	4	7.0

Source: [9.14, p. 222].

To save calendar time, much can be done toward developing alternate plans prior to and subject to completion of the models, which are the testing mechanism. In Fig. 9.1, for example, much of steps 2B, C, and D—the Transportation and Barriers Maps and the Principles Statements—as well as much of the measurement of Corridor Conditions (3C) could be done in advance of completion of Optimum Spacing (2D) or Testing of Alternates (4). The resulting gain of calendar time at the expense of efficiency is a question of strategy for a particular study.

As noted previously, the bulk of the work required to satisfy the first three requirements must be substantially completed before the systems synthesis stage can progress far. This is represented in Fig. 9.1 by step 1. However, readiness for the phase should be reviewed, undone work expedited, and any last minute changes in strategy or tactics made.

Requirement four, organization of data, is represented in Fig. 9.1 by step 2. The purpose of this step is to organize information needed for plan design so as to be (1) most meaningful to the planner or engineer and (2) "instantly" available to him. "Meaningful" organization of information recognizes that the manner in which data are displayed can stimulate ideas for solutions—and facilitate developing and checking them. "Instant availability" is required to reduce the time spent by the planner in securing the particular data he needs. If the data are not conveniently accessible, he may choose to do without them rather than take the time, with a resulting loss in creativity and realism in planning. What is needed is a "planning-oriented information system" in which the relevant information is displayed accessibly, coherently, and comprehensively for the plan-designer.

A plan generation information system is illustrated in Fig. 9.1 in step 2. Each block represents a set of information presented so as to convey to the planner or engineer the parameters of the problem he faces.

A. *Transportation factors map*

    1. Regional influences: Factors beyond the immediate urban area that must be taken into account include existing and potential transportation routes, cities, recreation areas, and other traffic generators, their size and probable growth; new town plans, natural factors shaping growth such as bodies of water and mountains. This information is displayed on a small-scale map so as to encompass an area at least 100 miles in each direction.

    2. Existing transportation facilities: Arterials, expressways, bus lines, rail transit, railroads, airports, ports, and terminal areas. What were the urban transportation facilities in existence at the time of data collection? What facilities have or are being added? What interfaces between modes?

    3. Committed transportation facilities: What proposed facilities must be taken as "givens" in planning new systems? Not always an easy question to answer. The safest indicator is that right-of-way acquisition or construction that has actually started. This map should also show the proposed facilities that are not so firmly committed—those in official

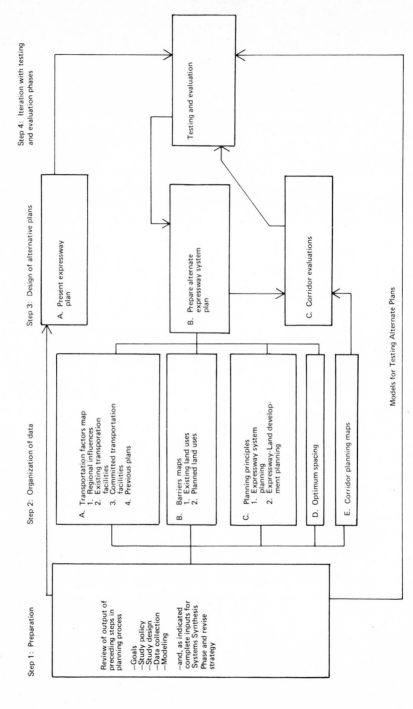

Step 1: Preparation

Review of output of preceding steps in planning process

—Goals
—Study policy
—Study design
—Data collection
—Modeling

—and, as indicated complete inputs for Systems Synthesis Phase and revise strategy

Step 2: Organization of data

A. Transportation factors map
   1. Regional influences
   2. Existing transporation facilities
   3. Committed transportation facilities
   4. Previous plans

B. Barriers maps
   1. Existing land uses
   2. Planned land uses

C. Planning principles
   1. Expressway system planning
   2. Expressway-Land development planning

D. Optimum spacing

E. Corridor planning maps

Models for Testing Alternate Plans

Step 3: Design of alternative plans

A. Present expressway plan

B. Prepare alternate expressway system plan

C. Corridor evaluations

Step 4: Iteration with testing and evaluation phases

Testing and evaluation

Fig. 9.1 Generalized steps for systems generation (synthesis) for metropolitan transportation planning.

plans or improvement programs, or for which engineering plans have been prepared.

In addition to providing the "given" base for the planning of new systems, the committed system performs two other functions: (1) To test the comparative value of alternate immediate improvements, and (2) To provide one alternative for the future, the "do nothing plan," or null hypothesis against which the benefits and costs of other plans can be measured.

4. Previous plans: This map or series of maps depicts historical transportation system or route plans, both those built and those not. In retrospect how realistic were the plans? What are the lessons?

B. *Barrier maps.* This map or series of overlays shows the location of existing or planned land uses that should be avoided by, or sometimes adapted to, or weighed against—new transportation facilities.

1. Existing land uses:

Cemeteries	Forest preserves
Railroad lines and yards	Scenic conservation areas
Public and private institutions	Historic sites
Water and wetlands	Neighborhood conservation sites
Poor soil condition areas	Shopping centers
Airports	Major industries
Parks	Ethnic and religious neighborhoods

2. Planned land uses:

Residential neighborhoods	Institutional expansion areas
Redevelopment areas	Industry and business expansion
School "enrollment" areas	areas

If all of these barriers are taken as impenetrable, construction of new transportation facilities often would be impossible, as may well be the case in some instances. Desirably, therefore, the map indicates the relative impenetrability or modifiability of each area.

C. *Planning principles.* The goals of the particular planning project should be translated into explicit principles and standards, and made available to all concerned. A considerable body of professional experience has been accumulated in recent years. Principles are well established for any one system, like the road system; principles are more general and still in the process of development governing the interface between the transportation system and land development.[3] By way of illustration, Creighton provides six planning principles in *Urban Transportation Planning* [9.14]:

---

[3] See [9.55, pp. 22-29]. The entire report, *The Freeway in the City*, is a summary of urban transportation-land development principles.

1. Continuity: Transportation systems should provide for direct, continuous motion and should not contain jogs, stops, or enforced changes in direction.
2. Lane balance: The number of lanes of expressway entering an interchange should be the same as those leaving it.
3. Even distribution of investment: Expressways should not be crowded together in some places and spaced too far apart elsewhere.
4. Dispersion: Concentration of traffic on segments of road systems (e.g., at the core of the city) is to be avoided.
5. Sufficient arterials: There should be a fine enough spacing of arterials so that they are not overloaded by traffic, forcing some travel to dangerous neighborhood streets.
6. Enclosed spaces: Spaces which exist within the mesh formed by major roadways should be areas which can readily contain efficient and pleasant groupings of activities or land uses.

Creighton also outlines some more specific principles, which can be found in his book.

D. *Optimum spacing.* How far apart should expressways and arterials be in each part of the region to carry the anticipated future travel volumes? Should the future system be rich or lean? Adequacy of transportation is the major goal of transportation planning. Since optimum spacing of expressways is a function of trip density, speed and length, and construction and right-of-way costs, it is possible to calculate it once the regional growth model stage of the process is complete. The result provides a "ballpark" estimate of richness or leanness of the future system as a guide to the planner [9.14].

E. *Corridor planning maps.* Air photos on detailed land use maps, at a scale of 400 ft to 1 in. or better and keyed to the information on the barriers maps, are required as the basis for measuring corridor conditions and costs affecting route desirability and feasibility.

Requirement five, actual development of alternative plans, is represented in Fig. 9.1 by step 3.

A. *Present expressway plan.* Every major urban area in the United States now has a transportation plan with some degree of commitment by the responsible agency and other officials. Because of the rapid changes in local conditions, U.S. policy requires that these plans be regularly reviewed and modified as necessary. For reasons of continuity, courtesy, and strategy, it is customary that the first alternative tested is the existing plan.

B. *Prepare alternate expressway system plan.* This is the system synthesis activity for which previous steps have been prepared and with which the model use and evaluation stages are iteratively linked. This linkage tends to balance creativity and realism. The number of alternatives to be developed must be determined by the strategy. In most metropolitan studies the number has varied from 2 up to the 28 in the Chicago Study [9.56]. These systems plans lead to two other steps in the synthesis process. The first of these is to abstract the proposed systems from their real world setting, represent them mathematically, and test their ability to carry future traffic (step 4).

C. *Corridor evaluations.* The other step, conducted in parallel, is to examine each of the proposed transportation systems in its real world setting. This is done through assessing the conditions in each corridor relevant to possible route locations and the goals of the project. The various conditions indicated on the Barriers map (2B) are evaluated in greater detail, and the impact of each alternative is measured.

The conditions revealed by this last step are of great importance in metropolitan planning and may determine whether a particular corridor—and therefore a particular system—is acceptable.

The sixth requirement, documentation of decisions in the development of alternatives, is important from several viewpoints. First, in the synthesis work that follows each iteration with model use and evaluation, good documentation facilitates building on the work previously done. Secondly, it facilitates preparing the defense of the recommended system in the face of anticipated public questions and criticism, a regular feature in metropolitan transportation planning these days. Finally, since plans must be reviewed and updated over the years, usually by different persons, documentation facilitates replication and verification of the original decision.

The final requirement, the cyclical or iterative relationship with the model use and evaluation stages, balances creativity with relevance of proposals to goals. Evolution makes possible a decision on an alternative in a way that directly relates the selected alternative to the goals of the project.

9.5 NONTRANSPORTATION SOLUTIONS FOR TRANSPORTATION PROBLEMS

The discussions in the previous two sections have emphasized the process by which transportation elements can be synthesized to form a modified system. It should not be assumed from these discussions, however, that congestion can be relieved and access improved only by altering the transportation system. In fact, there are many nontransportation means by which these objectives might be achieved. A few of these are:

1. Changing pricing mechanisms: If travel is made less or more expensive for a group of people through tolls, user charges, or other mechanisms, we would expect variations in the number of travelers [9.15].

2. Staggering of travel hours: If the peaks in traffic can be reduced as, for example, by inducing industries to release employees evenly over several 15-min intervals, less transport capacity would be needed [9.16].

3. Substitution with communication: If people can be influenced to use their telephone rather than travel, trip making would be reduced.[4]

---

[4] Interestingly, it seems that people end up increasing *both* travel and communication at the same time, so that this idea may not be that beneficial.

Still another nontransport solution is through the organization of land use either to decrease amounts and lengths of trip making or to induce changes of mode. The latter approach is demonstrated most aptly on many college campuses where buildings and open spaces are arranged to encourage pedestrian travel. On a regional scale, the same kind of idea has been attempted around Stockholm, Sweden, where satellite new towns have been organized in radial corridors emanating from the city [9.2]. Rapid transit lines have been constructed in the corridors so as to induce people to use the higher-capacity transit systems and forsake the purchase and/or operation of the automobile.

The arrangement of land use to reduce the amounts and length of travel has been attempted primarily in new town developments found mostly in Europe but increasingly in the United States and other parts of the world. Both Islamabad, the capital of Pakistan, and Chandiagarh, capital of the Punjab State in India, have been built on the "superblock" concept where major roads are spaced at approximately 1.25 mile intervals in both directions (see Fig. 9.2 and Refs. 9.3 and 9.4). A kind of self-contained community (Fig. 9.3) then is organized within each superblock so that few people need to travel outside the immediate area. The layout of Belconnen, a satellite new town to Canberra, the capital of Australia, follows somewhat similar principles (see Fig. 9.4 and Ref. 9.19). Neighborhoods, consisting of

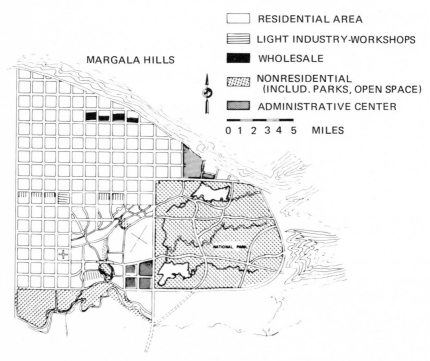

Fig. 9.2 Master plan of Islamabad. (*Adapted from Capital Development Authority, "Islamabad—The Project and Perspective," Government of Pakistan, Islamabad, 1970*).

Fig. 9.3 Layout of Shalimar—6, one of the communities within a superblock in Islamabad. *(Adapted from Capital Development Authority, "Islamabad—The Project and Perspective," Government of Pakistan, Islamabad, 1970).*

3,500 to 4,000 people, were organized so that almost everyone would be within 0.5 mile walking distance of local stores, primary schools, recreation areas, and so on.

Land use also can be organized for similar purposes around existing cities, although this has not been tried in many cases yet. The Stockholm plan is one exception. Some research has been done, however, to indicate the extent of travel savings that could be obtained through proper land use arrangement. One such endeavor [9.6] involves an application of TOPAZ (Technique for the Optimum Placement of Activities in Zones), a mathematical programming procedure. This will be discussed now to demonstrate both the types of results that can be obtained and the technique itself.

The objective function of TOPAZ is the minimization of establishment plus travel costs in an urban area. Establishment costs include those for building units, water and sewer, local streets, and electricity. Land value increments are perceived as negative establishment costs or benefits. Travel costs are predicted using a simple gravity model, and a constant cost per mile of travel. With these unit costs, TOPAZ is employed to allocate land acreages of various types (residential, commercial, etc.) predicted to be needed by 1990. The acreages are allocated to various zones where vacant land is available and, again, where total costs would be a minimum.

Fig. 9.4 Neighborhood of Aranda, Belconnen: 1. Shops; 2. Primary school; 3. Parish center and school; 4. Joint church; 5. Preschool, Mothercraft center; 6. Group housing; 7. Pedestrian underpass; 8. Recreation.

In applying TOPAZ, an initial feasible solution is needed as input. Such a plan for Blacksburg, Virginia, a town of roughly 10,000 population (1970), is shown in Fig. 9.5. This plan consists primarily of allocations of land to the northwest side of town in zones 9, 10, 13, and 17. The total cost of this solution, as noted in Fig. 9.5, is estimated to be $90 million (1970), of which $70.5 million is for establishment costs and $19.5 million for travel. We thus see that travel is a major expense in urban areas, accounting in this solution for about 22 percent of all costs [9.6].

The TOPAZ-generated minimum cost solution is displayed in Fig. 9.6. Total costs have been reduced to $84.1 million with about half of this reduction being in travel ($16.6 million). This result shows that it is possible to decrease travel costs about 14 percent through proper land use arrangement in this small town.

Interestingly, the minimum cost solution does not indicate a need for expansion to the zones utilized in the initial solution. Instead, growth is spread to those substantially developed zones fairly close to the town center.

TOPAZ also was employed in studies strictly to minimize and to maximize travel costs. The minimum was found to be $15.4 million, the maximum $20.7 million. If the latter value were used as a base, we would see that travel costs could

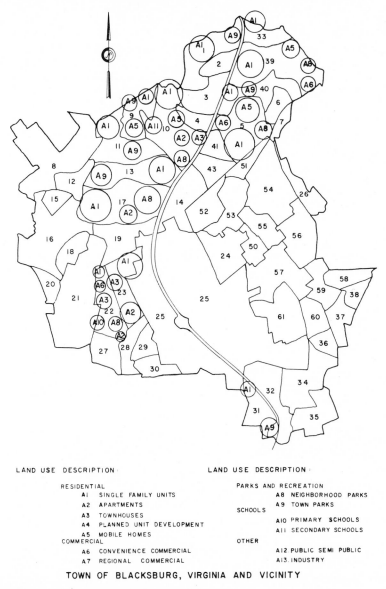

LAND USE DESCRIPTION

RESIDENTIAL
     A1   SINGLE FAMILY UNITS
     A2   APARTMENTS
     A3   TOWNHOUSES
     A4   PLANNED UNIT DEVELOPMENT
     A5   MOBILE HOMES
COMMERCIAL
     A6   CONVENIENCE COMMERCIAL
     A7   REGIONAL COMMERCIAL

LAND USE DESCRIPTION

PARKS AND RECREATION
     A8   NEIGHBORHOOD PARKS
     A9   TOWN PARKS
SCHOOLS
     A10 PRIMARY SCHOOLS
     A11 SECONDARY SCHOOLS
OTHER
     A12 PUBLIC SEMI PUBLIC
     A13 INDUSTRY

TOWN OF BLACKSBURG, VIRGINIA AND VICINITY

Fig. 9.5   Initial solution, 90.00×10^6. [9.6].

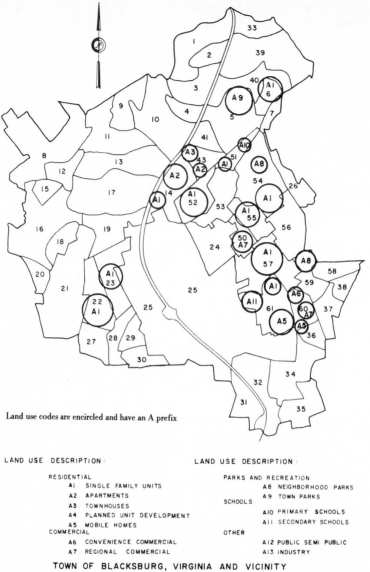

Land use codes are encircled and have an A prefix

LAND USE DESCRIPTION:

RESIDENTIAL
    A1. SINGLE FAMILY UNITS
    A2. APARTMENTS
    A3. TOWNHOUSES
    A4. PLANNED UNIT DEVELOPMENT
    A5. MOBILE HOMES
COMMERCIAL
    A6. CONVENIENCE COMMERCIAL
    A7. REGIONAL COMMERCIAL

LAND USE DESCRIPTION:

PARKS AND RECREATION
    A8. NEIGHBORHOOD PARKS
    A9. TOWN PARKS
SCHOOLS
    A10. PRIMARY SCHOOLS
    A11. SECONDARY SCHOOLS
OTHER
    A12. PUBLIC SEMI PUBLIC
    A13. INDUSTRY

TOWN OF BLACKSBURG, VIRGINIA AND VICINITY

Fig. 9.6 Minimum total overall cost solution, 84.1×10^6.

be as much as 25 percent higher in the most expensive arrangement (future development scattered to the far periphery). Improper land use arrangement thus can be seen as a significant contributor to traffic congestion and unneeded travel. However, proper land organization, especially if employed in connection with other nontransport schemes like these presented earlier in this section, could be of considerable help in alleviating these problems.

9.6 TRANSPORTATION SOLUTIONS FOR NONTRANSPORTATION PROBLEMS

While nontransportation solutions to transportation problems may be of great benefit, the opposite may also be useful: utilizing transportation to help solve other problems. Much of the literature dealing with developing countries gives heavy emphasis to the role of transportation in the development process [9.18]. Even in the United States, over $1 billion has been invested in highways in the Appalachian region primarily to induce economic development [9.9]. Transportation, then, is obviously thought to be a significant part of the solution to "development" problems, whether they be economic, social, or environmental.

We will not attempt to show how various transportation systems have been evolved to solve nontransportation problems. The possibilities and actualities are both so broad and pervasive that even an attempt simply to *list* applications would fall far short of being exhaustive. Instead, we will present one semihypothetical example that indicates the *potential* of utilizing transportation to achieve other goals.

9.6.1 Economic Segregation and the Transit System

The study to be described here [9.7] involved the use of the EMPIRIC land use model (see Chap. 5) in conjunction with goal programming, a particular type of mathematical programming technique (see Appendix). The EMPIRIC model can be employed to predict the number of families in each of four income classes that will reside in a given zone of an urban area in the future. Factors affecting the growth of residences in a zone include the future *regional* population and employment, the present number of families and employees of different types in the zone, land areas, water and sewer system types and availability, and, most important to this study, interzonal highway and mass transit travel times. The mass transit travel times were chosen for more intensive analysis in this study.

The objective of the goal program was to minimize the "extent of segregation" of families by income throughout all zones in the region. In other words, an attempt was made to create a more homogeneous distribution of poor and rich families throughout the metropolitan area. In an operational sense, this means that the proportion of families in each income level in each zone should be as close as possible to the corresponding proportion for the region as a whole. There could be a surplus of a given type of family in a given zone as compared to the regional proportion, or a dearth (slack), or no difference. The objective of the study thus became to determine how interzonal mass transit travel times could be changed to minimize the slack or surplus of families of all types in all zones.

Six zones out of the Boston metropolitan area were chosen for investigation. As shown in Fig. 9.7, zone 1 was Boston itself while the five other zones were surrounding suburbs. Where feasible, data were taken from the *Census* to make the study as realistic as possible. Three situations were investigated, the first in which segregation by income was to be minimized, the second in which there was no

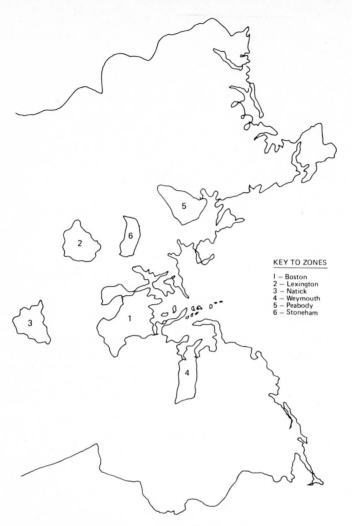

KEY TO ZONES

I — Boston
2 — Lexington
3 — Natick
4 — Weymouth
5 — Peabody
6 — Stoneham

Fig. 9.7   The eastern Massachusetts study region.

change made in future transit travel times, and the third in which segregation was to be maximized. These latter two situations were studied to provide bases by which to judge the relative impact of transit on segregation. The last case is particularly relevant since it shows the absolute worst condition of segregation by income levels and thus can be used as a yardstick for measuring the success or failure of the other two situations.

The outcomes of the three investigations are displayed in Tables 9.6 through 9.8. The top part of Table 9.6 shows the land use developments that take place as a result of efforts to minimize segregation. The bottom part shows the "desired" levels of development, that is, the levels that would occur if the regional *proportions* of families of each type were established in each zone.

The values of the slack or surplus for all three cases and for each family type and zone are presented in Table 9.7. A plus value indicates a surplus and a minus, slack. The total amount of slack and surplus for the minimum segregation case was 29,842. This can be compared to 37,317 for the "no change" and 49,021 for the worst segregation cases. The magnitude of these three totals leads to some interesting implications. First, and probably of foremost interest, is the fact that transit changes can have an effect on segregation. The difference between the best and worst cases is 19,189 families, which represents about 7.5 percent of the families in the region. This difference is not insignificant, especially since it is almost equivalent to the total amount of what might be called "inherent" segregation (the 29,842 families) that would be left if transit travel times were improved to their most desirable levels. In other words, proper transit improvements could reduce the amount of segregation by income in the region by approximately 40 percent as compared to what it would be if the transit changes with the worst impacts were implemented.

The actual effect of transit probably is not quite as significant, however. Comparison with the "no change" case, for instance, shows that the maintenance of the *status quo* insofar as transit is concerned would lead to a segregation level roughly in the middle between the best and worst situations (37,817 versus 29,842 and 49,021). The overall effect that transit might have in this situation would thus amount to a level of 7,975 families, which would be approximately 20 percent of the segregation by income that would exist if the "no change" alternative were followed.

Table 9.6   Minimum Segregation Numbers and Desirable Numbers of Families

Family income type	Zone						
	1	2	3	4	5	6	Total
Minimum segregation number							
$0–$4,999	71,222	404	927	1,671	2,593	643	77,460
$5,000–$9,999	95,834	4,061	6,114	8,035	9,443	3,342	126,829
$10,000–$14,999	22,266	2,609	2,865	2,800	3,093	1,333	34,966
$15,000 +	9,512	1,990	1,367	993	1,394	537	15,793
Total	198,834	9,064	11,273	13,499	16,523	5,855	255,048
Desirable number*							
$0–$4,999	68,902	2,919	4,393	5,777	6,789	2,403	91,185
$5,000–$9,999	95,834	4,061	6,114	8,035	9,443	3,342	126,829
$10,000–$14,999	22,639	960	1,444	1,898	2,231	789	29,961
$15,000 +	7,612	323	485	639	750	265	10,074
Total	194,987	8,263	12,436	16,349	19,213	6,799	258,049

*Those levels at which there would be no segregation by income in comparison to regional proportions.

Source: [9.7].

Table 9.7 **Slacks (−) and Surpluses (+) in Families**
in Each Income Class in Each Zone Resulting from Minimum
Segregation, No Change, and Maximum Segregation Solutions

Zone and income class	Minimum segregation	No change	Maximum segregation
Boston (1)			
$0–$4,999	+2,320	+1,047	+8,515
$5,000–$9,999	0	−4,631	0
$10,000–$14,999	−373	−1,306	+107
$15,000 +	+1,900	+1,636	+2,206
Lexington (2)			
$0–$4,999	−2,515	−2,236	0
$5,000–$9,999	0	+1,014	+5,419
$10,000–$14,999	+1,449	+1,258	+2,232
$15,000 +	+1,667	+1,725	+2,030
Natick (3)			
$0–$4,999	−3,468	−3,212	−4,661
$5,000–$9,999	0	+933	0
$10,000–$14,999	+1,421	+1,609	+1,328
$15,000 +	+882	+936	+823
Weymouth (4)			
$0–$4,999	−4,106	−3,683	−5,991
$5,000–$9,999	0	+1,541	0
$10,000–$14,999	+902	+1,213	+756
$15,000 +	+54	+442	+262
Peabody (5)			
$0–$4,999	−4,196	−4,067	0
$5,000–$9,999	0	+459	+7,219
$10,000–$14,999	+862	+957	+2,491
$15,000 +	+644	+670	+1,168
Stoneham (6)			
$0–$4,999	−1,760	−1,575	−2,502
$5,000–$9,999	0	+675	0
$10,000–$14,999	+544	+681	+486
$15,000 +	+272	+311	+235

Source: [9.7].

As an aside, there would seem to be a great deal of political palatability in the "no change" alternative. The impact on segregation is fairly neutral, not putting great pressure on communities to overcome defacto segregation in the housing market but at the same time not allowing for further segregation. Moreover, since no transit changes need to be made, the public would not get upset by the many alterations required to accomplish the minimum segregation solution. The maintenance of the *status quo* does not appear to be sufficient, however, if there is a serious interest in reducing segregation by income.

Table 9.8 1960 Zone-to-Zone Transit Times and 1970 Times Needed to Achieve Minimum or Maximum Segregation

Zonal pair	1960 transit times	1970 transit times Minimum segregation	1970 transit times Maximum segregation	Minimum possible transit time
1–1	15	9		6
1–2	25	17		13
1–3	25	13		13
1–4	20	11	18	9
1–5	45			21
1–6	20			10
2–1	25		13	13
2–2	6		4	4
2–3	25		13	13
2–4	60		35	35
2–5	30		17	17
2–6	12		7	7
3–1	25		13	13
3–2	25		13	13
3–3	5			4
3–4	40		21	21
3–5	45		26	26
3–6	30		17	17
4–1	20		9	9
4–2	60		35	35
4–3	40		21	21
4–4	6		4	4
4–5	52		30	30
4–6	40		21	21
5–1	45		21	21
5–2	30		17	17
5–3	45		26	26
5–4	52		30	30
5–5	6		4	4
5–6	15		9	9
6–1	20		10	10
6–2	12		7	7
6–3	30		17	17
6–4	40		21	21
6–5	15		9	9
6–6	6		4	4

Source: [9.7].

One other aspect of interest is that, even if all necessary transit changes were made, there still would be a discrepancy of 29,842 families from the most desirable levels. This amount possibly could be reduced by changes in other municipal services (highways, water systems, and sewer systems) shown to be relevant in the EMPIRIC model. Such changes probably would not cause a significant reduction, however. To reduce segregation to its absolute minimum probably would require the action of laws and politics not currently operative in urban areas (and thus generally not incorporated in the EMPIRIC model).

While the total slack and surplus for each case is important, the distribution of these totals also is relevant. It should be noted first that in all three cases the amount of slack exceeded the surplus, with the maximum segregation case having the biggest difference of 23,713 families. From this result comes the not too surprising inference that the process by which segregation is heightened involves the restriction of movement of families into a zone rather than an overexcessive migration of families. Yet this conclusion is not upheld in all zones and for all types of families. As should be expected, there are many variations which prevent generalities from being accepted unconditionally. Referring to Table 9.7, we see that the impacts on various zones can be quite different, with both large and small slacks and surpluses. The effect, though, on a per population basis is somewhat more noticeable. Boston, the zone having the largest number of families, is left with about the same amount of slack and surplus to overcome as the suburban zones, which means that, no matter what transit changes are made, the suburban zones will still be faced with a rather difficult task if they desire to overcome segregation by income.

The results when viewed in terms of the impacts on each type of family are a bit more explicit. In particular, families with annual incomes above $15,000 are always in surplus in every zone, and so, with two exceptions, are the families with annual incomes between $10,000 and $14,999. The opposite holds true for the very poor families. The latter problem could be partially overcome by somehow inducing the movement of the excess of poor families in Boston out into the suburbs where there is a dearth. But reducing the number of richer families would not be an easy task, mainly because the only apparent way would be to induce them to leave the region. This certainly is not feasible nor desirable from other viewpoints.

Another interesting aspect of the distribution of slacks and surpluses is that they vary according to the particular case under study—minimum segregation, "no change," or maximum segregation. Although large differences between the three are not common, one example does bring out an extraordinary result: if the "no change" strategy were chosen, there would be a large slack in the number of families with incomes between $5,000 and $9,999 in Boston, whereas, if either of the other two extreme strategies were chosen, there would be no slack or surplus. Similar results hold for zones 3, 4, and 6, except that there would be large surpluses instead of slacks. These results mean that in certain situations conservative policies, such as the "no change" one, may produce *much more exaggerated* conditions than if a policy involving some changes were followed.

The patterns of transit travel time reductions needed to bring about the impacts discussed above are very distinctive, as can be seen in Table 9.8. There are only four reductions needed to obtain minimum segregation, and these all relate to Boston. In contrast, maximum segregation is obtained by reducing most of the travel times within and between the suburban zones and by leaving Boston alone. These results are reasonable. To get minimum segregation, one must get the low income families out of Boston, and this is done by providing better transportation in these directions. On the other hand, to increase segregation, one simply isolates Boston travel time-wise and spends available funds on the intersuburban transit system. One result is perplexing, however; decreasing transit travel time from zone 1 to 4 helps both to decrease and increase segregation.

As a final remark, it should be mentioned that the improvements needed to achieve minimum segregation really are not as extensive as was first imagined. Only four changes are needed, and only one of these is to the lower travel time limit (corresponding to 70 mph speeds), although all four changes would be in Boston where improvement costs would be highest. What might be a significant finding at this point, though, is that attempts by low income groups to hinder or even stop construction and operation of transit facilities in the inner cities would only do harm to the cause of integration because the needed travel time improvements in and from the city would not be realized. We might also expect similar results insofar as urban highways are concerned.

9.6.2 Comments on the Boston Area Study

The preceding example obviously was highly oversimplified and could not be used in any real world application. On a more conceptual level, however, the example appears to be worthwhile in indicating the *potential* transportation can offer in helping to solve certain socioeconomic and environmental problems. The study shows, for instance, that mass transit can reduce segregation by income considerably. Yet there is some lower limit that can be reduced further only through modifications in other urban functions (law, government, schools, and so on). The study also points to the possibilities that:

1. If the transit system is not changed, a medium amount of segregation by income would be maintained.
2. Transit system changes would not have an even geographic distribution of impacts on segregation. Progress would not come through a smooth, even transition but rather with some forward motion and some backward.
3. Radial transit improvements are to be preferred over circumferential if segregation by income is to be reduced.

More elaborate studies would be needed to verify these possibilities in an actual situation, yet, as in previous sections of this chapter, we see some potential "principles" of solution generation or synthesis.

9.7 SUMMARY

In this chapter an effort has been made to display a variety of "principles" involved in developing solutions for transportation and related problems. The first section contained a brief discussion of the creative process, which is at the base of all solution-generating endeavors. In the following two sections several principles were evolved by reviewing the experiences of two transportation studies. One concerned a special central city transit system designed to aid the pedestrian. The other was concerned with a metropolitan area case. It was shown in both sections that potential impacts of transportation systems were considered first in the synthesis process, that is, before explicit attention was given to the potential user of the system and his needs.

In the final sections investigations were made of two often overlooked but extremely important synthesis situations:

1. Using nontransport means to help solve transportation problems, and
2. Using transport means to help solve nontransport problems.

Examples employed relative to these approaches indicated that the potential benefits to be achieved were significant. For instance, if land use arrangements were set so as to minimize travel, the result would be a 25 percent reduction over the worst possible case. If transit changes were employed to help reduce segregation by income in a region, it is possible that a 40 percent reduction over the worst situation could be obtained. As noted, these potential benefits are significant.

BIBLIOGRAPHY

9.1   Owen, W.: *The Accessible City*, The Brookings Institution, Washington, D.C., 1972.
9.2   Genteli, G.: *The Satellite Towns of Stockholm*, Department of Planning and Building Control, Stockholm, 1960.
9.3   Doxiadis, C.: "Islamabad, the Creation of a New Capital," *Town Planning Review*, vol. 36, no. 1, April, 1965.
9.4   Evenson, N.: *Chandiagarh*, Univ. of California Press, Berkeley, 1966.
9.5   Hugh, W. L.: *Cumbernaud New Town Traffic Analysis Report*, Cumbernaud Development Corporation, Glasgow, 1958.
9.6   Dickey, J. W., P. A. Leone, and A. R. Schwarte: "Use of TOPAZ for Generating Alternate Land Use Schemes," *Highway Research Record* 422, 1973.
9.7   Dickey, J. W.: "Minimizing Economic Segregation Through Transit System Changes: A Goal Programming Approach," in G. Newell (ed.), *Proceedings of the Fifth International Symposium on Traffic Flow Theory and Transportation*, Elsevier, New York, 1972.
9.8   Nugent, C. E., T. E. Vollman, and J. Ruml: "An Experimental Comparison of Techniques for the Assignment of Facilities to Location," *Operations Research*, vol. 16, no. 1, Jan.-Feb., 1968.
9.9   Wohl, M., and B. Martin: *Traffic Systems Analysis for Engineers and Planners*, McGraw-Hill, New York, 1967.
9.10   Harrisberger, L.: *Engineersmanship: A Philosophy of Design*, Brooks/Cole, Belmont, Calif., 1966.
9.11   McPherson, J. H.: "The Relationship of the Individual to the Creative Process in the Management Environment," *ASME Paper* 64MD12, May, 1964.

9.12 Raudsepp, E.: "Removing Barriers to Creativity," *Machine Design*, May 24, 1962.

9.13 Working Party on the Introduction of a New Mode of Transportation in Central London: *An Aid to Pedestrian Movement*, Westminster City Council, London, 1971.

9.14 Creighton, R. L.: *Urban Transportation Planning*, Univ. of Illinois Press, Urbana, Ill., 1970.

9.15 Bellomo, S. J.: "Toll Pricing and Its Relationship to Travel Demand, Elasticity, and Distribution of Economic Activities for Hampton Roads, Virginia," *Highway Research Record* 348, Washington, D.C., 1971.

9.16 O'Malley, B.: "Staggered Work-Hour Project in Lower Manhattan," *Highway Research Record* 348, Washington, D.C., 1971.

9.17 National Capital Development Commission: *Tomorrow's Canberra*, Australian National University Press, Canberra, 1970.

9.18 Owen, W.: *Distance and Development*, The Brookings Institution, Washington, D.C., 1968.

9.19 Friedmann, J.: "Poor Regions and Poor Neighbors: Perspectives on the Problem of Appalachia," *Appalachia*, vol. 1, no. 8, April, 1968.

9.20 Osborn, A. F.: *Applied Imagination*, Charles Scribner's Sons, New York, 1963.

9.21 Lagemann, J. K.: "How We Discourage Creative Children," *Redbook Magazine*, March, 1963.

9.22 "The Impact of Appalachian Development Highways," *Appalachia*, vol. 3, no. 7, April, 1970.

9.23 Richards, B.: *New Movement in Cities*, Reinhold Publishing Corporation, New York, 1966.

9.24 Canty, E. T., and A. J. Sobey: *Case Studies of Seven New Systems of Urban Transportation*, General Motors Corporation, Warren, Mich., January 13-17, 1969.

9.25 Davidson, H. O., J. L. Crain, and E. W. Davis: *Comparative Analysis of Rapid Transit Vehicle Systems*, Operations Research Incorporated, Silver Spring, Md., July, 1962.

9.26 Millar, J., and J. Dean: "Practical Considerations of Rapid Transit—A Summary of the Manchester Study," *Journal of the Town Planning Institute*, vol. 54, no. 4, April, 1968.

9.27 *AMF–Safege Monorail: The Transportation of Tomorrow—Today*, American Institute of Planners 1964 Convention, Robert Treat Hotel, Newark, N.J.

9.28 Beller, W. S.: "Megalopolis Transportation—Attacking the Systems Problem," *Space/Aeronautics*, Sept., 1967.

9.29 Chilton, E. G.: *Future Urban Transportation Systems*, vol. 2, Stanford Research Institute, Menlo Park, Calif., May, 1967.

9.30 Transportation Research Institute, Carnegie-Mellon University: *Urban Rapid Transit Concepts and Evaluation*, Pittsburgh, Pa., 1968.

9.31 *Popular Science*, vol. 199, no. 5, Nov., 1971.

9.32 Barton-Aschman Associates, Inc.: *Study in New Systems of Urban Transportation. Guidelines for New Systems of Urban Transportation. Urban Needs and Potentials*, vol. 1, Chicago, May, 1968.

9.33 "Highballing on Air," *Compressed Air Magazine*, vol. 71, no. 3, March, 1966.

9.34 "Monorail Guides Air-Cushion Car," *Engineering News-Record*, vol. 174, no. 24, June 17, 1965.

9.35 Ross, H. R.: "Newer Transportation Technology," *Science and Technology*, 1966.

9.36 Tube Transit, Inc.: "Gravity-Vacuum Transit System," (as presented at Expo '67), Palo Alto, Calif., 1967.

9.37 Edwards, L. K.: "Urban Gravity-Vacuum Transit," Tube Transit, Inc., Palo Alto, Calif., Sept. 30, 1968.

9.38 Steiner, J. E.: "Jumbo Jets and SST's," *Civil Engineering Magazine*, vol. 38, no. 3, March, 1968.

9.39 "Boeing 747: The Aircraft," *Engineering*, vol. 206, no. 5342, Sept. 6, 1968.

9.40 "The Amazing Future for Air Travel," *U.S. News & World Report*, vol. 65, no. 13, Sept. 23, 1968.

9.41 Richards, B.: "Urban Minisystem," *Architectural Forum*, vol. 128, no. 1, Jan./Feb., 1968.

9.42 General Motors Research Laboratory: *New Systems Implementation Study, Vol. 1, Summary and Conclusions*, Research Publication GMR-710A, Warren, Mich., Feb., 1968.

9.43 Transit Research Foundation of Los Angeles, Inc.: *City and Suburban Travel*, issue 3, June, 1970.

9.44 Operations Research, Inc.: *Requirements for Transit Car Specifications*, Report 24, Federal Clearinghouse, Springfield, Va., PB 169 564, April, 1964.

9.45 The Dashaveyor Company: *Dashaveyor, Revolution in Transportation*, Venice, Calif., 1967.

9.46 Meyer, J. R., J. F. Kain, and M. Wohl: *The Urban Transportation Problem*, Harvard Univ. Press, Cambridge, Mass., 1965.

9.47 "Motor Transportation," *Encyclopaedia Britannica*, 1967.

9.48 Maxtone-Graham, J. A.: "Flying the English Channel: Altitude 7 feet," *Popular Mechanics*, Jan., 1969.

9.49 "Hovercraft Proved," *Engineering*, vol. 208, no. 5393, Sept. 5, 1969.

9.50 U.S. Department of Commerce, National Bureau of Standards: "The Shirley Highway Express Bus-on-Freeway Demonstration Project—Project Description," Washington, D.C., Aug., 1971.

9.51 Northern Virginia Transportation Commission: "Project Status Report—Shirley Highway Express Bus-on-Freeway Project," Alexandria, Va., 1969.

9.52 Dickey, J. W.: *Mass Transit*, Council of Planning Librarians Exchange Bibliographies 98 and 99, Monticello, Ill., Sept., 1969.

9.53 Berry, D. S., G. W. Blomme, P. W. Shuldiner, and J. H. Jones: *The Technology of Urban Transportation*, Northwestern Univ., Evanston, Ill., 1968.

9.54 Stuart, R. C., and J. W. Dickey: "Modeling the Group Goal Component of the Plan Evaluation Process," Confer-In West, American Institute of Planners, San Francisco, Oct., 1971.

9.55 The Urban Advisers to the Federal Highway Administration: *The Freeway in the City*, U.S. Government Printing Office, Washington, D.C., 1968.

9.56 *The Chicago Area Transportation Study*, vols. 1–3, Chicago, 1959, 1960, and 1962.

9.57 *The Cleveland–Seven County Transportation Study*, Cleveland, 1969.

9.58 *The Niagara Frontier Transportation Study*, vols. 1 and 2, Albany, N.Y., 1963 and 1964.

9.59 Miki, T.: "Kama-kura's Shonan Monorail," *Permanent Way*, no. 45, 1971.

10 Solution Specification: Some Techniques and Examples

When solutions to urban transportation problems are generated, perhaps along the lines of some of the principles presented in Chap. 9, they often are still too general to be made immediately operational. For example, transportation plans on a metropolitan-wide scale usually show highway and major transit systems located in certain 1-to-3-mile-wide corridors. Usually the actual placement of the facilities within the corridor is determined through separate route location studies. In many final designs, the coordinates of the center line of a route would be specified to the nearest hundredth of a foot at 50-ft intervals along the proposed alignment. There is thus a need in almost any planning process to translate the more general plans or solutions generated into detailed enough instructions so they can be implemented without much misunderstanding. This process of specifying solutions in more detail is the subject of this chapter.

As has been the case throughout this book, there are a great many more types of situations falling under the topic of concern than could possibly be discussed here. This problem is compounded in this chapter because what is detail to one person in one transportation planning situation is generality to another person in another situation. Highway design engineers, for instance, usually are concerned with specific route locations in a corridor, whereas, the planner would consider this to be detail. In any case, we have chosen to present five sample situations we feel represent what is commonly understood as "solution specification." These samples are not necessarily connected in any way, but have been chosen for their variety and to demonstrate some common techniques used in the solution specification process.

10.1 TRAFFIC SIGNAL SIMULATION

The solution specification procedure to be presented here is an example of simulation, a process by which a model or set of models is utilized to make predictions of values of some desired variables. The concept of simulation as commonly understood has another aspect, however: that of *probabilistic* or *stochastic* events or values. What is implied by these two terms, often used interchangeably, is that there is some variation associated with all variables and parameters, a variation which usually cannot be explained through relationship with other variables. For example, transportation facility construction costs, usually assumed constant, never can be determined exactly: there are differences in affecting factors such as topography, labor practices, weather, and even managerial abilities, which many times are difficult to identify and incorporate in models but which, when taken together, would cause significant variations in construction costs. Moreover, if we were simulating a bus operation, for example, there also would be variations in other inputs such as distances which buses must travel, acceleration and deceleration rates, turnaround times, the number of people who can sit in each bus, and, in what will be important to us in our forthcoming example, variations in the number of arriving passengers at line haul stations during individual time periods within each peak hour. Thus, to make more realistic models, we must attempt to take into account variability. In other words, we must try to determine not just whether a certain value of a variable will occur or not, but what the probability of occurrence of that value is.

The idea of simulation perhaps can be explained best by means of an example, which in this case will relate to the operation of a left turn bay at an intersection controlled by a *fixed-time* traffic signal (a signal for which the time for each type of green and red phase has been preset to certain values). It will be our task to determine the delay to left turn vehicles resulting from any particular setting. Figure 10.1 shows a diagram of the situation.

In the figure there is a left turn bay, an opposing traffic lane, and a set of traffic signals. The signal phase for left-turning traffic can be red (R), yellow (Y), green (G), or left turn arrow green (LTAG), whereas the opposing traffic, which for this simple example is limited to a straight through movement, only has the first three of these phases. It is also assumed that the left turn arrow will come in sequence *before* the full green for that approach to the intersection and that left turns can be made during the green period for the opposing traffic *if* there is a time gap of 5 or more seconds available in the opposing traffic stream. These and several additional "rules" for the simulation will become more evident as this description progresses. Most also are listed in Table 10.1.

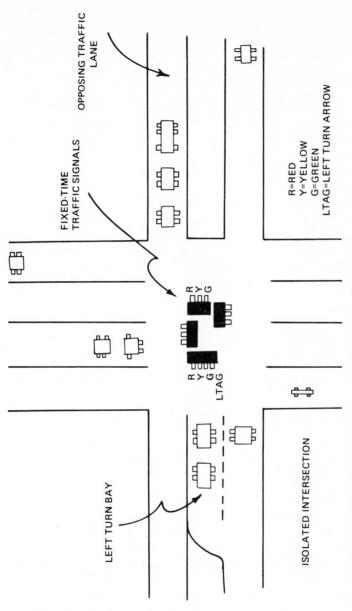

Fig. 10.1 Hypothetical intersection controlled by fixed-time traffic signals.

OPPOSING TRAFFIC LANE

FIXED-TIME TRAFFIC SIGNALS

R = RED
Y = YELLOW
G = GREEN
LTAG = LEFT TURN ARROW

R
Y
G

R
Y
G
LTAG

LEFT TURN BAY

ISOLATED INTERSECTION

Table 10.1   Rules for Simulation "Game"

1. During any respective green phase, one vehicle can clear the intersection every 2.5 sec (two in 5.0 sec).
2. During the opposing traffic green (OTG) phase, one left turn vehicle requires a gap of 5.0 sec in the opposing traffic stream before it can proceed through the intersection. However, an additional left turn vehicle can clear the intersection *with the previous vehicle* if an additional gap of 2.5 sec is available. (The use of the variable "note" in the decision tree allows for this possibility. See Fig. 10.3.)
3. If there is no left turn arrow phase, one left turn vehicle, if present, can clear the intersection at both the beginning and the end of the OTG phase.
4. If there is a left turn phase, one left turn vehicle, if present, can clear the intersection at the end of the OTG phase.
5. The left turn arrow green (LTAG) phase always will be a "leading" green, coming in sequence before the OTG phase.

The major question to be discussed at this point is, Where does variability enter into the simulation situation portrayed in Fig. 10.1? The answer lies in the nature of the arrival patterns of vehicles at the left turn bay and opposing lane approaches to the intersection. It should be noted that we are going to be interested in looking at these two approaches at intervals corresponding to 5 seconds of real time, so that we will need to know how many arrivals will come in each 5-second period. *This would be extremely difficult to predict.* Could anyone really estimate with any reliability the number of arrivals at a given intersection between, say, 3:05.45 p.m. and 3:05.50 p.m. on a given day? Obviously, to make such estimates would be treacherous since the expected variation in arrivals would be great. Nevertheless, all is not lost, since traffic engineers and planners have been able to predict with fair success both the *hourly* arrival volume and the statistical *distribution* of the number of arrivals in any small time period (like 5 seconds), the latter prediction being more applicable for an isolated[1] intersection, a situation assumed in our example. Figure 10.2 shows several cumulative arrival distributions found from empirical studies in Texas. It turns out that the cumulative Poisson probability function, discussed in the Appendix, happens to fit the data nicely. The equation for the Poisson density function is

$$p(X = x, T = t) = \frac{(\lambda t)^x e^{-\lambda t}}{x!} \tag{10.1}$$

where, for the example simulation
$p(X = x, T = t)$ = probability that there will be exactly x vehicular arrivals during time interval $t(x = 0, 1, 2, \ldots,)$
λ = mean number of arrivals

[1] An isolated intersection is one which is so distant from any other intersection that each arrival is random and independent of other arrivals, that is, arrivals would not come in "bunches" or platoons as would happen at closely spaced signals.

Thus for a 5-second interval and, say, 600 arrivals/hr, we would have

$$\lambda = \frac{600 \text{ arrivals/hr}}{3{,}600 \text{ sec/hr}} = 0.167 \frac{\text{arrivals}}{\text{sec}}$$

Thus

$$\lambda t = 0.167(5) = 0.835$$

and

$$p(X = x,\ T = 5) = \frac{(0.835)^x e^{-0.835}}{x!} \tag{10.2}$$

From this equation the probability of having, say, two arrivals in 5 seconds, $p(X = 2, T = 5)$, given 600 in 1 hour is 0.15. Now we must determine artificially a value for the number of arrivals in any 5-second period. This objective is accomplished by picking a random number, associating it with a given probability, and then finding the number of arrivals corresponding to that probability. To be more specific about this procedure, we will need to work with a cumulative Poisson probability distribution like that shown in Fig. 10.2. The cumulative distribution is given by

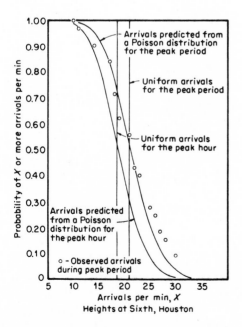

Fig. 10.2 Relationship between observed and predicted arrivals during morning peak periods. [10.12, p. 136].

Table 10.2   Random Numbers

0.10	0.09	0.73	0.57	0.01	0.11	0.91	0.69	0.35	0.86	0.34	0.67	0.35
0.37	0.54	0.20	0.01	0.50	0.43	0.69	0.44	0.42	0.96	0.24	0.80	0.52
0.08	0.42	0.26	0.97	0.29	0.99	0.48	0.72	0.93	0.03	0.23	0.20	0.90
0.99	0.01	0.90	0.33	0.54	0.62	0.07	0.11	0.07	0.15	0.33	0.21	0.13
0.12	0.80	0.79	0.64	0.46	0.32	0.64	0.37	0.61	0.48	0.64	0.03	0.23

$$p(X \leqslant x, T = t) = \sum_{x=1}^{X} \frac{(\lambda t)^x e^{-\lambda t}}{x!} \tag{10.3}$$

where $p(X \leqslant x, T = t)$ is the probability that the number of vehicular arrivals in time period t is less than or equal to X arrivals. Thus in our example above we find that the probability of having less than or equal to two arrivals in 5 seconds (i.e., 0, 1, or 2 arrivals) is

$$p(X \leqslant 2, T = 5) = \frac{(0.835)^0 e^{-0.835}}{0!} + \frac{(0.835)^1 e^{-0.835}}{1!} + \frac{(0.835)^2 e^{-0.835}}{2!} = 0.95$$

Further calculations would show that

$p(X \leqslant 0, T = 5) = 0.44$

$p(X \leqslant 1, T = 5) = 0.80$

$p(X \leqslant 2, T = 5) = 0.95$

$p(X \leqslant 3, T = 5) = 0.99$

$p(X \leqslant \infty, T = 5) = 1.00$

Now by choosing a random number between 0.00 and 1.00, either by drawing it from a hat, spinning a roulette wheel, or, as is usually done, by looking in a prepared table such as Table 10.2, it is possible to obtain an estimate for the number of arrivals in any 5-second period. For instance, the first number in Table 10.2 is 0.10, and since this falls between 0.00 and 0.44 we can say that there are no arrivals in the first 5-second interval. On the other hand, if the random number chosen for the second 5-second period happened to be 0.97, the number of arrivals could be assumed to be three. This selection process then would continue for as many 5-second intervals as needed.

0.48	0.76	0.80	0.95	0.90	0.91	0.17	0.39	0.29	0.27	0.49	0.46
0.40	0.37	0.20	0.63	0.61	0.04	0.02	0.00	0.82	0.29	0.16	0.65
0.25	0.00	0.15	0.95	0.33	0.47	0.64	0.35	0.08	0.03	0.36	0.06
0.11	0.65	0.88	0.67	0.67	0.43	0.97	0.04	0.43	0.62	0.76	0.39
0.66	0.53	0.98	0.95	0.11	0.68	0.77	0.12	0.17	0.17	0.68	0.33

The reader should be cognizant of the subtleties which exist in the above selection process, for if the random numbers given us are truly random, we should find that after a large number of picks, the distribution of number of arrivals per period should be fairly close to that of the Poisson. However, within any one period, an estimate of the number of arrivals depends strictly on a randomly chosen value for $p(X \leqslant x, T = t)$.

Having described the procedure by which arrivals are generated for an approach to an intersection, we now are ready to summarize the remaining operations of the simulation procedure. These are presented by means of the *decision tree* in Fig. 10.3. In this figure, each *node* of the tree represents a point at which a certain decision must be made. For example, at the node denoted by the asterisk (*), if a left turn arrow green (LTAG) phase exists for the signal, then the upper branch is chosen. If not, the lower. To understand the rest of the decision tree, we must take into account the specifications summarized in Table 10.3.

At this point the reader can appreciate the complexity of the logic of any apparently simple simulation and also realize that most simulation exercises require a considerable amount of effort. Nevertheless, continuing with the left turn bay example, we must now set the values of the independent variables. Let us choose

LTV = 300 vehicles/hr
OTV = 800 vehicles/hr
LTAG = two 5-sec periods
OTG = eight 5-sec periods
RED = four 5-sec periods

Thus, CYCLE = 2 + 8 + 4 = 14 5-second periods and λt for the left turn is 300 (5)/3600 = 0.083 (5) = 0.415 while for the opposing traffic it is 800 (5)/3600 = 0.222 (5) = 1.110. These lead to the cumulative Poisson arrival probabilities shown in Table 10.4.

We now are in a position to set up a chart like that shown in Table 10.5 where each column represents one 5-second interval and the first two rows indicate the duration and sequencing of red and green signals on the respective approaches. The third and fourth row are reserved for counting the number of vehicles stopped on each approach, whereas the final row is for recording, for the left turning vehicles, the delay encountered (only) within the particular 5-second period.

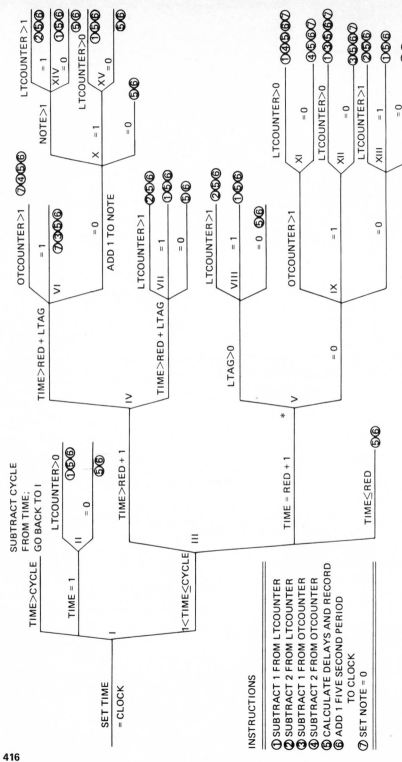

Fig. 10.3 Decision tree for left turn bay simulation example.

Table 10.3 Specifications for the Left Turn Bay Simulation Example

1. There are five independent variables for each simulation trial:
   a. the left turn traffic volume, LTV (vehicles/hr),
   b. the opposing lane traffic volume, OTV (vehicles/hr),
   c. the left turn arrow green time, LTAG (number of 5-sec periods),
   d. the opposing traffic green time, OTG (number of 5-sec periods), and
   e. the red time, RED (number of 5-sec periods).

2. The dependent variable is the delay to left turn vehicles (sec/hr of traffic signal operation time).

3. There are four major steps to be traced in each 5-sec period of the simulation:
   a. generation of vehicles in the left turn bay and on the opposing traffic lane,
   b. testing both for the phase of the traffic signal currently in operation on each approach and for the presence of opposing traffic in the opposing traffic lane (done through the logic of Fig. 10.3),
   c. moving of eligible vehicles through the intersection, and
   d. recording of delays to vehicles still stopped in the left turn bay.

4. There is a clock which starts at 0 and moves ahead 5 sec after each loop through the 4 steps outlined in 3 above.

5. There is a CYCLE for the traffic signal which equals the sum of LTAG, OTG, and RED.

6. There is a TIME variable which indicates the position of the clock time within the cycle time.

7. There is a left turn counter and an opposing traffic counter (LTCOUNTER and OTCOUNTER). These are incremented each time a vehicle arrives on the respective approach and decremented each time a vehicle clears the intersection from that approach.

8. During any green phase, one vehicle can clear the intersection every 2.5 sec (or two every 5 sec).

9. During the OTG phase, one left turn vehicle requires a gap of 5 sec in the opposing traffic before it can proceed through the intersection. However, an additional left turn vehicle can clear the intersection *with a previous vehicle* if an additional gap of 2.5 sec is available. (The use of the variable "note" in the decision tree of Fig. 10.3 creates the logical structure to allow for this possibility in the simulation exercise.)

10. If there is no left turn arrow phase, one left turn vehicle, if present, can clear the intersection at both the beginning and the end of the OTG phase.

11. If there is a left turn phase, one left turn vehicle, if present, can clear the intersection at both the beginning and the end of the OTG phase.

12. The LTAG always will be a "leading" green, coming in sequence before the OTG phase.

**Table 10.4 Cumulative Poisson Arrival Probabilities
for Left Turn Bay Simulation Example**

X	0	1	2	3	4	5
$p(X \leqslant x, T = t)$ for left turning traffic	0.66	0.93	0.99	—	—	—
$p(X \leqslant x, T = t)$ for opposing traffic	0.33	0.69	0.90	0.97	0.99	—

Table 10.5   Calculations for Left Turn Bay Simulation Example

Clock	1	2	3	4	5	6	7	8	9	10	11	12	13	14
Left turn	RED				←LTAG→		←					OTG		→
Opposing	RED						←					OTG		→
LTCOUNTER	0	0	1	1	0	0	0	0	0	0	1	1	1	1
OTCOUNTER	0	2	3	6	7	8	7	5	7	5	4	2	1	0
Delay	0	0	5	5	0	0	0	0	0	0	5	5	5	5

To perform the simulation we trace through the four steps outlined in item 3 of Table 10.3, utilizing Fig. 10.3 as an aid in the process. To start, we generate vehicles in the left turn bay and on the opposing traffic lane by choosing a random number from Table 10.2 and comparing it to the values in Table 10.4. For this purpose, and also to insure that there are a sufficient number of arrivals to provide a good example, let us pick the first random number from the top of the third column of Table 10.2 and continue down that column as the need arises. Thus the first random number picked is 0.73, which lies between the 0.66 and 0.93 numbers in Table 10.4. This gives one arrival in the left turn bay for the first 5-second period. For the opposing lane, the next random number is 0.20, which is less than 0.33 in Table 10.4, so that *no* arrivals will be considered to have come in the opposing traffic lane in this period.

Going on to the remaining three steps in item 3 of Table 10.3, we trace through Fig. 10.3 as far as possible and do all the operations we are instructed to do by the circled numbers at the end of the particular branch we happen to follow.[2] Thus, for the first 5-second period now being studied, TIME = CLOCK = 1 so that we follow the middle branch from the first node. At the next decision node we compare the value of LTCOUNTER to 0, and since LTCOUNTER = 1, we follow the upper branch to the circled numbers, 1, 5, and 6. Referring to the INSTRUCTIONS box in the chart, we see that 1 vehicle should be subtracted from the LTCOUNTER, a step which says that in a real world situation one left turn vehicle (if present) would clear the intersection and that the remaining ones would be stopped. Consequently we should calculate the delays to any remaining vehicles (of which there are none) and go on to the next 5-second period, that is, make CLOCK = 2.

The reader may have noticed an apparently odd circumstance in this first period—a left turn vehicle making its movement when the light phase was red. This situation is a result of the assumption made in item 11 of Table 10.1, which states

---

[2] It is assumed in the use of Fig. 10.3 that the first phase in the cycle always will be red. The first four periods in the example simulation thus will be times when there will be vehicles stopped in the left turn bay and the opposing traffic lane.

that a left turn vehicle, if present, can go through the intersection when the light is just turning red[3]—this action supposedly corresponding to the way most left turning drivers would behave under the circumstances. Whether this assumption is valid or not, the important point to emphasize at this stage of the simulation is that, for the first 5-second period, we have had to consider superficially the preceding (OTG) phase of the previous (actually nonexistent) cycles of the signal. In other words, in any simulation, there is a need to "warm up" from some initial point which may or may not correspond realistically to the initial conditions of the actual situation. The discrepancies between the two usually are not significant and tend to fade as time progresses.

Continuing to the second 5-second period, we pick the random numbers 0.26 and 0.90 which, when matched against the numbers in Table 10.4, lead to 0 and 2 arrivals in the left turn bay and opposing traffic lane respectively. Then, entering Fig. 10.3 with TIME = CLOCK = 2, we take the lower branch from node I since TIME is less than CYCLE but not equal to one, and we also take the lower branch from node III since TIME is less than RED. Having reached this point we are instructed to calculate and record delays to left turn vehicles, of which there are none, and put CLOCK ahead to three.

In the next two periods we find there is one left turn arrival and four more opposing traffic arrivals, with the left turn arrival being delayed five seconds *in each period*. This delay is recorded in the fifth row of Table 10.5. In period 5, the random numbers chosen are 0.33 and 0.64, which indicate an additional arrival in the opposing traffic lane. Then, in tracking through Fig. 10.3, we go first from node I to node III, then to node V and the middle branch of node VIII, whereupon we subtract one from LTCOUNTER and record any delays that still may exist (in this case there are none). The reader can see the logic of the path we have traced by referring to Table 10.5, where it is seen that TIME = CLOCK = 5 is less than CYCLE = 14 but greater than one (branch from node I to III) and that the signal is in the first phase after the red, which might be either the OTG or LTAG depending on the particular light phase scheme being tested. In the example case, we do have an LTAG phase (LTAG $>$ 0), so that the signal presently must be in this phase since, according to item 12 of Table 10.3, the LTAG phase always comes before the OTG phase. We therefore are led to node VIII in Fig. 10.3, where we are asked to find out how many vehicles currently are in the left turn bay. The LTCOUNTER for period 4 is one, and this vehicle, because of the LTAG phase, can proceed freely through the intersection (leaving LTCOUNTER = 0). It should be noted, however, that if there were two vehicles in the left turn bay (LTCOUNTER = 2), both of them could have made it through the intersection since each vehicle is assumed to take only 2.5 seconds for this movement (item 9, Table 10.3).

The results for the simulation in the rest of the cycle are exhibited in the remainder of the spaces in Table 10.5. The total delay to left turn vehicles in this

---

[3] Actually, what is meant is that the vehicle starts to make his turn in the yellow phase (left out of this simulation for simplicity) and finishes his turn after the light has gone to red.

cycle is 30 seconds or 30/(14) (5) = 0.43 seconds for each second of operation of the signal. Of course more reliable estimates of the delay could be obtained by using the simulation for more than one cycle—1 hour or about 52 cycles might be a good length of time—yet manual simulations for this length of time often become tedious. Consequently many engineers and planners have turned to the digital computer for doing most of the numerical labor. In fact, in a simulation done at Virginia Tech of 324 hours of operation of various left turn signal schemes, the digital computer (IBM 7040) took 17 minutes, 17 seconds. To do the same amount of calculation by hand would require in the neighborhood of 3,000 manhours. Many other interesting and successful simulations have been run, including those of traffic flow through a network of fixed time signals [10.14], the location and operation of downtown terminals [10.13], and the flight paths of supersonic aircraft [10.1].

10.1.1 Comments on Simulation

While simulation has found a multitude of uses such as those referenced in the preceding paragraph, it does have several difficulties associated with it which should be recognized. First, any simulation program has contained within it a model and therefore is subject to all the problems inherent in models. For example, the 12 items in Table 10.3 represent a verbal model of the behavior of traffic at a certain type of intersection—in this case one with a left turn bay and an opposing traffic lane. Yet in this model most of the factors[4] deemed to have an effect on capacity, and therefore on flow and delay at an intersection, are disregarded. All vehicles are assumed to be similar in acceleration and speed characteristics, whereas in reality there are automobiles, trucks, buses, and so forth in the traffic stream. No pedestrian crossing interference is taken into account. Changes in weather have not been considered. So the list goes on, but the point to be made is that no simulation results should be taken as being absolutely accurate and reliable, simply because there is a model, oftentimes somewhat camouflaged, at the base of every simulation.

A second set of difficulties with simulation is the money, time, and effort required to elaborate on its logical structure, that is, on the nature of the underlying model. The decision tree in Fig. 10.3 is significant in that it is fairly complicated considering the apparently simple situation to which it corresponds. When larger models are developed as, for example, for traffic flow through a network of signals, the structure of the decision tree may become very large, so large in fact that many illogical steps inadvertently creep in and cause unforeseen and untold problems which cannot be avoided except through prodigious effort. Some general simulation programs exist [10.1], but the same problems may arise and there is the added (and usually difficult) task of understanding the general programs themselves.

---

[4] See Chap. 5 for a list and discussion of these factors.

Boundary conditions also present a problem to the person who wishes to simulate. A good example of this type of difficulty can be found in the left turn bay simulation, for in that exercise we assumed that at the start of simulation there would be no vehicles already present in the left turn bay or in the opposing traffic stream (i.e., the intersection would be completely unsaturated). However this may or may not be the actual situation. It might be that if we were to use the traffic signal phasing scheme from the above simulation exercise in the field, the results might be much worse than anticipated due to an initial oversaturated condition at the actual intersection. Moreover we might have simulated only 1 hour of operation of the intersection, whereas, the scheme might be utilized for more than 1 hour. If the occurrences which take place in succeeding hours are significantly different from those in the first, the simulated scheme may turn out to be very inefficient.

A final criticism of simulation is that it is still a trial and analysis technique. The best scheme for the operation of the traffic signal in the left turn bay example cannot be found except by repeated trials utilizing different schemes. Even then, it would be difficult to *know* that the optimum scheme had been found because the next trial may produce a better one. Consequently, there is a need for a technique (or set of techniques) that will give optimum solutions that we know are optimum. This argument sets the stage for dynamic programming, which is discussed in the next section.

10.2 TRAIN DISPATCHING AND DYNAMIC PROGRAMMING

A need has been identified for optimization techniques to aid in the specification process. The calculus serves well in many cases where an optimum is desired, yet the presence of *constraints* and *discontinuous functions* in any real world situation often make utilization of the calculus cumbersome and sometimes impossible. As it turns out in the study of transportation, both of these difficulties are accentuated because of ever-present restrictions on budgets and operating policies and also because of the discrete nature of vehicles—there are either 1 or 2 or 3, etc., but certainly not 1.236.

As aids in solution specification situations where the calculus is not applicable, the techniques of linear and dynamic programming have been developed (see the Appendix). An example using the former technique was presented in Chap. 9. Here we will illustrate a dynamic programming application involving scheduling of trains from a central terminal.

10.2.1 The Vehicle Dispatching Problem

As in the simulation section, we will outline a simple problem which will provide a basis both for the understanding of the technique and for a demonstration of a potential application in the field of transportation. The example to be used [10.11] concerns the dispatching of sets of vehicles, either rapid transit, railroad, or, in a more inventive case, bus trains, from a center city terminal to some outlying stations lying along a line haul route. A known number of passengers arrive at the center city terminal at certain specified time intervals, and a train of vehicles is provided for them at the same or at a later period. The question to be answered is that of how many passengers should be provided service or, conversely, how many vehicles should be in each train dispatched during each time interval. The objective is to minimize the cost of delay to passengers plus the cost of having to run each train. A tradeoff is involved since a greater number of vehicles per train means a greater cost to the company but also means less cost of delay to passengers. However, there is a constraint on the company that if a train is dispatched at any time, there must be enough vehicles on it to carry all the passengers accumulated at the terminal up to the departure time. In other words, the choice at each time interval is to provide transportation for all the accumulated passengers or for none. In the last time period all passengers must be given service.

In Tables 10.6 and 10.7 are shown the input data on arrivals and costs. For simplicity, the arrivals are specified in terms of number of vehicle loads of passengers. The cost component for delay is figured roughly on the basis of a $1.50/hr of delay per person for a hypothesized 50-passenger vehicle. Dispatching costs for a train composed of different numbers of vehicles were chosen strictly for the sake of making an interesting example. Three points should be emphasized at this juncture: (1) The train dispatching cost function is *discrete;* there is no cost for, say, a 1.32-vehicle train because such cannot exist. (2) The train dispatching cost function is nonlinear, meaning that there is no constant rise in costs as additional vehicles are added to the train. (3) There is the aforementioned constraint on the company.

Considering each time interval to be one stage[5] of the dynamic programming progress, we can picture the decisions which must be made at each stage through the network structure shown in Fig. 10.4. Before the 3–4 p.m. stage there are no

[5] See the Appendix for a discussion of the terminology used in this section.

Table 10.6   Passenger Arrival Data for the Dispatch Example

Stage	Time interval	Passenger arrivals (*vehicle loads*)
I	3–4 p.m.	2
II	4–5	1
III	5–6	2
IV	6–7	3

Table 10.7   Component Cost Data for the Dispatch Example

Number of vehicles	Delay to vehicle loads (C_{pw})	Train dispatching (C_{vd})
0	$ 0	$ 0
1	75	200
2	150	400
3	225	500
4	300	520
5	375	540
6	450	560
7	525	580
8	600	600

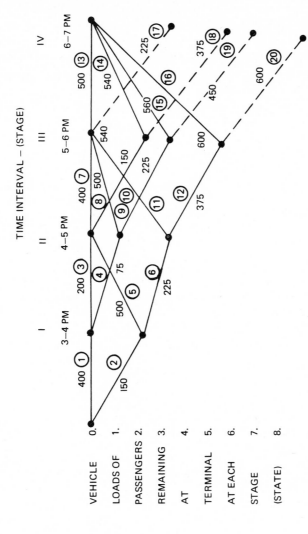

TIME INTERVAL – (STAGE)

Fig. 10.4 Decision network formulation of dispatch example.

passengers waiting to be served nor any vehicles dispatched. Then 2 vehicle loads of passengers arrive (Table 10.6), leaving the dispatcher with the choice of providing a 2-vehicle train or no train for the 3–4 p.m. stage. The first alternative would result in no passengers being left (link 1) in the terminal but would cost $400 for the 2-vehicle train operation, whereas the choice of the second alternative would mean that two loads of passengers would be delayed (link 2) at least 1 hour until the next possible departure time. This would result in a delay cost of $150. Continuing on from stage I to stage II, link 3 represents one possibility open to the dispatcher. He could send off a 1-vehicle train, taking with it the passengers arriving in stage II. On the other hand, the dispatcher could let these arrivals wait, at a cost of $75, and save the $200 of sending the train.

If we were to elaborate on all the possible decisions that could be made in all stages, we eventually would arrive at the complete network in Fig. 10.4 and, with a cost associated with each line, our objective would be to determine the shortest cost route through the network.[6] Hence, we have a problem structure similar to the one demonstrated in the Appendix.

There is one significant difference between the dispatching problem and the problem in the Appendix—the output state of one stage of the dispatching problem is not necessarily the input state to the next. However the two are related easily by means of the equation

$$PW_t = PW_{t-1} + A_t - VD_t \tag{10.4}$$

where PW_t = vehicle loads of passengers waiting at stage t (output state)
PW_{t-1} = vehicle loads of passengers waiting at stage $t-1$ (input state)
A_t = number of arrivals at stage t
VD_t = number of vehicles in train dispatched at stage t

Equation (10.4) is a simple accounting equation which indicates that the numbers of passengers waiting at a given time period t must equal the number waiting in the previous time period $(t-1)$ plus the arrivals during the present period minus the departures in that time period. Note, however, that either PW_t or VD_t must be 0 if the requirement for dispatching all accumulated passengers or none is to be met. Moreover, PW_{IV} must be 0 in order that no passengers are left at the terminal after the train departure at the last stage.

Having designated the stages, states, and interstate relationships for the dispatch problem, we now are ready to obtain a solution by means of the functional equation

$$f_t(PW_t) = \min_{PW_t} [r_t(PW_t) + f_{t-1}(PW_t)] \tag{10.5}$$

---

[6] In fact, most dynamic programming problems can be formulated as decision networks.

where PW_t represents both the input state for each stage and the decision variable. The value of the term $r_t(PW_t)$ is found through

$$r_t(PW_t) = C_{pw} \cdot PW_t + C_{vd} \cdot VD_t \tag{10.6}$$

or, from Eq. (10.4)

$$r_t(PW_t) = C_{pw} \cdot PW_t + C_{vd}(PW_{t-1} + A_t - PW_t) \tag{10.7}$$

where C_{pw} and C_{vd} are the costs given in Table 10.7. The direct use of the functional equation is rather cumbersome, so that a tabular arrangement similar to that shown in the Appendix becomes convenient. Such an arrangement is presented in Table 10.8, where all the necessary calculations are made and the minimum cost path (strategy) is shown by the boldface numbers in each subtable. The best route costs $1,260 and runs from 0 to 0 to 1 to 3 to 0. Consequently, the dispatcher should have these many vehicle loads of passengers on the terminal platform after each respective time interval. These figures imply, through the use of Eq. (10.4), that the number of vehicles to have in each train is 0, 2, 0, 0, and 6.

An interesting concomitant output from this particular example is the information contained in rows 1 to 8 of the expanded stage IV subtable shown in Table 10.9. The "min" column in the table gives the minimum total delay and dispatching costs if there were no constraint on having all passengers served by the time the last train departed. In other words, if this limitation did not exist, the total cost could be reduced to $925 from the present $1,260, a saving of $335. Such added features of dynamic programming tabulations allow the planner or engineer to give some consideration to the consequences of removing various constraints or of taking the second or third best routes. If, for example, one of the latter two options were available, the costs would be $1,280 and $1,285, respectively, as shown in the stage IV subtable. In general, the ability to test the *sensitivity* of various solutions to possible changes in constraints and costs is a valuable asset of any optimization technique such as dynamic programming.

10.3 GEOMETRIC CONSIDERATIONS

In the design of the guideway for a transportation conveyance, there are many important considerations that must be taken into account, some of the more important being the geometric design of the facility, its structural design, and the effects of weather on both the performance of the system and the durability of the physical facility. Here we will discuss those aspects of these considerations that are common to more than one specific type of transportation with only passing comments made on special aspects for specific types of systems.

The geometric design of a guideway or roadway has to do with its physical layout and concerns such things as width, curvature (horizontal and vertical),

Table 10.8 Tabular Arrangement for Solution of Dispatch Problem

Stage I

	PW_o	
PW_I	0	min
0	(400)	400
1	(150)	—
2		150

Stage II

	PW_I			
PW_{II}	0	1	2	min
0	200 + 400 = (600)	—	500 + 150 = 650	600
1	75 + 400 = (475)	—	—	475
2	—	—	—	—
3	—	—	225 + 150 = (375)	375

Stage III

	PW_{II}				
PW_{III}	0	1	2	3	min
0	400 + 600 = 1,000	500 + 475 = 975	—	540 + 375 = (915)	915
1	—	—	—	—	—
2	150 + 600 = (750)	—	—	—	750
3	—	225 + 475 = (700)	—	—	700
4	—	—	—	—	—
5	—	—	—	375 + 375 = (750)	750

Stage IV

	PW_{III}						
PW_{IV}	0	1	2	3	4	5	min
0	300 + 915 = 1,415		540 + 750 = 1,290	560 + 700 = (1,260)		600 + 750 = 1,350	1,260

Table 10.9 Expanded Version of Stage IV Subtable of Table 10.8

				PW_{III}			
	0	1	2	3	4	5	min
0	500 + 915 = 1,415	—	540 + 750 = 1,290	560 + 700 = 1,260	—	600 + 750 = 1,350	1,260
1	—	—	—	—	—	—	—
2	—	—	—	—	—	—	—
3	225 + 915 = 1,140	—	—	—	—	—	1,140
PW_{IV} 4	—	—	—	—	—	—	—
5	—	—	375 + 750 = 925	—	—	—	925
6	—	—	—	450 + 700 = 1,150	—	—	1,150
7	—	—	—	—	—	—	—
8	—	—	—	—	—	600 + 750 = 1,350	1,350

superelevation or banking, and the need to conform to terrain and other environmental factors.

10.3.1 Design Speed

Whether it is a highway, airport taxi-way, subway system, or other type of transportation system, the basic geometric design of the guideway or roadway is based upon knowledge of the planned design speed of the vehicle involved. Simply put, design speed is the maximum speed the vehicle or conveyance can travel on the road or guideway with safety and comfort, where only geometric considerations govern. In most cases this means that horizontal and vertical curvature will be the main geometric features that will act as a constraint on design speed. As a rule, design speed will not be selected so as to be higher than the physical capabilities of the vehicle or conveyance.

For Interstate highway construction where 80 mph frequently is selected as a design speed standard, the selection approaches the physical limitations of the vehicle. Whether 80 mph should be used as design speed in the future, however, is open to question. In rugged topography where highways of lesser importance are constructed, generally much lower design speeds are selected. This is done to affect economics in traversing the rugged terrain. If money were available for these lower class roads, it would be physically possible to maintain a much higher design speed through rugged terrain by using long sweeping curves, but normally the expense is not justified. Therefore, it can be said in many instances, the economics of the situation also affect the selection of the design speed.

In airport taxi-way design, the physical characteristics of the aircraft are such that turning movements can be made from the runway, following landings at velocities as high as 60 mph, if the taxi-way turnoffs are properly designed. With this in mind, the Federal Aviation Administration recommends that all taxi-way turnoffs be designed for 60 mph so that aircraft may vacate the runway as quickly as possible in order to make room for others attempting to land. So in this case the need for greater runway capacity makes it important to have the highest possible design speed for these taxi-way turnoffs.

With specification of any transportation system, the selection of a design speed is essential so that the geometric design of the guideway may be carried out. The selection may be affected by many of the same factors given in these examples: economics, terrain considerations, and capacity limitations, as well as the physical limitations of the vehicle or conveyance itself.

10.3.2 Effect of Grade

The vertical gradient of a guideway or roadway can have a very pronounced effect on the performance characteristics of the vehicle or conveyance on the system. It can be shown that for a given power to weight ratio, a certain constant velocity can be maintained at a given grade: change the gradient and a different velocity can be maintained. In other words, the steeper the hill, the slower the vehicle will go. It is important that once a design speed has been selected the gradients be kept low enough so as not to cause the vehicle to slow below the design speed. For highways, speed reduction curves have been developed for different weight categories of trucks. Figure 10.5 illustrates the relationship between power-weight ratio, gradient, and maximum sustained speed. The speed distance curves shown in the upper part of the figure were developed from the basic relationships shown in the lower part of the figure for a typical large truck. Similar curves could be developed for any vehicle or conveyance desired.

10.3.3   Effect of Curvature

The details of the effect of curvature as a physical factor affecting design were discussed in some detail in Chap. 5. Essentially, it is the equation

$$e + f = \frac{V^2}{15R} \tag{10.8}$$

that is used for design purposes. In this equation e is the superelevation, f is the side friction coefficient, V is the speed in miles per hour, and R is the radius in feet. Having selected a design speed and having decided upon desirable values for e and f, it is simply a matter of solving for the desired radius of curve. The value thus obtained represents a minimum radius that could be used under the prescribed conditions. Where topography and other objects are not an obstacle, however, there is no reason to keep to the minimum radius obtained from the equation. But it is usually desirable to use as large a radius as environmental conditions will permit. Nonetheless, especially in urban situations, it is often important to use the minimum curve. In this case, the design formula would be used with maximum acceptable values of e and f and with the desired design speed.

It may be necessary to introduce curvature as a vehicle or conveyance begins to decelerate from the design speed down to a terminal point. Since a terminal point is often in a congested urban area, quite sharp curvature may be desired. It is practical, therefore, to take advantage of knowledge of the change in velocities during deceleration in order that a smaller curve radius can be used for each incremental drop in velocity. It has been found in highway design that it is practical to use compounded horizontal curves under similar situations just described by reducing curve radii in increments of a maximum of 2 to 1; that is to say, one could go from a 500-ft radius curve to a 250-ft radius curve to a 150-ft radius curve, with the curves compounded and without any unusual transition discomfort felt by the passenger. The actual radius of curves used would be based upon knowledge of the velocity at various points along the deceleration path, with the main criteria being that the ratio of one curve radius to the next not exceed two.

10.3.4   Superelevation

Whenever curvature is introduced on the road or guideway, and where superelevation is used properly with smaller radius curves, there is always the problem of the transition from the tangent section of the road or guideway where

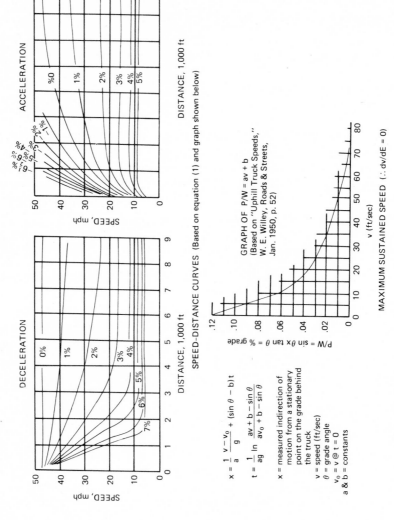

Fig. 10.5 Effect of gradient upon velocity of trucks.

ACCELERATION

DISTANCE, 1,000 ft

SPEED-DISTANCE CURVES (Based on equation (1) and graph shown below)

DECELERATION

DISTANCE, 1,000 ft

GRAPH OF P/W = av + b
(Based on "Uphill Truck Speeds,"
W. E. Willey, Roads & Streets,
Jan. 1950, p. 52)

MAXIMUM SUSTAINED SPEED (∴ dv/dE = 0)

v (ft/sec)

P/W = sin θ x tan θ = % grade

$x = \frac{1}{a} \cdot \frac{v - v_0}{g} + (\sin \theta - b)t$

$t = \frac{1}{ag} \ln \frac{av + b - \sin \theta}{av_0 + b - \sin \theta}$

x = measured indirection of
motion from a stationary
point on the grade behind
the truck

v = speed (ft/sec)
θ = grade angle
v_0 = v @ t = 0
a & b = constants

there is no superelevation to the curved portion with full superelevation. Figure 10.6 illustrates the simplest of procedures for obtaining full superelevation for a highway, and there is no reason why the same illustration could not apply to almost any kind of roadway or guideway. This particular illustration represents a compromise between a completely smooth transition and full superelevation for the full length of the horizontal curve. One can easily visualize that it would be undesirable to obtain full superelevation while still on the tangent portion of the roadway so that full superelevation would be available at the time the vehicle reached the curve. This situation would give the passengers an uncomfortable sense of sloping in the wrong direction and, for driver-directed vehicles, it could adversely affect the driver's performance. In the illustration the *PC*, or beginning of the horizontal curve, is placed somewhere between 60 and 80 percent of the superelevation runoff; or in other words, only about $\frac{3}{4}$ of superelevation is obtained by the time the beginning of the curve is reached. This is a compromise in that some superelevation is obtained while the vehicle is on the tangent and the vehicle has to traverse a small part of the horizontal curve without the benefit of full superelevation. However, from a practical standpoint, the compromise is not a serious one, especially in open areas where superelevations tend to be relatively low and the length of curve radii long. If the designer were working out a solution for a situation where absolute maximum superelevation was required with the shortest possible radii of curves, it would be easy to use a transition spiral from the tangent to the horizontal curve. By doing this, it would be possible to go from 0 to full superelevation while the vehicle is on the spiral, with full superelevation obtained when the beginning of the horizontal curve is reached.

Figure 10.6 also illustrates another principle useful to the designer: one element of the roadway is used for control. In the illustration given, the center line is used for control and, as can be seen, that element is not affected by superelevation. By having one element unaffected by superelevation, it is then easy to combine horizontal and vertical alignment, by first working out the details of superelevation, ignoring vertical alignment, and then finding the vertical alignment of the unaffected control element. Then it is a simple matter of adding or subtracting (as the case may be) the vertical distances the affected elements are from the unaffected element. Or, as in the case of Fig. 10.6, the vertical distances are measured from the outside and inside edges to the center line to determine the height of the superelevated elements.

In highway design, the rate of superelevation is often controlled by the formula

$$S = 75 + 2.5V \tag{10.9}$$

where V is the design speed in mph and S is the slope of the superelevated section as shown in Fig. 10.6. It has been found that with automobiles this formula gives a rate of superelevation that is comfortable to the passenger under a wide range of conditions. It is possible that in certain transportation systems where passengers are involved in activities other than sitting securely in their seats, a lower

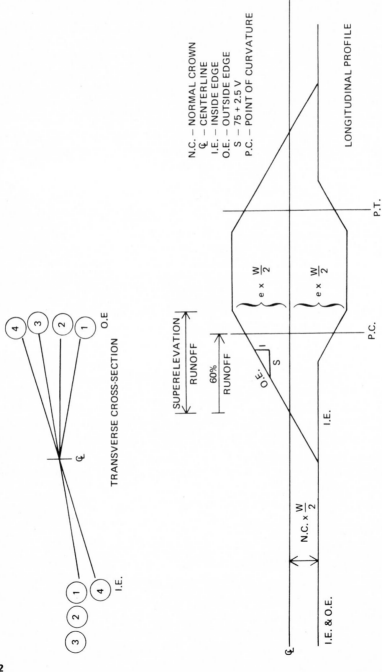

N.C. – NORMAL CROWN
℄ – CENTERLINE
I.E. – INSIDE EDGE
O.E. – OUTSIDE EDGE
S – 75 + 2.5 V
P.C. – POINT OF CURVATURE

TRANSVERSE CROSS-SECTION

LONGITUDINAL PROFILE

Fig. 10.6 Example of highway superelevation.

superlevation would be necessary. Conversely, in systems where the passengers are even more secure in their seats than in the average automobile, it might be quite permissible to use greater superelevation.

10.3.5 Sight Distance

Whether a vehicle or conveyance is under the full manual control of a person or whether it is under complete mechanical or electronic control, the geometric design of the road or guideway must provide enough distance to bring the vehicle to a stop when an emergency condition exists on the guideway ahead. This sight distance may be of the straight, line-of-sight type or it could relate to some sort of electronic sensing mechanism which would not depend upon line-of-sight detection. Where line-of-sight detection is important for the particular system being designed, the effects on the geometric design of the guideway are quite significant. It is this condition which will be discussed here. For illustration, the automobile will again be used because the techniques for handling sight distance for the auto are well defined and the same principles apply to any other conveyance system that requires line-of-sight type distance.

The minimum sight distance available on a road or guideway should be sufficiently long to insure a vehicle traveling at or near the likely top speed (usually the design speed) can stop before reaching an object in its path. In a vehicle, such as an automobile, where the operator has complete manual control, minimum stopping sight distance is the sum of two distances: (1) that traveled from the instant the operator sights an object for which a stop is necessary to the instant he applies the brakes; and (2) that required to stop the vehicle after the brake application begins. The first of these distances is often referred to as the *PIEV* distance, which is described as follows: (1) *P* for perception—the lapse between the observation and realization that braking (or some other operation) is required; (2) *I* for intellection—the time for an evaluation of the situation; (3) *E* for emotion—the condition of the driver as it affects his reflexes, and (4) *V* for volition—the time required for the action of response to the situation. The *PIEV* distance is often thought of as the brake reaction and perception time. Although the actual time required to make a brake application would vary with the type of conveyance involved, the perception, intellection, and emotion parts of *PIEV* should be about the same, regardless of vehicle. For highway design, the American Association of State Highway Officials [10.15] recommends that the time for perception be taken as 1.5 seconds and that the total of perception and brake reaction time be taken as 2.5 seconds.

In computing the second part of required safe stopping distance, the braking distance, certain assumptions are made, the most important of which is that the brakes lock the wheels immediately after application, and sliding commences. At first thought this may not seem to be a very good assumption since maximum friction is obtained without sliding, and a definite reduction in available friction takes place when sliding commences. Also, the question might be asked, is it safe to slide a vehicle on a dry roadway? The answer to this question is that when deceleration rates exceed about 16.1 ft/sec^2, they are sufficiently high to cause passenger discomfort and, if he is not strongly strapped in his seat, may actually throw him to the floor of the vehicle. Theoretically this means that the full mobilization of a friction value greater than 0.5 is not practical—so we design for values of less than 0.5. In the case of an automobile, design certainly should be based for a wet pavement where sliding friction may easily drop below 0.4. Since sliding on wet pavement in an emergency stop situation is most common, friction values used for highway design purposes are about 0.3, depending upon velocity. Actually, according to the American Association of State Highway Officials, friction values would vary from 0.27 at 80 mph up to 0.36 at 30 mph, these being based on experimental tests which take into account variations in sliding friction with vehicular velocity. Further development of equations presented in Chap. 5 concerning maximum deceleration would show that the standard braking distance formula is

$$S = \frac{V^2}{30(f \pm g)} \tag{10.10}$$

where S = braking distance in feet, V = velocity in mph, f = coefficient of friction, and g = the gradient of the roadway. The $\pm$ gradient is to take into account whether it is uphill or downhill, with the minus sign being for a downhill condition, resulting in a longer braking distance.

If the required safe stopping sight distance is known, by assuming a horizontal line of sight, by knowing the height of the observer's eyes, and by making an assumption of the height of object to be observed in the roadway, the required length of vertical curve may be found by the following formulas

    1. Crest vertical curves
        a. When S (sight distance) is less than L (length of vertical curve)

$$L = \frac{AS^2}{100(\sqrt{2h_1} + \sqrt{2h_2})^2} \tag{10.11}$$

        b. When S is greater than L

$$L = 2S - \frac{200(\sqrt{h_1} + \sqrt{h_2})^2}{A} \tag{10.12}$$

where L = length of vertical curve in feet, S = sight distance in feet, A = algebraic difference in grades in percent, h_1 = height of the eye above the roadway surface in feet, and h_2 = height of the object above the roadway surface in feet.

    2. Sag vertical curves
        a. When S is less than L

$$L = \frac{AS^2}{400 + 3.5S} \qquad (10.13)$$

b.   When S is greater than L

$$L = \frac{400 + 3.5S}{A} \qquad (10.14)$$

In developing the second pair of equations, it was assumed that an automobile is traveling at night and the headlight is aimed at a required angle and showing up a definite portion of the road ahead of the vehicle. S in the second pair of equations is thus equal to both safe-stopping sight distance and to the length of roadway that the headlights of the vehicle illuminate.

In highway design other sight distances are taken into account, such as passing sight distance. But in the design of future transportation systems, separation of directional traffic should be required, making such considerations unnecessary.

10.4 STRUCTURAL CONSIDERATIONS

The design of the structural components of a guideway for a transportation system can be based upon principles used in previously developed technologies. For example, the design of an elevated guideway, whether it be monorail or duorail, will utilize principles already practiced in the design of bridges and highway overpasses.

Roads or guideways on the ground surface itself would make use of principles of pavement design now in use in the highway field. Those who would subscribe to the development of an underground pneumatic tube transportation system would make use of principles already in use in the construction of tunnels. It is not the intent to elaborate on the details of these three areas, but instead to touch on the principles of the second example: the guideway built on the ground surface. The reason for this is that the principles of bridge design are well illustrated and documented in advance textbooks on the subject. The third example concerning tunneling is an area that depends so much on specific localized conditions that it is beyond the scope of this discussion to elaborate upon it. The second example concerning guideways constructed on the ground perhaps represents the greatest portion of transportation system construction and thus some benefit can be derived from some elaboration on the principles that are known.

10.4.1 Required Properties of a Guideway Substructure

The substructure for a road or guideway of almost any type would consist mainly of mineral aggregates base courses resting upon a prepared subgrade. There are certain properties that should and can be built into the subgrade and base course components of a substructure for any kind of transportation road or guideway.

The subgrade must be compacted or stabilized to an extent that it has sufficient strength to resist significant deflections when loads are applied by the vehicle. In highway design where deflections of more than five hundredths of an inch occur in the subgrade, quite frequently distress occurs in the pavement. Perhaps certain guideway surfaces could be designed so as not to show distress from such low deflections, but it is usually not too difficult to prepare the subgrade in such a way to keep deflections well below this minimum.

Compaction with heavy construction equipment to an optimum density is the most common means of preparing subgrade soils so that they will have sufficient strength. When plastic clay subgrade soils are prevalent, it is often necessary to stabilize them with an admixture such as hydrated lime. Hydrated lime [$Ca(OH)_2$] will raise the pH of the plastic subgrade soil to the extent where aluminum and silica components of the clay mineral go into solution and are able to react with the available calcium to form calcium aluminates and calcium silicates. These components are identical to the cementing compounds formed by the hydration of Portland cement in concrete, and the result is a plastic clay soil having greatly improved strength. The addition of hydrated lime to the clay soil also greatly improves its workability by making it less plastic.

Another important property for subgrade materials is that they be as little frost susceptible as possible. For example, a subgrade material composed mostly of silt size particles will be very frost susceptible in areas that have at least some freezing weather. These soils have particle sizes that are very conducive for the capillary rise of ground water from below up through the soil to a point in the subgrade where freezing temperatures occur. At this point, the water in the soil pores freezes and attracts additional water from below, causing the accumulation of frozen water in what are called "ice lenses."

A soil which has either larger grain sizes than silts, and thus which are very permeable, or soils which have very small grain sizes, such as with the clays, are not particularly frost susceptible. The permeable larger grain size soils will not permit water to rise by capillarity up to the soil layer. The impermeable clay soils that have small grain sizes have high capillarity but are so impermeable that not enough water will rise up to form significant ice lenses. This phenomenon which is most prevalent with silt soils, is called "frost heave." Therefore, in areas that will be exposed to any amount of freezing temperatures and where there is a water table within a reasonable distance of the surface (the Corps of Engineers suggest that within 10 ft of the subgrade surface is close enough to cause damage), it is important to remove silt soil which could cause severe detrimental frost heave, which would result in severe distress in the guideway. Where the silts cannot be removed and replaced with other materials, it sometimes is necessary to stabilize these materials with Portland cement. Hydrated lime will not work as a stabilizer with silt because the action of lime will not cause the aluminum and silica of the silts to go into solution as it does with the clay soils. The use of Portland cement as a stabilizer of silts will generally cause the material to have sufficient strength to cut down the amount of frost heave that occurs to an acceptable level. Portland cement generally cannot be used as a stabilizer of plastic clay soils because of the difficulty of working the cement into the soil.

The requirements of the base course layers will depend a great deal on the type of guideway constructed at the surface. In most cases the base course layers will be the main structural component and will have the function of distributing the load that is applied on the guideway over the subgrade to the surface and base courses. This structural function is not as important if the guideway construction was similar to that of a rigid Portland cement concrete slab as is frequently used in highway construction. In this case, the beam action of the concrete slab performs most of the structural function. However, in either case, certain basic properties are required, with the main difference between the two cases being that one requires greater structural stability than the other.

Where the base course performs an important structural function, it is very important to optimize stability as much as possible. To actually optimize this property would require having the fines (soil fraction) just filling the void between the aggregate particles, with the entire gradation curve representing a very dense mixture resembling that of the so called "Fuller's Curve." This optimum gradation curve can be represented by the equation

$$P = \left(\frac{d}{D}\right)^{0.5} \tag{10.15}$$

where P = percent passing, d = the size of particle in question on the grain size curve, and D = maximum size aggregate particle in the gradation. Unfortunately, when stability is optimized, other important properties are sacrificed, in particular, permeability and quite frequently susceptibility to frost action. Generally a base course should be able to drain to the extent that when loads are applied, pore water pressures are not developed. Further, when excessive amounts of water are retained in the base course, the freezing temperatures can cause frost heave and subsequent loss of strength during the thaw period.

On the other hand, in order to optimize permeability and resistance to frost action, the best design would be a base course that had only sand and coarse aggregate size particles in its gradation. With no fines (soil fraction) to clog up the voids among the aggregate particles, free drainage would be permitted and frost action would not be a problem. This can be done when the structural function of the base course is not important, such as with a Portland cement concrete slab; however, when the structural function is important, this type of design lacks stability. Stability is lacking in part because the base course material does not have the cohesive properties of the fines, which tends to hold the particles together and maintain the natural grain-to-grain contact of the aggregate particles. Lacking this, when a load is applied, the tendency is for the aggregate particles to shove or push out. Where it is essential to optimize drainage as much as possible and yet still have some stability, it is important to have as dense a gradation of the aggregate portion as possible, while still omitting the fine fraction. In most base course designs, it is suitable to strike a compromise between stability and drainage and have the fine fraction partially fill the voids of the aggregates, thus providing some stability and some drainability.

In regard to the design of the road or guideway, in this discussion reference will be made only to a few guiding principles. Specifics about various guideway types in use or in prospect are treated elsewhere. One very important factor that must be considered is the area over which a load is applied. With rubber wheeled vehicles, this area is for practical purposes nothing more than the total load on a given wheel divided by the tire pressure. When tire pressures are very high and thus the applied area small, it is of utmost importance to select a surface material that has extremely high stability. Portland cement concrete is an inherently good material to use for small loaded areas resulting from high tire pressures. Bituminous concrete can be satisfactory, providing a high stability design is used. In the case of railroad type of vehicles where the load is applied to rails and the rails spread the load on ties or something similar, again the loaded area is well defined.

In these cases there is not surface material as such that the designer is concerned with, and attention must be directed to whether the base course has sufficient stability and is thick enough to properly reduce the stresses that reach the subgrade. In most cases, simple Bousinesq stress distribution theory [10.17] is applied in checking out distress levels at the interface of the various components. As a rule, when a given load is spread over a large area, the stresses in the various components of the structure are small, yet on the other hand they do reach to greater depths. With small loaded areas with resulting high levels of stress at the surface, stress concentrations rapidly diminish to be negligible at small depths. Thus with wheeled vehicles, for example, where high tire pressures are used, greater attention must be given to the surface component, and where low tire pressures are used for the same road, greater attention must be given to the underlying structure.

10.4.2 Effects of Weather

Weather must be considered when designing a road or guideway for a transportation system. In previous sections it was pointed out how in highway design superelevation is limited in states where snow and ice is prevalent so that if for some reason a vehicle became slowed or stalled, it would not slide down the cross slope of the highway. The problem of ice and snow can have similar effects on other types of guideways and in many instances should be taken into consideration. It should be pointed out that if a snow or ice problem similar to the example given for highways can be expected, then geometric design can be worked to minimize its effects. When designing curvature and using Eq. (10.8) and when designing using a side friction value of 0, the effects of ice and snow can be eliminated providing the designer can be assured that the vehicles or conveyances almost always will be maintaining design speed around the curve. Under such circumstances it would not matter if there were ice on the guideway or not, since the weight component of the vehicle would actually balance out the centrifugal force component. For such a design, it would be necessary to provide for a method to protect the vehicle in the rare circumstance it was not able to keep its design speed around the curve.

Also previously discussed were some of the effects of weather on certain structural characteristics. Where freezing temperatures are prevalent, care must be taken to design the substructure of the road or guideway to prevent severe frost heave or loss in strength due to the thawing of frozen ground. Since in most cases the road or guideway will be out in the open, it is certainly important to have proper weather protection for the vehicle and any electronic equipment that may be installed along the guideway. For the most part weather that has to be taken seriously is that which produces water and freezing temperatures, which results in ice and frost action and snow. In the design of the guideway, adequate provision must be made for snow removal.

One other component of weather not mentioned previously is that of wind. In most areas of the United States rather high winds are obtainable at relatively frequent intervals. Although in most cases it has little effect on the design of the road or guideway, it has obvious effects on the design of the vehicle, which in turn has significant effects on the guideway. Stability of the system in wind is of course essential.

Another consideration of weather that affects the design of a transportation road or guideway is the durability of its components. Especially the action of alternate cycles of freezing and thawing can have rather serious effects on the durability of the materials that make up the structure. In highways, for example, when certain highly weathered aggregates are used in Portland cement concrete, alternate cycles of freezing and thawing can reduce the strength of the concrete in a matter of two or three seasons of cyclic freezing and thawing. In these cases often the causes of distress are the pressures developed by the movement of water within an aggregate particle advancing in front of water being frozen and expanding as it freezes. The resistance to movement of this unfrozen water in front of the frozen water produces pressures that have been shown to be sufficiently high to disrupt the aggregate, with the resulting disruption of the surrounding mortar of the concrete.

The ability to find adequate aggregate materials to put in the structures necessary for the guideway will become an increasing problem in years to come, whether the structure is made up primarily of base course aggregates or concrete or asphalt or similar types of materials, aggregate is the main component. Aggregate sources having satisfactory performance as far as weather is concerned are being depleted in many areas of the United States. To make matters worse, particularly near urban areas, excellent aggregate sources are being zoned out of existence by being reserved for residential areas and other similar construction. Thus, in many cases, use must be made of aggregate sources that may not have known a good service record.

10.5 ENVIRONMENTAL DESIGN CONSIDERATIONS

In addition to the aspects of cost, scheduling, geometric design, and structural considerations already discussed in this chapter, there are a number of factors that relate to the user and to the acceptability of a transport system to the nonuser. These factors are of less obvious importance and have in the past generally been overlooked. For the purpose of this discussion, we have grouped these factors under the heading of "environmental design" considerations. Although no attempt has been made at completeness, it is believed that the following discussion touches upon those areas of widespread concern.

10.5.1 Privacy

Perhaps the most common argument offered in favor of mass transit is that it moves people instead of vehicles. In 15 of the nation's 25 largest cities, however, 60 percent or more of all riders arriving at the central business district do so in automobiles [10.19]. One of the chief reasons for this preference is privacy.

Physical privacy might be described as that need for people to establish definite spatial regions between themselves and others. The size and configuration of this territoriality is a function of the activity being engaged in and the sociological background of the persons involved. Although territorial ownership is a very complex thing, investigation has produced evidence of norms related to given circumstances. Optimum conversational distance, for example, seems to vary inversely as both the size of the space in which it is taking place and the level of noise or distraction. People who want to converse tend to sit opposite each other, but this preference is only true when the distance across is equal to, or less than, the side-by-side distance [10.20]. Such norms are more easily maintained or are less important in a private automobile than in public transit. In fact, the personal space that could be identified with a rush-hour commuter is often so minimized as to cause stress.

Stress may be any influence, whether attributable to the interal or external environment, which interferes or even threatens to interfere with a persons's ability to satisfy basic needs or maintain equilibrium [10.21]. Such stress may result from the close proximity of others on the train or, for example, from the fear of passing by an unfamiliar stop in the subway. Strain, on the other hand, refers to an individual's reaction to stress, and may be evidenced by a passenger's move to a less crowded part of the vehicle.

It is not necessary for conditions to reach the "noxious" level beyond the user's physical tolerance in order for him to suffer discomfort. The impact of the physical configuration of seats and windows in a train or bus upon the stress-strain relationships developed by the public users is great. Upon these subtle relationships rests, in part, the degree of acceptability of a transport vehicle.

The second kind of privacy that is relevant to transport vehicle design is often called cultural privacy. It refers to the user's apparent need to establish homogeneity in his surroundings. He will do this by sitting with persons of his own socioeconomic background, or with acquaintances who share his opinions or general life style. Certain groups of commuters will congregate in the club car for an en-route martini, while others prefer the observation car or their newspapers.

Provision for cultural privacy can be made by designing seats in such a way as to promote group conversations or by defining various kinds of activity spaces within the vehicle.

10.5.2 Orientation

Only those who have ever been lost in a bustling Paris Metro, armed with an insufficient French vocabulary, can understand the importance of orientation to transportation design. It is essential that transport information be clearly and legibly presented to the public. What is more, the communication must be quick and should not depend on the particular language. Color coding is a good device for expediting understanding of even the most entangled route map. The most legible color combinations are as follows: black on white (most legible), black on yellow (gains most attention), green on white, red on white, and white on blue.

It is wrong to assume, however, that abundant super-graphics will satisfactorily explain where the passenger is or where he is going. Landmarks or simple physical points of reference might be used to increase the passenger's sense of orientation. A church steeple or radio tower clearly seen along a freeway will offer assurance to the visitor and local resident alike. Landmarks are more easily identified, and thus more significant, if they have a clear and comprehensible form [10.22].

The most successfully designed (and sometimes indigenous) artifacts seem to possess a spatial organization that enables the user to "sense" where he is in relation to the entire complex. Exit signs, for example, although usually required by fire underwriters, are superfluous in a well-organized building. Properly designed transportation facilities, as well, will attain some innate qualities of direction and orientation. This is of primary importance where transportation routes venture underground, because familiar points of reference are no longer available. In Boston, large photographs and murals have been used with some success to assist in associating an underground platform with the peculiar characteristics of the street above.

10.5.3 Convenience

If convenience is indeed an important criterion of transportation design, then the automobile would seem to be the paragon of comparative excellence. Cars are readily available to an ever-increasing number of Americans. For those more interested in basic transportation than snobbery, a very few dollars buys a surprisingly intricate machine. Cars are as accessible as your garage; they require a minimal number of transfers in getting from one place to another.

Public transportation convenience is usually considered simply as a matter of vehicular capacity and frequency of stops. Another, and perhaps more appropriate attitude to transportation convenience is that held by Ehrenthal [10.23]. He believes that transportation systems can be made more convenient, as well as safer and more comfortable, by analyzing the pedestrian-passenger/public transportation interface situations. The most common interface situation exists where the pedestrian enters, leaves, or waits for the transport vehicle. Simple, comfortable shelters that are heated, well-lighted, and in a safe environment might make waiting, even for extended periods, tolerable and perhaps enjoyable.

10.5.4 Comfort

As regards transport facilities design, comfort can be defined as that state acquired which sets both the mind and body at ease. In practice, concern has been limited largely to the anthropometrical relationships that exist between man's body and his physical environment. A great deal is being learned about the optimum dimensions of seats, heights of arm-rests, and the degree of slope of back-rests, etc. The paths traced by a seated man as he swings his arms in a horizontal arc, for example, tell the designer a great deal about where the ashtray or handrail should be placed. The position of information both inside the vehicle and out is similarly related to sight lines projected from the seated or standing passenger through windows or other openings.

Anthropometric information is a necessary ingredient of transportation design, but is not sufficient to insure its complete suitability. There are many physiological problems which confront the designer that demand considerable sophistication before they are recognized—much less solved. These problems often relate to the physical safety of the user and can be demonstrated by the following examples:

1. The engineer of a modern, high-speed train is enclosed by transparent glass or plastic. Although he serves only to monitor the train's computerized operation, it is important for the passenger's tranquility that he be visible.
2. Structural members, especially those made of concrete, are often "over-sized." This is sometimes done for convenience of construction, but just as often to correct the proportions or assure the user of its stability.
3. The bumper on automobiles serves little use in a crash, but offers a semblance of protection to the owner of the vehicle.

Few people suffer from agoraphobia, but most are quick to feel uncomfortable in tight or over-crowded spaces. Generally it is good design practice to create a feeling of openness by careful use of windows, color, and generous space where appropriate.

Vehicular motion also can contribute to discomfort of the user. Using the automobile for an example, if one were to drive around a curve and actually mobilize all of the available friction up to the point of sliding (which on a wet road might be on the order of 0.3 to 0.4), the passengers, unless they were strapped in, would be thrown to the side of the vehicle. In order for the passengers to be comfortable in such conditions, they would have to have a complete compliment of straps to eliminate the side sway of the body and needless to say they would have to have complete confidence in the driver. Standards set for highway design by the American Association of State Highway Officials [10.7] and those set for airport design by the Federal Aviation Administration [10.4] specify that the maximum amount of side friction mobilized while going around a curve at 60 mph should not be more than about 0.12 or 0.13.

Having such a maximum limit on side friction makes the discomfort of the passenger minimal. Where lower speeds are involved, somewhat higher side friction values can be tolerated for normal operations. In highway design, when a special situation is encountered, such as a ramp leading off a freeway, higher side friction values are permitted in an effort to make the vehicle operator conscious of the fact that he is going into a special situation. On such curves, side friction values are permitted to range from 0.16 at 40 mph all the way up to 0.32 at 15 mph. This illustrates the principle that the passenger can tolerate far greater side friction being mobilized at very slow speeds. At higher speeds the side friction mobilized must be kept very low.

10.5.5 Ecological Considerations

A comprehensive study of natural processes is important to the highway planner and engineer. Different rocks have a variety of compressive strengths; some areas are subject to inundation during heavy storms; certain soils are more susceptible to erosion than others. These factors and many more considerations indicate the necessity to evaluate and rank natural resources in the solution specification process.

Physiographic factors important to transportation design are as follows:
1. Degree of slope for grading and drainage.
2. Surface drainage including streams, lakes, and ponds.
3. Soil drainage, to indicate areas with poor drainage to be avoided.
4. Bedrock foundation to determine the most suitable foundation material.
5. Soil foundation for high compressive strength.
6. Susceptibility to erosion from cuts and fills.

In addition to these physiographic factors, McHarg suggests a number of other factors of social importance in locating and designing highways [10.24]. These are listed as low land economic values; areas above flood levels; low historic, scenic, and recreation value; urbanized watersheds of important streams; unforested lands and poor wildlife habitat areas; and low residential and institutional value. By utilizing these additional values, McHarg feels that the highway will inflict the least social cost and, therefore, assume the most appropriate location.

One of the problems in strictly following the procedure outlined by McHarg is that quite often the highway is so far from existing development that it cannot be used efficiently. Thus, although the above factors are important to consider in road location endeavors, each design situation is unique and must be planned in a balanced manner stressing some values and diminishing others.

Once the survey of physiographic, biotic, and social factors is complete, the information may be put on map overlays or computer programmed for synthesis of the various factors. The computer programming method allows for the weighing of this multiplicity of factors and printouts can be produced for alternative locations.

10.5.6 Landscape Design Considerations

Landscape design for highways must be based upon kinetic spatial organization. In other words, we must develop a sense of movement through the landscape by incorporating continuous expressions of open and closed spaces or transitions and the development of features to indicate progression and climax of arrival at a destination.

On high speed roads the design must be bold, set back from the highway, and utilizing major tree forms. This is because at high speeds the eye focuses far ahead of the vehicle, and the range of vision is very limited. The view of the roadway is very narrow and hence only large, significant forms can be interpreted.

In contrast to the above, the design of low speed roads can be quite diverse, utilizing major trees, small flowering trees, and large and medium shrubs to form intimate plant compositions for the driver's enjoyment. The road focus at slow speeds, say 30 mph, is only a few hundred feet ahead, and peripheral vision is reasonably wide. Thus scenic roads are normally subject to speed limitations of 40 mph in order that the driver may successfully comprehend highway aesthetics.

There are a number of considerations to be included in spatial design, each of which must relate to the others. Twelve points with which the designer is involved are: color, texture, value, scale, space (both negative and positive), light and shadow, ecology (plants and humans), climate (micro and macro), area use, material use, historical implications, and movement and time. All of these factors involve the psychology and physiology of seeing.

Landscape design of highways should begin with road alignment analysis. It is in this stage that the landscape architect can determine the best alternatives for aesthetic value in compliance with economy of construction based on points mentioned earlier in the description of the ecological survey. In a 40-mile stretch of landscape, a road can be located as much as 5 miles off the "bee line" and only contribute 1.24 additional miles to a trip. If this alignment contributes to road interest and aesthetic value with little extra labor or expense, it is certainly worth it. It is at this stage of planning that design possibilities can be foreseen. After the road is aligned, there may be additional expense in trying to beautify a dull landscape.

The right-of-way width is the second important landscape design decision which must be made. The right-of-way width should vary to make the highway better, safer, and often more economical. This variation may take place for high fills or deep cuts to give a better sense of spaciousness, to include sand and gravel deposits for use in construction, to preserve a grove of trees or even a lone tree around which a roadside park might be formed. It is important to have sufficient control of surrounding lands so that unique settings and views may be preserved. One highway department has made a practice of excess condemnation, not just for the purpose of creating roadside parks and rest areas, but at limited access highway interchanges to control future land use development.

Clearing the right-of-way is also an assignment that needs prechecking by the landscape architect to determine which trees and ground cover should be preserved. Each tree worthy of preservation should be tagged before the bulldozers arrive. A principle which should be borne in mind is that it is much easier to preserve a tree than it is to grow one, and the same holds true for native shrubs and ground cover, though to a lesser extent. Trees and plants marked for preservation are then carefully trimmed and pruned under the direction of a competent foreman.

The early designation of trees and shrubs for preservation determines many construction features like ditches, cuts, and fills. These features are not wholly determined from physical conformation of the land. With the new shallow cross-sections of the roadway, the drainage ditches are meaner among trees. After the highway area has been graded and the roadbed constructed, the role of the landscape architect is one of planting design and erosion control to maintain slope stability.

The two methods of erosion control are prevention and restoration. Obviously, prevention is the most important action that can be taken. If the possibilities of erosion are controlled, no hillside channels will develop during a heavy rainstorm to threaten the highway with fast flowing water at certain points.

Once slopes are established, the best means of erosion prevention is sodding the more gentle slopes with grass and planting steeper ones with shrubs and other forms that develop thick root mats. There are many different types of grass or ground cover, and techniques for planting depend upon soil types. Consultation should be obtained from an agronomist or turf specialist. In addition to planting, precautions should be taken by installing concrete drainage troughs on the top of all long, steep cut and fill slopes and in the bottom of ditches or median strips of divided highways where erosion is likely.

Landscape design of completed highways consists of functional as well as aesthetic considerations. Plants can serve functions of glare reduction, acoustical control, erosion control, air conditioning, and traffic control if they are well chosen and judiciously placed. It is well known that plants absorb some noxious gases, act as receptors of dust and dirt particles, and generally cleanse the air of impurities. Certain plants are relatively effective in muffling traffic noise. Plants also can be effective as structures for creating and defining spaces, complementing, expanding or negating land forms, masking undesirable views, helping direct wind (windbreaks) and snow, and controlling precipitation and humidity.

The functional aspect of landscape design, other than erosion control, is that of influencing speed through control of road focus. Danger lurks at intersections and on curves with insufficient warning. Signs may help, but the warning must be more subtle, more effective, less obvious and yet more imperative. The warning must be built into the environment of the highway so that it cannot be ignored.

At intersections of a minor and major road, the problem is to warn the motorist on the minor road long before he reaches the intersection. This can be done on a straight road by installing a grove of trees on the other side of the main highway.

An alternative on a curving road is to install a reverse curve, the first curve of 5° slowing speed from 60 to 50 mph, and the second curve of 9°, thereby reducing the speed to 40 mph and then a straight section to the intersection. In addition to the curves, the designer must reinforce the alignment by heavy tree and perhaps shrub planting on the outside of each curve.

10.5.7 An Example

The considerations presented in the previous subsections are difficult to illustrate because so little transportation design incorporating them has been implemented to date. One good example, however, is the Nicollet Avenue Mall in Minneapolis. Planned by Barton-Aschman Associates in conjunction with Lawrence Halprin Associates, of San Francisco, the project was conceived as a transit mall and addresses itself jointly to problems of accessibility and the environment.

Nicollet Avenue, Minneapolis, Minn., before renovation. (*Downtown Council of Minneapolis*)

Nicollet Mall, Minneapolis, Minn., after renovation. (*Downtown Council of Minneapolis*)

Private vehicular traffic is prohibited along the 8-block section of Nicollet Avenue where the roadway has been replaced with an undulating transitway that introduces a pleasant sense of rhythm and continually changing vistas. The curved transitway minimizes the feeling of distance and encourages walking block to block. The roadway has been reduced to 22 ft in width so that the adjacent pedestrian space is not only more generous than it had been, but also much more safe and useful. The pedestrian capacity of the sidewalk is increased three or fourfold.

Nicollet Mall is for people, not cars. Up to 40,000 bus passengers per day arrive where a meager 9,000 were previously brought by automobiles, taxis, and buses combined. It is expected that the increased accessibility will dramatically increase retail sales and decrease the number of store vacancies. Studies are being made of a minibus system that would augment the present parking facilities and bus transit in the central business district.

The mall includes a sculpture-clock, automated post office, fountains, a weather station, and a Mobile-Stabile by Alexander Calder. These serve as landmarks and provide easy orientation to pedestrians and passengers. Thirty-three variously boxed trees, 63 unboxed trees, and 80 large concrete flower pots add color and variety.

Granite bollards, resembling hitching posts, are used at appropriate spots to channel pedestrians to mid-block crossings. There are 16 heated, well-lighted bus shelters on alternate sides of the street, which contribute to safety and comfort at the pedestrian/passenger interface as well as generally enhance the street.

The cost of the project, originally estimated at nearly $4 million, is borne by the property owners who benefit from it financially. A special commission appointed by the city council assesses the benefits to merchants on Nicollet Avenue and adjacent streets under terms of the Elwell proceedings. This procedure insures the cooperation of a majority of property owners along the mall and provides opportunity for them to participate in the planning and design process.

Most importantly, Nicollet Mall underlines the value of total transportation design; it represents the new trend toward comprehensive and simultaneous consideration of both traffic accessibility and the environment. It symbolizes the commitment of a growing number of professionals to offering better alternatives to our present way of urban life.

10.6 SUMMARY

In the preceding sections, examples and techniques were presented that related to the solution specification process. It was noted in the beginning that what is broad design or planning to one person is detail to another. Consequently, we will not take a hard stance by saying exactly which items we feel fall under the heading of "solution specification."

In the same vein, many of the techniques demonstrated in this chapter are not necessarily relegated only to the solution specification stage. Both simulation and dynamic programming (and many other operations research techniques) can be employed in other stages, particularly in the model development and solution generation stages. Yet these techniques are, in our minds, most valuable *after* the major outlines of the solution have been set and the need arises to mold the details of the outlines to form a finished product.

A final comment relates to the breadth of factors to be considered and to teamwork needed in the solution specification stage. It should have occurred to the reader that it would be difficult if not impossible for any one individual or professional to specify a solution suitable to all concerned. There are simply too many factors like privacy, convenience, police and fire access, and so on to be considered in too little time. The conclusion thus arises that a design *team* is essential. In addition, the engineer or planner should not forget to consult willing citizens, for often they have suggestions that can improve the details (and sometimes the broad outline) of a solution considerably (see [10.25] for examples). In any case, solution specification is a difficult task, requiring on the one hand the expertise of a large number of professionals and on the other hand inputs from those whom the specification might effect. It is at the solution specification level, in fact, that the impacts are "closest to home" and thus must be handled with great care.

BIBLIOGRAPHY

10.1   Department of Engineering, Univ. of California at Los Angeles: *Transim-General Purpose Transportation System Simulator-User's Manual*, Federal Clearinghouse, PB 173 016, Springfield, Va., May, 1966.

10.2   T.R.W. Systems Group: *Transportation System Optimization Program Demonstration Problem, (for the Office of High Speed Ground Transportation)*, Department of Transportation, Washington, D.C., June 1, 1968.

10.3   Baerwald, J. E. (ed.): *Traffic Engineering Handbook*, Institute of Traffic Engineers, Washington, D.C., 1965.

10.4   Horonjeff, R.: *Planning and Design of Airports*, McGraw-Hill, New York, 1962.

10.5   Charnes, A., S. C. Littlechild, M. J. Kirby, and W. M. Raike: "Chance Constrained Models for Transport Pricing and Scheduling under Competition," *Transportation Science*, vol. 2, no. 1, Feb., 1968.

10.6   Browne, J. J., and J. J. Kelly: "Simulation of Elevator System for World's Tallest Buildings," *Transportation Science*, vol. 2, no. 1, Feb., 1968.

10.7   American Association of State Highway Officials: *A Policy on Arterial Highways in Urban Areas*, Washington, D.C., 1967.

10.8   Hay, G. A., E. K. Morlok, and A. Charnes: "Toward Optimal Planning of a Two-Mode Urban Transportation System: A Linear Programming Formulation," *Highway Research Board Record*, 148, 1966.

10.9   Meyer, J. R., and J. F. Kain, and M. Wohl: *The Urban Transportation Problem*, Harvard Univ. Press, Cambridge, Mass., 1965.

10.10 Naylor, T. H., and J. L. Balintfy, D. S. Burdick, and K. Chu: *Computer Simulation Techniques*, Wiley, New York, 1968.

10.11 Bisbee, E. F.: *Operations Analysis of System Specification, Part I Passenger Scheduling*, Federal Clearinghouse, PB 173 635, Springfield, Va., Nov., 1966.

10.12 Drew, D. R.: *Traffic Flow Theory and Control*, McGraw-Hill, New York, 1968.

10.13 Hoel, L. H., F. Di Casare, and J. W. Hoag: "On the Interface of a Regional Transportation System and the Central Business District." Presented to the Meeting of the *Operations Research Society of America*, San Francisco, May, 1968.

10.14 Wagner, F. A., F. C. Barnes, and D. L. Gerlough: *Improved Criteria for Traffic Signal Systems in Urban Networks*, N.C.H.R.P. Report 124, Highway Research Board, Washington, D.C., 1971.

10.15 American Association of State Highway Officials: *A Policy on Geometric Design of Rural Highways*, Washington, D. C., 1965.

10.16 Yoder, E. J.: *Principles of Pavement Design*, Wiley, New York, 1959.

10.17 Walker, R. D., and R. D. Krebs: *Highway Materials*, McGraw-Hill, New York, 1971.

10.18 Roberts, P. O., and J. H. Suhrbier: *Highway Location Analysis: an Example Problem*, M.I.T. Press, Cambridge, Mass., 1966.

10.19 Editors of Fortune: *The Exploding Metropolis*, Doubleday Anchor Books, Garden City, N.Y., 1958.

10.20 Sommer, R.: *Personal Space—The Behavioral Basis of Design*, Prentice-Hall, Englewood Cliffs, N.J., 1969.

10.21 Wolpert, J.: "Migration as an Adjustment to Environmental Stress," *Journal of Social Issues*, vol. 22, no. 4, 1966.

10.22 Lynch, K.: *The Image of the City*, M.I.T. Press, Cambridge, Mass., 1960.

10.23 Ehrenthal, F. F.: "An Investigation and Development of Design Concepts for Public Transit Passenger Shelters," D.O.T./U.M.T.A. Project No. VA-MTD-3 (Mid-term Report), July, 1970.

10.24 McHarg, I.: *Design with Nature*, The Natural History Press, New York, 1969.

10.25 Smith, D. C.: *Urban Highway Design Teams*, Highway Users Federation for Safety and Mobility, Washington, D.C., Feb., 1970.

11 Implementation Procedures

While it is important to develop solutions which are technically feasible, the real test of a good solution is its implementability. Far too many plans and designs have been developed only to gather dust in some remote corner of an agency office or library. There are many reasons for such occurrences. Political actions, or the lack thereof, is one. Such actions often lead to approved legislation, which is the topic of the first section in this chapter. Of course no legislation is ever final and irreversible since it can be tested in courts of law to determine its constitutionality. The courts also provide *interpretation* to clarify and otherwise fill in missing spots in the legislation. Several court decisions in regard to state and local laws for land use control are discussed in the second section of this chapter.

The third and final section deals with finance, perhaps the most important ingredient in the implementation of any solution. The emphasis there is on different sources of funds at the federal, state, and local level.

11.1 URBAN TRANSPORTATION LEGISLATION

Public policy in the United States with respect to urban transportation is in a state of dramatic change. The full impact of these changes and the directions in which they are aimed can only be appreciated in historical perspective. The evaluation of local-state-federal governmental attitudes toward urban transportation can be blocked into three historical stages:

1781–1944	Exclusive local responsibility; federal laissez-faire attitude toward cities.
1944–1964	Federal and state aid to cities for highway purposes only.
1964–	Federal and some state aid for transit; concern for social, economic and environmental impacts of transportation.

11.1.1 Local Responsibility, 1781–1944

Not until the end of World War II was there any regular state or federal financial aid for urban transportation, and then it was solely for highways. There seemed to be generous federal aid for homesteaders, farmers, roads, railroads, and canals; why not for urban transportation? First of all, during most of the 19th century such aid would have been unthinkable. Federal "intervention" of this sort would have been contrary to the prevailing faith in laissez-faire and the idea that "least government is the best government," a faith sustained by rapid progress and broadening prosperity. However, in view of the aid given other purposes, it appears that these principles were selectively applied. When the unseen hand of the market place could be assisted by governmental promotion, aid was forecoming. When the "evil" cities were involved, the pursestrings were closed.

Secondly, cities were politically weak. A major source of their impotence is traceable to the anti-urban bias of American intellectuals. Jefferson stated the widespread view of large cities "as pestilential to the morals, the health, and the liberties of man." Accordingly, the Constitution had reduced the strong colonial cities to mere legal creatures of the states. Rural and small town populations exceeded those of cities. Even so, state legislatures usually had a disproportionate number of rural representatives.

Finally, urban transportation was not the serious problem it became with the automobile. In large part it was a profitable private endeavor. Cities were relatively wealthy and providing but a small fraction of today's municipal services; they were usually able to pave streets and build bridges, especially in the business and "better" residential neighborhoods.

Nevertheless, even in the laissez-faire era, we can identify the antecedents of later policies in regard to urban transportation. First, governmental support, both national and local, of transportation as an instrument of economic expansion and national defense had been accepted as a legitimate public function since colonial times. From the beginning the States were active in road and canal building, often jointly with private enterprise. By 1850 over 3,700 miles of canals were built. Where turnpike construction costs exceeded private and state capacities, the federal government assumed the role. This was the case with the most ambitious early road project, the Cumberland Road (National Pike) which ran from Cumberland, Maryland, to Vandalia, Illinois. The project, financed through land sales and completed in 1852, totaled $6,821,200. Cities too were active. Cincinnati, for example, financed the Cincinnati and Southern Railroad partly with municipal bonds to tap southern markets.

A second trend during this period was the slow evolution of explicit transportation policies, reflected in laws. Railroads, a major force in city development, were *the* dominant inter-city mode from roughly 1840 to 1940. As such they were the principal concern of emerging national transportation policy. Norton [11.1] discerns three states of public policy relative to railroads. During the promotion, roughly 1840–1870, governmental aid for railroad construction was so popular that policies were often more implicit than explicit. In the second era, 1870–1920, goals of public regulation—general economic welfare, railroad efficiency and stability (e.g., avoiding excessive competition)—were more clearly spelled out, notably in the Interstate Commerce Act of 1887. The third stage can be dated from the Transportation Act of 1920, the first really *comprehensive* transportation regulatory act to be passed in the United States. Unlike the simply negative, even punitive, nature of previous policy, the Act of 1920 was "a rational and constructive approach . . . a remarkable piece of legislation . . . maturity of view . . . and constructive, not merely negative" [11.1, pp. 6, 7].

The Act of 1920 was more outstanding as a statement of national purpose than as an effective instrument. The rise of the automobile, a competing mode to the railroads, which had helped make the Act of 1920 possible and necessary also helped contribute to its demise. Just as Congress attempted to reconcile a wide variety of interests, often conflicting, in the railroad regulatory acts, it responded starting in 1916 to a new coalition of interests supporting federal aid to inter-city highways. The coalition included the farmers, other agricultural interests, auto owners and manufacturers, bicycle enthusiasts, mail order businesses, postal interests, and the railroads themselves.

Like the Act of 1920, the Transportation Act of 1940 was more of a policy statement than an implementation vehicle. Until 1940 governmental regulation was restrictive and punitive in nature and without a formal policy statement of the needs, directions, and purposes of the transportation industry. The 1940 Act represented a realization on the part of the Federal government that the transportation needs of the country were multimodal, not simply a problem of highway construction. (Highway travel had become a more and more dominant mode with the decline of the railroads.) The Act was intended to be an overall guide to the direction of policy making agencies and organizations (especially Congressional) and was an attempt to enable them to work toward a common goal of maximum efficiency in the transportation industry. The Act was to serve as a rough indicator of intended allocation of natural resources between the various transportation modes and other industries.

The third of the forerunner policy trends, federal aid for roads, can be dated from the Federal-Aid Road Acts of 1916 to 1920. The Act of 1916 was the first authorizing federal funds for inter-city highways, giving great impetus to state road-building projects. It initiated a 30-year period in which federal road aid was almost exclusively for rural and inter-city roads. In fact the 1916 Act specifically prohibited aid to urban areas of 2,500 or more, except routes where the houses averaged more than 200 ft apart [11.2, p. 553]. The coalition of interests which successfully supported the federal aid bills did not want to share the funds available with cities, or worse, risk defeat in an unpopular cause.

The 1916 Act established a basic framework of federal-state cooperation in road construction. Indeed, for three decades all federal aid highway acts were amendments to the 1916 Act. It set a Constitutional basis for federal-state cooperation by requiring specific assent by state legislatures to obtain and use funds in compliance with federal law.

The Federal Highway Act of 1921 did little to carry out the comprehensive policy expressed in the Transportation Act of 1920. Instead, it rather single purposedly amended the 1916 Act to establish a system of "federal-aid highways" to be built or improved by the states with matching federal funds. In each state the system was limited to 7 percent of the total nonurban road mileage.

A fourth forerunner policy trend during the pre-World War II period was the gradual evolution of the federal road aid to cities. The transportation situation in urban areas worsened rapidly during the 1920's and 30's. Ownership of automobiles soared, as shown by registration figures below:

1910[1]	458,000
1920	8,132,000
1930	22,973,000

A star-like pattern of urban settlement had been engendered by decades of transport service by railroads and interurban lines. The railroad's commuter services were usually incidental to and subsidized by their intercity freight business. As a result of automotive competition they were no longer able to do this. Fares increased and service contraction resulted. The interurban railroads, based on electric streetcar technology, had spawned a vast rail network, particularly during the period 1900-1910. By the end of the Depression most of the service as well as the rights-of-way had been abandoned.

Urban transit companies experienced similar pressures. In the decade 1910-1920, squeezed between rapidly increasing operating costs and a franchise-fixed fare (usually 5 cents), 116 companies with over 2,000 miles of trackage went into receivership. These unhappy events were typical of urban transit during the next four decades. Although buses replaced streetcars and fares increased substantially, with the exception of the Depression and War Years which curtailed private auto use, transit ridership steadily declined.

Other forces contributed to a critical and mounting transportation problem, particularly in the larger and middle sized cities. Among these, growing affluence,

---

[1] Henry Ford began production of the low-priced Model T in 1909. Source for figures is J. G. Coke, "Antecedents of Local Planning," in W. I. Goodman and E. C. Freund (Eds.), *Principles and Practice of Urban Planning*, International City Management Association, Washington, D. C., 1968.

popularly priced autos and federally insured home mortgages accelerating new patterns of suburban and exurban settlements created a life style heavily dependent on the automobile. Traffic congestion became a major economic and political problem.

Often public policies changed slowly in response to needs. Urban transportation provided one such case. Despite these new conditions, the strength of the anti-urban bias persisted, as illustrated by the 1928 amendment of the Federal-Aid Highway Act. Federal-Aid routes could be extended into cities of 2,500 population or more, again *provided* that the adjoining houses were more than 200 feet apart on the average [11.3, p. 61].

During the Depression of 1930 to 1940 federal funds did go into highway construction in cities, not in recognition of their now serious transportation problems, but to provide work. "It was one of the 'radical' schemes born out of the desperate national plight. 'When Franklin D. Roosevelt began the vast New Deal program to relieve unemployment, highway construction was among the first items on the list—especially those highways going in and out of our great cities' " [11.4, p. 124].

The legislative basis for urban highway construction in 1933–1936 was emergency work relief. The Highway Act of 1936 regularized the basis by authorizing extension of federal-aid intercity highways into and through urban areas. However there was no requirement that funds be spent where most needed (as in cities). Nor was there any specific allotment of funds (until 1944) that must be spent in cities. Within rurally dominated state legislatures this meant that relatively little regular federal highway aid actually found its way into urban areas until the decade following World War II. Nevertheless, during the preceding 20 years the urban problem was recognized and the initial groundwork for federal aid was laid; only inertial social and political mechanisms held back effective aid.

11.1.2 Highways-only Aid, 1944–1964

The Federal-Aid Highway Act of 1944 is the milestone legislation marking the start of the period of federal aid to urban road systems. While the 1936 Act had authorized urban extensions of the federal aid system, cities were completely dependent on rural dominated state highway agencies for actual funds.

The 1944 Act created a new appropriation category, the federal-aid urban system, with monies apportioned among the states according to their urban populations. Authorized annual sums for the several federal-aid systems were:

$225 million	45%	Primary system (intercity) including urban extensions
150 million	30	Secondary and feeder system (rural farm-to-market roads, mail and school bus routes)
125 million	25	Urban system
$500 million	100%	Total annual authorization

Each state had the option of shifting up to 20 percent of its funds from one system to another. The percentage portions among the three systems were constant for the next quarter century. Federal aid was limited to 50 percent of construction and $33\frac{1}{3}$ percent of right-of-way costs.

The Act of 1944 is also noteworthy for providing for the creation of a 40,000-mile "National System of Interstate Highways" to connect "the principal metropolitan areas, cities and industrial centers, to serve the national defense . . . " [11.4 and 11.5]. Following the 1944 Act, the state highway agencies prepared, often for the first time, comprehensive highway plans for urban areas, indicating the preliminary locations of the proposed Interstates.

Implementation of the Interstate System was not specifically financed until the Federal Highway Act of 1956. It provided for an extraordinary 90–10 split of costs. For most of a 13-year period, appropriations of $2,200 million were authorized to cover the federal 90 percent. It expanded the system by 1,000 miles to 41,000 to accommodate urban bypasses and connectors.

The authorization for the primary, secondary and urban systems was raised to $875 million for 1959. An important innovation in the 1956 Highway Revenue Act was the creation of the Highway Trust Fund, which for the first time linked federal tax income from user charges, such as the gasoline tax, with highway expenditures to make the program self-financing [11.4, pp. 131–133].

11.1.3 Transit and Comprehensive Planning, Since 1964

The decade of the 1960s saw four major trends affecting urban transportation legislation—federal funding of transit, protection of the environment, comprehensive planning, and the creation of departments of transportation (DOTs) at the state and federal levels.

11.1.3.1 Municipal efforts Local efforts by the 1950s, burgeoning human and auto populations, and deteriorating transit service forced the larger cities to undertake planning for transit. Several cities were outstanding in terms of intensity of effort and actual results. The San Francisco–Oakland Bay area counties in 1951, through the California Legislature, set up a Transit Commission with a $750,000 state grant. The resulting studies led to creation of the Bay Area Rapid Transit District (BART) and construction of the first new rapid transit system in the United States in 50 years. It is noteworthy that the project was initiated through a local bond issue and surplus Bay Bridge auto tolls, with no federal aid.

Philadelphia created the Urban Traffic and Transportation Board in 1953 and, after rebuff from the state legislature, in 1958 started leasing improved commuter service from the railroads through a technique that was later (1960) institutionalized as the Passenger Service Improvement Commission [11.5, pp. 142–145]. Cleveland in 1954 began rail rapid transit service financed by revenue bonds repaid completely from the fare box.

Chicago has a history of land use and transportation planning that can be traced back to the Burnham Plan of 1906. In the 1950s the city launched two projects of note here. The first was the inclusion of rail rapid transit in the median of the Eisenhower Expressway running due west from the Loop, in a real sense a realization of some aspects of the Burnham Plan. The second was initiation of the Chicago Area Transportation Study (CATS 1955-1961), financed jointly with local, state, and federal funds, which set the prototype model for the comprehensive planning studies of the 1960s.

These cities of course were exceptional in terms of on-the-ground accomplishment in instituting transit service. Many more cities, however, gave the transit issue serious study during the 1950s. Atlanta began transportation policy studies through its Metropolitan Planning Commission in 1955, leading to creation of the Metropolitan Atlanta Rapid Transit Authority (MARTA) and construction of a regional rapid transit system (1971-   ). A unique feature of the Atlanta approach is a 15 cent bus and rapid transit fare supported by an areawide 1 percent sales tax.

Similarly in Washington, D.C., transportation planning studies initiated in the 1950s led to congressional appropriations for METRO construction in the 1970s. Interestingly, the appropriations were delayed for years by congressional efforts to tie them to construction of several freeways opposed by many District residents.

11.1.3.2 Federal aid The Bay Area, Philadelphia, Cleveland, and Chicago accomplishments are noteworthy not only because they pioneered the resurgences of rapid transit but also because initial action was taken without the incentive and help of federal or state monies. The first federal aid for transit was contained in the Housing Act of 1961, which provided $25 million for mass transportation demonstration projects. In addition it provided for low-interest loans to states, localities, and other authorities for land-acquisition, facilities, and equipment for mass transportation. This was very limited funding for very limited purposes, especially compared with the billions for highway transportation, but it was a start.

Appropriations large enough to aid urban transit on a significant scale date from the Urban Mass Transportation Act of 1964, with appropriations totaling $375 million. Improvements such as the 1965-1968 extension of rapid transit to the Cleveland Airport were funded under this Act. The federal share of a project could be as much as two-thirds, provided there was a comprehensive transportation plan. Otherwise the federal share would be 50 percent.

This expanded program of grants, loans, and demonstration projects was conducted by the Urban Mass Transportation Administration of the Housing and Home Finance Agency. Most important, the Act marked a turning point in the generally pessimistic outlook for transit by creating a hospitable climate for planning and action.

The 1966 Amendments to the 1964 Act required (1) more rigorous technical studies as a prerequisite to grants, (2) transit management training grants, (3) university research and training grants, and (4) the Secretaries of Housing and Urban Development and Commerce (this was just prior to creation of DOT) to work together in research and development of new transportation modes and systems [11.5].

The Urban Mass Transportation Act of 1970 represented an even greater federal commitment to transit. It authorized $10 billion over a 12-year period with a limit of $3.1 billion after fiscal 1975. In addition a program of 18-year loans was established for purchase of real property or equipment for transit purposes. Applications for loans and grants are subject to mandatory review by the Secretary of Transportation and the governor in states which have comprehensive planning programs.

As will be noted later, the proposed Federal Transportation Act of 1972, which was carried over into the 1973 congressional session, would further strengthen local transit efforts by placing a portion of the Highway Trust Fund monies for transit use at the discretion of elected local officials.

Probably the most troublesome gap in existing transit legislation is the lack of any device to maintain local transit operations as a stop-gap measure. In many middle-sized cities transit operations have or are about to cease operations. The resulting consequences included increased automobile usage, congestion, and deprivation of transportation services for people who do not own cars or drive, particularly the young, the elderly, the handicapped, and the poor. While, given the level of public concern, an ultimate solution may be found, the inability to finance interim transit operations deprives these groups of an essential service and eliminates a going operation that may facilitate the ultimate solution.

The beginnings in many cities during the 1950s of a much more comprehensive approach to transportation federal policy gave some support to environmental and comprehensive planning efforts. Most of the studies utilized either "701" or "HPR $1\frac{1}{2}$ percent" funds. The former were initiated in Section 701 of the Housing and Urban Redevelopment Act of 1954, which provided Urban Planning Assistance to communities under 50,000 population and to metropolitan planning. Highway Planning and Research (HPR) Funds were first authorized by the Federal Highway Act of 1934. Both acts require matching state or local funds according to prescribed formulas.

In November, 1960, the intensified efforts to improve urban transportation led to the identification of a number of additional factors in the problem or solution to be considered. This led Congress to require comprehensive planning as a prerequisite to federal aid. The transit grants and loans provided in the Housing Act of 1961 could be obtained only where a plan for a coordinated mass transportation system, as an integral part of a metropolitan comprehensive plan, had been or was being developed. The Federal Aid Highway Act of 1962 contained a similar requirement, which because of the magnitude and prestige of the highway program, had a greater impact. Section 302 of the Act reads in its entirety as follows:

Highway Act of 1962, Public Law 87–866

It is delcared to be in the national interest to encourage and promote the development of transportation systems, embracing various modes of transport in a manner that will serve the States and local communities efficiently and effectively. To accomplish this objective the Secretary shall cooperate with the States, as authorized in this title, in the development of long-range highway plans and programs which are properly coordinated with plans for improvements in other affected forms of transportation and which are formulated with due consideration to their probable effect on the future development of urban areas of more than fifty thousand population. After July 1, 1965, the Secretary shall not approve under section 105 of this title any program for projects in any urban area of more than fifty thousand population unless he finds that such projects are based on a continuing comprehensive transportation planning process carried on cooperatively by States and local communities in conformance with the objectives stated in this section.

Congress continued to refine these comprehensive planning requirements. In the Demonstration Cities and Metropolitan Development Act of 1966, Title II requires that federal funds for any project in 34 program categories, including highways, transit, and airports, be dependent upon (a) existence of a metropolitan body composed of at least 50 percent of local elected officials of general government and (b) the body having at least 60 days in which to recommend approval, disapproval, or otherwise comment on the project. This Act was further strengthened in 1968 and was implemented by Bureau of the Budget (now Office of Management and Budget) Circular Letter A-95. Hence these area-wide reviews have come to be known as "A-95 reviews."

An extremely important refinement was added by the National Environmental Policy Act of 1969. Section 203 of the Act requires the federal agency responsible for any federally aided project to submit a draft Environmental Impact Statement on a project to any affected local, state or federal agency and to the general public comment. The Act, enforced in nearly 200 courts during its first 2 years, has been highly significant in forcing (1) interagency and intergovernmental planning, (2) attention to the entire range of impacts on social, economic, natural, and physical aspects of the projects' environment and (3) a more open public decision process.

As a result of the A-95 and Environmental Impact Statement requirements most states have established an interagency, intergovernmental Project Notification and Review System (PNRS) to assure all affected agencies and groups (1) information about any forthcoming decision on a state or federal aid project and (2) the opportunity to comment. The net effect of the Congressional and state actions during this decade has been to force a public decision process that is more comprehensive, in that it takes into account the full range of relevant factors, and more open in that there is a fuller disclosure of the basis for any decision and a better opportunity for participation.

11.2 LEGAL POWERS FOR IMPLEMENTING PLANS

The tools available for implementing urban transportation plans are many and varied and include control of land use as it affects transportation. Most persons do not realize the kinds of devices available to exert control over urban development. Cities and counties are creatures of the states, and they have only that authority conferred on them by the state. Therefore, not all cities or counties will have all these powers, and when they do, the powers may be limited in various ways. Tools for plan implementation may be divided into several major categories. The basis for plan implementation is, of course, governmental authority, which is exercised through a number of important, long established powers possessed by governments, whether they engage in conscious planning or not.

It must be realized that planning per se adds nothing to the substantive powers a government possesses. The powers described briefly below may be exercised whether there is a planning program or not, but planning may determine the need and afford the occasion for exercise of certain of these powers. It is necessary to have an understanding of the nature of these powers and the legal limitations that restrict their use.

11.2.1   Fiscal Powers

Every government must have the power to raise and expend money in order to carry out its responsibilities. Governments can raise revenue, incur debt, borrow, make expenditures, collect and distribute funds, and make appropriations. They can levy taxes and special assessments.

Under the financial power there are three important considerations for planning: (1) assessment and other taxes can powerfully influence patterns of urban development and redevelopment; (2) similarly the power to expend money for capital improvements, such as transportation, utilities, schools, and parks, can shape land development; and (3) the powers to spend money for, construct, and operate public transportation facilities implies the power to plan for the wise exercise of these powers.

11.2.2   The Power of Eminent Domain[2]

Eminent domain is used to acquire land or easements by condemnation. In the early history of highway building in America this tool was used rarely since land generally was available through voluntary sale by the owner or in many instances by owner dedication of private land to the public use. In recent years, however, these two forms of acquisition have not been able to fulfill increasing transportation land needs. Thus the exercise of eminent domain has become a measure of frequent use.

Through the power of eminent domain a unit of government, within its jurisdiction, may take private property for public use without the consent of the owner, subject to payment of just compensation as prescribed by law. As an inherent attribute to sovereignty, states are granted by constitutional provision the power of eminent domain. Political subdivisions of states—counties, cities, towns, and villages—are not sovereigns and must receive such power by delegation of the state legislature.[3]

Condemnation law can be divided into two very broad categories: administrative or judicial condemnation. The administrative method involves the condemner

---

[2] Adapted in part from [11.6].

[3] In all highway projects, except the National System of Interstate and Defense Highways, condemnation is a power vested only in States and their political subdivisions. As provided by the Federal Aid Act of 1966, land condemnation disputes involving Interstate highways may be settled by action of the Secretary of Commerce.

filing with specified public officials papers showing the plot of land with proposed improvement and a tender to the landowner or deposit in court of an award of compensation. Should the landowner wish to contest either the right to take the property or the amount given in compensation, then court proceedings may begin by his action with the burden of proof being the responsibility of the landowner.

The judicial approach requires the condemnation to be commenced by an agency petitioning the court for a judgment on the right to take and the amount of compensation to be awarded. The court must assure itself that if the property owner is not satisfied, he is fully heard. Once the court issues an order of condemnation and the landowner receives payment, the title of the property becomes the possession of the condemner, unless appealed within a specified time.

Statutory provisions in state law may fall under the general framework of either the administrative or the judicial law procedure. However, a great deal of variation exists among the various state constitutions and in enabling legislation for their respective political subdivisions. For this reason, the student desiring to have a more detailed knowledge in methods of condemnation would be advised to consult the various state codes. In a more general sense, four aspects of condemnation can be identified as key problems in statutory provisions as they apply to states, counties, cities, towns, and special authorities:

1. Who has the authority to condemn?
2. Which property may be taken?
3. Which type(s) of legal estate may be acquired?
4. What procedure is to be followed?

11.2.2.1 State highway department

Delegation of authority   The power of eminent domain is an inherent attribute of the state in its role as a sovereign, but the right to authorize the exercise of eminent domain is a legislative function. Thus, in order to make use of this sovereignty, the state legislature must confer the power of eminent domain in express terms or by necessary implication to any state agency in need of this authority. Doubtful inferences will not sustain exercise of eminent domain and without this authority there can be no taking of private property for public use without the consent of the owner.

In general, once the state legislature grants the power of eminent domain to an agency, that agency subsequently will be responsible for its own defense should any court litigation occur as a result of exercise of condemnation. The exception to this is the case in which a highway commissioner has been granted condemnation power by the state. Because a highway commissioner is identified so closely with the state, the courts generally have contended that any act of condemnation by a commissioner is done not in the "nature of a private individual" but rather as an act of the State itself.

Property which may be acquired   The legislature must establish by state statutes that the state highway department may condemn property and then define the kind of property that may be condemned. The definitions vary greatly from state to state and even an all-inclusive statute, such as "land may be condemned for any highway purposes" does not insure that condemnation can proceed always in the absence of court interference.

The two categories adopted most commonly are "right-of-way" property and property containing "necessary road building materials." While all states have provisions for acquiring road rights-of-way through condemnation of the actual real estate and any interest therein, there are differences in language (e.g., "land and/or property" or "land, easements, rights, franchises, and property"). Forty-two states have statutes authorizing the power to condemn land containing such necessary road building materials as gravel and rock (that is, the right to purchase such at a "reasonable" cost). In situations, however, where the state statutes have not made explicit the distinction between "property" and "real estate," landowners have been able to sue condemnation authorities from the viewpoint that gravel and rock in fact are "property," not "real estate."

A third category of more recent origin is condemnation by highway departments of marginal land. In terms of road building, land is considered marginal if it is not a part of the actual right-of-way. Before the emergence of widespread urbanization as well as the increased use of the automobile, the condemnation of such land was an infrequent practice but in recent years the benefits of such acquisition have become much more obvious. The acquisition of marginal land may serve the following benefits:

1. To effect economy, by acquiring an entire tract of land when the necessary portion plus the severance damages to the remainder would involve an equal or greater expenditure than if the entire tract were acquired with the right to salvage the remainder later.
2. To prevent the creation of small, uneconomical remnants of land.
3. To remove unsightly buildings and obnoxious uses and to assist landscaping.
4. To control the use of adjoining property for aesthetic, safety, or future highway development objectives by incorporating restrictive easements on a later sale of property.
5. To diminish right-of-way costs through the sale of acquired marginal land.

About two-thirds of the states have either constitutional provisions or statutes delegating in a specific manner the authority to condemn marginal land. Of these states, roughly half are concerned primarily with controlled access. Even those remaining states having no specific provisions may enter into condemnation of marginal land on occasion, as courts generally seem to support the assumption that such land is in the interest of public health and safety as concerns highway development. However, such litigation is a costly expense in time regardless if the ruling is in the favor of the highway department.

Legal interest or estate acquired   Two general types of estates may be acquired by state highway departments through the process of condemnation. These are the "fee simple" estate in which the state has title (full ownership by deed) to the land condemned and the "estate in easement," wherein the state has a limited right (i.e., for highway right-of-way only) to use land held in title by the original owner. While all states have provisions giving the state highway department an option on which type of estate to acquire, this is not always the case in cities, towns, and villages. A fee simple estate, of course, requires more initial investment, but it is preferred increasingly by state highway departments since easements usually always have reverter clauses requiring the return of the use of property (and therefore, loss by the state of any financial investment incurred) to the landowner should the highway in question not be constructed within a specified period of time.

Procedure The procedure by which state highway departments may acquire land is always established by legislative statutes, but varies greatly from state to state. In practice it makes little difference which procedure the state highway department must operate within as long as the language is clear and conditions are spelled out carefully. This, of course, reflects a problem in legislative drafting and much confusion as well as questions of policy may arise when precautions are not taken to insure clarity in procedure. In general, the procedure used will fit into one of the six following categories:

1. The general condemnation procedure followed by the state for any exercise of eminent domain is incorporated specifically by reference in the highway statutes.
2. The general condemnation procedure specifies the various public uses for which land may be condemned, transportation or highways being one of these uses.
3. Reference is made in the highway statutes that the general condemnation law is to be followed unless another procedure is specified for a particular transportation use.
4. A special condemnation procedure separate from the general condemnation law is established for transportation agency uses.
5. A special procedure is established for use by the state in transportation purposes.
6. The railroad condemnation law is made available to the state highway department.

11.2.2.2 Counties

Delegation of authority As mentioned previously, the power of eminent domain is an inherent attribute of state sovereignty, whereas a county is not a sovereign and must have authority delegated by the state. Nor is this authority always granted; in seven states—Connecticut, Delaware, New Hampshire, North Carolina, Rhode Island, Vermont, and West Virginia—counties have little or no role in highway development.

In those states granting counties the power of eminent domain the authority granted always is less than that retained by the state highway department. The power given may take numerous forms, but in a very simplified fashion three types of grants seem prevalent:

1. The most comprehensive power is that of establishing, laying out, opening, altering, changing, widening, and improving public roads and ferries in the county.

2. The power to condemn property for county roads.
3. Power, under certain prescribed conditions, to acquire property *for* the state.

Property which may be acquired As with state highway departments, the legislative language designating what property a county highway department may acquire often means the difference between costly court litigation and relatively simple administrative or judicial condemnation. Apparent as this may seem, the legislative definitions of property that a county highway agency may condemn are often less clear than those found in statutes of the state highway department. In many cases it is a semantic interpretation made by the court during a condemnation proceeding that determines how narrow or broad the powers given to a county agency will be. A review of county condemnation statutes reveals six general classifications of property that a county may condemn subject to its enabling legislation. Except for the last category, there is evidence of some obscurity in the term "property":

1. Property acquired must be for the road "right-of-way" (23 states).
2. Counties may acquire "land" for county highways and roads (21 states).
3. "Private property" may be acquired for county highways and roads (8 states).
4. The county may condemn "property" for county highways and roads (5 states).
5. The county may condemn "real property or interest therein" for county highways and roads (5 states).
6. "Public or private property" may be condemned by the county for highways and roads (Arizona, Pennsylvania).
7. "Land, rights or other property" may be taken for county highways and roads (Illinois, Wisconsin).

Only 19 states permit counties to acquire land in excess of actual right-of-way, with 2 of these (Alabama and Nebraska) permitting acquisition only when the offer is a voluntary action of the landowner.

Legal interest or estate acquired Acquisition of land in either "fee simple" or "easement," as discussed in the section on state highway departments generally, is not at the option of a county highway department. In 21 states the type of legal estate that may be acquired is specified by legislative statute. In the remaining states a general principle is that an easement be made when it accomplishes the purpose required.

Procedure The approaches used by states to provide a procedure for condemnation by counties vary widely. The most common method is to incorporate by reference the general condemnation law and make it applicable to county officials.

11.2.2.3 Cities, towns, and villages

Delegation of authority Cities, towns and villages, like counties, must be granted condemnation powers by the state. In the absence of these powers, they are without any power to exercise eminent domain. Legislation concerning cities, towns, and villages is even more fragmented than that directed toward counties since the former may have special charters, "home rule" legislation, or statutes named for special cities and class legislation aimed at specific communities. In a very general sense, however, the most common form of authority when granted is the power to "lay out, open, extend, widen, and improve public streets and alleys," and in furtherance of such power to acquire property through eminent domain.

Property which may be acquired In general, cities, towns, and villages have been empowered to condemn land for public streets and alleys in one of the following classifications:

1. Property
2. Land/real estate
3. Private property
4. Right-of-way

In 16 states, cities, towns, and villages (as applicable) have been granted the right to condemn land in excess of that needed for the road right-of-way. In all cases, however, this authority falls under provisions for limited access.

Legal interest or estate acquired Generally, cities, towns, and villages are given the same grant as counties. Easements are preferred unless fee-simple estates are permitted or specified.

Procedure The same trend concerning procedure discussed with state and county highway departments exists with cities, towns, and villages. Thus a procedure may be created that is unique to the city (e.g., in home rule legislation), or the general condemnation law may be incorporated by reference, or a provision may be made designating officials of the procedure and/or uses for which property may be condemned.

11.2.2.4 Special authorities

Delegation of authority The latest expression of legislative intent in the transportation field can be found in the establishment of functionally separate authorities whose existence concerns a single purpose such as turnpikes, bridges, and tunnels, and some more recent mass transit projects. In general, the power of eminent domain is made explicit in a broad manner.

Property which may be acquired The legal definition of property that may be acquired by special authorities has been handled in most cases in a manner much less likely to arouse litigation. The most common description reads "land, other property, public property, franchises, easements, buildings, interest in land, and land devoted to public use" may be condemned for purposes of the respective project.

Legal interest of estate acquired Of those states having special authorities only Kansas limits in enabling legislation the estate to an easement. Otherwise, all such states provide for fee simple absolute acquisition.

Procedure The procedure to be followed by special authorities in condemnation is provided for in four ways:

1. The most common procedure is specific incorporation or allusion to the general condemnation law by providing that laws applicable to eminent domain proceedings are to apply.
2. A procedure distinct and separate from other procedural laws.
3. A procedure followed by the state highway department (usually turnpike authorities).
4. A procedure following the condemnation power delegated to railroads (used in "special improvement districts" in Arkansas and Oklahoma).

The problems as discussed with the exercise of eminent domain in each category of political jurisdiction reflect the increased use of this tool to effect acquisition of land needed for public facilities. It should be stressed, however, that in most cases enabling legislation generally has given a large amount of descretion to condemnation authorities in both the manner in which they may use their power and the land they may condemn. Although the exercise of eminent domain is an important device, especially as it concerns providing improved transportation facilities, there are other tools that complement this authority and in themselves serve as important measures of keeping stride with the improvements needed in urban society. These are the powers of proprietorship, the police power, and controls over land use.

11.2.3 The Power of Proprietorship

Governments are engaged in many enterprises and are the owner of considerable property. For example, a city owns streets which, as noted, it acquires by dedication, purchase, or condemnation; it owns land and buildings; and it owns or operates utility systems. All three of these broad areas are of importance to planning because of the tremendous bargaining power they allow the city, particularly in dealing with land developers. It could well be that the bargaining position the city possesses by virtue of its power of proprietorship may be more significant in terms of development control than the police power.

11.2.4 The Police Power

The general police power is the most comprehensive and pervasive of all powers of government. It is a regulatory power which restricts the use of private property in the public interest and can prevent a property use that is harmful to public welfare. In its original and broadest sense, the police power denoted the inherent power of every sovereign to control man and things, but it is not quite so broadly defined today. It is "limited" to the power to establish the social order, protect life and health, secure a person's existence and comfort, and safeguard him in the enjoyment of private and social life and the beneficial use of his property.

This power governs the manner in which each person may use his property when regulation becomes necessary in the public interest, and it may be broadly used to promote the general welfare of the state or the community. It is a flexible power, not rigid or fixed, but elastic enough to meet new conditions that arise from changes in the social and economic order.

The police power is important for planning because no other power available to a city is so far reaching with respect to relationships between government and the individual's personal and property interest.

11.2.5 Land Use Controls

This major category consists of exercise of the police power in subdivision regulations, zoning ordinances, building and construction codes, housing codes, architectural controls, and mapped streets ordinances. Each of these is designed for a specific purpose, and the most effective plan implementation is achieved if they are used to supplement each other. Each has some relevance to transportation planning. These have traditionally been local powers, but recently they have been used increasingly at the state level.

11.2.5.1 Mapped streets ordinance Under this, projected future streets or other public areas are designated on an official map, which is recorded; this prevents erection, within the boundary lines of designated areas, of structures that would have to be removed when a street or area is opened. In some jurisdictions only streets are included; in others, streets, parks, playgounds, school sites, and other uses are designated.

11.2.5.2 Architectural controls The purpose of architectural controls is to prevent excessive uniformity or excessive disparity in architectural styles. Many communities have adopted a method of architectural controls, some preferring to use private covenants, some relying on an ordinance which appoints a board of review. Decisions upholding boards of review have been based largely on the general welfare aspects of the police power and not solely on the basis of esthetics. Some states do not allow aesthetics as a valid legal consideration; in others, aesthetics may be considered only in conjunction with other recognized bases for the exercise of the police power.

11.2.5.3 Building, construction, housing, plumbing, gas, fire, and electrical codes The primary function of the various kinds of codes is to safeguard public health and safety through the regulation of building construction, use, and maintenance, and through the installation of utilities and the provision of certain kinds of services. Such codes reduce hazards—quake, wind, fire, flood, lightning and disease, accident, and injury due to carelessness and neglect. Basically, the objective is to provide a sound building.

11.2.5.4 Zoning Zoning is one of the major tools of plan implementation. While its original purposes relate to the regulation of land use, it is frequently used to serve a number of transportation related functions: requirement of adequate off-street parking and limitation of intensity of trip generation, among other functions. Zoning is basically

... the governmental regulation of the uses of land and buildings according to districts or zones. It is a means of insuring that land uses within the community are properly situated in relation to one another, that adequate space is available for various types of developments, and that the density of development in each area is held at a level which can be properly served by governmental facilities and will permit light, air, and privacy for persons living and working within the community [11.7].

To accomplish its purpose a city can zone with regard to land usage, lot area, population density, size of all yards and open spaces, building setbacks, parking, signs, and billboards; it can prohibit some uses, can eliminate some existing uses. In addition to controlling industrial and commercial noises, fumes, smoke and particle emission, zoning can even control erection of structures in the air space approaches to airports. Zoning has become an infinitely sophisticated tool, with new approaches and techniques being developed all the time to meet new needs emerging in a complex society.

Planning and zoning often are misunderstood, and many times the words are used interchangeably. The distinction between planning and zoning is a most important one, and it should be clearly understood. A leading court decision states that zoning

> ... is a separation of the municipality into districts, and the regulation of buildings and structures in the districts so created, in accordance with their construction and the nature and extent of their use ... it is the dedication of the districts limited to particular uses designed to subserve the general welfare. It pertains not only to use but to the structural and architectural design of buildings.[4]

Planning, as opposed to zoning,

> ... is a term of broader significance. It connotes a systematic development contrived to promote the common interest in matters that have from the earliest times been considered as embraced within the police power.[5]

Planning is conceptual and goal oriented. It is concerned with systematic development of a municipality along lines determined by the people in the common interest. Zoning is implementive. It is concerned exclusively with land use regulation, aiming at the most effective utilization of land.

Zoning has been known as a "preventive" device, intended to deter community blight and deterioration by prescribing standards for uses in separate areas and by assisting in the control of new buildings. It requires similar uses in given areas and thereby helps keep out blighting factors and keep up property values in all areas. It must be pointed out here that this concept is changing somewhat, though not rapidly. Some courts are now more prone than ever before to allow zoning "for the future" rather than using it as a preventive tool.

Zoning is the oldest tool of plan implementation. It was known as far back as the Romans, who used zoning to restrict the location of certain buildings and businesses. Zoning in the United States had its forerunners in the 17th century, when towns regulated tenements, factories, garages, theaters, and billboards. Boston, Salem, and Charleston, among others, controlled the location of slaughter-houses and distilleries, and in the 18th century the premises of changlers, couriers,

---

[4] *Mansfield & Swett* v. *Town of West Orange*, 120 N.J.L. 145, 198A. 225 (1938).
[5] *Ibid.*

and potters were added to the list of those regulated. Most of this early zoning was based on the use of the "nuisance technique," starting with the practice in colonial cities of zoning such nuisances as gunpowder storage out of the center of town. Other nuisances appeared as time went on.

Modern zoning, however, is purely a product of the 20th century. Attesting to this is the fact that the first comprehensive zoning ordinance in the United States was not enacted until 1916, and not until 1926 did the United States Supreme Court uphold the concept of zoning, in the landmark case *Euclid* v. *Ambler Realty Company.* The late start of comprehensive zoning in this country has been attributed to ". . . the tendency of our courts down through the years to protect and preserve individual rights in property against the arbitrary control thereof by municipalities."[6]

The theory of zoning is to generate land use improvements by confining specific classes of buildings and uses to certain localities without causing owners undue hardship. Prior to general public acceptance of zoning in this country, haphazard location and use of buildings existed in all our municipalities. Zoning attempted to remedy this situation by imposing regulations that would exclude new uses and structures prejudicial to the preservation of the true character of a neighborhood.

Zoning which regulates the *use* of land, irrespective of its ownership, aims not primarily at protecting the value of property of particular individuals, but instead at promoting the welfare of the whole community. Zoning does protect property values, of course, but it is intended to do more: to insure the availability of adequate light, air, and accessibility to all property. It protects the public health and minimizes the number of fire hazards.

> The essential considerations of zoning require the municipality to adhere to basic purposes (including security from fire, panic and other dangers; promotion of health, morals, and general welfare; adequate light and air; prevention of overcrowding and of undue concentration of population; the character of the district and its peculiar suitability for particular purposes) with a view to conserving the value of property and encouraging the most appropriate use of land throughout such municipality.[7]

Inquiry shows that comprehensive zoning has been generally accepted in the United States, but some other devices for plan implementation have not been accepted. Why has zoning gained this acceptance? It has been said that "zoning is an offspring of urgent urban necessity." But urban necessity today is so urgent as to call for recognition of other tools of plan implementation, too, those which are vital to planning but which have not yet received judicial support. One may wonder why zoning has been more acceptable. One experienced planner has said that

> . . . [action] in the field of planning for the small community frequently begins with ideas of zoning because the abuses to be corrected by this device are most painfully obvious to the average citizen. The zoning ordinance appears to be a very direct attack upon

---

[6] 272 U.S. 365 (1926).
[7] *Thornton* v. *Village of Redwood* 111A. 2d 899 (N.J., 1955).

undesirable situations. It is readily understood and enthusiasm for its enforcement can be generated easily.[8]

It seems, then, that zoning has three characteristics which give it a certain advantage: it may correct clearly undesirable conditions, it is a very direct attack upon abuses, and it can gather very enthusiastic adherents.

Our antipathy for regulation of private property notwithstanding, when it became obvious that such damage to the community was occurring as the result of failure to regulate urban land use and when the many benefits of zoning became evident, its popularity increased. There can be no doubt that zoning was a most radical departure from traditional concepts of private property, but the need for it—arising from increasing population density and multiplying forms of business activity and the increasing complexity of our civilization—was so great that conservatives, liberals, and progressives all accepted zoning. Originally very radical in its departure from our customary ways of thinking and doing, zoning has now become the standard method of insuring the efficient use of land and it is the first—and probably the only—device considered by the general, uninformed, uncritical public for implementation of the comprehensive plan. Other devices for implementation, equally valuable, should be granted acceptance, but apparently the need is not obvious to very many people.

While many view the zoning ordinance as the most important tool to provide land use controls in planning, there are other devices and techniques that potentially offer at least as much promise as zoning, and probably more promise under specific types of developmental circumstances. Competent planning and zoning alone do not guarantee a "city beautiful," nor can they insure the most efficient utilization of urban lands.

11.2.5.5 Subdivision regulation Of all the land use control devices available, the potential of subdivision regulation is probably the greatest. One experienced planner has this to say about its value:

> In the process of exercising this planning implement (zoning) in the public interest, municipal authorities are prone to overlook a planning tool capable of greater accomplishments with far less efforts. The process of subdivision control is a powerful and effective device for achieving a desirable community environment and all communities both large and small would do well to examine their position in this regard. If they are now exercising subdivision control, the process should be reviewed for maximum effectiveness. For those communities that have not adopted this device, it is highly recommended because nothing is more fundamental to the proper growth of the community.[9]

Again, the same planner says that

> . . . when compared with zoning, a well-administered subdivision control is more useful in achieving planning goals and its influence is far more lasting.[10]

---

[8] Address by Ronald Scott at the National Planning Conference, May, 1958.
[9] *Ibid.*
[10] *Ibid.*

Subdivision regulation is the control by a public authority of the platting and conversion of raw land into building lots. A city can control the subdivision of real estate by forcing the developer to meet requirements and standards established by the city in return for the privilege of recording a plat and selling off lots. The cumulative effect of land subdivision is so extensive that public control of this activity is required. The impact of unregulated subdivision of land is felt in tax burdens, the high cost of extending utilities, street and traffic problems, overloaded schools, health hazards caused by sewage disposal systems unsuited to a particular area, and so on.

Subdivision regulation is crucial because, once large tracts of land are broken up into individual parcels, the pattern of development is irretrievably set. Thus a subdivider is taking action that is of great importance to the community—to the homeowner, to the governing body, and to the general public, the taxpayers. It is through subdivision regulations that the community interest is expressed—and protected.

Subdivision control plays a fundamental role in the development of a community because, although a city is something more than a total of its land subdivisions, much of the form and character of the city will be determined by the quality of those subdivisions and the standards which are built into them.

The subdivision of land is clearly the first step in building communities.

Once land has been cut up into streets, blocks, and lots, and publicly recorded, the dye is cast and the pattern is difficult to change. For generations the people who occupy such land will be influenced by the character of its design [11.8].

Perhaps it seems odd that the influence of subdivisions on the community is not more widely recognized. This lack of recognition is due in part to the nature of the subdivision process. It occurs largely on paper, and the quality or lack of quality in the land involved is not obvious to the public. It is also quite true that rather loud and long objection by real estate speculators to public control of the subdivision process has tended to hamper and delay the public acceptance of this planning device.

At any rate, it is quite clear that today most large cities are paying high costs for their failure to establish adequate public controls over the subdivision of land. Traffic congestion, blighted areas, slums, increased cost of public improvements, and other defects are attributable in large measure to imperfect land subdivision. Because they did not regulate years ago, cities now must ask their planners to work on the rehabilitation of blighted areas and slums. This is work of a curative kind, and cities might instead be working on preventive aspects of urban problems. In spite of a preponderance of evidence which shows the costs to the community of failing to exercise control over its own growth, a number of communities have engaged in costly replanning and redevelopment projects without having put into effect adequate subdivision controls to prevent a repetition of the same process in other areas. It seems that growth, surge, decay, and recuperation have characterized most of the world's urban centers from their beginnings. Good planning and the use of all tools of plan implementation, particularly subdivision control, could enable us to change this traditional cycle in our cities. Much of the decay could be prevented, and thus the recuperation would be unnecessary.

The purpose of subdivision control is to prevent congestion of population and to provide land development in accord with established design standards, to create sound neighborhood patterns, and to integrate the area involved—sooner or later—into the community as a whole. For this purpose, the regulations usually establish standards to be met in construction of public improvements and often require the developer to provide basic improvements before he can sell any of his lots.

Early attempts at subdivision control are likely to be clumsy and inefficient, as is the case with many new devices, but continued use will prove its value. Maximum effectiveness can be obtained only if there is a land use plan and a mapped streets plan because these are prerequisites to good subdivision control. All these tools of planning implementation must be coordinated for best results.

How does subdivision control fit into the context of planning? Subdivision control is closely connected to the process of comprehensive community planning. Subidivision control, like zoning, could be carried out without long-range planning, but would be limited to the prevention of obvious mistakes—such as excessive street grades, awkward intersections, and substandard improvements—in an individual plan. This would be subdivision control at its weakest. While this alone would be of considerable value,

> ... the true measures of success are the creation of sound neighborhood patterns; integration of residential development with other land uses; acquisition of sites for public parks, schools, and other facilities; and the continuation of the transportation network, among others [11.9].

Subdivision control, therefore, is an integral part of the planning process, an important tool of plan implementation, and if the municipality has not developed a comprehensive plan, intelligent subdivision control is not possible. It is in this broad operation, based on a comprehensive plan, that subdivision control's greatest contribution to orderly community growth can be made.

Unpleasant experiences with uncontrolled subdivision have taught some people in this country a lesson. Control of the subdivision process has been recognized in some areas as an important part of land use plans and controls. However, the extent of this recognition certainly varies from state to state and depends upon a number of factors. The statutes of all states, save one, make some sort of provision for subdivision regulation, but an examination of these statutes indicates a wide variation in their provisions and the extent of enforcement also varies greatly from state to state.

Why the great variation in acceptance of and reliance on subdivision regulations? The need for public regulation, in the public interest, has not been equally visible in all areas. The effects of poor subdivision practices are not immediately seen by the general public, there is a traditional respect for private property, and many developers apply considerable pressure on councils and commissions to avoid regulation.

Subdividers tend to think of a development as a complete, separate project, not as a unit of the city with a definite relation to other streets, utilities, parks, schools, and so on. But these subdivisions are a part of the city and have a tremendous impact on that city. Therefore, local governments—and in some cases state governments—ought to be able to exert some influence on new subdivisions to make them meet minimum requirements and comply with the comprehensive plan and the established subdivision regulations. When localities cannot or do not control the subdivision of land, the result is low-grade, substandard subdivision, excessive or premature development of land, or partial development.

11.3 FINANCING TRANSPORTATION

Of all the powers to implement transportation plans a government's power to spend is probably the most potent. The following section will discuss the current federal, state, and local laws and practices in regard to financing urban transportation, followed by an exploration of current trends affecting future laws and practices. It is useful to group sources of income for financing transportation into four categories: use taxes, general fund, borrowings and grants.

Dedicated user charges, in the case of automotive travel, include gasoline taxes, vehicle registration fees, driver's license fees, tolls, vehicle sales taxes, etc. For commercial air travel there is the federal transportation tax, local embarkation fees, etc. General aviation (i.e., nonscheduled airlines) pays a fuel tax.

General fund sources are the common central treasuries existing at all levels of government, from which discretionary budgets are fashioned by the executive and adopted by the legislature. Into the general fund may go property taxes, sales taxes, income taxes and a wide variety of other revenues, including user fees in those states which do not dedicate these sources. Prior to the Highway Act of 1956 all federal highway user charges were placed in the General Fund of the U.S. Treasury and appropriations for highways made therefrom.

Borrowings include bond issues and short-term notes.

Grants, or grants-in-aid, are intergovernmental transfer payments, the most important of which flow from federal to state, and from state to local governments. Local governments occasionally transfer funds to state highway or other agencies for the construction of specific projects.

11.3.1 Financing Highways

All levels of government raise revenues for automotive transportation facilities. Table 11.1 shows the total receipts and disbursements for highway purposes by all levels of government. Two items are of special note: (1) the states raise more money for highways than the other three levels combined, and (2) the states receive (but do not necessarily keep) 82 percent of the federal revenue collection. The $1,007 million placed on reserve represents largely moneys raised by the Highway

Table 11.1 Total Receipts and Disbursements for Highway Purposes by All Levels of Government, 1970

Item	Highway trust fund (federal)	States and D.C.	Counties and townships	Munici-palities	Total
Receipts (collecting agencies)					
Highway-user revenues[1]	$ 5,295	$ 8,854	$ 44	$ 134	$14,327
Other[2]	152	563	1,193	1,713	3,621
Bonds[3]	—	1,159	196	375	1,730
Subtotal	5,447	10,576	1,433	2,222	19,678
Intergovernmental payments					
Federal	-4,412[4]	4,412	—	—	—
State	—	2,423[5]	1,487	936	—
Counties and townships	—	60	120	60	—
Municipalities	—	50	3	53	—
Subtotal	-4,412	2,099	1,370	943	—
Funds drawn from (+) or placed in (−) reserves	-954	-86	-27	+60	-1,007
Total funds available	81	12,589	2,776	3,225	18,671
Expenditures (expending agencies)					
Maintenance	—	1,694	1,522	1,212	4,428
Administration	81	679	203	157	1,120
Other[6]	—	1,467	232	815	2,514
Total fixed costs	81	3,840	1,957	2,184	8,062
Expended for capital outlay	—	8,749	819	1,041	11,609

Note: All figures in millions of dollars.

[1] Net of collection costs and nonhighway expenditures.

[2] Includes other state imposts, general fund appropriations, property taxes, investment income, premium and discounts on sale of bonds, and miscellaneous receipts.

[3] Proceeds of short-term notes and refunding issues.

[4] Excludes highway activities of other federal agencies financed from general fund revenues.

[5] Represents grants-in-aid paid to local governments.

[6] Includes highway law enforcement and safety, interest on debt, and debt retirement.

Source: [11.10, Table VII-1, Part II].

Trust Fund but postponed for disbursement by the President as an anti-inflation measure.

Of considerable interest are the trends at each level of government in raising revenues for highways (Table 11.2). Creation in 1956 by Congress of the Federal Highway Trust Fund and authorization of the Interstate System caused the federal share to increase substantially, from 12 percent to 27 percent between 1956 and 1960, with all other levels reduced. Since 1960 the county share has steadily declined, the state share remained steady, and city share decreased.

11.3.1.1 Sources by governmental level The sources of highway income at each level of government provides valuable perspective for urban transportation finance. It should be kept in mind that since metropolitan areas, as such, do not raise revenues, the following sections do not offer a picture of past highway expenditures in urban areas. Metropolitan highways are financed by revenues from all levels of government.

The major historic trend revealed by Table 11.3 is the doubling of the proportion of revenues received from grants-in-aid as a result of the 1956 Federal Highway Act. In actual amounts, grants tripled from $839 million in 1956 to $2,589 million in 1960, and doubled again to $5,136 million in 1970. Also of great interest is the tripling of total receipts for highways during the 14-year period. Bond financing was apparently rendered less important in the early 1960s by the increased federal grants, but greatly increased use in the late 1960s put it back up above its 1956 level by 1970. The increase in state borrowings reflected the increased costs of maintenance and administration (not federally aided) and the rising costs of construction.

Local government contributions to highway purposes are relatively small, with counties raising 6.8 percent and cities 12 percent in 1970 (Table 11.1). Perhaps the real story here is that cities make a considerably greater effort than counties to raise money for highways, yet receive much less federal and state aid relative to need. (See Table 11.4) Their greater effort is reflected by their higher appropriation from property tax and other general fund sources (in 1970, 58.9 percent versus 39.8

**Table 11.2 Percent of Revenues for Highways
Raised by Each Level of Government, 1956–1970**

Level of government	1956	1960	1965	1970
Federal	12.0	27.3	30.8	28.0
State	64.3	53.2	51.2	53.2
County	10.1	8.3	7.4	6.8
Municipal	13.6	11.2	10.0	12.0
Total	100.0	100.0	100.0	100.0

Note: Percentages exclude toll facilities and all borrowing.

Source: [11.10, Table VII-2, Part II].

Table 11.3 Source of Receipts of the States for Highways, 1956-1970

Year	Highway user	Other taxes	Grants[1]	Bonds[2]	Total	Actual[3]
1956	73.3%	3.8%	15.9%	7.0%	100.0%	$ 5,274
1960	60.1	2.3	33.3	4.3	100.0	7,784
1965	56.4	2.2	37.1	4.3	100.0	10,714
1970[4]	57.3	2.4	33.1	7.2	100.0	15,510

Note: Excludes toll facilities.
[1] Includes small amount of transfers from local government.
[2] Excludes refunding issues.
[3] Millions.
[4] Estimates.
Source: [11.10, Table VII-3, Part II].

percent in the counties), higher borrowing (12.1 percent versus 9.5 percent county and 7.2 percent state), and lower grants-in-aid (29.0 percent versus 50.7 percent county and 33.1 percent state).

That state and federal governments have been responsive to the mounting transportation problems of cities is evidenced by the dramatic rise in grants for highways from 19 percent to 29 percent of the 14-year period. The greater effort

Table 11.4 Source of Receipts of Local Governments for Highways, 1956-1970

Year	Property tax and other general funds	Bonds and notes[1]	State grants	Total	Actual[2]
Counties and local rural agencies					
1956	42.7%	8.2%	49.1%	100.0%	$1,461
1960	44.0	6.6	49.4	100.0	1,686
1965	40.3	9.2	50.5	100.0	2,175
1970[3]	39.8	9.5	50.7	100.0	2,910
Municipalities					
1956	57.8	23.2	19.0	100.0	1,459
1960	55.7	21.8	22.5	100.0	1,782
1965	55.8	16.2	28.0	100.0	2,258
1970[3]	58.9	12.1	29.0	100.0	3,414

Note: Excludes toll facilities.
[1] Excludes refunding issues.
[2] Millions.
[3] Estimated.
Source: [11.10, Tables VII-4 and VII-5, Part II].

being made by the cities in terms of general fund appropriations and borrowing, despite demands of the many competing municipal services, indicates that this trend needs to continue. For comparison, over 50 percent of the daily vehicle miles of travel in the United States and therefore of the earned state and federal tax is attributable to urban streets.[11]

11.3.1.2 Legal constraints on user funds Highway-user revenues in most states are placed in escrow accounts and generally spent for highway purposes. Some 28 states have limited the discretion of the state legislature by approving anti-diversion or "Good Roads Amendments" to their constitutions that provide "safeguards" on the user charges, requiring that they be used exclusively for highways and closely related purposes. Another method is diversion of user funds from which the legislature makes appropriations for highways as well as for other public purposes. Although this flow of user fees through the general fund is not the general practice, it is the preferred method of most political scientists so as not to limit the ability of elected officials to adapt the budget to particular circumstances.

An example of such circumstances can be found in many of the larger cities where it has become apparent that relief of congestion will require not only improvement of highways but the attraction of some motorists to public transportation. In 1969 and 1970 nine states introduced legislation to use a portion of highway-user revenues for transit. One state, Maryland, has in fact established a "Single Transportation Fund."[12] Efforts have been made to repeal the "Good Roads Amendments" in several states; these efforts to date have failed. It is likely that future legislatures and electorates will over time take a broader view of "transportation" and "highway related purposes."

The federal government through congressional and administrative actions has provided an example of this broader view. Eligibility for expenditures from the Highway Trust Fund has gradually been extended beyond the original concept of physical roadway and bridge construction to include land acquisition, relocation of housing assistance, environmental enhancement, additional safety and capacity features, bus facilities and many others. While these are all solid advances toward a more viable federal-aid highway system, progress has been slow in some states due in large part to the need for enabling state legislation to participate in the new transportation purposes.

11.3.1.3 Apportionment of highway funds "Apportionment" is the term given to the geographic or jurisdictional allocation (dividing) of appropriated funds. Highway Trust Fund moneys are apportioned to the states and thence urban areas for all federal systems.

Forty-five percent of the Interstate expenditures were to be in urban areas, and apportionments have been running about 10 percent below that figure. However, upon completion, the urban portion of Interstate System will approximate 15 percent of the system and account for 45 percent ($18.45 billion) of the overall

[11] [11.10, Table 1, Part II].
[12] See Sec. 11.4.

expenditures [11.4, p. 137]. Urban roads are also financed by the ABC program (federal aid primary [FAP], secondary [FAS], and urban highways). Authorizations for the urban segments of the ABC program have exceeded a quarter of a billion dollars per annum [11.4, p. 137].

As of 1970, the present apportionment scheme for the ABC program from the Highway Trust Fund to each state conforms to the following four formulas:

    a. Federal-aid primary system (FAP)—one-third area; one-third rural post miles, with a minimum apportionment of 0.5 percent per state.

    b. Federal-aid secondary system (FAS)—one-third area; one-third rural population; and one-third rural post miles, with a minimum apportionment of 0.5 percent per state.

    c. Urban extensions of FAP-FAS systems based on urban population in all urban places above 5,000 people, and with no minimum apportionment per state.

    d. New (1970) federal-aid urban system based on urbanized area, population 50,000 or more [11.10, pp. 30–31].

11.3.2 Financing Air Travel Facilities

Public aid for airports and airway facilities is steadily increasing, a trend that is likely to continue, given the costs of more sophisticated technology for safety, comfort, and convenience, and airport acquisition in the face of metropolitan sprawl. An example of the latter cost, the new Dallas–Fort Worth Airport, the only new major airport under construction in the United States, covers an area larger than Manhattan. Like highways, the major share of air travel facilities are publicly financed by user fees, general fund appropriations, borrowings, and grants.

11.3.2.1 Federal aid Congress has recognized the urgency of working out the problems of the nation's airports by creating a National Airport System and providing matching funds for airport construction and improvements. Funds available under the Airport and Airway Development and Revenue (AADR) Act of 1970 are as follows: $250 million in matching funds per year for the 5-year period starting July 1, 1970, for airports served by air carriers certified by the Civil Aeronautics Board (CAB); $30 million in matching funds per year for segments of aviation other than air carriers certified by the CAB; $15 million in matching funds per year for planning grants for airport systems planning and airport master planning; not less than $250 million annually for the next 5 fiscal years ending in 1975 for acquisition, establishment, and improvement of air navigation facilities. After 1975 the Act declares the policy to continue obligating authority for airway development at no less than $250 million/year to 1980, and airport assistance from 1970 to 1980 to be $2.5 billion. Funds are to be apportioned as follows: one-third to states on area population formula; one-third to sponsors of airports served by air carriers; one-third at the discretion of the Secretary; $30 million exclusively for general aviation; and $15 million for planning grants [11.11, pp. 1–4].

The revenue part of the Act, Title II, provides for increased support from the users of aviation facilities. Funds come from the following sources: an increased passenger tax (from 5 percent to 8 percent); a $3 tax on passengers leaving the United States on international flights; a 5 percent tax on freight bills; a tax of 7 cents per gallon for gasoline and jet fuel in noncommercial aircraft; and a $25 aircraft registration tax plus a tax of 3.5 cents/pound for all turbine aircraft and a tax of 2 cents/pound on all piston aircraft over 2,000 pounds, certified gross takeoff weight.

The federal share of project cost is 50 percent except in public land states. Nevada, at 62.5 percent, is the maximum. High-density runway lighting, touchdown zone and center lighting, and land for ILS approach lighting systems are computed at 82 percent U.S. share.

Environment requirements A project must be consistent with the comprehensive planning of the area and must give consideration to communities near the airport. A public hearing must be scheduled, if requested, to consider economic, social, and environmental effects on all projects involving a new airport, new runway or runway extension. An air and water quality certificate issued by the governor must be submitted with a project involving a new site, new runway or major runway extension. A project must also consider preservation of the natural beauty of the countryside, public parks and recreation lands, wildlife and water foul refugees and historic sites. No project will be approved which requires the use of publicly-owned land from the above areas unless there is no feasible alternative.

Airport certification The AADR Act required all airports serving air carriers certified by CAB to be certified by May 21, 1973. Certification is concerned with such things as conditions of paved areas including marking and lighting; fire and rescue facilities and adequate emergency plans; self-inspection program of airport maintenance; adequate obstruction lighting; maintenance of air navigation and ground control facilities; public protection; and, smoke and bird hazard control.

National Airport System Plan The Act also required that a National Airport System Plan (NASP) be published by July 1, 1972, to set forth needs for a 10-year period, including costs. An Aviation Advisory Commission was established to formulate recommendations concerning long range needs and to consider the relationship of airports to other means of transportation. No project for fund allocation can be approved unless it is in the NASP.

Eligibility requirements Some of the costs that are eligible or ineligible under the Airport and Airways Development Aid Program are as follows:

Land. Eligible: land for entire airport including building areas as outlined on layout plan, landing aids if included in the airport boundary, approach protection, airport utilities, and clear zones including navigation easements
Ineligible: land for industrial or nonairport purposes, awards made on damage flowing from noise or trespass

Site preparation. Eligible: clearing, grubbing and grading, drainage, erosion control, grading for NAVAIDS, and dredging or seaplane channels
Ineligible: air hangars, public parking for autos, and industrial and nonairport purposes

Runways. Eligible: reconstruction required to obtain either (1) a desired capability in a runway beyond that of its original construction or (2) capability lost through age or latent deficiencies in design or construction

Ineligible: construction work classified as maintenance

Taxiways. Eligible: exit and bypass taxiways, runway pads, and primary taxiway systems providing access to hangar and other building areas delineated on an approved layout plan

Ineligible: taxiways providng access to an area not offering aircraft storage or service to the public and lead-ins to individual storage hangars

Aprons. Eligible: loading ramps, aprons available for public parking storage and/or service, and aprons serving hangars (including privately owned) which offer aircraft storage and/or service to the public

Ineligible: aprons serving installation for nonairport use, inside a hangar or on the proposed site of a hangar, and aprons/services (pits or pipes for chemicals)

Lighting. Eligible: runway and taxiway edge lights, in-runway and taxiway lights, guidance signs, obstruction lights, apron flood lights, beacons, wind indicators, conduit and duct systems, control panels, offsight obstruction lighting, and economy approach lights

Ineligible: certain navigational aids under other programs, horizontal lights, isolated repair and reconstruction, and lighting of public paving areas

Airport buildings. Eligible: (1) fire and rescue buildings if equipment is on hand or ordered and (2) snow removal equipment buildings if in areas where temperature has not exceeded $0°$ F for at least 20 days/year for 5-year period preceding the request

Ineligible: terminal buildings, hangars, industrial buildings, and sidewalks

Utilities. Eligible: where they serve eligible buildings, utility tunnels if incidental to eligible airport development, and water systems for fire protection to air carrier operations

Airport roads. Eligible: entrance roads, acceleration-deceleration strips, street lighting, and bus stops if necessary

Ineligible: public roads used in common with airport traffic, roads to exclusive use areas, and auto parking construction, alteration or repair

Fencing. Eligible: property line fencing, blast fencing, and security fencing

Ineligible: fencing leased plots

Obstruction removal. Eligible: all structures in clear zones although not for hangar removal and location

Ineligible: cost of erection of new hangars

Offsite work. Eligible: outfall drainage ditches, relocation of roads, and lighting of obstructions

11.3.2.2 State and local aid Patterns of state and local financing of air travel facilities, while conforming to the four general categories, vary considerably. A California state tax on general aviation fuel provides state grants, which when locally matched, can be used for public airport land acquisition and development. In Oregon a similar program is supported through an aviation fuel tax and registration and license fees. Wisconsin has an "airport-aid channeling act" under which the State Division of Aeronautics acts as agent for all localities seeking federal and state aid. Many states have similar revenue sources and channels.

Local governments have financed most airport development from franchises and concessions given airline and other commercial enterprises at airports. These user charges are often used to underwrite revenue bonds or match state and federal grants. A recently enacted source is airport embarkment fees (Philadelphia, Roanoke, Newport News) paid by each commercial airlines passenger, a tax that is widespread in Europe.

11.3.3 Financing Transit

Financing of urban public transportation has been a reoccurring and often acute problem since World War I. After the peak transit years of World War II a decline in ridership and revenues set in, which accompanied by rising costs has forced increased attention at all levels of government to what once was essentially a private enterprise. While most transit companies in the United States are still privately owned, the very large urban rail and bus systems are now publicly owned. Consequently, most of the ridership is carried on publicly owned lines. The trend toward public ownership has accelerated in recent years as private companies have used up their capital investment to offset operating losses. From 1959 to 1970, of the 235 private companies that have gone bankrupt, 89 have been taken over by public authorities and 146 have gone out of existence completely [11.12, p. 6]. This has left many smaller communities without any public transportation except for taxicabs, which typically have considerably higher fares than transit.

Federal aid for urban public transportation has increased steadily with the Acts of 1961, 1964, 1966, and 1970 previously described. The Urban Mass Transportation Administration (UMTA) in the U.S. Department of Transportation administers the five major programs provided by the Acts, namely

1. Capital improvement grants
2. Capital loans
3. Technical studies
4. Demonstration projects
5. Research and training grants

Prerequisites for aid are matching local grants, generally on a $\frac{2}{3}$ to $\frac{1}{3}$ basis, and, in the case of the first three categories, a comprehensive transit plan as part of comprehensive areawide planning. Transit projects in Virginia, for example, received $1.2 million in federal aid from UMTA during the first 5 years of the program, while localities contributed about $250,000 and universities about $12,800 [11.13, p. 77].

Three of the five types of aid have been used and each developed to meet specific local needs. Bristol and Martinsville, Virginia, used capital improvement grants to upgrade publicly owned bus systems. Federal study grants have been used by the Richmond Regional Planning Commission and the Fairfax County, Virginia, Board of Supervisors to improve transit service. Demonstration grants to improve transit systems and service have been used by the Metropolitan Washington Council of Governments (COG). One University received a demonstration grant to develop training techniques for transit management, a technical study for bus shelter design, and a series of University Research and Training Grants [11.13, pp. 92-93].

As noted earlier, Congress authorized in 1970 some very limited aid from the Highway Trust Fund for rubber-tired transit facilities. In a preceding action, the Federal Highway Administration (FHWA) in June, 1968, entered into an agreement with Washington COG for a feasibility study of bus rapid transit in the Shirley Highway (I-95) Corridor in Northern Virginia. The study was completed in October, 1969, and funded at a cost of $207,000 entirely with FWHA funds rather than the usual state-federal highway planning funds. As a result exclusive bus lanes are now in operation on the Shirley Highway. Minor sources of federal aid to transit include the Department of Housing and Urban Development, the National Science Foundation, and the Small Business Administration [11.3, pp. 94-95].

State and local assitance for urban public transportation varies greatly around the country. New York State has passed statewide bonds to aid public transportation, particularly in New York City. Many of the larger cities have approved bond referendums for this purpose (See Sec. 11.1). Occasionally there have been direct grants as a stopgap measure. Local tax reductions for private companies have been more frequent. The public purchase of transit equipment for its own operation, or for lease for private operation in some larger cities, takes advantage of lower interest rates on public borrowing, particularly when backed by the full faith and credit of the local government. As noted elsewhere, it is likely that increasingly state and local transit aid will come from some variation of the single transportation fund already in operation in Maryland.

11.4 SUMMARY

In this chapter an attempt has been made to discuss several of the major considerations relevant to implementation of solutions to urban transportation problems. Included are the topics of legislation (especially at the federal level), local legal controls of transportation and land use through zoning, subdivision and the like, and finance. Not included in this chapter, but far from unimportant, were such factors as "politics," the establishment of relevant organizations and institutions, marketing, construction management, and so on. The reader is referred to other publications for information on these topics.

In the legislation section an historical perspective was offered. Until 1944, local and private responsibility for urban transportation was dominant. From 1944, to 1964 federal aid for highway flowed to urban areas. Also, the Interstate system was created. From 1964 on, emphasis in legislation was on funding for transit, protection of the environment, comprehensive planning, and the creation of departments of transportation at the state and federal levels.

The second section of the chapter dealt with several types of legal powers, especially at the local level. These included

1. Fiscal powers
2. Eminent domain
3. Proprietorship
4. The police power
5. Land use controls

The emphasis in the section was on identification of these powers which could be of most use in particular transportation and related situations.

The final section dealt with financing of transportation. The four major sources of funds identified were

1. Deducted user charges
2. The general fund
3. Borrowings
4. Grants

It was found that in most of these categories federal support for highways, airports, and mass transit had increased substantially over the last decade, along with relatively detailed descriptions of the exact types of goods that could be purchased using these funds.

BIBLIOGRAPHY

11.1 Norton, H. S.: *National Transportation Policy: Formation and Implementation*, McCutchan, Berkeley, Calif., 1966.

11.2 Johnson, E. R., G. G. Huebner, and L. G. Wilson: *Transportation: Economic Principles and Practice*, Appleton-Century-Crofts, New York, 1940.

11.3 Hudson, W. J., and J. A. Constantin: *Motor Transportation*, Ronald Press, New York, 1958.

11.4 Smerk, G. M.: *Urban Transportation: The Federal Role*, Indiana Univ. Press, Bloomington, Ind., 1965.

11.5 Smerk, G. M.: *Readings in Urban Transportation*, Indiana Univ. Press, Bloomington, Ind., 1963.

11.6 Feldman, H. G.: "Condemnation of Property for Highway Purposes," *Highway Research Board Special Report 32*, Washington, D.C., 1958.

11.7 League of Kansas Municipalities: *Planning Tools: Theory, Law, Practice*, vol. 15, Topeka, Kans., 1962.

11.8 American Society of Civil Engineers: *Land Subdivision*, Manual of Engineering Practice, no. 16, New York, 1946.

11.9 International City Management Association: *Local Planning Administration* (3d ed.), Chicago, 1959.

11.10 U.S. Department of Transportation, Federal Highway Administration: *Highway Needs Report 1972*, U.S. Government Printing Office, Washington, D.C., 1972.

11.11 Hand, C. G.: "Federal Aid for the Planning and Construction of Airports," Airport District Office, Federal Aviation Administration, San Francisco, Calif. 1969.

11.12 U.S. Department of Transportation: *1972 National Transportation Report Executive Summary*, U.S. Government Printing Office, Washington, D.C., 1972.

11.13 Virginia Metropolitan Areas Transportation Study Commission: *Urban Transit in Virginia*, Richmond, Va., 1969.

12 Transportation Systems Operation and Maintenance

After a transportation system modification has been implemented, all is not done. In fact, the task is never complete since it is always necessary to operate and maintain any changes (along with the original system). This stage of operation and maintenance involves, among other matters, the collection of new data to assess the effects of the modifications as they occur in reality (not as forecasted through a model). This stage also involves the continual solution of small-scale problems related to the plan developed as part of the overall planning process (minor rescheduling and rerouting of buses being one example of such "small-scale" problem solving). Thus in many ways the operation and maintenance stage implies a continual reorientation to the problem-solving process.

The material in this chapter is divided into two main sections, operations and maintenance. Under operations is found the topics of scheduling, terminal operations, and traffic control. The discussion under maintenance is divided according to mode: (1) streets and highways, and (2) transit. A few examples are given of specific techniques, although the description must remain somewhat general.

12.1 TRANSPORTATION SYSTEM OPERATION

Operations covers a broad variety of topics. Among these are the scheduling of personnel, vehicles, guideway usage, and control systems. Also involved is the whole realm of agency or firm administration: accounting, advertising, purchasing, and the like. The discussion in this section is directed mainly to concepts in scheduling.

12.1.1 Systems Scheduling

The problem of efficient scheduling of transportation system operations is very complex and also very important if the utilization of the system is to achieve any minimum set of service objectives. The following discussions attempt to bring to light some of the more salient considerations involved in systems scheduling.

12.1.1.1 Frequency and regularity It is obvious that the movements of most modes are regularly or irregularly spaced and the intervals of time between movements may be short or long. Schumer defines regularity in transport service as meaning that the movements are either at evenly spaced intervals or at known times [12.15]. In modern society regularity of transport service is generally assumed, though not always realized, and thereby people are able to organize their personal movements and activities accordingly.

Frequency of scheduled service yields a number of advantages including the following: the delays encountered waiting for service are minimized; the necessity to store people or goods before or after transport is reduced or avoided; a personal movement or dispatch of goods which is unexpected but urgent can be expedited; and, if transport is in a number of stages, each with frequent service, the loss of time in storage or waiting where the journey is broken will be reduced.

12.1.1.2 Scheduling algorithms With the increasing interest in transportation problems, specialists in many other fields have made significant attempts toward solving specific problems by applying their own well-developed methods and techniques. For example, mathematicians and operations research specialists, among others, have provided numerous solutions to two specific problems encountered in the scheduling of transportation systems operations.

One example is that of *routing,* wherein one seeks an optimal route in a system network based upon a selected measure of performance such as cost, time, or distance. The routing problems include those in which the terminal location of a trip differs from the starting location and also those in which the terminal location and the starting location coincide.

Another type of problem is that called *scheduling,* in which the task sequence is fixed but the task cost is time-dependent, and one wishes to allot times to each task which minimize total cost for a specific total completion time.

Obviously, however, the scheduling of transportation system operation is much more complex in nature than those idealized systems solved by such approaches. A more thorough analysis must include the various factors (and possibly, others) discussed below.

12.1.1.3 Factors affecting scheduling Complete analyses of system scheduling requirements is certainly essential to optimum system operation. In view of this fact, consideration must be given to the following variables to provide a sound basis for schedule determination.

1. Demand for service—identification of the level of demand for transportation service, the type of demand, i.e., passenger or commodity, where the demand exists, the origin-destination nature of the demand and the acceptable alternatives for supply
2. Desired levels of service—the desired type of service to perform the specific function of each trip and the tolerance levels which can be anticipated by users
3. Personnel requirements—labor costs, crew requirements, etc.
4. Station characteristics—number, spacing, and type of station are significant determinants in either the passenger or the commodity transport situation
5. Transport vehicle—the kind, type, and size of vehicle available and the limitations that these characteristics present to the flexibility of the system
6. System automation—the extent to which the human operator is eliminated from the system greatly affects the minimum allowable operational headway and thereby increases the scheduling alternatives
7. Available power—type of operating power system as a function of availability and cost
8. Operating concept—determination of stop–nonstop schedule for individual vehicles and resulting schedule for the entire system
9. Operating costs for each alternative
10. Federal, state, and local regulation

12.1.2 Terminal Operations

Since many intraurban as well as interurban trips involve a change-of-mode, the importance of the operation of terminal facilities cannot be minimized. In fact, multimodal terminals which provide an interface between combinations of a number of modes have become prominent in transportation plans. As a result, an introduction into the operational characteristics of various terminal facilities is essential to those engaged in the transportation planning process.

12.1.2.1 Automobile terminals

As the population of persons and automobiles grows, a recent publication entitled *Parking Principles* [12.11] points out, the need for adequate parking facilities also grows. Parking facilities are needed *off-street* simply because increasing travel demand in urban areas requires the fullest utilization of streets and highways and because of the high number of urban accidents associated with curb parking, typically 20 percent of all accidents. Furthermore, unless urban travel characteristics change drastically in a short period of time, parking requirements in urban areas will remain for some time. This presentation relies heavily on the information gathered for the aforementioned report and another entitled *Parking in the City Center* [12.10].

The supply of parking spaces has been shown to increase with city size, although at a decreasing rate. Furthermore, the nature of parking supply alters with city size as illustrated in Fig. 12.1. Any specific planning analysis must also take into account certain parking characteristics such as purpose of the parkers' trips, accumulation of parkers at specific locations and within the general urban area, parking duration,

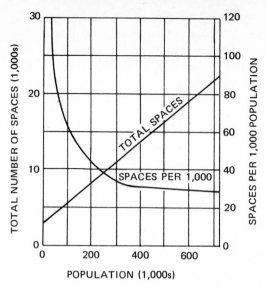

Fig. 12.1 Number of parking spaces in the CBD as related to population of the urbanized area. [12.11, p. 95].

and the parking turnover rates for the type and size of location under study. Furthermore, parking demand for a certain area is influenced by a number of factors including population characteristics, land and building use, alternative transportation modes, traffic access, parking facility congestion, supply shortages, location, and cost.

Information is available to guide transportation planners in establishing sensible parking requirements. Suggested standards such as those shown in Table 12.1 are useful for zoning purposes, but it is essential that local analyses be prepared to establish proper values for local conditions.

A general-purpose public parking facility has as its goals the enhancement of local economic values, increase of production, and reduction of street congestion, all in various combinations. As a result, numerous factors determine the appropriateness of specific facility locations, and they include degrees of parking shortages and types of nearby parking generators, user considerations (walking distances, security, and access convenience), development costs, and street system elements such as capacity, directional flows, and turn restrictions. The specifics of parking terminal design are determined by the selection of a self-parking or attendant-parking facility. Self-parking is common in new garages, and is increasingly acceptable to all types of parkers. It is also possible to develop facilities which combine the parking function with one or many other functions including retail establishments, offices, and schools.

Beyond the simple off-street parking lot, the types of parking terminals include underground garages, mechanical garages, and ramp garages. The design of specific parking terminals is dependent upon the size, weight, and turning characteristics of the automobile. Building codes throughout the United States have been established to accommodate the loading characteristics required in final designs for both multideck and roof level parking garages. Typical design configurations are shown in Fig. 12.2.

Parking terminal designs must also be evaluated in light of certain other needs within the terminal. Sufficient reservoir space must be allocated where drivers are required to stop so that cars do not block other automobile or pedestrian movements. The movements of pedestrians within the terminal, be they horizontal or vertical, must be considered in the design stage. Also necessary is an adequate lighting system in order to promote vehicle and pedestrian safety, to maximize operating efficiency, and to promote user security. Consideration should also be given to the requirements of ventilation and heating, fire protection, and adequate informational and directional signing.

12.1.2.2 Transit station terminals It is well established that mass transportation is well suited to commuter transportation to and from the CBD. Recent studies have also shown that many daily commuters can be encouraged to ride public

Table 12.1 Zoning Standard Guidelines

Use of building or site	Minimum number of parking spaces required
Residential	
Single family	2.0 per dwelling unit
Multifamily*	
Efficiency	1.0 per dwelling unit
One or two bedrooms	1.5 per dwelling unit
Three or more bedrooms	2.0 per dwelling unit
Commercial	
Offices* and banks	3.3 per 1,000 sq ft GFA
General retail	4.0 per 1,000 sq ft GFA
Shopping centers	5.5 per 1,000 sq ft GLA
Restaurants	0.3 per seat
Hotels, motels*	1.0 per rentable room plus 0.5 per employee
Industrial	0.6 per employee
Auditoriums and theaters*	0.3 per seat
Churches	0.3 per seat
College/university	
Good transit access	0.2 per student
Auto access only	0.5 per student
Senior high school	0.2 per student plus 1.0 per staff member
Elementary and junior high school	1.0 per classroom
Hospitals	1.2 per bed

*Exceptions permitted in CBD if adequate public transportation is available.

Source: [12.11, p. 39].

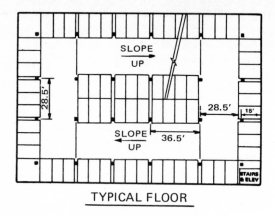

TYPICAL FLOOR

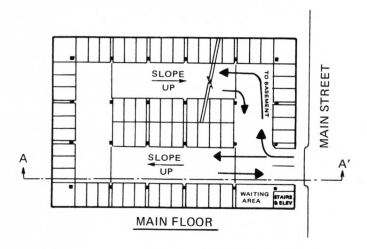

MAIN FLOOR

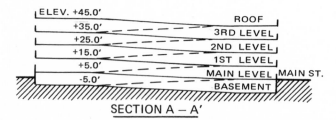

SECTION A — A'

Fig. 12.2 Typical ramp garage design (functional plan—sloping floor garage), [12.4, p. xxiv-9 and R. E. Whiteside, *Parking Garage Operations*, The Eno Foundation, Westport, Conn., 1961].

transportation for at least a portion of the commuting trip. Provision of change-of-mode parking which is convenient to quick, reliable transit service gives the commuter an alternative to CBD traffic and parking congestion. Furthermore, it has been pointed out [12.10] that such facilities result in certain advantages to the community, namely:

1. Automobiles are taken off the road in and near the central area, where the transportation problems are most acute.
2. The addition of the new passengers may allow increased frequency of transit service during at least the rush hour.
3. Downtown parking problems of the central city are eased, and more spaces can be available for shoppers and other persons desiring midday parking.
4. The reduction in demand for CBD parking has secondary benefits in that more space is then available for primary land uses. This results in greater development efficiencies by allowing a more compact central area. Higher tax yields may also be achieved with retention of strong property values, which benefits the entire city.

The actual design of a change-of-mode facility depends upon the variety of modal changes involved. Consideration must be given to the interrelationships as well as design of areas of train boarding, bus or taxi loading, and private automobile pickup-dropoff. The location of areas for these various activities must minimize pedestrian-vehicular conflicts and can be developed according to the following suggested schedule of priorities:

1. Bus loading–unloading
2. Taxi loading–unloading (may intermix with buses or cars)
3. Passenger car unloading–loading
4. Short-term parking
5. Long-term parking

A suggested plan for a rapid transit change-of-mode terminal, shown in Fig. 12.3, illustrates these considerations.

12.1.2.3 Airport terminals

The terminal area of an airport can be defined as that portion of the airport other than the landing area. Requirements of a terminal area include the need for a terminal building for processing passengers and baggage; facilities for loading and unloading passengers, baggage, and cargo; aprons for parking aircraft; vehicular parking areas; cargo storage buildings; and maintenance hangars.

The passenger terminal building is a focal point in the terminal area. To ensure smooth operation of the terminal functions, comprehensive planning must precede the development and construction of the terminal building. There are two approaches to terminal building arrangement. In a *centralized* terminal all passengers and baggage are processed in one building. The *unit* terminal concept utilizes a single terminal building for each airline or group of airlines and is particularly appropriate where traffic volumes are very high.

The terminal building should provide space for the following activities: (1) airline operations; (2) facilities for the convenience of the passengers; (3) offices for

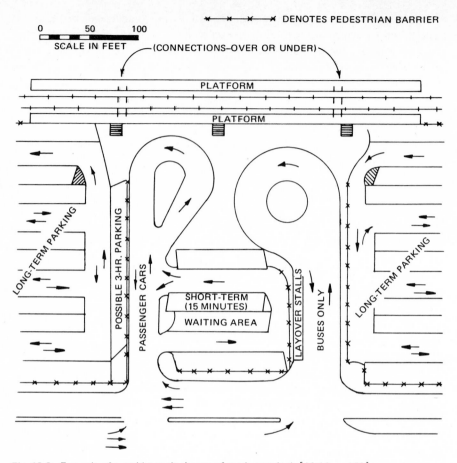

Fig. 12.3 Example of a rapid transit change-of-mode terminal. [12.11, p. 158].

the airport management; (4) aeronautical functions of the federal government; and (5) nonaeronautical functions of the federal government, including postal facilities, and passport and customs control. The actual amount of space required for the various activities in the terminal building varies considerably among different terminals. An estimate of the peak-hour passenger volume can be determined to assist in ascertaining the space requirements. The Federal Aviation Agency (FAA) has attempted to establish space requirements for the various activities through observation of operations at U.S. airports. This information provides a useful guide for planning and should be supplemented with local demand data.

Servicing the terminal building, and an essential component in the operation of an airport terminal, is the vehicular traffic circulation system. Vehicular traffic is composed of three main categories, passenger, visitor and spectator, and service; and the circulation system must be well planned or congestion and delays will result. Furthermore, parking facilities must be provided for (1) passengers, (2) visitors accompanying passengers, (3) spectators, (4) people employed at the airport, and (5) car rental. Consideration must be given to the location of parking facilities for each of the categories and for the resulting walkway connecting facilities. Directional information for parking lots and the various terminal facilities should be well-planned and executed; pedestrian routes should be direct, well-marked, and adequately lighted. Further information regarding circulation system alternatives and requirements is available from the FAA (see, for example, [12.20]).

12.1.2.4 Bus terminals An essential component of a bus–rapid transit system serving downtown areas is a set of bus-stop locations of adequate capacity. These locations may be provided in single terminals, where all passengers destined to the central area are loaded or unloaded, or as a series of off-street bus-stop locations where only part of the load may be handled.

Downtown bus terminals include space requirements for bus loading and unloading areas, passenger concourses, ticket sales and other passenger services, necessary cargo facilities, administrative functions, and parking facilities as required in all terminal locations. Space requirements for loading and unloading depend upon the design of the loading area and the operational level of the facility. Loading configurations which require operational improvements such as centralized bus fare collection systems and double-side loading and unloading are aimed at reducing travel time and cost by reducing loading and unloading delays and their attendant acceleration-deceleration time losses [12.7].

It has been noted that when arrangements are made for rapid transit buses to stop at each of two or more off-street terminals in the downtown area to load or unload passengers, the total area devoted to bus terminals in the downtown area will be greater than with a single-stop terminal. However service would be better with more than one terminal as most passengers would have a shorter distance to travel to a terminal.

12.1.2.5 Downtown rail terminals Three types of downtown facilities are in general use for rail-rapid transit operations: the distribution loop, through routing, and the stub-end terminal. In the first two types, the transit vehicles operate within and through the downtown area along a particular track or lane. Stops are made to discharge inbound passengers and pick up outbound passengers, and the vehicles then continue on their way. The elevated railway loop in downtown Chicago is an excellent example of a downtown distribution loop. Trains operate along elevated railroads, circling the loop, making necessary stops, and then returning to outlying areas. In stub-end terminals, such as New York's Grand Central Terminal, trains pull into a dead-end platform berth at the terminal. After the passengers are unloaded, the train—if equipped with double-end controls—may then be loaded and dispatched by reversing direction along the incoming terminal track. Trains pulled by locomotives, such as is common in some commuter train operations, are generally turned around before loading for the outbound trip.

Downtown rail terminal space requirements include platform space for train loading and unloading passengers, baggage, and cargo (though limited), facilities for ticket operations and passenger convenience, administrative functions, vehicular parking, and taxi operations. Because of the commuting nature of most downtown-oriented rail passengers specific attention should be paid to the needs of such travelers in order to minimize delay and encourage rail transit use.

It has been pointed out [12.7] that future demand for rail cargo transportation may well result in bands circumscribing the city just beyond presently built-up environs. Moreover, it has been concluded [12.7] that it would not be surprising if railroads (and bus companies) began relocating their intercity passenger terminals at points near the intersections of railroads and urban circumferential highways. It is unlikely that all railway tracks will be eliminated from the urban centers since some will be needed to serve heavy raw-material-consuming industries, such as iron and steel, and those warehousing activities that find it advantageous to be located in the city center.

12.1.2.6 Commodity terminals For commodity traffic a terminal is the operational origin or destination of the traffic and is often the point to which the traffic is actually brought from outlying areas for consolidation prior to road movement or for distribution to those outlying points following a road haul. From the standpoint of time alone terminals possess more significance than line haul. The average daily movement of a railroad freight car is about 44 miles, a distance requiring little more than 1 hour of travel time. A significant portion of the remaining 23 hours is spent in or at some terminal activity or facility—in yards, at the shipper's or consignee's door, in transfer, on repair tracks, etc.

An elementary function of terminals is the concentration of traffic to enable efficient and economic handling. Even though shippers and transportation companies often have their own individual terminal facilities, it is often helpful if freight can be concentrated in one freight house. The location of terminal facilities, ideally in close proximity to the sources of traffic, is of great concern to traffic and urban planners. Inadequate zoning regulation, and the resultant scattered location of industry and commerce, has resulted in a complex crisscrossing of traffic routes and increased interference with passenger traffic.

There are only a few solutions for a large urban complex with a well-established land-use pattern. Utilization of elevated, depressed, or tunnel structures, consolidation and abandonment of duplicated facilities, and the development of union truck and bus facilities all reduce cross haul interference and route duplication. Smaller communities with developing land-use patterns can bring about readjustments of land-use, defining industrial and commercial areas and planning transport routes to give maximum service to those areas and reducing the interference to other land uses within the community.

12.1.2.7 New technology Future developments in transportation systems, cargo-handling equipment, and urban structure may greatly alter transportation terminal requirements. Many writers have suggested that the key to mobility in the central city is separation of the like from the unlike in time and in space. This includes separation in space of modes of movement, whether auto, subway, bus, or train, and separation in time of functional movements, particularly that service vehicles operate at hours when large numbers of people are not present. Implementation of such an obvious, though radical, concept would result in a significant change in terminal area functional and space requirements.

12.1.3 System Traffic Control

The need for control and regulation of complex traffic systems is apparent to transportations planners and engineers. Different levels of control are possible in order to provide for economic movement and minimization of delay within the system. Several types of control systems and levels of controls are discussed in the following sections.

12.1.3.1 Street and highway control systems Urban street systems are controlled by a number of techniques which serve essentially the same purpose, that of eliminating conflicts between opposing flows of traffic. These techniques include the utilization of traffic control devices, such as stop and yield signs and traffic signals. Properly installed and adjusted, traffic control devices can minimize delays and accidents to motorists as well as improving the overall capacity and performance of the urban street network. Stop and yield signs are used to control traffic at intersections, thereby giving definite priority to one of the intersecting roads over the others. In this type of operation, the major flow suffers almost no delay and the minor flow is delayed while waiting for acceptable gaps or openings in the main flow. As the main flow increases, the number of acceptable gaps decreases and hence minor-flow vehicles are delayed longer. Or, if the minor flow increases, queues will develop and minor-flow vehicles will be delayed in crossing the main flow and in queuing.

By contrast, the use of signal controls will eliminate some delays to side street vehicles waiting for acceptable gaps, but it will cause delays while waiting both for a green signal and for the vehicles in front to clear the intersection. Moreover, signal control causes delay to the main-flow vehicles as well.

Traffic signals are generally classified [12.9] as follows:

1. Pretimed signal, which directs traffic to stop and permits it to proceed in accordance with a single, predetermined time schedule or a series of such schedules. The traffic signal is set to repeat regularly a given sequence of signal indications. The advantages of pretimed signals include simplicity of equipment, providing for easy adjustment, servicing, maintenance, and the capability of being coordinated to provide continuous flow of traffic at a definite speed along a certain route. The pretimed signal does not, however, recognize short-term fluctuations in traffic demand and as a result often causes excessive delay to vehicles and pedestrians during off-peak periods.

2. Traffic-actuated signal, whose operation is varied in accordance with the demands of traffic as registered by the actuation of vehicle or pedestrian detectors on one or more approaches. The advantages of traffic-actuated controllers include reduction of total vehicle delay and increase in capacity when properly timed, adaptability to short-term fluctuations in traffic demand, and continuous traffic responsive operation under low traffic

demand conditions. The primary disadvantages of these signals are related to cost, since installation costs are from two to five times that of a pretimed signal and maintenance and inspection costs of actuated controllers and detectors are higher because of the complexity of the equipment. Control of traffic-actuated signals is accomplished through the utilization of semi-actuated, fully actuated, or volume-density controllers.

Semi-actuated controllers are used at intersections where a major street, having high or uniform traffic demand, is crossed by a minor street with low demand but with some short, sporadic peaks. Stop sign control is inadequate during the peaks. Operating characteristics include

1. Detectors on minor approaches only.
2. Major phase receives a minimum green interval.
3. Major phase green extends indefinitely after minimum interval until interrupted by minor phase actuation.
4. Minor phase receives green after actuation providing major phase has completed minimum green interval.
5. Minor phase has minimum initial green period.
6. Minor phase green extended by additional actuations until preset maximum is reached.
7. Memory features remembers additional actuations if maximum has been reached on minor phase and will return green after major phase minimum interval.
8. Amber intervals are preset for both phases.

Fully actuated controllers are used at isolated intersections of streets that carry approximately equal traffic volumes, but where the distribution of traffic demand between approaches fluctuates. Thus this system takes into consideration the traffic demand on all approaches. Operating characteristics include

1. Detectors on all approaches.
2. Each phase has a preset initial interval which allows starting time for standing vehicles.
3. Green interval is extended by a preset vehicle interval for each actuation after the expiration of the initial interval.
4. Green extension is limited by preset maximum interval.
5. Amber intervals are preset for each phase.

Volume-density controllers provide for the maximum demand responsiveness for signalization of isolated intersections. Green time is allocated on the basis of relative volumes on approach legs. Not only does the volume-density controller react in a predetermined fashion to an actuation, but it is able to record and retain information regarding volume, queue length, and delay times. It also records the time gap between vehicles on an approach, measures it against a maximum standard, thus providing a "density" control function. The operating characteristics include

1. Detectors on all approaches.
2. Assured green times for each phase as set by three dials on the controller.

    a. Minimum green interval.

    b. Number of actuations before minimum green starts to increase.

    c. Increase of minimum green for each added actuation.

3. Passage time (the extended green time created by each additional actuation after the assured green time has elapsed). This time is set as the time required to travel from the detector to the stop line. This time interval can be reduced in the following ways:

    a. A predetermined low limit of passage time is reached when red phase vehicles have waited a preset time.

    b. A predetermined low limit of passage time is reached when the number of vehicles waiting on the red phase exceeds a preset value.

    c. A predetermined low limit of passage time is reached when the number of green phase vehicles per 10 seconds is less than a preset value.

4. Platoon carry-over effect. This remembers a preset percentage of the previous green period traffic and synthetically applies that number of vehicles waiting on the red phase, thus insuring a more prompt return to the green phase when the next platoon of vehicles hits the detector.

5. Maximum green extension. This can also be predetermined and set on the controller. This feature seldom operates because of the reduction factors on passage time.

6. Amber intervals set for each phase.

7. A recall switch for each phase that operates in the same manner as described for the full-actuated controller above.

12.1.3.2 Traffic signal systems Individual signalized intersections can be interconnected to form signal systems [12.4]. A *simultaneous signal system* is one in which all signals along a given street always give the same indication (red, green, or amber) at the same time. An *alternate system* is one in which alternate signals, or groups of signals, give opposite indications to a given street at the same time. In *progressive signal systems* the various signal faces controlling a given street give green indications in accordance with a time schedule to permit (as nearly as possible) continuous operation of groups of vehicles along a route at a planned rate of speed, which may vary in different parts of the system. A time–space diagram, Fig. 12.4, is often useful in determining and illustrating a progressive system on a two-way street. While progressive systems work reasonably well for light to medium-heavy traffic, they have been found to break down under very heavy traffic demand.

    The most sophisticated signal systems are those where entire networks are computer controlled. A truly traffic-responsive signal system should employ control decisions which result from continual sampling of traffic volume and density and with such speed as to gather and process the pertinent data, calculate the decision, and actuate the controls in real time. To process the large quantities of data obtained from a network of signal controlled intersections and perform the many calculations within required time intervals a high-speed computer is essential. The computer, working in real time through specially prepared and programmed

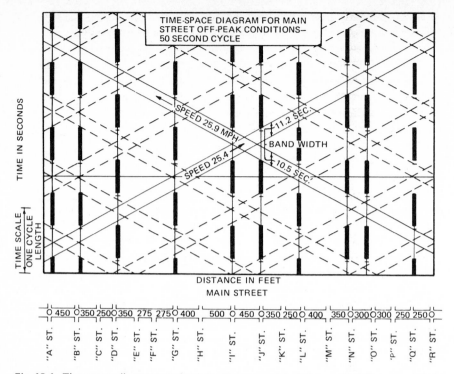

Fig. 12.4 Time-space diagram treating both directions of traffic equally. [12.4, p. xvi-12].

equations implementing some form of delay minimization criterion, computes the optimum signal display at a given time for the entire network. A number of cities have successfully experimented with this form of signal control and have shown that computer control can appreciably reduce delays by using methods not possible with existing controllers [12.19].

12.1.3.3 Air traffic control The transportation planner must be aware of the importance of air traffic control in airport planning since any extensive reorientation of runways on existing airports or the construction of entirely new airports requires consultation with the people controlling air traffic, namely, the Federal Aviation Agency. Air traffic control facilities provide the basis for communications with aircraft and the relay and clearance of flight plans for air traffic.

There are three basic types of manned air traffic control facilities:

1. Air route traffic control center: There are 33 air route traffic control centers (ARTC) in the United States, each controlling the movement of aircraft along the airways of a definite geographical area. The ARTC is concerned primarily with the control of aircraft operating under instrument flight rules (IFR).

2. Airport traffic control towers: These facilities are used to supervise, direct, and monitor air traffic within the airport area up to 15 miles from the

airport. The control tower provides a traffic control function for aircraft arriving at or departing from an airport.

3. Flight service stations: These facilities, located along the airways and at airports, provide the en route instructions to aircraft from the ARTC center personnel. Briefly, their functions are to relay traffic control messages between en route aircraft and the ARTC centers, to brief pilots before flight and in flight on weather, navigational aids, airports that are out of commission, and changes in procedures and new facilities, to disseminate weather information, and to monitor navigational aids.

A number of traffic control and navigational aids provide for positive traffic control within the air terminal area. These include the following:

1. Instrument landing system (ILS): The ILS is an adaptation of the very-high-frequency omnidirectional range (VOR) navigational aid system for landing purposes. It consists of two radio transmitters located on the airport, with one radio beam called the localizer and the other the glide slope. The localizer indicates to the pilot whether he is left or right of the correct alignment for approach to the runway; the glide slope indicates the correct angle of descent to the runway.

2. Precision approach radar (PAR): Also called ground control approach (GCA), precision approach radar was developed by the military during World War II in order to provide a mobile unit which is not dependent on airborne navigation equipment. The PAR radarscope gives the controller a picture of the descending aircraft in azimuth, distance, and elevation to enable determination of the aircraft's correct alignment and glide slope. Instructions from the controller to the pilot are given by voice communication.

3. Airport surveillance radar (ASR): This radar system, with a range of 30 to 60 miles, provides the control tower operator with an overall picture of what is going on within the airspace surrounding the terminal.

4. Approach lights: Lights are installed on the approach to the runways and on the runways because in every instrument landing the pilot must change from instrument to visual conditions and only a few seconds are available in which to make the transition and complete the landing.

5. Airport surface detection equipment (ASDE): A specially designed radar which gives a pictorial display of the runways, taxiways, and terminal area, ASDE is particularly useful at large, high-density airports where controllers have difficulty in regulating taxiing aircraft because they cannot be seen in poor visibility conditions.

12.1.3.4 Railroad traffic control   Although the primary objective of railway signaling was originally safety, wider development and use of signaling and control devices and techniques have resulted in greater economy, efficiency, and flexibility within the system. This has been achieved through increases in speed, greater line capacity, improved control and economy of train operation by consolidation of interlockings, remote control and optimum use of trackage (sometimes effecting a reduction), automation of marshalling yards, and automatic train control.

Railway signaling and control, having evolved from the original use of policemen to modern, sophisticated, and complex systems, is a highly specialized technique and as such does not lend itself to other transport systems [12.3]. Obviously, as long as a single train is in possession of a stretch of track, no signaling or control is needed, but as soon as more than one train is involved, prevention from collision becomes necessary. The original method of handling traffic was by a time interval, whereby successive trains were dispatched after a specified length of time. This method, however, is neither speedy nor efficient if train characteristics are different and speeds are other than slow. As a result, it was not long before an interval of space became established such that the trackage was divided into convenient sections, each one under the control of an individual with some form of signal, and fundamentally arranged so that only one train at a time could occupy one section. If the section were blocked by a train (or part of a train), a second was not permitted to proceed. The space interval became known as a block section. It still exists today, both on lines signaled by the older mechanical methods and on those lines where high speeds obtain and the most modern signaling is installed.

With improved and faster track (due largely to continuous welded rail) and longer switches, train speeds are rising, and it stands to reason that rail traffic control has to be geared accordingly. This involves not only apparatus design, but also appropriate train spacing and quicker control. All these are essentially demanding of power working to provide complete route selection and immediate clearing of signals under safe conditions. Brake control is also becoming more important and the link between the train and the control system assumes larger proportions. Automatic warning systems are now in the forefront of development. Speed and its reciprocal, brake power, are important in consideration of line capacity; as more traffic offers, so utilization of the line has to be increased.

Signaling is one method (but not the only one) of increasing line capacity and may be introduced on its own account or in conjunction with modernization. Power signaling installations are used not only to concentrate control in the hands of a central authority, thereby obtaining higher efficiency and greater safety, but also to economize in operating manpower and other measures. The greater use of electronic equipment for supervision and transmission of command and data is enabling the areas under control to be considerably extended, the ultimate being one central control for a complete railway system. It must be accepted that technical maintenance is often thereby increased, both in number and skills, but the overall result is usually well worthwhile.

The system called centralized traffic control (CTC) is one by which a single operator directly controls an almost unlimited number of stations and length of track, usually over a single line, having a complete display of all conditions on a diagram before him. These systems have been widely adopted in the United States.

Railways, being a system of transportation that moves in a single dimension and being guided by rails, appear to lend themselves freely to automatic operation. But practice is complicated by the very large number of separate linear movements involved, which must not conflict and which, depending on the type of system involved (e.g., main line, suburban, urban), must accommodate a variety of ancillary processes such as loading, unloading, revenue collection and checking, booking of traffic, marshalling, and many others, not least of which is the behavior of customers. It goes without saying, too, that safety must not be sacrificed; on the contrary, an automatic railway must be safer than the conventional one.

In some measure, automation on railways is already an accomplished fact. The following are examples of automated systems of an urban nature at present in operation:

1. London Transport already controls several of its junctions by "program machine" (a purely signaling exercise), but its Victoria line, operating since 1969, runs automatically.
2. The so-called "automatic pilot" on the Stockholm Underground assists the driver in optimum safety and control and in obtaining precision, reliability, and running economy.
3. Experimental systems on the Paris Metro have automatic driving and also automatic traffic control.
4. The automatic train control selected for the BART system at San Francisco.

Automation offers real advantage in railway operations, bringing improvements and financial savings to justify its implementation. The main advantages of railway automation are

1. *Safety* is increased since human error is eliminated; automatic systems replace the human operator as the controlling element either partially or completely—at most his task is reduced to a supervisory function.
2. *Economy* is achieved through optimum train running, requiring less energy and protecting equipment against undue wear.
3. *Line capacity* is maximized by increasing traffic density, reducing or eliminating completely delays, and by greatest use of trackage in minimizing the distance between trains.
4. *Punctuality* is ensured since the schedule is kept under constant supervision and adjusted as necessary.
5. *Traveling comfort* is maintained at the same high level for all trains as acceleration and especially braking are no longer dependent on an individual driver's skill.
6. *Saving of personnel* is effected by their release from routine work, thus reducing recurrent costs.

12.2 TRANSPORTATION SYSTEM MAINTENANCE

Any structure or facility which is subjected to usage or exposure to the elements is bound to deteriorate. While such deterioration cannot be completely prevented, it can be arrested to the point where the expected life of a facility can be realized, consistent with the durability which went into its original design and construction. Timely and effective maintenance is one sure means by which this deterioration can be reduced to its least detrimental minimum.

12.2.1 Street and Highway Maintenance

The purpose of highway maintenance is the preservation of each type of roadway, roadside, structure, and facility as nearly as possible in its original condition as constructed or as subsequently improved, and the operation of highway facilities and services to provide satisfactory and safe transportation [12.8]. An estimated one-fourth of all highway funds go to highway maintenance, which is generally performed by the various highway agencies themselves. Since World War II, highway maintenance has emerged as a major industry. It utilizes over 200,000 personnel, 300,000 to 400,000 pieces of equipment, and billions of dollars each year. About half of this total is accounted for by the 50 state highway departments.

The organization for highway maintenance for most states has more or less grown up without much formal planning. A look at the history of highway usage makes evident why this has been the case. Early roads in the horse and buggy era were built solely for local travel. Roads were mostly only graded and drained earth with possibly some stabilization of surfaces with gravel or crushed rock. A very common practice was to require that each landowner spend a certain number of days per year working on maintenance of the road in front of his property or furnish a team of horses and a wagon for a certain number of days.

As automobile production increased, and with it travel, both in volume and speed, more work was required for the maintenance of roadways. Farmers and landowners then logically asked the local unit of government, county or townships, to hire men to do the maintenance work and the landowners paid taxes to cover the costs. As traffic volumes increased, an ever decreasing percentage of the traffic passing any one point was of local origin, and maintenance became even more logically a governmental responsibility.

The improvement of roadway design and construction procedures resulted in the need for improved maintenance procedures and equipment. Trucks replaced horses and wagons, and then with the harnessing of steam, gasoline, and diesel power there has gradually been developed even more sophisticated and expensive equipment. This modern equipment can perform a better job of maintenance only if there is enough volume of work assigned to one piece of equipment to keep the machine busy and if it is run by a skilled operator.

The fact that maintenance is performed for the most part by the various highway agencies themselves is in direct contrast to construction, where 95 percent of the work, exclusive of engineering, is done by contract. The principal explanation is that maintenance work is so diverse, so subject to variation from the expected, and on occasion so hurried, that it does not lend itself to competitive bidding. Sometimes maintenance forces also perform "betterment" work that might also be done by contract. Common betterment projects include grading and paving for small line changes, resurfacing, and mulching, planting, or other erosion-control work.

Maintenance by most of the state highway departments and many local, rural and urban agencies is a well-organized operation. Without question, however, there are still many instances where maintenance positions are used to discharge political obligations. Among the state highway departments, there is an encouraging trend toward making maintenance a well-paid and profitable career.

12.2.1.1 Relationship between design and construction practices and maintenance costs There is a close relationship between design and construction practices and maintenance costs. For example, insufficient pavement or base thickness or improper construction of these elements soon results in expensive patching or surface repair. Shoulder care becomes a serious problem where narrow lanes force heavy vehicles to travel with one set of wheels off the pavement. Improperly designed drainage facilities mean erosion or deposition of materials and costly cleaning operations or other corrective measures. Sharp ditches and steep slopes required hand maintenance whereas flatter ditches and slopes permit machines to do the work more cheaply. In snow country, improper location, extremely low fills, and narrow cuts that leave no room for snow storage can create extremely difficult snow-removal problems. Even more specifically, some of the problems of this relationship were studied in a National Cooperative Highway Research Program Project entitled, "Snow Removal and Ice Control Techniques at Interchanges" [12.15], which was undertaken to identify the factors affecting snow removal, to study the problems and current procedures for solution of these problems, and to suggest improved techniques for snow removal and ice control in interchange areas. Although the problems of snow removal and ice control on interchanges are basically similar to those on the main line, there are special considerations, and the problems which can result from such considerations or from poor design or construction practices often result in excessively high maintenance costs.

12.2.1.2 Maintenance costs Of the maintenance dollar, about 45 cents is spent on care and repair of the roadway surfaces, 25 cents on shoulders, roadside, and drainage, 10 cents on control of snow and ice, 5 cents on bridge maintenance, and 15 cents on traffic services—signs, markings, and lighting [12.5]. The total costs for highway maintenance, however, are accelerating beyond the expectation of most state administrators. As a result, and because of the necessity for an objective quantification of future highway maintenance financial needs, a Minnesota highway engineer has recently attempted to prepare a reliable yardstick for determining within broad limits the extent of future resource requirements for highway maintenance. Because of the general applicability of these results, the following discussion relies heavily on the analysis [12.17].

Maintenance costs on the Minnesota state highway system for each year beginning in 1957 and continuing through 1969 were identified. The annual cost per mile over the 13-year period was expressed as an index number, with 1957–1959 serving as the base time period to show explicitly the magnitude of fluctuations in cost. The results are shown in Table 12.2. The index shows the

Table 12.2 Annual Unit-Mile
Index of Highway Maintenance
Direct Operational Costs

Year	Cost per mile	Index
1957	$1,305.90	101.03
1958	1,338.96	103.62
1959	1,232.15	95.35
1960	1,328.55	102.82
1961	1,428.81	113.67
1962	1,522.89	117.85
1963	1,643.22	127.17
1964	1,785.12	138.15
1965	2,426.69	187.80
1966	2,425.97	187.74
1967	2,529.02	195.72
1968	2,289.13	177.15
1969	2,876.96	222.65

Note: 1957–1959   (index 100.00) average cost per mile was $1,292.14.
Source: [12.17, p. 2].

relative increase in the cost of all factors affecting highway maintenance over the cost that would result had these factors remained static.

The most prominent influence on maintenance costs proved to be fluctuations in the quantity and type of labor, equipment, and materials needed for direct maintenance operations and the effect of economic factors on the "going rate" for these resources. Changes in the "going rate" for labor, equipment, and materials were computed and expressed in the form of index numbers for purposes of analysis. The recent increase in the cost of labor is clearly evident, and the 1969 compensation rates represent a 97 percent increase over the base period (Fig. 12.5). At the same time the increase in equipment costs has been very modest; they have risen only about 13 percent over the base period (Fig. 12.6). The cost of maintenance materials is still below base-period levels despite a small but steady increase since 1965 (Fig. 12.7). An overall index (Fig. 12.8) was developed to express the composite impact of rising labor compensation and changes in equipment and material prices.

It should be pointed out that in this particular study a single measure of output, namely centerline miles of highways maintained, was chosen. It should be realized that not all centerline miles are equal in terms of maintenance complexity. Thus, any change in this makeup from one year to another could obviously have a substantial effect on the average overall centerline mile maintenance cost.

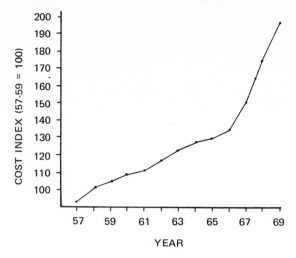

Fig. 12.5 Labor compensation index. [12.17, p. 3].

The study also resulted in the quantification of the effect of rising costs, changing roadway system mix, and increased traffic on maintenance costs. The values of unit-mile highway maintenance direct operational costs, as given in Table 12.3, thus were statistically adjusted to indicate the cost level that would have resulted had these factors remained static. A plot of the adjusted index is shown in Fig. 12.9 by the light dashed line superimposed over the original index. It can be readily seen that with these influences removed, the cost index in 1969 drops from 223 to 132. If the impact of rising compensation and prices is excluded, the systems mix and increased traffic together leave a residual that is considered a

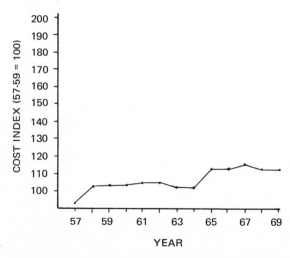

Fig. 12.6 Equipment cost index. [12.17, p. 3].

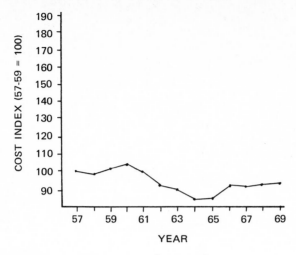

Fig. 12.7 Materials cost index. [12.7, p. 3].

change in the basic cost level. Further, when the influence of cost changes caused by differing winter severity was negated, the unit-mile highway maintenance direct operational costs increased 19 percent between 1957 and 1969.

As a final step, highway maintenance direct operational costs were formulated for 1975 and 1986 for the State of Minnesota. Total direct operational costs were forecast at $53.5 million by 1975 and $106 million by 1986. The awesome fact about these forecasts is that in the current 6-year period (1970–1975), highway maintenance direct operational costs will increase by $5 million more than they did

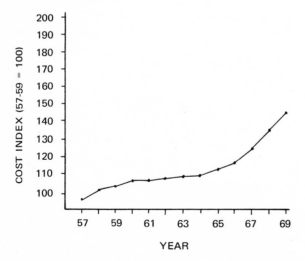

Fig. 12.8 Composite cost index: labor, equipment, and materials. [12.17, p. 3].

Table 12.3 Formulated Highway Maintenance Direct Operational Costs, 1957–1986

Item	1960	1962	1964	1966	1969	1975	1986
Cost* at 1957–1959 levels†	$15,300	15,400	15,500	15,600	15,800	16,200	11,000
Increases*							
Caused by changes in the basic cost level	0	400	2,900	5,200	3,000	5,500	11,000
Caused by changing system mix	0	400	700	1,000	1,500	2,700	4,300
Caused by changing traffic volume	100	600	800	1,200	1,800	4,800	8,400
Caused by interstate and freeway aging	0	0	0	0	0	200	800
Caused by rising labor compensation rates and higher prices	1,000	1,300	1,800	3,900	9,900	24,500	65,300
Total formulated normal year direct operational costs	$16,400	18,100	21,700	26,800	31,800	53,500	106,000
Actual costs	15,700	18,100	21,400	29,200	34,700		

*Expressed in 1957–1959 dollars per centerline mile.
†The cost if all factors remained static except the number of centerline miles maintained.
Source: [12.17, p. 7].

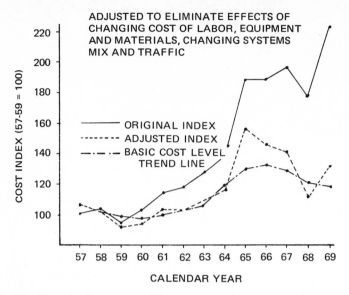

Fig. 12.9 Adjusted index of unit-mile highway maintenance directed operational costs showing the basic cost level. [12.17, p. 5].

during the preceding 10 years. The anticipated increase between 1969 and 1986 will be 4.5 times greater than the $16.5 million increase that occurred between the base period and 1969.

12.2.1.3 Highway maintenance practice Since a major portion of the state and local highway maintenance dollar goes toward care of the roadway surface, surface maintenance problems are of continued concern. The specific maintenance requirements for roadway surfaces vary with pavement surface. For gravel roads, blading and occasional resurfacing is required. Calcium chloride is often necessary during dry weather when much of the fine material is beaten out by traffic and blown from the roadway material in the form of clouds of dust.

For surface treatments and low-type bituminous surfaces, patching, seal coating, or possibly loosening, oiling, remixing, and relaying are necessary. Where surface failure is due to weakness beneath the surface, possibly in the subgrade, the weak material must be removed and refilled (or back filled) with more stable materials.

In the case of high-type surfaces, such as bituminous concrete and Portland cement concrete, removal and replacement of failed areas and resurfacing are often required. Any adverse subgrade conditions which may have directly or indirectly caused the failure must first be corrected. Filling and sealing of joints and cracks to prevent seepage of water into the subgrade constitutes a major item of maintenance of concrete pavements.

12.2.1.4 Roadside and drainage maintenance Mowing of grass, weeds, and brush on the roadside within the limits of the right-of-way is necessary to improve sight distances and to provide a better appearance along the roadway. Picking up litter thrown or blown along the roadside or into wayside areas is another annoying but necessary chore.

Special roadside areas—parks and turnouts—should be maintained so as to meet approved aesthetic and health standards. Many state highway organizations have roadside improvement and forestry departments that have charge of planting, trimming, spraying, and fertilizing of turf, trees, and shrubs in roadside and park areas.

Drainage maintenance involves keeping ditches, culverts, structures, and appurtenances such as drop inlets and catch basins clean and ready to carry the next flow of water. Sediments deposited during periods of heavy flow must be removed. Brush, branches, and other debris that collect in trash racks or at culvert and structure entrances must be disposed of. Badly eroded channels and dikes must be repaired, and paving, seeding, sodding, riprap, bank protection, or other means must be adopted to prevent recurrence. After extreme storm damage, maintenance forces may be called upon to reconstruct much of the drainage system.

Periodic inspection of bridges—superstructure, substructure, and the stream bed—is made to determine what maintenance work is necessary. Inspection should be complete enough to discover any undermining of footings and damage to or deterioration of substructure by corrosion, erosion, floating debris, or attack by organisms.

Frequent cleaning and painting of all surfaces of steel superstructure is essential for protection from the elements; bridge floors must be repaired and replaced; damage caused by traffic accidents should be repaired promptly and damaged members replaced; and expansion elements—bridge seats, rockers, and rollers—must function properly.

Shoulder and approach maintenance procedures depend on the surface character of these areas. Sod shoulders must be mowed and occasionally bladed down to the level of the roadway so that water is not trapped in the traveler's way. The grass must be fertilized, reseeded, and otherwise treated to keep it in good condition. Care of shoulders protected by bituminous blankets or surface treatments is the same as for roadways with like surfaces. Gravel and earth shoulders are maintained by blading under proper weather conditions.

Rutting or settling of the shoulders that leaves a drop-off at the pavement edge creates a serious accident hazard. If this condition develops, it should be corrected as soon as possible by reconstruction, resurfacing, or other appropriate means.

12.2.1.5 Snow and ice control In a large section of the country, various types of snowplows, large trucks, and power graders must be kept in working order for removal of snow from the highway. To solve the major winter maintenance problem requires careful organization and advance training. Often "dry runs" are held in the fall to discover and correct deficiencies in equipment or plans that would cause serious trouble during a storm. Communications equipment has been a major step forward in coordinating snow-removal operations.

Snow fences are used in areas where drifting of snow occurs and on the side of the roadway from which the wind blows during storms. Their purpose is to drift or pile up the snow before it reaches the roadway. Natural snow fences or windbreaks may be made in critical areas by planting rows of trees and shrubs parallel to the roadway where rights-of-way or property easements may be procured.

Ice-control abrasives such as coarse sand and cinders should be placed in stockpiles or containers at strategic points along the roadway where icing of the surface is likely to occur. Normally, the abrasives are treated with calcium chloride in solid or liquid form before storage to prevent freezing in the stockpile or bin and insure penetration of the particles into the icy surface. Experience has shown that untreated aggregates, even if heated before application, whip or blow off the roadway.

12.2.2 Airport Maintenance

The organization for maintenance activities for airports will vary with the size of the facility, but the general types of maintenance are relatively the same regardless of airport size or extent of development. The scope of maintenance work varies, therefore, in complexity and degree, but general maintenance is required at all airports in the following areas:

Grading and drainage   Buildings and furnishings
Pavements   Landscaping and grounds
Lighting and electrical facilities   Sewage disposal facilities

The Federal Aviation Agency has provided an explicit manual outlining the necessary procedures for airport maintenance [12.2]. Table 12.4, which summarizes the procedures for this area of maintenance, provides an indication of the extensive nature of the requirements for airport maintenance.

A scheduled periodic on-ground inspection should be conducted by trained personnel in order to detect and record defective conditions of off-pavement surfaces and of surface and subsurface drainage facilities. The inspection, as a minimum, should be conducted at intervals of 6 months, or less following any major storm or meteorological disturbance.

The inspection should provide a means of identifying (1) signs of wind, water, or blast erosion; (2) ponding of water in undesired areas; (3) build-up of soil at pavement edges preventing runoff; (4) eroded ditches and spill basins; (5) clogged and overgrown ditches; (6) broken or displaced inlet grates or manhole covers; (7) clogged or silted inlets; (8) broken or deformed pipe; (9) backfill settlement over pipes; (10) erosion around inlets; and (11) generally poor shoulder shaping and random erosion.

The trouble-shooting guide (Table 12.4) indicates common problems found on airports and suggests possible cures. The equipment and manpower requirements are also outlined for this and other specific maintenance tasks [12.2].

In general, maintenance is required regardless of use. Certain items may require less maintenance when operations are reduced, but the deterioration of most facilities is caused by the passage of time rather than activity.

Table 12.4   Trouble-shooting Guide for Grading and Drainage Maintenance

Problem	Probable cause	Cure
Ditch erosion	Excessive flow velocity; absence of ditch lining	Reestablish lining (sod, rip rap, etc.); install ditch checks
Erosion around structure	Poor backfill compaction; improperly designed inlet	Refill and compact; install apron; redesign inlet entrance
Settlement over pipes	Poor backfill compaction	Fill and recompact (removal and replacement of fill may be required if condition is recurring)
Crushed or broken pipe	Overload on pipe: (1) Insufficient cover (2) excessive fill load	Replace pipe: (1) In concrete bedding or encasement (2) Use "elastic" cover (imperfect trench) in backfill
Surface erosion	Flowing water concentrating in wrong areas; poor ground cover; poorly designed grades	Remove cause (obstruction to intended flow); fill ruts and gullies; reestablish ground cover; reshape surfaces
Obstructed ditches or structures	Presence of foreign material; vegetation	Remove obstructions and debris; trim vegetative growth; remove debris sources
Runoff trapped on pavement edges	Soil or turf accumulation at pavement edge	Reshape pavement shoulder
Blast erosion	Unprotected, erosion-susceptible soil	Provide surface protection (turf, bituminous surfacing, etc.), consistent with operational requirements
Broken or displaced grates or manhole covers	Improper seating in frame; loose or broken fastening bolts or anchors	Clean cover recesses or grind cover to prevent rocking; replace broken units; anchor firmly

Source: [12.2, p. 7].

12.2.3   Transit System Maintenance

Maintenance is a very significant factor in the operation of mass transportation facilities, but in spite of this very little attention has been focused on the topic. As an example of its magnitude, the cost estimates for operations and maintenance of the Metro System in Washington, D.C., for the 40-year period between 1980 and

2020 call for $1.4 *billion.* Moreover, construction cost estimates have since been modified upward, and it is reasonable to assume that the foregoing operating and maintenance cost estimates need also to be modified upward [12.18].

The costs associated with the maintenance of all fixed facilities of a system—tracks, tunnels, bridges, buildings, power distribution systems, signal and communication systems, and so forth—are generally classed under the heading "maintenance of way and structures." They comprise from 10 percent to 15 percent or more of total operating and maintenance costs. All those way and structures costs would include some or all of the following components (and possibly others): ballast, ties, rails, rail fastenings and joints, special trackwork, electric track switch, track grinding, shop expense, paving, cleaning track, removal of snow and ice, ventilating equipment, escalator equipment, water removal, subway bridges over tracks, signals and interlockers, third rail maintenance, track bonding, and station maintenance.

The maintenance costs associated with power distribution commonly include the following components: signal system, communication systems, supervisory control equipment, underground conduits, feeders—overhead and underground, miscellaneous electric line expenses, and emergency crews.

Maintenance-of-equipment costs are those associated with the repair and upkeep of the vehicles on a rail transit system. They include the following: maintenance of passenger car bodies, painting, accident repairs, electric motive equipment, shop expenses, car cleaning, oiling, inspection and maintenance of fare collection equipment.

Table 12.5 shows annual cost of maintenance of way and structures, estimated annual gross tonnage, and track mileage for five operating mass transport properties as obtained by Lang and Soberman [12.6]. The authors point out that the variation in the resulting unit costs per ton-mile and per track-mile is probably due to the different characteristics of the properties involved. Table 12.6 shows maintenance-of-equipment costs for these same companies [12.6]. The authors point out that for the three companies using new (1960) equipment (Cleveland, Toronto, and Philadelphia), maintenance costs per car-hour are seen to decrease with increasing car mileage, which suggests there are economics of scale to be obtained with higher utilization.

In the planning of the Washington Metro System, modern 75-ft air-conditioned cars operating in pairs were assumed. Car equipment such as train controls, air-conditioning equipment, and compressors was designed to be of modular construction for ease of removal, bench repair, and reinstallation. Car inspection and cleaning is to be conducted at 10,000-mile intervals. A summary of the estimated labor and material expenses for vehicle maintenance is shown in Table 12.7. A perusal of the salaries, employee benefits, and material costs, indicates that these estimates are conservative.

The Bay Area Rapid Transit District has included in its development a major maintenance facility known as the Hayward Yard and Shop. The maintenance yard will be an automated operation and will have the capacity for and capability of

Table 12.5 Maintenance-of-way Costs, 1960

City	Annual revenue (in car-miles)	Revenue track-miles	Annual car-miles per revenue track-mile	Approximate car weight*	Annual ton-miles per revenue track-mile	Total annual m-of-w cost	Unit annual m-of-w cost†	Cost per track-mile	Cost per car-mile
Cleveland	7,703,000	29.8	158,000	65,000	5.1×10^6	$ 266,000	$1.75	$ 8,900	$0.057
Toronto	7,053,000	8.82	800,000	96,000	38.4×10^6	1,060,000	3.13	120,200	0.15
Philadelphia‡	10,200,000	26.0	392,000	59,000	11.6×10^6	1,100,000	3.65	42,300	0.108
Chicago	44,633,000	160.7	278,000	53,000	7.4×10^6	3,678,000	3.09	22,900	0.082
New York	305,570,000	723.4	422,000	92,000	19.4×10^6	40,211,000	2.86	55,600	0.132

*Using a 40 percent load factor applied to maximum rated car capacity and assuming an average passenger weight of 150 pounds.

† Per TGTM (thousand gross ton-miles) per mile.

‡Due to a change in equipment used on this line during 1960, Philadelphia figures quoted in this and in following tables are based on a projection of the first 7 months in 1961.

Source: [12.6, p. 71].

Table 12.6 Maintenance-of-Equipment Costs, 1960

City	Total annual maintenance-of-equipment costs*	Cost per car-mile	Average car speed (mph)	Car length (ft)	Car-miles per car	Car weight (1,000 pounds)	Total number of cars	Average car age (years)	Cost per car-hour
Cleveland	$ 194,000	$0.041	28.9	48	53,400	57	88	6	$1.18
Toronto	602,000†	0.085	16.0	57	50,700	84	140	6	1.36
Philadelphia	700,000	0.069	21.0	55	37,800	59	270	1	1.45
Chicago	4,431,000	0.099	22.0	48	40,200	44	1,110	19	2.17
New York	29,984,000‡	0.098	18.0	51–60	46,500	74–84	6,565	23	1.82

*Accounting procedures are not entirely standard from one property to another. Some properties, for example, include the cost of car cleaning under equipment maintenance while others include this cost under transportation. Car hostling (the forming or breaking up of trains) is also charged to one or the other of these accounts. To account for these differences the authors have included car-servicing costs under equipment maintenance, and car-hostling costs under transportation. The available cost data have therefore been adjusted to make accounts comparable as detailed in the following footnotes.

†Excluded approximately $324,000 for car hostling added to Table 12.5.

‡Includes $2,797,000 for car servicing deducted from Table 12.5.

Source: [12.6, p. 72].

Table 12.7 Estimated Labor and Material Expense for Equipment Maintenance in the Washington, D.C., Metro System, by Functional Departments

		Labor expense		Material and other expense	Total expenses
Job classification	Quota	Pay rate	Annual cost		
General superintendent	1	$22,800/yr	$ 22,800		
Superintendent, equipment	1	18,200/yr	18,200		
Superintendent, repairs	1	18,200/yr	18,200		
Superintendent, inspection	1	18,200/yr	18,200		
Foremen, repair shop	3	9,800/yr	29,400		
Foremen, inspection shop	3	9,800/yr	29,400		
Foremen, running repairs	6	9,800/yr	58,800		
Mechanics	28	3.93/hr	228,900		
Electricians	17	4.12/hr	145,700		
Welders	3	3.93/hr	24,500		
Machinists	6	3.93/hr	49,000		
Helpers	14	3.51/hr	102,200		
Repairmen	23	4.12/hr	197,100		
Helpers	7	3.51/hr	51,100		
Car inspectors	55	3.82/hr	437,000		
Car cleaners	44	3.44/hr	314,800		
Car washers	11	3.62/hr	82,800		
Chief clerk	1	8,600/yr	8,600		
Secretary	1	6,600/yr	6,600		
Clerks	3	6,600/yr	19,800		
Janitor	1	6,800/yr	6,800		
Stenographer	1	5,800/yr	5,800		
Total	231		$1,875,700		
Vacation pay			89,500		
Holiday pay			27,600		
Labor contingency			100,000		
Total payroll expense					$2,092,800
Repair and inspection of cars				$ 737,000	
Shop heating				29,400	
Miscellaneous office material and expense				10,300	
Material and other contingency				38,800	
Total material and other expense					$ 815,500
Maintenance of equipment expense					$2,908,300

Source: [12.8, Table XI-10].

performing functions such as storage, dispatch and receipt of cars, cleaning of cars, minor maintenance, safety inspection, and train washing.

To supplement the modern equipment and facilities, a separate Maintenance Planning Organization has been formed to establish and perform what BART has labeled "Maintenance Management" [12.13]. The prime product of the organization is information which will be used to improve the efficiency of the maintenance operation.

But transit systems have experienced many years of maintenance operations by a vast number of agencies. Recent declines in bus transit passenger ridership and subsequent declines in operating revenues have forced the systems to improve the efficiency of their maintenance operations, particularly in the area of preventive maintenance.

The maintenance procedures used by Bi-State Transit Company in St. Louis are considered among the best in the transit industry. The company and its principal predecessor, the former St. Louis Public Service Company, have won the top award for bus maintenance efficiency for the past 22 years. The schedule of preventive maintenance performed by the company is based on the following principal phases of an effective preventive maintenance:

1. Daily servicing, consisting of refueling, cleaning, and checking drivers' reports
2. Mileage inspections at 1,500, 3,000, 9,000, and 27,000 miles
3. Overhauling of units on a condition inspection basis
4. Body overhaul and painting at 4- to 5-year intervals [12.13]

As a result of the experience obtained by mass transit maintenance operations it has been shown that preventive maintenance reduces repair costs, improves the reliability of service, prevents accidents, and prolongs the life of the vehicles. It seems logical that any transit authority can benefit from a well-organized maintenance program, and, when considering the amount of funds required for construction, operation, and maintenance of the system, such a program is essential. Furthermore, such a program must provide the flexibility whereby the continuous analysis of output can be effectively utilized in the updating and modification of the program, which should result in maximum efficiency.

12.3   SUMMARY

The purpose of this chapter has been to familiarize the student of transportation planning with the operation and maintenance of transportation facilities. Although of primary interest to the transportation engineer, these facets of metropolitan transportation systems are of importance to the planner because of their impact upon the effectiveness of any system plan.

Transportation systems scheduling, though a complex problem, is of importance if system utilization is to be maximized within any set of operating constraints. Similarly, the provision of adequate change-of-mode terminals is important to system utilization as well as to making system and terminal facilities an integral part of the community.

The operation of any transportation system requires some form of operational or traffic control for safe and efficient movement. Such operational control results in constraints upon the system, although improved types of control provide for more economic movement and the minimization of delay within the system.

The maintenance of transportation system facilities is of concern to the planner since any facility subject to usage is bound to deteriorate. The halting of deterioration or the replacement of deteriorated facilities can be costly in economic terms and also in terms of efficient operation of the systems. Excessive delays or stoppages of system operation due to maintenance requirements must be avoided if operation is to be efficient. Nevertheless, a conscientious program of maintenance must be adhered to in order to protect and sustain the system.

BIBLIOGRAPHY

12.1   American Association of State Highway Officials: *A Policy on Maintenance of Roadway Surfaces*, Washington, D.C., 1948.

12.2   Federal Aviation Agency: *Airport Maintenance*, Publication AC 150/5380-1, Washington, D.C., 1963.

12.3   Cunliffe, J. P.: "A Survey of Railway Signaling and Control," *Proceedings of IEEE*, vol. 56, no. 4, April, 1968.

12.4   Kennedy, N., J. H. Kell, and W. Homburger: *Fundamentals of Traffic Engineering—7th Edition*, The Institute of Transportation and Traffic Engineering, Univ. of California, Berkeley, 1969.

12.5   Hennes, R., and M. Ekse: *Fundamentals of Transportation Engineering*, McGraw-Hill, New York, 1969.

12.6   Lang, A. S., and R. M. Soberman: *Urban Rail Transit*, Joint Center for Urban Studies through the M.I.T. Press, Cambridge, Mass., 1963.

12.7   Meyer, J. R., J. F. Kain, and M. Wohl: *The Urban Transportation Problem*, Harvard Univ. Press, Cambridge, Mass., 1965.

12.8   Oglesby, C., and L. Hewes: *Highway Engineering*, Wiley, New York, 1964.

12.9   Paquette, R. J., N. Ashford, and P. Wright: *Transportation Engineering*, Ronald Press, New York, 1972.

12.10 Smith, W., and Assoc: *Parking in the City Center*, New Haven, Conn., 1965.

12.11 Highway Research Board: *Parking Principles*, Special Report 125, Washington, D.C., 1971.

12.12 American Association of State Highway Officials: *Policy on Maintenance of Shoulders, Road Approaches, Sidewalks and Roadside*, Washington, D.C., 1958.

12.13 Bi-State Transit System: *Preventive Maintenance*, St. Louis, 1968.

12.14 Robertson, R. N.: "Maintenance of Mass Transit Systems," Dept. of Civil Engineering, V.P.I. & S.U., Unpublished Research Paper, Spring, 1972.

12.15 Schumer, L. A.: *The Elements of Transport*, Butterworth, London, 1964.

12.16 Highway Research Board: *Snow Removal and Ice Control Techniques at Interchanges*, NCHRP Report 127, Washington, D.C., 1971.

12.17 Tessman, T. F.: "Minnesota Highway Maintenance Costs: A Study of Financial Requirements through 1986," *Highway Research Record*, 359, 1971.

12.18 Washington Metropolitan Area Transit Authority: *Traffic Revenue and Operating Costs*, Federal Clearinghouse, Springfield, Va., Feb., 1969.

12.19 Wagner, F. A., F. C. Barnes, and D. L. Gerlough: *Improved Criteria for Traffic Signal Systems in Urban Networks,* NCHRP Report 124, Highway Research Board, Washington, D.C., 1971.

12.20 U.S. Department of Transportation, Federal Aviation Administration: *Airport Master Plans,* Report AC 150/5070-6, Washington, D.C., Feb., 1971.

Appendix
Mathematical Tools

Planners and engineers involved in the study of transportation often use mathematical techniques or tools which differ from those utilized in many other endeavors. For example, calculus traditionally has played an important role in engineering work in such efforts as the analysis of structures, fluids, and soils. But other techniques, such as those of regression and mathematical programming, have greater application to the unique kinds of problems which evolve from the analysis of transportation systems. It is to these latter methods that this appendix is directed. However, the presentation made here will dwell on each one of the several topics only lightly and should not be construed as an all-encompassing work. References to more complete discussions are given at the end of the appendix.

A.1 MEANS, STANDARD DEVIATIONS, AND DISTRIBUTIONS

There are several types of averages that can be calculated; the mean, the mode, and the median are three. We will deal only with the mean in this discussion. The mean can be obtained through the equation

$$\bar{x} = \sum_{i=1}^{n} \frac{x_i}{n} \tag{A.1}$$

where $\bar{x}$ = arithmetic mean of n observed values of variable X

$\quad\quad x_i$ = value associated with observation i of variable X.

The simplest way to measure variability would be to take the average of the deviations of each observation from the mean. This procedure is essentially what is done in computing the standard deviation. However, we want to make sure that positive and negative deviations do not cancel themselves out. The usual procedure thus is first to square the deviations, thereby making all positive numbers, and then to sum the squared deviations, divide by the number of observations (minus one, to account for lost degrees of freedom), and finally take the square root of the resulting number (in order to compensate for the squaring done initially). Symbolically, this procedure reduces to

$$s = \pm \sqrt{\sum_{i=1}^{n} \frac{(x_i - \bar{x})^2}{n-1}} \quad\quad\quad\quad (A.2)$$

where s = standard deviation

$\quad\quad x_i$ = value associated with observation i of variable X

$\quad\quad \bar{x}$ = arithmetic mean of n observed values of variable X

After computation of means and standard deviations, the next step in converting empirically derived data into a more usable form is to create a *histogram,* which is a simple graph depicting a set of mutually exclusive and exhaustive classes of a variable on the abscissa and the frequency (number of times) that the observed values of the variable fall within each class as the ordinate. Figure A.1 shows the prescribed transformation of a set of highway speed data. This

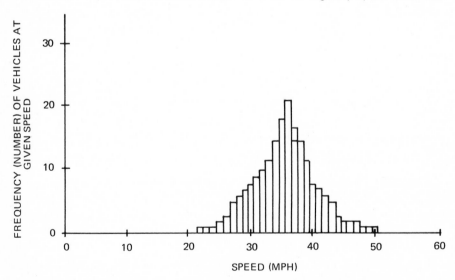

Fig. A.1 Frequency (number) of vehicles passing a point on a roadway at a given speed.

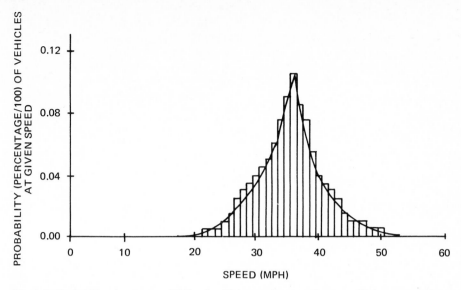

Fig. A.2 Probability (percentage/100) of vehicles passing a point on a highway at a given speed.

transformation is only the first stage of a three-stage procedure, however. The next stage involves the division of frequencies within each class by the total number of observations, to produce the *percentage* of observations falling within each class. This percentage also can be considered to be an empirically derived *probability* of an observation belonging to a given class. Figure A.2 shows the transformed histogram.

The third and last stage in the three-stage transformation is the construction of a smooth curve through the midpoints of the columns corresponding to each class, as has been done in Fig. A.2. In essence, what is assumed in this smoothing process is that if enough further data were available, we could (1) make a greater number of classes, and (2) make each class infinitesimally small so that, in the limit, the result would be a *continuous* function corresponding to the continuous nature of the variable (speed, in the example) under consideration. The name given to such a function is the *probability density function.*

The probability density function of the speed data in Fig. A.2 has the familiar bell-shaped appearance characteristic of the normal distribution, the general equation for which is

$$p(X = x) = \frac{1}{s\sqrt{2\pi}} \, e^{-(x-\bar{x})/25^2} \tag{A.3}$$

where $p(X = x)$ = probability that variable X takes on value x
   x = value of variable X

$\bar{x}$ = arithmetic mean of variable X

s = standard deviation of variable X

e = base of natural logarithms

Not all variables are continuous in nature. Some may take on only discrete values. Such is the case for the previously discussed variable "number of vehicles arriving per minute." One probability density function[1] commonly used in traffic analysis which is a good example of a discrete function is the Poisson distribution, the equation for which is

$$p(X = x) = \frac{\bar{x}^x e^{-\bar{x}}}{x!} \tag{A.4}$$

where $p(X = x)$ = probability that discrete variable X takes on integer value x (x = 0, 1, 2, . . . , ∞)

$\bar{x}$ = arithmetic mean of the discrete variable X

x = integer value of discrete variable X

As can be seen in Fig. A.3, the form of the Poisson distribution depends to a considerable extent on the value of $\bar{x}$. It should be noted in this figure that the values of the function $p(X = x)$ for each integer value of x have been joined by a dotted line. This has been done for the purpose of clarity only.

---

[1] For discrete variables, the name "probability mass function" usually is employed in place of "probability density function."

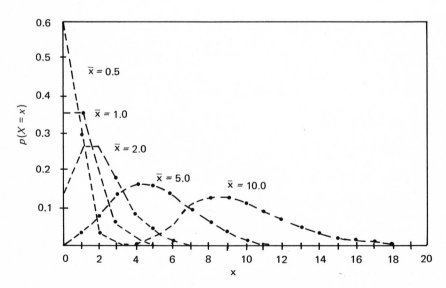

Fig. A.3   The shape of the Poisson distribution for various values of $\bar{x}$.

Probability density, or mass functions, may incorporate more than one variable. A common example of a multivariate function is another version of the Poisson distribution in which the dimension of time has been included. Equation (A.4) becomes

$$p(X = x, T = t) = \frac{(\lambda t)^x e^{-\lambda t}}{x!}$$ (A.5)

where $p(X = x, T = t)$ = probability that discrete variable X takes on integer value x ($x = 0, 1, 2, \ldots, \infty$) during time interval t

t = time interval over which x occurs

x = integer value of discrete variable X

λ = mean rate of occurrence of X (or total number of occurrences divided by total time)

An example of a set of data usually assumed to follow the Poisson distribution, Eq. (A.5), is that of arrivals of vehicles at an approach to an isolated intersection. If we know the value λ, this alone would be sufficient to enable us to determine $p(X = x, T = t)$, the probability of a given number of arrivals x during time interval t. For example, if we wanted to know the probability that there would be 1 arrival in any 5-second period, given that there are 600 arrivals in an hour, the calculations would proceed as follows:

$$\lambda = \frac{600 \text{ arrivals}}{(1 \text{ hr}) (3{,}600 \text{ sec/hr})} = 0.167 \frac{\text{arrivals}}{\text{sec}}$$

Thus

$$p(X = 1, T = 5 \text{ sec}) = \frac{[(0.167)(5)]^1 e^{-(0.167)(5)}}{1!} = 0.363$$

Similarly, for two arrivals

$$p(X = 2, T = 5 \text{ sec}) = \frac{[(0.167)(5)]^2 e^{-(0.167)(5)}}{2!} = 0.151$$

and so forth.

A third property of probability density functions is the ability to form from them *cumulative probability distributions,* formally known as *distribution functions.* For a continuous random variable, such as that found in the normal distribution, the distribution function $p(X \leqslant x)$ is related to the probability density function through the relationship

$$dp\left(X \leqslant x\right) = p\left(X = x\right) dX \tag{A.6}$$

or

$$p\left(X \leqslant x\right) = \int_{-\infty}^{X} p\left(X = x\right) dX \tag{A.7}$$

Comparing these equations with Eq. (A.3), we see that the cumulative probability distribution is equivalent to the area under the probability density function curve up to point x or, more specifically, to the probability that a given value of the variable X is *less than or equal to x.*

A.2 SAMPLING

In many transportation studies, the amount of data that can be collected is extremely large. For example, if it were desired to know the origins, destinations, times, and modes of all trips made in a day in a metropolitan area of 1 million population, a substantial data-collection effort would be needed. Since there are approximately 2.5 daily trips per person, the metropolitan area would generate 2.5 million trips in a day. If the information about each trip were put on an individual computer card, the total volume of cards would fill an average-sized bedroom. The expense of collection of these data would be prohibitive. Interviews would have to be made at residences, and the cost for interviewers and assorted staff, averaging about 25 cents for each of the 2.5 million trips, would total roughly $625,000. The cost of collecting all data pertinent to a given topic thus often becomes exorbitant when compared to the benefits to be gained from the information. A need therefore arises to risk some uncertainty by taking a *sample* of the data rather than collecting all that is available.

Some definitions often employed in sampling endeavors are

Universe: a specified set of individuals, objects, or reactions

Population: the totality of all possible values (measurements or counts) of a particular characteristic of those individuals, objects, or reactions in the universe [A.4]

Sample: a part of the population selected according to some rule or plan

In the preceding discussion of trip making, the *universe* would be the 2.5 million trips made in a given day in the metropolitan area. A *population* might be the travel times corresponding to each of these trips. A *sample* would be any part or portion of the travel times of those trips. It would be reasonable, for example, to take a random sample of 10 percent of the 2.5 million trips. This could be done as follows:

1. Each trip would be numbered on a slip of paper.
2. All the slips would be placed in a big box.
3. The box would be carefully shaken so that there would be an *equal chance* of each slip being chosen.

4. Ten percent of the slips (250,000) would be drawn from the box.[2] Information then would be obtained on the travel times of each of the 250,000 trips corresponding to the chosen slips.

Several points should be noted here. First, it must be possible to *identify* each individual, object, or reaction in the universe before a sample can be taken. This in itself would not be either easy or inexpensive in the example we have been using. It would be necessary to survey all residents just to determine *how many* trips they had made so the trips could be numbered.[3] Nevertheless, in many other situations the universe can be identified without as much effort, and the sampling can proceed from there. Second, there must be a choice of the sample size (and corresponding percentage). This choice depends to a great extent on the amount of allowable inaccuracy or uncertainty. Obviously if only one trip out of the 2.5 million were sampled (a 0.00004 percent sample), it probably would not be very representative of the entire population. On the other hand, if all 2.5 million trips were sampled (a 100 percent "sample"), it would be completely representative of the population. Sample size, therefore, relates to inaccuracy of estimation and uncertainty. The greater the size, the less the inaccuracy (this will be demonstrated in more detail later). The question of sample size thus becomes one of choosing between greater accuracy and greater cost.

The third point concerns the *type* of sample. In the example a *random* sample was specified. This is one in which each individual, object, or reaction has an equal chance of being chosen. There are other types of samples, however. One commonly used in transportation studies is the *systematic random* sample, in which the first item is chosen at random and then succeeding ones are picked at a set interval. Suppose that in the above example a 10 percent sample still were desired. To get a systematic random sample, all 2.5 million slips would be arranged in a single row. We then would select the first slip at random from the first 10 in the row. Suppose this were the 8th slip. Thereafter, we would select the 18th, 28th, 38th, etc., slips until the universe were exhausted. If we then were to calculate, say, the percentage of trips by transit in this sample, we probably would find that the number would differ somewhat from that calculated from a purely random sample. This difference would be due in part to the different types of samples.

A final point concerning sampling has to do with "replacement." In the preceding example, no mention was made as to whether a slip, when chosen, was replaced in the box or kept out. In some situations, especially when the universe is small in size and the sample large, the decision to replace or not to replace the sampled items can be significant. By way of illustration, suppose there were a universe consisting of just 10 households, with 9 making 2 daily trips by transit and the remaining 1 making 12 trips, giving an average of 3. If a sample of 8 households

---

[2] In a real-world application, sampling could by done by computer.

[3] Because of this problem, in most urban transportation studies the universe consists of *dwelling units* rather than *trips* themselves. Some inaccuracy thus is introduced in order to decrease data collection costs.

were taken randomly *without* replacement, there would be an 80 percent chance that the household with 12 trips would be selected. On the other hand, if the sampling were done *with* replacement, a constant universe would be maintained (the 10 households); in sampling without replacement the universe decreases from 10 to 9 to 8, . . . , to 3, respectively, after each slip is drawn. We would therefore expect that in this situation any sample drawn *with* replacement would be more likely to give an average number of daily trips by transit different from 3 than would the sample drawn *without* replacement.

A.2.1 Sample Size and Errors

The most important point to be gained from the discussion in this section is that there is a relationship between sample size and "errors," or inaccuracies in the quantities being estimated from the sampled items. To demonstrate, consider a hypothetical situation in which there is a population of 10 households which produce the following numbers of daily trips:

Household number   1   2   3   4   5   6   7   8   9   10

Number of daily trips   3   4   4   5   5   5   5   6   6   7

The mean number of trips is 5.0 and the standard deviation is ±1.15 trips. Now suppose that two kinds of samples are taken, each ten times. The first kind is a sample of 5 households taken randomly without replacement. The second kind is analogous, but the sample size is only 1. The samples chosen of each kind are presented in Tables A.1 and A.2, respectively.

Table A.1 Standard Error of Means for Samples of Five Households

Sample number	Household numbers in sample					Corresponding trips in sample					Sample mean
1	10	3	8	7	6	7	4	6	5	5	5.4
2	5	8	7	2	6	5	6	5	4	5	5.0
3	2	5	7	3	1	4	5	5	4	3	4.2
4	8	4	3	10	9	6	5	4	7	6	5.6
5	5	8	2	1	9	5	6	4	3	6	4.8
6	6	10	3	1	5	5	7	4	3	5	4.8
7	7	9	8	6	1	5	6	6	5	3	5.0
8	4	7	5	2	10	5	5	5	4	7	5.2
9	4	8	6	10	9	5	6	5	7	6	5.8
10	8	9	5	6	7	6	6	5	5	5	5.4

Mean of sample means   5.1

Standard deviation (error) of sample   ±0.47
   means (from population mean)

**Table A.2 Standard Error of Means
for Samples of One Household**

Sample number	Household number in sample	Corresponding trips in sample	Sample mean
1	3	4	4
2	9	6	6
3	5	5	5
4	9	6	6
5	1	3	3
6	6	5	5
7	6	5	5
8	8	6	6
9	2	4	4
10	3	4	4

Mean of sample means	4.8
Standard deviation (error) of sample means (from population mean)	±1.05

In comparing the two tables it can be seen that the standard deviation of sample means is about twice as great (±1.05 versus ±0.47) for the samples of size 1 than for those of size 5. In other words, the mean for a small sample is much more likely to deviate from the "real" (population) mean than is that from a large sample. There thus is a tradeoff between likely accuracy of estimation (in this case, of the population mean) and sample size (and hence cost of collection). If extreme accuracy or certainty were desired, a large-scale and (probably) expensive survey would be needed.

In general, the standard deviation (error) of sample means can be estimated from the following equations, the first for random sampling *with* replacement and the second for sampling *without* replacement

$$\sigma_{\bar{x}} = \sqrt{\frac{\sigma^2}{n}} \tag{A.8}$$

and

$$\sigma_{\bar{x}} = \sqrt{\frac{\sigma^2}{n} \frac{N-n}{N-1}} \tag{A.9}$$

where $\sigma_{\bar{x}}$ = standard error of sample means
  σ = population standard deviation
  n = size of sample
  N = size of universe

Of course, if a sample were taken, the *population* standard deviation would not be known. The usual procedure then is to substitute the *sample* standard deviation (error) for it (with some inaccuracy involved).

Errors in sampling are of primary concern in *hypothesis testing*, which will not be covered in detail here. As a short example, however, suppose it were suspected that in a certain transportation study one of the interviewers gathering data on daily numbers of trips by households was not actually doing the interviews, but instead was making up the data. Suppose further that, according to his data, the mean number of daily trips in his sample of 5 out of 10 households was 6.5. Yet another interviewer, whom we trust and in a similar situation, has found a mean of 5.0 trips and a standard deviation of 0.5. Assuming that such trips are normally distributed, we would find that there is less than a 1 percent chance that a difference of 3 standard deviations $[(6.5 - 5.0)/0.5 = 3]$ would occur. Our hypothesis that the suspected interviewer is collecting the correct data thus is highly improbable and must be rejected in favor of the alternate hypothesis that he is not.

This example was short, but hypothesis testing is not of great *direct* importance in this book. Such testing is of importance in most advanced planning endeavors, however, and the concerned student might study examples in [A.1, A.2, A.3, A.16, and A.17].

A.3 REGRESSION AND CORRELATION

While the emphasis in the previous sections was on direct estimation of probabilities associated with a given variable, the main goal to be pursued in this section is that of estimating the value of one variable, *given the value of another.* This situation is common in all endeavors in science and engineering where, for example, we might wish to predict the strain on a steel bar, knowing the stress, or to predict the pressure in a cylinder, knowing the temperature. To establish a relationship between two (or more) variables, two questions must be answered— first, what is the nature of the relationship (linear, nonlinear, direct, inverse, and so forth), and second, how reliable is it for purposes of estimation? Regression and correlation are methods often employed to answer these questions.

In Figs. A.4 and A.5 are presented two scatter diagrams which are plots of pairs of observations collected in the field. If we were to attempt to fit a straight line among the points of Fig. A.4, that is, to form a *linear relationship* between average number of resident vehicular trips per dwelling unit (the dependent variable) and average income (the independent variable), we would find that the line more than likely would have a positive slope *and* that most points would not lie very close to it. We then would conclude that the general nature of the relationship, as indicated by the slope, is direct, but that due to the probable dispersion of points about the line, the relationship could not be considered to be very reliable for making any estimates of the dependent variable. In Fig. A.5 similar conclusions would be reached except that the relationship would be inverse. What is lacking in the above conclusions,

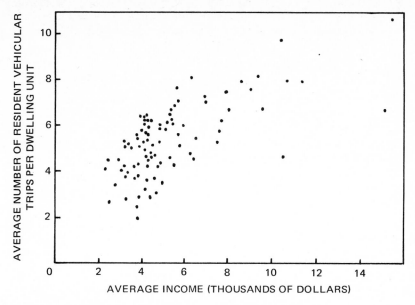

Fig. A.4 Relationship between average income per household and average trip production per household in Washington, D.C. [A.14, p. 10].

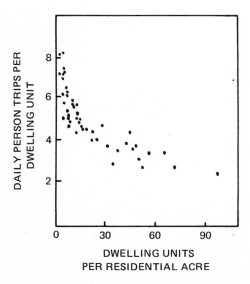

Fig. A.5 Effect of residential density on trip productions by districts in Washington, D.C. [A.14, p. 8].

however, is a more precise way to describe the phrases "direct," "inverse," and "not very reliable." The development of such descriptions is the main objective of this section.

A.3.1 Linear Regression

The first question posed above was that of determining or describing the nature of a relationship between two variables, say X and Y, with the purpose in mind of employing the relationship for making future estimates of Y given X. If the relationship appears to be linear, then the procedure to be discussed below can be utilized to give the slope and intercept for the line which "fits" the data best. This procedure is known as *linear regression*, and the resulting line is called a *regression line*.

Referring to Fig. A.6, where several data points are given, we assume that a linear relationship between X and Y is reasonable and that our objective is to find a line of the form

$$Y = aX + b \tag{A.10}$$

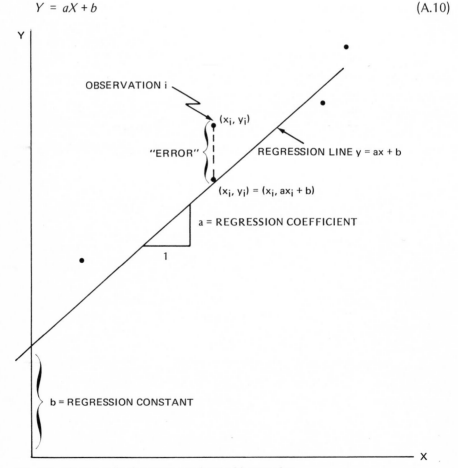

Fig. A.6 Diagram indicating terms associated with regression.

which lies closest to all of the points. Thus, a and b are the unknowns to be determined. If any observation point, indexed by i, is denoted by (x_i, y_i), and the corresponding value of Y falling on the regression line directly below (x_i, y_i) is denoted by $\hat{y}_i$, then $(y_i - \hat{y}_i)$ represents the "error" that would be made in estimating Y when $X = x_i$. In other words, knowing x_i, we would estimate that $Y = ax_i + b = \hat{y}_i$, but from our observations we know that $Y = y_i$ when $X = x_i$, so that our estimate is in "error" by the amount $(y_i - \hat{y}_i)$. Adding all of the errors from each observation point then would give the *total error* in estimating Y.

One drawback in utilizing the term $(y_i - \hat{y}_i)$ as a measure of "error" is that there may be both positive and negative values for the term, and these may cancel each other out when the addition is made to find the total error. A similar situation arose in regard to the standard deviation discussed in Sec. A.1, where the tack taken was that of squaring the deviation term in order to obtain all positive numbers. Applying the same strategy here we obtain the quantities $(y_i - \hat{y}_i)^2$ which, when summed, give the error sum of squares (ESS)

$$\text{ESS} = \sum_{i=1}^{n} (y_i - \hat{y}_i)^2 \tag{A.11}$$

Since ESS is a measure of the total error, it is desirable to set the linear regression line (that is, determine a and b) so that ESS is a minimum. Thus, from Eq. (A.10)

$$\hat{y}_i = ax_i + b \tag{A.12}$$

and then

$$\text{ESS} = \sum_{i=1}^{n} (y_i - ax_i - b)^2 \tag{A.13}$$

so that to minimize ESS, it is necessary to take the partial derivatives of ESS with respect to a and b and set then equal to 0. Before this can be done, ESS must be expanded further to

$$\text{ESS} = \sum_{i=1}^{n} y_i^2 - 2a \sum_{i=1}^{n} x_i y_i + a^2 \sum_{i=1}^{n} x_i^2 - 2b \sum_{i=1}^{n} y_i$$

$$+ 2ab \sum_{i=1}^{n} x_i + nb^2 \tag{A.14}$$

where the last term is obtained because

$$\sum_{i=1}^{n} b^2 = \sum_{i=1}^{n} \frac{i}{i} b^2 = \frac{1}{1} b^2 + \frac{2}{2} b^2 + \ldots + \frac{n}{n} b^2 = nb^2 \qquad (A.15)$$

Therefore

$$\frac{\partial(\text{ESS})}{\partial a} = -2 \sum_{i=1}^{n} x_i y_i + 2a \sum_{i=1}^{n} x_i^2 + 2b \sum_{i=1}^{n} x_i = 0 \qquad (A.16)$$

and

$$\frac{\partial(\text{ESS})}{\partial b} = -2 \sum_{i=1}^{n} y_i + 2a \sum_{i=1}^{n} x_i + 2bn = 0 \qquad (A.17)$$

Multiplying Eq. (A.16) by $n/2$ and Eq. (A.17) by

$$\frac{1}{2} \sum_{i=1}^{n} x_i$$

we obtain

$$-n \sum_{i=1}^{n} x_i y_i + na \sum_{i=1}^{n} x_i^2 + nb \sum_{i=1}^{n} x_i = 0 \qquad (A.18)$$

and

$$- \sum_{i=1}^{n} x_i \sum_{i=1}^{n} y_i + a \left(\sum_{i=1}^{n} x_i \right)^2 + nb \sum_{i=1}^{n} x_i = 0 \qquad (A.19)$$

Subtracting Eq. (A.19) from Eq. (A.18) and solving for a gives

$$a = \frac{n \sum\limits_{i=1}^{n} x_i y_i - \left(\sum\limits_{i=1}^{n} x_i \right) \left(\sum\limits_{i=1}^{n} y_i \right)}{n \sum\limits_{i=1}^{n} x_i^2 - \left(\sum\limits_{i=1}^{n} x_i \right)^2} \tag{A.20}$$

Knowing the value of a, we then can find b from Eq. (A.17) as

$$b = \frac{\sum\limits_{i=1}^{n} y_i - a \sum\limits_{i=1}^{n} x_i}{n} \tag{A.21}$$

As a result of all these manipulations, we find that for a given set of observations, $[(x_1, y_1), (x_2, y_2), \ldots, (x_i, y_i), \ldots, (x_n, y_n)]$, we can determine the slope and intercept of the line which has the best[4] fit to the observations from Eq. (A.20) and Eq. (A.21). An example of calculations involving these two equations is presented in Table A.3, where the number of average daily auto trips per dwelling unit (Y) is found to be related to the average number of autos owned per dwelling unit (X) by

$$Y = 5.489X - 2.996 \tag{A.22}$$

The minimum value of ESS equals 0.1334.

While the actual determination of this equation is an important finding, the greatest benefit is yet to come since it is through the *utilization* of Eq. (A.22) that many useful predictions can be made. If, for instance, it were known that in a certain section of a city the average number of autos owned per dwelling unit in 1985 would be 0.76,[5] then by entering this value for X in Eq. (A.22) the average daily auto trips per dwelling unit could be calculated as

$$Y = 5.489 \, (0.76) - 2.996 = 1.17$$

Thus, to repeat what was stated before, by having available a relationship like Eq. (A.22) it is possible to make *predictions*, thereby relieving us from the chore of collecting further data to obtain the desired estimate[6] and also relieving us from the

[4] "Best" is defined in terms of the criterion of Eq. (A.11).

[5] The question of whether the regression coefficient and constant will be the same in 1985 as in the present is not raised at this point. See Chap. 6 for discussion of this dilemma.

[6] Notice that the 0.76 value for X is not found in Table A.3. Strictly speaking, this situation should dictate that more data should be collected to determine the value of Y with X set exactly at 0.76.

**Table A.3 (Hypothetical) Sample Data on
Auto Trips and Ownership Used to Estimate
a Linear Regression Equation**

Observation number (i)	Average daily auto trips per dwelling unit (y_i)	Average autos owned per dwelling unit (x_i)
1	1.24	0.75
2	1.31	0.78
3	1.04	0.76
4	1.56	0.84
5	0.53	0.68
6	1.47	0.80
7	0.49	0.65
8	0.86	0.71
9	1.60	0.82
10	1.15	0.75
11	1.47	0.80
12	0.39	0.60
13	0.80	0.70
14	1.72	0.84
$n = 15$	1.80	0.89

$$\sum_{i=1}^{n} y_i = 16.54 \qquad \sum_{i=1}^{n} x_i = 11.20$$

$$n \sum_{i=1}^{n} x_i y_i - \left(\sum_{i=1}^{n} x_i\right)\left(\sum_{i=1}^{n} y_i\right) = 193.4820 - 185.2479 = 8.2341$$

$$n \sum_{i=1}^{n} x_i^2 - \left(\sum_{i=1}^{n} x_i\right)^2 = 126.939 - 125.439 = 1.500$$

$$a = \frac{8.2341}{1.500} = 5.489$$

$$b = \frac{16.54 - (5.489)\,(11.20)}{15} = -2.996$$

min   ESS $= 0.1334$

situation in which we would have *no number to use* since the event about which we seek information is yet to occur (as is the case in the above example where the auto trips will not be made until 1985). These then are two of the major reasons for developing relationships through regression.

A.3.2 Multiple (Multivariate) Linear Regression

Extensions of the linear regression technique can be made in several directions, two of which will be discussed briefly in the following subsections. The first involves the expansion of the general model of Eq. (A.10) to the situation where there is more than one dependent variable, as is exemplified by the equation [A.13, p. 220]

$$Y = 3.79X_1 - 0.0033X_2 + 3.80 \qquad\qquad (A.23)$$

where Y = daily person trips per family
X_1 = autos per dwelling unit
X_2 = dwelling places per residential acre

An equation like Eq. (A.23) can be obtained in an operation similar to that performed in going from Eq. (A.13) to Eq. (A.21) where, as before

$$\text{ESS} = \sum_{i=1}^{n} (y_i - \hat{y}_i)^2 \qquad\qquad (A.24)$$

but where $\hat{y}_i$ now is the ordinate on a *plane* of the form

$$Y = cX_1 + dX_2 + e \qquad\qquad (A.25)$$

Therefore

$$\text{ESS} = \sum_{i=1}^{n} (y_i - cX_{1i} - dX_{2i} - e)^2 \qquad\qquad (A.26)$$

where X_{1i} = value of variable 1 for observation i
X_{2i} = value of variable 2 for observation i

Taking the partials $\partial(\text{ESS})/\partial c$, $\partial(\text{ESS})/\partial d$, and $\partial(\text{ESS})/\partial e$, setting them equal to 0, and solving for c, d, and e would give the equaion of the plane which best fits the three-dimensional array of observations. Corresponding calculations can be performed for three or more independent variables.

A.3.3 Nonlinear Regression Equations

Up to this point only linear or supposedly linear functions have been explored. However, many relationships cannot be considered to be linear. The one underlying the data in Fig. A.5 is a good example of such a case.

Two nonlinear forms commonly found in relationships relevant to transportation are

$$Y = aX_1^{b_1} X_2^{b_2} \ldots X_n^{b_n} \tag{A.27}$$

and

$$Y = b_1 X_1 + b_2 X_1^2 + \ldots + b_n X_1^n + a \tag{A.28}$$

The parameters (a and b_1 through b_n) for the first equation can be established using logarithmic transformations of both sides of the equation whereas those for the second equation are found in a manner similar to that utilized in the preceding section. An explanation for a 2-variable situation will be given for the first case and an example of a specific equation for the second.

The general form of Eq. (A.27) when there are 2 independent variables is

$$Y = aX_1^{b_1} X_2^{b_2} \tag{A.29}$$

Taking the logarithms of both sides of Eq. (A.29) yields

$$\log Y = \log a + b_1 \log X_1 + b_2 \log X_2 \tag{A.30}$$

Letting $Z = \log Y$; $g = \log a$; $W_1 = \log X_1$; and $W_2 = \log X_2$, the preceding equality becomes

$$Z = g + b_1 W_1 + b_2 W_2 \tag{A.31}$$

which is exactly similar to Eq. (A.25) in Sec. A.3.2. As a consequence, the slopes and intercept of the plane, Eq. (A.31) are equivalent, respectively, to the exponents and coefficient in Eq. (A.27). Subsequently, if a regression plane is fit to the *logarithms* of the values of each multivariate observation, values for a_1, b_1, *and* b_2 can be determined and utilized directly in Eq. (A.27). This procedure thus provides us with a direct technique for establishing the specific form of Eq. (A.27).

In the case of Eq. (A.28), the general relationship Eq. (A.24) becomes

$$\text{ESS} = \sum_{i=1}^{n} (y_i - b_1 x_1 - b_2 x_1^2 - \ldots - b_n x_1^n - a)^2 \tag{A.32}$$

The partial derivatives $\partial(ESS)/\partial b_1$, $\partial(ESS)/\partial b_2$, ..., $\partial(ESS)/\partial b_n$ are taken and set equal to 0, thereby forming a set of simultaneous equations which can be solved for the needed values of the parameters. In one example found in the literaure [A.13, p. 221], an empirical relation

$$Y = 38 + 2.53X_1 - 0.0111\, X_2^2 \tag{A.33}$$

where Y = percentage of urban trips via transit
    X_1 = net residential density per acre
was determined using this technique.

A variety of regression techniques not discussed in this subsection can be found in most statistics books. Reference should be made to such often-used techniques as stepwise and simultaneous regression and to hypothesis testing relative to these techniques.

A.3.4   Correlation

The previous sections on regression have shown techniques useful for answering the question posed earlier concerning the *nature* of a relationship between a dependent variable and one or more independent variables—the nature was specified by means of the parameters (coefficients, exponents, and so forth) in the equation. The other question, that of the reliability or accuracy of the relationships, has yet to be answered. The correlation coefficient is a measure or index commonly used for this purpose.

If it were desired to estimate the value of a variable for some time in the future and nothing were known about any inherent relationships, the only reliable prediction method would involve the use of the *mean* from previous measurements of the variable. For example, if it were known from past experience that shopping centers generated an average of 500 trips per acre per day, then we would have no reasonable alternative other than to use the same figure in estimating the number of trips to a shopping center about to be constructed. Nevertheless, previous measurements might have shown considerable *variations* in trip generation rates, say from 200 to 700 trips per acre per day, so that our estimate might not be very accurate. Consequently, it is this *variation* we would like to reduce or eliminate by means of some relationship in order to obtain reliable and accurate forecasts.

The expression

$$TSS = \sum_{i=1}^{n} (y_i - \bar{y})^2 \tag{A.34}$$

where TSS represents the "total sum of the squared deviations from the mean," or, more concisely, the "total sum of squares," is a good indicator of the *total* variation to be found in the variable[7] Y and thus, from the preceding discussion, also

---

[7] Note that the *average* variation has been presented in sec. A.1 as being the *standard deviation* and that the TSS in Eq. (A.34) is included in the expression for the standard deviation, Eq. (A.2).

indicates the quantity we would like to reduce as much as possible. Returning to Sec. A.3.1 on linear regression, we find that ESS, the "error sum of squares," is a measure of the variation that remains *after* a linear regression has been performed, so that the quantity (TSS − ESS) would represent the variation that has been *eliminated* by the establishment of the linear relationship between Y and X. Therefore

$$r^2 = \frac{TSS - ESS}{TSS} \tag{A.35}$$

shows the *part* (or, if multiplied by 100, the *percentage*) of the total sum of squares eliminated by means of the relationship. Thus, r^2, referred to as the *coefficient of determination*, is a good index of the reliability of the relationship. A regression line which lies extremely close to all the observation points will give a low ESS which will lead to a high value of r^2, whereas a scatter of points around a regression line will give a high ESS and a low r^2.

If the square root of Eq. (A.35) were taken, we would obtain

$$r = \pm \sqrt{\frac{TSS - ESS}{TSS}} \tag{A.36}$$

where r = the commonly used *correlation coefficient*

For the case of *linear* regression, the plus sign is employed when the slope of the line is positive, the minus when the slope is negative. It should be noted that the range of r is between −1 and +1 since the *least* the ESS can be is 0, which gives (TSS − 0)/TSS = 1. Thus, an r of ±1 corresponds to a relationship with the *highest possible* reliability whereas an r equal to 0 would imply that ESS = TSS so that (TSS − TSS)/TSS = 0, which is the *worst possible* reliability.

Figure A.7 gives some representations of linear relationships having various degrees of correlation. These can be utilized to obtain a rough idea of the magnitude and direction of a correlation coefficient in a given situation. However, to calculate an exact value for r, one must return to Eq. (A.36) and its relevant predecessors or else use the following general equation for a linear relationship, which yields the same results

$$r = \frac{n \sum_{i=1}^{n} x_i y_i - \left(\sum_{i=1}^{n} x_i \right) \left(\sum_{i=1}^{n} y_i \right)}{\sqrt{\left[n \sum_{i=1}^{n} x_i^2 - \left(\sum_{i=1}^{n} x_i \right)^2 \right] \left[n \sum_{i=1}^{n} y_i^2 - \left(\sum_{i=1}^{n} y_i \right)^2 \right]}} \tag{A.37}$$

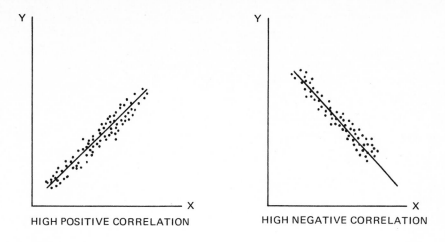

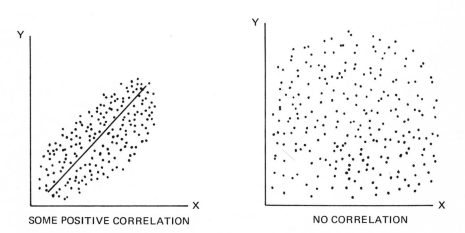

Fig. A.7 Schematic representation of various degrees of correlation.

where the x_i and y_i are pairs of observations on the independent and dependent variables, respectively. The sign of r comes out automatically, and no knowledge of the underlying regression equation is needed.

As an example of an application of the correlation coefficient, consider the four data points portrayed in Fig. A.8. The calculations are given in Table A.4. A high, "+" value of r is expected since most of the points lie close to the regression line, which has a positive slope. This prediction turns out to be correct, with the correlation coefficient found to be +0.993. As a consequence, we can feel fairly certain that the regression equation will yield fairly reliable estimates of the average

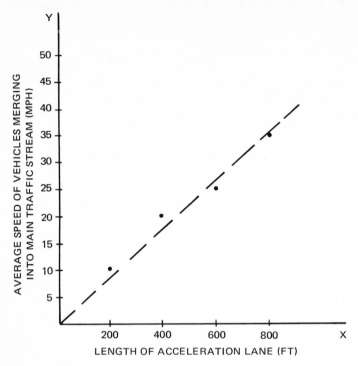

Fig. A.8 (Hypothetical) observed data on average speeds of merging vehicles and lengths of acceleration lanes.

speed of vehicles moving into the main traffic stream (from a ramp) *knowing* the length of the acceleration lane leading onto the main trafficway.[8]

A.3.5 Standard Error of Regression

While the correlation coefficient is one of the most frequently used measures of the reliability or accuracy of a relationship, it has one major drawback—it is a relative rather than an absolute measure. Looking back to Eq. (A.35) and Eq. (A.36) it can be seen that the correlation coefficient deals essentially with the *percentage* of the total sum of squares, TSS, that is eliminated through the regression relationship. There is no indication that the TSS, a measure of initial variability, is large in absolute terms. Nor is there a similar indication for the ESS. The consequence is that a relationship could produce a low ESS and yet have a low r if the initial TSS also were low. In most cases we would expect a low ESS to indicate a fairly reliable relationship.

---

[8] The possibility of "errors" in determining the example correlation coefficient due to the use of a *sample* of data instead of the entire set (e.g., all the ramps in the world) has not been discussed here nor will it be. The student is directed to most elementary statistics books for discussions on variations attributable to sampling.

What is lacking in the correlation coefficient, which deals with *total* deviation and *total* error, is a measure of the *average* deviation of observation points from the regression line. Thus, in a situation similar to that under which the *standard deviation* (average deviation from the mean) was derived,[9] we could define a *standard error of regression*, s_E, as

$$s_E = \pm \sqrt{\frac{ESS}{n-2}} = \pm \sqrt{\frac{\sum\limits_{i=1}^{n} (y_i - \hat{y}_i)^2}{n-2}} \tag{A.38}$$

where y_i = observation i of variable Y
  $\hat{y}_i = f(x_i)$
  n = number of observations

The error sum of squares, ESS, is divided by the total number of observations (minus 2) to get an "average" error per observation. The square root of this figure then is taken in order to balance the previously performed squaring operation. We subsequently obtain a measure of the average deviations of points from the regression function $Y = f(X)$.

The reason for subtracting 2 from n in the denominator inside the radical is similar to the reason for subtracting 1 when computing the standard deviation. *Assuming a linear regression functin with one independent variable*, we would see that if only two observations were available, the function would pass through both points. This situation is unsatisfactory since it will happen *no matter what the values corresponding to the two observations*. Therefore, that standard error should reflect this undefined situation by becoming similarly undefined, $\sqrt{0/0}$, when $n = 2$.

An example of the calculations involved in determining a standard error of regression can be constructed for the hypothetical relationship shown in Fig. A.8. The equation of the linear regression line portrayed there is

[9] See Sec. A.1.

Table A.4   Calculation of Standard Error of Regression Using Example Given in Fig. A.8

x_i	y_i	$\hat{y}_i$*	$y_i - \hat{y}_i$	$(y_i - \hat{y}_i)^2$
200	10	10.5	−0.5	0.25
400	20	18.5	1.5	2.25
600	25	26.5	−1.5	2.25
800	35	34.5	0.5	0.25
Sum			0	5.00

$$s_E = \pm \sqrt{\frac{5.00}{4-2}} = \pm \sqrt{2.50} = \pm 1.59$$

*Calculated from the equation $Y = 0.04X + 2.5$.

$$Y = 0.04X + 2.5 \tag{A.39}$$

The standard error comes out to ± 1.59. Standard errors also could be calculated for other than linear or univariate (one-independent-variable) relationships. One unit should be subtracted from n in the denominator of Eq. (A.38) for each parameter (coefficient, exponent, constant, and so forth) in the estimating equation.

A.4 LINEAR PROGRAMMING

The statistical procedures presented in the preceding sections of this appendix have proven valuable in the study of transportation, especially in simplifying the description of large sets of data and in establishing relationships to be used for predictive purposes. In this section we turn from descriptive and predictive techniques to *prescriptive* or *normative* techniques, the foremost of which is *linear programming.*

It often happens that in the synthesis and design of various structures, machines, or any general system, an effort is made to maximize or minimize some objective function. For instance, in the determination of how much traffic signal green time should be assigned to each approach to an intersection it often is desirable to minimize the average delay to all vehicles on all approaches or to maximize the hourly volume that will pass through the intersection. In a more complex situation, the purpose may be to minimize the maximum number of stops that might be required. The design conditions usually are not completely determined, however, when the relevant objective has been specified, for it often turns out that certain *constraints* exist which must be considered. For example, two important constraints which loom heavily over all design efforts are those on the time and the budget of the designer himself. Another, more concrete example of a constraint can be found in the traffic light timing problem outlined above since, in most actual cases, the traffic engineer is constrained to have *at least* enough green time in each direction to allow pedestrians to cross the street.

A linear program is a *mathematical* expression of both an objective function and a corresponding set of constraints in which all the variables involved are related to each other in a linear fashion. An example probably would be most instructive at this point. The set of equations (A.40) comprises a *program,* and, since the equations are linear, the set is known as a *linear* program.

$$\min Z = 3X_1 + 2X_2$$

subject to

$$X_1 + X_2 \leqslant 30$$
$$X_1 \geqslant 10 \tag{A.40}$$
$$X_2 \geqslant 10$$
$$X_1, X_2 = 0$$

The coefficients of X_1 and X_2 in the objective function generally are referred to as *costs*, while the constants 30, 10, and 10 are known as the *righthand side* (RHS) of the constraints. The equations (A.40) may not correspond to any real-world situation but, to show a practical use for linear programming, we could think of a hypothetical situation that would lead to the same program (A.40):

> Suppose that the delay in seconds at a simple two-way intersection with a fixed-time traffic signal is equal to three times the red time in one direction and twice the red time in the other direction. Moreover, the green time in each direction cannot be less than 10 seconds and the total of the two red times must not exceed 30 seconds. How much red time should be allotted to each direction in order to minimize delay? No negative red times are allowed and, for simplicity, yellow times are ignored.

In the example, X_1 would be the amount of red time allocated to direction 1 and X_2 would be the corresponding amount for direction 2. The second and third constraints in (A.40) are obtained by noticing that the *green* time in one direction, which must not be less than 10 seconds, is of equal duration to the *red* time in the other direction. The first constraint corresponds to the statement concerning the total of the two red times.

The solution of the linear program (A.40) can be obtained through a graphical procedure shown in the series of diagrams in Fig. A.9. The general approach begins with the establishment of the region of the $X_1 - X_2$ plane, within which all points would meet the given constraints, and then terminates when that point or set of points within that region which give the lowest value for Z is found. Tracing through the process in more detail, we start by noticing that $X_1, X_2 \geqslant 0$, thus implying that a feasible solution must fall within the upper righthand quadrant of the $X_1 - X_2$ plane. As a second step, a determination is made of all those points meeting the first constraint. This set of points can be established through the following device:

> Assume that $X_1 + X_2$ is equal to some value less than 30, say 20. All positive points on the resulting line shown in Fig. A.9(a) fall within the constraint of being less than or equal to 30. Thus it is easy to see that all positive points on *any* line whose *slope is the same as that of the constraint* and whose *righthand side is between 0 and 30* will fall within the constraint. The shaded region in Fig. A.9(a) represents the set of points meeting those two requirements.

A similar argument can be used to find regions associated with the two remaining constraints in (A.40). It should be noted, however, that our interest centers on determining a region that meets *all* the constraints so that part of the shaded region in Fig. A.9(a) must be eliminated by the constraint

$$X_1 \geqslant 10 \tag{A.41}$$

since these points correspond to values of X_1 which are less than 10. The region remaining after all the constraints in (A.40) have been considered is shown in Fig. A.9(c). Each point within this region is known as a *feasible solution*.

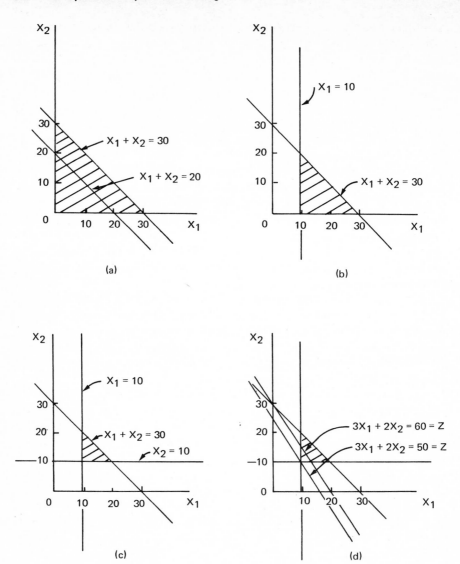

Fig. A.9   Solution to hypothetical two-variable linear programming problem.

We now turn our attention to finding that single feasible point (or possibly a set of feasible points) which gives the lowest value for Z. Notice that in Fig. A.9(a) the righthand side of the first constraint equation *decreased* as the line was brought closer to the origin. Consequently, the value of Z in

$$Z = 3X_1 + 2X_2 \qquad\qquad\qquad (A.42)$$

also would become smaller as this line is moved toward the origin, a situation that indicates that a minimum Z would occur at the feasible point nearest the origin. From Fig. A.9(d) this point is (10, 10). Therefore, $X_1 = 10$, $X_2 = 10$, and $Z = 3(10) + 2(10) = 50$ is the optimal (min Z) solution to the program (A.40).

Linear programming has several distinct advantages. First, many design situations arise in which the goal is to optimize some objective while working within some constraints. These real-world situations often can be adapted neatly to a linear programming format. Second, there is no need to worry about the possibility of obtaining only local optima or points of inflection as solutions to linear programs as would be the case in many nonlinear and, perhaps, unconstrained problems approached by means of calculus. Solutions to linear programs are always *global* optima.[10] Finally, with further knowledge of the mathematics involved in linear programming, an analyst becomes capable of investigating the *sensitivity* of solutions to *changes* in various costs and constraints in the program, an advantage which is highly desirable since most of these are not as firmly set in a real-world situation as they would appear in the program.

Most computing centers have linear programming programs (codes) available which can be utilized to obtain solutions for programs of great variety and size and also to produce relevant sensitivity measures. Extensions of common linear programming techniques into the more general area of *mathematical programming* also can be made. Such extensions might include

1. The use of nonlinear functions in the objective function or in the constraints
2. The introduction of probabilistic elements in the objective function or constraints; and
3. The employment of variables some or all of which may take on only integer values.

Further elaboration on these possibilities can be found in [A.9].

A.5 DYNAMIC PROGRAMMING

In linear programming, solutions are obtained essentially by solving for the values of all the variables at once. This type of attack on a program often is beneficial, yet another approach might be to attempt to *decompose*, or break down, the program into a series of smaller programs each one of which is solved individually and then combined again with the others. This type of approach is characteristic of *dynamic programming.*

An example probably will best explain the general technique of dynamic programming. Suppose a person wishes to travel from his home to city X over a route on the transportation network shown in Fig. A.10. He would like to spend as little time as possible in making the trip. Which route should he take? Before

---

[10] For a further discussion of this and several other characteristics of linear programming see [A.8], one of many valuable works in this field.

starting the search for an answer, we first note that the number in the box over each node in the network is a code designation for each stage (first digit) and each state (second digit). The number on each link is the travel time in minutes over that link; for example, from home, at 01, it takes 9 minutes to go to node 11. The general dynamic programming approach to the problem proceeds as follows: the traveler imagines himself placed at each of the stage-1 nodes. He determines the best (minimum time) path *into* the particular node at which he has placed himself from *any* of the stage-0 nodes (of which there is only one in this example). Having done this for all stage-1 nodes, he then moves forward and imagines himself at each stage-2 node. Again he searches for the minimum time path into each node, except that at this (and each succeeding) stage, the minimum path is found by adding (a) the travel time over the link from each node in the preceding stage to the present node and (b) the minimum time path into the preceding node. That link with the minimum sum is taken as optimum, and after all the stage-2 nodes have been evaluated, the traveler imagines himself at the next stage. The entire procedure continues until the last stage, at which point the overall optimal path becomes known.

Table A.5 shows the stage-by-stage calculations for the example problem. In stage 1 in Table A.5, the minimum time paths into nodes 11, 12, and 13 are found. To do this, we first record the travel time from each of these three nodes to all nodes in the previous stage (node 01) and then take the minimum for each stage-1 node. Continuing on to stage 2, Table A.5, we take the minimum from stage-1 row and place it in each row of the corresponding column of stage 2. For example, the 9 from the first row (node 01) of stage 1 has been placed in each row under column 1 (node 11) in stage 2.[11] To these minimums then are added the respective internodal link travel times, and new minimums subsequently are established for each node at this stage. This addition has been made, for example, in the top-left element of Table A.5, stage 1, where the travel time of 11 minutes from node 11 to node 21

---

[11] Except where no link connection exists between node 11 and the stage-2 node.

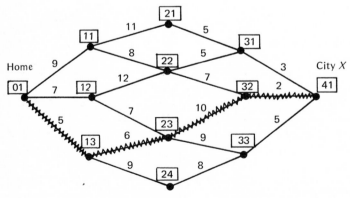

Fig. A.10 Network travel example.

Table A.5 Stages in Dynamic Programming Solution to Example in Fig. A.10

Stage 1

	01	min
11	(9)	9
12	(7)	7
13	(5)	5

Stage 2

	11	12	13	min
21	9 + 11 = (20)	X	X	20
22	9 + 8 = (17)	7 + 12 = 19	X	17
23	X	7 + 7 = 14	5 + 6 = (11)	11
24	X	X	5 + 9 = (14)	14

Stage 3

	21	22	23	24	min
31	20 + 5 = 25	17 + 5 = (22)	X	X	22
32	X	17 + 7 = 24	11 + 10 = (21)	X	21
33	X	X	11 + 9 = (20)	14 + 8 = 22	20

Stage 4

	31	32	33	min
41	22 + 3 = 25	21 + 2 = (23)	20 + 5 = 25	23

has been summed with the minimum travel time to node 11, which is 9 minutes. This path to node 21 turns out to be the minimum (and only) one. The dynamic programming procedure continues through stages 3 and 4 until, at this latter stage, the overall minimum time route of 23 minutes duration is determined.

What remains to be done is to locate the optimal route. This is accomplished by tracing backwards through each stage. The columns in which the row minimums occur in each stage of Table A.5 are circled for convenience in this endeavor. For instance, in stage 4 it can be seen that the *last* part of the optimal route goes from node 32 to node 41. Looking along the second (node 32) row in stage 3, we further determine that *the next to last* part of the optimal route is from node 23 to 32. Similarly, the second leg of the journey should go from node 13 to 23, with the initial leg being from 01 to 13. The complete optimal route then can be summarized as

$$\boxed{01} \longrightarrow \boxed{13} \longrightarrow \boxed{23} \longrightarrow \boxed{32} \longrightarrow \boxed{41}$$

This route has been overhatched in Fig. A.10.

The dynamic programming procedure demonstrated by means of the preceding example can be generalized into a set of seven entities, five of which are portrayed in Fig. A.11. The seven include

Stages	Stage returns
Input states	Functional equations
Output states	Transformations
Decision variables	

The nature of these entities can be understood by returning to the example problem in Fig. A.10. Each *stage* in the example network is representative of a set of nodes at which decisions must be made by the potential trip maker as to which link should be traversed in *reaching* each one of the nodes at that stage. An *output state*, X_n, would be any node at a particular stage, n, at which a link travel decision, D_n, is made. This decision results in the accrual of a link travel time (stage) *return* or cost, $r_n(X_n, D_n)$, and a *transformation*, t_n, of the potential trip maker from an *input state* in the preceding $(n-1)$ stage, X_{n-1}, to the given output state X_n. This output state then becomes one of the input state nodes for the next stage, $n + 1$. The objective at each state of each stage is to decide on the input node at which travel should progress to each output node in order to minimize total travel time. The specification of this process is contained in the *functional equation*

$$f_n(X_n) = \min_{D_n} \left[r_n(X_n, D_n) + f_{n-1}(X_{n-1}) \right] \tag{A.43}$$

subject to the *transformation*

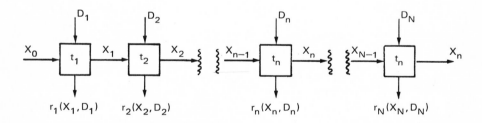

$$
\begin{aligned}
X_{n-1} &= \text{input state X at stage } n-1 \\
X_n &= \text{output state X at stage } n \\
D_n &= \text{decision possibilities at stage } n \\
r_n(X_n, D_n) &= \text{stage return at stage } n \\
t_n &= \text{transformation of input state } X_{n-1} \text{ to state } X_n \text{ at stage } n
\end{aligned}
$$

Fig. A.11 Diagrammatic display of stages in the dynamic programming process.

$$X_n = t_n(X_{n-1}, D_n) \tag{A.44}$$

where $f_n(X_n)$ = optimal return for output state X at stage n

Equations (A.43) and (A.44) together compose the nucleus of the *principle of optimality* [A.10] which, when liberally translated, reads:

> the optimum return, $f_n(X_n)$, for any output state X at stage n is the optimum, over all decision (input state) possibilities, of the sums of (a) the individual return, $r_n(X_n, D_n)$, for the given output state and decision possibility, and (b) the optimum return, $f_{n-1}(X_{n-1})$ up to the respective input state.

A good example of the use of the principle of optimality is in stage 2 of Table A.5. We assume that we are at node (state) 22 and look back toward nodes 11 to 13 to decide on which of the corresponding links we should travel to get to 22. There actually are only two choices—the link from 11 to 22 and the link from 12 to 22. If we look at the first choice, the *total* return would be the time on the link from 11 to 22 of 8 minutes *plus* the time on the *best* path up to node 11, which turns out to be 9 minutes (from node 01). For the second choice, we have 12 minutes from 12 to 22 and the time on the best path to 12, which is 7 minutes. Therefore

$$f_2\left(\boxed{22}\right) \; \min_{\boxed{11},\;\boxed{12}} [8+9,\ 12+7] = 17 \text{ with } D_2 \text{ being } \boxed{12}$$

as shown in the minimum column for node 22 at stage 2.

Several remarks concerning both dynamic programming and the example problem discussed here should be proffered at this time:

1. The example problem actually can be solved by mathematically simple techniques. If we were to examine the network in Fig. A.10 in more detail, we would find that there were exactly 12 routes from 01 to 41. All we really need do is add up the travel times on all four links of each of these 12 routes and then find the one that has a minimum total travel time. This approach would require 36 simple arithmetic additions.

2. One major advantage of dynamic programming is that it can be used to reduce the number of calculations required. To obtain the example problem solution, only 15 additions were needed, less than one-half the 36 needed for the complete elaboration proposed in the preceding paragraph. Savings in calculations required usually become greater with larger-sized problems.

3. Dynamic programming is difficult to understand. There is little doubt that by looking at a problem in stages and by working forward and backward through these stages, one will become confused.[12] Consequently, the additional effort needed to understand the process of dynamic programming

---

[12] In light of this comment, it should be remarked that it is certainly difficult to imagine a traveler plotting his path by jumping one node away from his starting point and looking back to find the best way of getting to the point he's just reached. This type of approach, being the basis for dynamic programming, contradicts the usual one of beginning at the starting node and *looking ahead* to succeeding nodes.

has to be balanced against the anticipated computational savings that may occur.

4. The dynamic programming approach has great flexibility in that it can be adjusted to fit different situations. The flexibility is exemplified in Table A.6, where the entire example problem has been reworked by starting at node 41 and proceeding *backward* through the network.

Table A.6   Stages in Backwards Dynamic Programming Solution to Example in Fig. A.10

Stage 1

Input state—Decision

	41	min
31	③	3
Output state 32	②	2
33	⑤	5

Stage 2

Input state—Decision

	31	32	33	min
21	$5 + 3 =$ ⑧	—	—	8
22	$5 + 3 =$ ⑧	$7 + 2 =$ 9	—	8
Output state 23	—	$10 + 2 =$ ⑫	$9 + 5 =$ 14	12
24	—	—	$8 + 5 =$ ⑬	13

Stage 3

Input state—Decision

	21	22	23	24	min
11	$11 + 8 = 19$	$8 + 8 =$ ⑯	—	—	16
Output state 12	—	$12 + 8 =$ 20	$7 + 12 =$ ⑲	—	19
13	—	—	$6 + 12 =$ ⑱	$9 + 13 = 22$	18

Stage 4

Input state—Decision

	11	12	13	min
Output state 01	$9 + 16 = 25$	$7 + 19 = 26$	$5 + 18 =$ ㉓	23

5. Nonlinearities, integer variables, and probabilistic elements often can be handled nicely through dynamic programming.
6. With only a small number of additional calculations, the second-, third-, etc., best routes through a decision network can be located, thereby providing a measure of *sensitivity* that often is useful in many analyses.

A.6 MINIMUM TIME-PATH ALGORITHMS

The determination of minimum time paths (in particular) can be done even faster than with dynamic programming by using algorithms (computing techniques) such as that by Moore [A.18]. Such paths are needed as inputs to most of the land use and travel models discussed in Chaps. 5 and 6. The full sequence of steps necessary to determine minimum time paths will be presented here. For an example, we will use the street classification and base map shown in Fig. A.12. After the important thoroughfares have been identified, as in that figure, and zone centroids, corresponding roughly to the geographic centers of the zones, have been located, another map showing the major network links and their measured lengths (top number) and speeds (bottom number) can be prepared (Fig. A.13).[13] The problem, then, is to find the minimum travel time path between each and every zone centroid. It is easy to see that without some kind of logical procedure to do this, many tedious and perhaps incorrect calculations would be made before the best path were found.

The most common technique employed for determining minimum travel time paths is that developed by Moore [A.18]. As an example of his approach we will take the overly simplified network in Fig. A.14 representing the highway system in the nine counties of the San Francisco Bay Area. Travel times are marked on the links, and our interest is centered on finding the minimum time route between centroid 1 and centroid 7. We start by determining the minimum path from centroid 1 over all links connecting to it. Thus, min (21, 20, 10) = 10 on the link from 1 to 2. In the second stage, we find the minimum total (from 1) time path from centroids 1 and 2 to all centroids directly connected to 1 or 2. So, min (10 + 15, 10 + 20, 20, 21) = 20, which corresponds to the 1-4 path. Continuing in a similar manner, we take the minimum total time from 1 to 2 to all connecting centroids except 4, from 1 to 4 to all connecting centroids except 2, and from 1 to all connecting centroids except 2 and 4. This gives min (10 + 15, 20 + 10, 20 + 10, 21) = 21, which is the time on the link from 1 to 9. The remaining calculations along with those shown above are presented in detail in Fig. A.15, with the resulting minimum time paths shown together in Fig. A.14. An interesting outcome of Moore's algorithm is that in finding the minimum time path to the farthest centroid, it is also necessary to find the minimum time paths to all other centroids.

---

[13] Notice in Fig. A.13 that some centroids might not lie on a major thoroughfare so that some reasonable, yet arbitrary speeds must be given to the travel distance to the nearest actual street nodes.

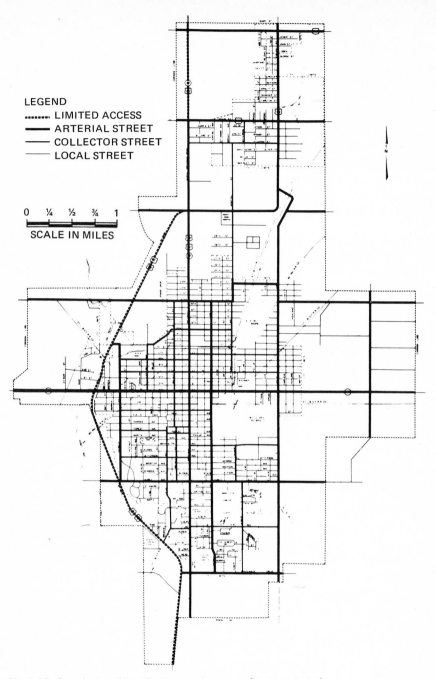

Fig. A.12 Sample street classification and base map. [A.15, p. iv-10].

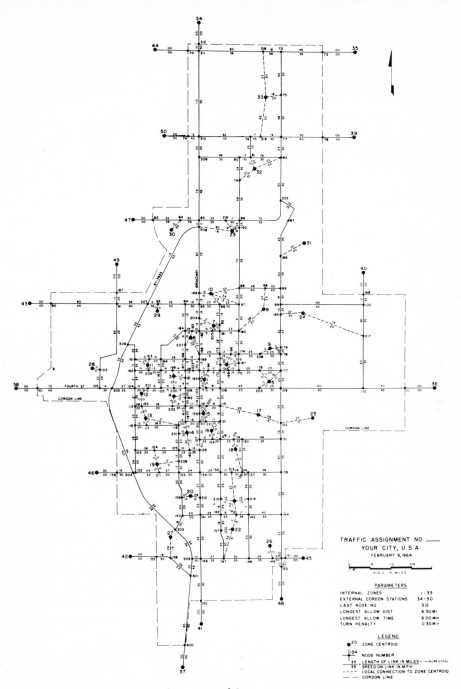

Fig. A.13   Sample network map. [A.15, p. iv-11].

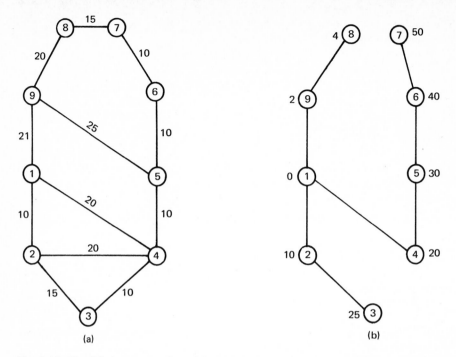

Fig. A.14 Simplified representation of the highway network in the San Francisco Bay area.

The output of the algorithm therefore is a set of minimum travel time paths known as a *minimum path tree*, emanating from one centroid. Figure A.16 displays the tree for the first centroid in the network in Fig. A.13. It should be noted that in both the example problem and in Fig. A.16, the tree is developed for only one centroid. A complete analysis would require the building of trees from all centroids.

A.7 COMPUTER APPLICATIONS

Many of the techniques discussed in this appendix and especially in Chaps. 5 and 6 probably owe their existence to the computer, for without it most of the extensive and cumbersome calculations could not be done. In addition, most of the large-scale data handling inherent in the collection and processing procedures presented in Chap. 7 would not be possible. It thus seems appropriate to discuss computer applications briefly in this section.

The types of computers available vary widely, but what is important with respect to the type of analyses discussed here is the "software" (preprogrammed material) provided. It would be extremely time consuming and expensive for an individual agency or firm to program for itself something like the gravity model or multiple regression or a linear programming algorithm. In fact, the gravity model program package supplied by the Federal Highway Administration has over 50 subroutines or subprograms, each one of which is somewhat complex. Most agencies therefore make use of the "canned" programs.

The most commonly utilized "canned" programs for correlation and regression are the BMD [A.17] and the SPSS [A.19]. These are readily available and have a wide range of options covering most of the situations that might arise. For linear programming, the MPS code [A.20] is just one example of many available from computer manufacturers. Dynamic programming codes usually are written directly by the user.

Minimum time path algorithms can be found in programs developed by the Federal Highway Administration. These also include codes for the gravity model [A.21, A.23], the BPR assignment model [A.22], and several others. Programs also

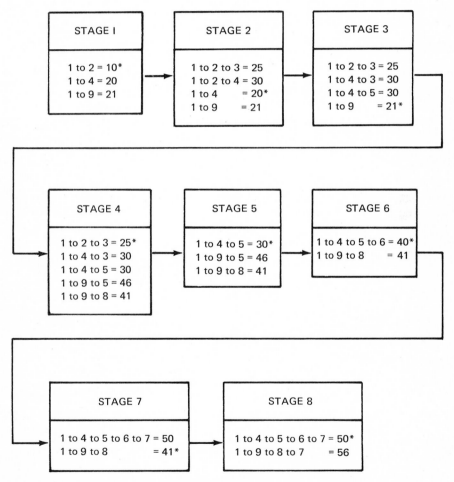

Fig. A.15 Complete set of calculations to obtain minimum time path tree from network in Fig. A.14. (Asterisks indicate minimum time at each stage.)

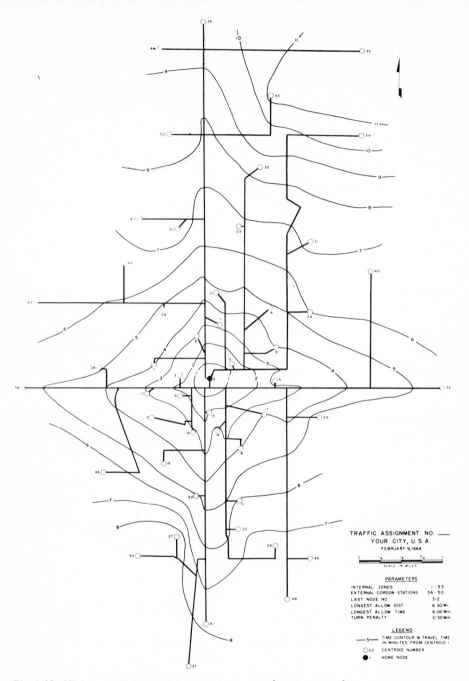

Fig. A.16. Minimum path tree with isochronal contours. [A.15, p. iv–13].

useful in transportation analysis are the UMTA Transportation Planning System [A.26] and ROADS [A.25], TRANSET [A.24], and related programs from M.I.T.

Costs for obtaining and running the programs mentioned here vary, but some are not inexpensive. For example, computer time on certain facilities ranges from $200 to $500 per hour. A trip assignment program, perhaps the most expensive to run, might take from one-half hour to an hour, thereby costing from $100 to $500. It should not be expected that the program will run without any difficulties. Even beginning programmers realize that four to five runs usually are necessary just to get a simple program operating correctly. Then too, input data errors often are found, thus requiring additional runs. If mistakes in the program are indicated, moreover, it is not an easy task either to find or fix them, especially if one is not totally familiar with the "workings" of the program (which usually is the case since the program has been prepared elsewhere). These then are just a few of the problems that must be faced in attempting to employ many of the computer-oriented techniques discussed in this text.

A.8 SUMMARY

An attempt has been made in this appendix to describe as briefly and clearly as possible those mathematical and statistical tools of assistance to the transportation planner and engineer as they attempt to understand transportation problems. The first section of the appendix dealt with measures of central tendency and dispersion in a set of data. Generally, when we have some observations, for instance on vehicular speeds, we want to know what an "average" speed is and how much a given vehicle deviates from this average. The mean and standard deviation, respectively, are the measures of these two aspects.

Of course it may also be valuable to determine the complete range of vehicular speeds. Histograms and probability distributions provide such information. They also serve as an underlying basis for those situations in which it is too expensive or time consuming to collect data on all members of a universe. Sampling then is required, and some additional inaccuracy or uncertainty of estimation often results.

Regression and correlation provide a means by which one variable can be related to another. If, for example, car ownership can be predicted better than daily trips from home, it might be desirable to correlate car ownership with trip making and predict the latter by means of a regression equation.

The final three sections of the appendix dealt with linear and dynamic programming and with minimum time path algorithms. These are optimization techniques useful in situations where objectives and constraints are relatively clear and concise. These techniques then can be employed to determine solutions that give minimum costs or whatever kind of optimum is desired. Examples of these techniques can be found in the text of this book and in much of the literature on transportation planning and design.

BIBLIOGRAPHY

A.1 Guilford, J. P.: *Fundamental Statistics in Psychology and Education*, McGraw-Hill, New York, 1956.

A.2 Ackoff, R. L., and M. W. Sasieni: *Fundamentals of Operations Research*, Wiley, New York, 1968.

A.3 Schwar, J. F., and J. Puy-Huarte: *Statistical Methods in Traffic Engineering*, Special Report 26, Engineering Experiment Station, Ohio State Univ., Columbus, Ohio, September, 1962.

A.4 Wohl, M., and B. V. Martin: *Traffic System Analysis for Engineers and Planners*, McGraw-Hill, New York, 1967.

A.5 Seshu, S., and M. B. Reed: *Linear Graphs and Electrical Networks*, Addison-Wesley, Reading, Mass., 1961.

A.6 Ford, Jr., L. R., and D. R. Fulkerson: *Flows in Networks*, Princeton Univ. Press, Princeton, N.J., 1962.

A.7 Busacker, R. G., and T. L. Saaty: *Finite Graphs and Networks—An Introduction with Applications*, McGraw-Hill, New York, 1965.

A.8 Hadley, G.: *Linear Programming*, Addison-Wesley, Reading, Mass., 1962.

A.9 Hillier, F. S., and G. J. Lieberman: *Introduction to Operations Research*, Holden-Day, San Francisco, 1967.

A.10 Nemhauser, G. L.: *Introduction to Dynamic Programming*, Wiley, New York, 1966.

A.11 Ostle, B.: *Statistics in Research* (2d ed.), Iowa State Univ. Press, Ames, Iowa, 1963.

A.12 Wilde, D. J.: *Optimum Seeking Methods*, Prentice-Hall, Englewood Cliffs, N.J., 1963.

A.13 Baerwald, J. E. (ed.): *Traffic Engineering Handbook* (3d ed.), Institute of Traffic Engineers, Washington, D.C., 1965.

A.14 U.S. Department of Transportation, Federal Highway Administration, Bureau of Public Roads: *Guidelines for Trip Generation Analysis*, U.S. Government Printing Office, Washington, D.C., June, 1967.

A.15 U.S. Department of Commerce, Bureau of Public Roads: *Calibrating and Testing a Gravity Model for Any Size Urban Area*, U.S. Government Printing Office, Washington, D.C., Oct., 1965.

A.16 Institute of Traffic Engineers: *Manual of Traffic Engineering Studies* (3d ed.), Washington, D.C., 1964.

A.17 Dixon, W. J., (ed.): *BMD: Biomedial Computer Programs*, Univ. of California Press, Berkeley, 1970.

A.18 Moore, E. F.: "The Shortest Path Through a Maze," *Proceedings*, International Symposium on the Theory of Switching, Harvard Univ. Press, Cambridge, Mass., April 2–5, 1957.

A.19 Nie, N., D. H. Bent, and C. H. Hull: *Statistical Package for the Social Sciences*, McGraw-Hill, New York, 1970.

A.20 International Business Machines Corp: *Mathematical Programming System*, White Plains, N.Y., October 15, 1971.

A.21 U.S. Department of Transportation, Federal Highway Administration: *Trip Distribution and Peripheral Programs*, U.S. Government Printing Office, Washington, D.C., 1969.

A.22 U.S. Department of Transportation, Federal Highway Administration: *Traffic Assignment and Peripheral Programs*, U.S. Government Printing Office, Washington, D.C., 1969.

A.23 U.S. Department of Transportation, Federal Highway Administration: *Program Documentation, Urban Transportation Planning, System 360*, U.S. Government Printing Office, Washington, D.C., June, 1970.

A.24 Ruiter, E. R.: *ICES TRANSET 1; Transportation Network Analysis, Engineering User's Manual*, M.I.T. Press, Cambridge, Mass., March, 1968.

A.25 Suhrbier, J. H., T. C. Prokopy, and E. C. Sullivan: *ICES Roads 1, Roadway Analysis and Design System, Engineer's Reference Manual*, M.I.T. Press, Cambridge, Mass., March, 1968.

A.26 U.S. Department of Transportation, Urban Mass Transportation Administration: *UMTA Transportation Planning System Reference Manual* (a Computer Program), U.S. Government Printing Office, Washington, D.C., September, 1972.

Index